OCCUPATIONAL HEALTH AND SAFETY FOR TECHNOLOGISTS, ENGINEERS, AND MANAGERS

SECOND CANADIAN EDITION

DAVID L. GOETSCH

Vice-President Emeritus and Professor Northwest Florida State College

GENE OZON, MBA, CRSP

 Pearson

For my colleagues who have taught me so much about occupational health and safety.
For my family and friends who inspire me with their love and wisdom.

—Gene Ozon

VICE PRESIDENT, EDITORIAL: Anne Williams
ACQUISITIONS EDITOR: Mark Grzeskowiak
MARKETING MANAGER: Leigh-Anne Graham
CONTENT MANAGER: Madhu Ranadive
PROJECT MANAGER: Sarah Gallagher
CONTENT DEVELOPER: Christine Langone
PRODUCTION SERVICES: Cenveo® Publisher Services

PERMISSIONS PROJECT MANAGEMENT: Integra Publishing Services, Inc.
PHOTO PERMISSIONS RESEARCH: Integra Publishing Services, Inc.
TEXT PERMISSIONS RESEARCH: Integra Publishing Services, Inc.
INTERIOR AND COVER DESIGNER: Anthony Leung
COVER IMAGE: aarrows/Shutterstock
VICE-PRESIDENT, DIGITAL STUDIO: Gary Bennett

Pearson Canada Inc., 26 Prince Andrew Place, North York, Ontario M3C 2H4.

978-0-13-468171-9

1 18

Library and Archives Canada Cataloguing in Publication
Goetsch, David L., author
   Occupational safety and health for technologists, engineers, and
managers / David L. Goetsch, Gene Ozon. — Second Canadian edition.

Includes index.
ISBN 978-0-13-468171-9 (hard cover)

   1. Industrial safety—Canada. 2. Industrial hygiene—Canada.
I. Ozon, Gene, author II. Title.

T55.G63 2018   658.4'08   C2017-907302-8

Brief Contents

Contents

PART 2 MANAGEMENT OF OCCUPATIONAL HEALTH AND SAFETY

Preface

BACKGROUND

The field of occupational health and safety has undergone significant change over the past three decades. There are many reasons for this. Some of the more prominent include the following: technological changes that have introduced new hazards in the workplace; proliferation of health and safety legislation and corresponding regulations; increased pressure from regulatory agencies, environmental groups and the public, and labour organizations and employees in general; growing understanding by managers that workers in a safe and healthy workplace are typically more productive; health care and workers' compensation cost increases; improvement in the ability to correlate diseases to a worker's occupation; a growing interest in ethics and corporate responsibility; professionalization of health and safety occupations; rapidly mounting costs associated with product safety and other types of litigation; and increasing incidents of workplace violence.

All of these factors, when taken together, have made the job of the modern health and safety professional more challenging and more important than it has ever been. These factors have also created a need for an up-to-date book on workplace health and safety that contains the latest information for Canadians who have a stake in this profession in the age of global competition and rapid technological change.

WHY WAS THIS BOOK WRITTEN AND FOR WHOM?

This book was written to fill the need for an up-to-date, Canadian, practical teaching and learning resource that focuses on the needs of modern health and safety professionals. It is intended for use in universities, colleges, and corporate training settings that offer programs, courses, workshops, and seminars in occupational health and safety. Educators and students in such disciplines as industrial technology, manufacturing technology, industrial engineering, engineering technology, occupational safety, management, and supervision will find this book both valuable and easy to use.

This book will also serve as an excellent reference for human resource personnel who want to gain a better understanding of how health and safety integrates with their role. The direct, straightforward presentation of material focuses on making the theories and principles of occupational health and safety practical and useful in a real-world setting. Up-to-date research has been integrated throughout in a down-to-earth manner.

ORGANIZATION OF THE BOOK

The text contains 28 chapters, each focusing on a major area of concern for modern health and safety professionals. The chapters are grouped into four sections, dealing with specific areas of health and safety.

The order in which the material is presented begins with a broad view of health and safety, progresses to general principles adapted by the profession, and next examines more deeply specific hazards commonly found in the workplace. The last section looks at current and developing trends and emerging issues in health and safety.

- Part 1: General Principles of Health and Safety
- Part 2: Management of Occupational Health and Safety
- Part 3: Chemical, Biological, and Physical Hazards
- Part 4: Contemporary Issues in Health and Safety

A standard chapter format is used throughout the book. Each chapter begins with a list of major topics and ends with a comprehensive summary. Following the summary, each chapter offers review questions, key terms and concepts, useful Weblinks, and endnotes.

Within each chapter are case studies to promote classroom discussion, as well as at least one safety fact or myth. These materials are provided to encourage review, stimulate additional thought, and provide opportunities for applying what has been learned. In addition, key terms appear in bold within the text, with their definitions provided in the page margin to reinforce comprehension.

HOW THIS BOOK DIFFERS FROM OTHERS

This book was written to address health and safety issues in the Canadian workplace. In the age of global competition, health and safety in the Canadian workplace has changed dramatically. Many issues, concerns, and factors relating specifically to modern workplace environments have been given more attention, greater depth of coverage, and more illumination here than in other textbooks. Some of the areas receiving more attention and specific occupational examples include:

- Globally Harmonized System (GHS), WHMIS 2015
- Expanding Worker's Compensation Boards (WCB) coverage
- Psychological health and safety in the workplace
- Post-traumatic stress disorders (PTSD)
- Life safety
- Evolving roles of health and safety and human resource professionals
- Health and safety training
- Human factors in safety
- Computers, robots, and automation
- Ethics and safety
- Bloodborne pathogens in the workplace
- Ergonomics and safety
- Relationship between safety and quality
- Workplace violence
- Repetitive strain injuries (RSIs)
- Terrorism threats in the workplace
- Workplace wellness
- Impact of alcohol and drugs in the workplace

NEW TO THE SECOND CANADIAN EDITION

Along with changes to the order in which the material is presented, the reader will notice that this second Canadian edition of *Occupational Health and Safety* contains much new and updated material, including the following:

- **Part 1 (Chapters 1–5)** provides a Canadian perspective on the evolution of health and safety, using the latest statistics available and current examples to frame the state of health and safety in Canada. While legislation continuously changes across the country, we endeavor to provide the most recent references and, in some instances, identify trends to predict future changes. Recent changes to Workers' Compensation increased coverage for psychological injuries and presumptive coverage is also covered in this section.
- **Part 2 (Chapters 6–10)** looks at safety management systems and explores safety management from a Canadian perspective and how it is impacted by the increasing globalization of the marketplace. More recent accident causation models are used to complement the long-standing theories that are still used. This section also highlights the growing reliance on the hazard assessment process and safety management systems.

- **Part 3 (Chapters 11–22)** makes specific references to Canadian legislation and compares the differences among different Canadian jurisdictions; for example, it compares noise regulations for each province and territory. Specific problems posed by our diverse country, such as temperature extremes, are also discussed. Chapter 12 explains the new Globally Harmonized System of Classification and Labelling of Chemicals (GHS) and WHMIS 2015. This section notes numerous hazards created as products, processes, and tools in the workplace evolve.

- **Part 4 (Chapters 23–28)** explores at issues facing Canada today. Floods, power blackouts, ice storms, terrorism, and border security are just some of the challenges facing workplaces and government agencies. Psychological health and safety, whistle-blower protection, violence, ethics, and the impact alcohol and drugs have on the workplace are issues that Canadian health and safety professionals must deal with more frequently. The growing concern with drug use on the workplace, and new hazards created by the proliferation of synthetic drugs, is covered. This section explores the impact of these contemporary workplace issues and the growing role of the workplace on the workers' overall well-being.

Canadian-specific content is also incorporated into the following features:

- Useful Weblinks, related to topics discussed, provide an additional learning resource for teachers and students.
- Safety Fact, Safety Myth, and Safety Tip boxes, Case Studies, and Discussion boxes use Canadian examples, where appropriate.
- Metric measurements along with references to Canadian legislation, associations, and organizations are used throughout.

Accident vs *Incident*

Traditionally, in the occupational health and safety field, the term *accident* was used to describe an event where unexpected injury or loss occurred, whereas *incident* was used to describe a "near-miss" event. As the philosophical view on occupational health and safety evolves, so does the terminology used in the field. The term *accident* is avoided by many health and safety professionals because of the potential perception or implication that the injury or loss was unavoidable—contrary to fundamental accident causation theories. The author agrees with the assertion that some form of mitigation or intervention could have averted these injury or loss events.

The term *accident* is universally understood among human resource professionals, corporate leaders, and safety practitioners to mean an event where injury or loss had occurred, but does it not imply inevitability. Further to the prevalence and acceptance of the term, it is used in the workers' compensation and safety legislation in most Canadian jurisdictions. Therefore, you will see the term throughout the text with due consideration for the context in which it is used.

SUPPLEMENTS

Instructor's Manual: This manual includes answers to the Review Questions at the end of each chapter (9780134855738).

Test Item File: The Test Bank contains 10 true/false and 5 multiple choice questions for every chapter (9780134855752).

Both the Instructor's Manual and Test Item File are available for downloading from a password-protected section of Pearson Education Canada's online catalogue (pearson.com/higher-education). Navigate to your book's catalogue page to view a list of those supplements that are available. See your local sales representative for details and access.

Acknowledgments

The author acknowledges the invaluable assistance of the editors and staff at Pearson Education Canada in developing the Canadian edition of this book: Mark Grzeskowiak, Acquisitions Editor; Madhu Ranadive and John Polanszky, Content Managers; Christine Langone, Content Developer; Sarah Gallagher, Project Manager; Kathleen Reed, Copy Editor; and Audrey Dorsch, Proofreader.

Finally, the author would like to thank the following people who took time and effort to provide thoughtful and meaningful reviews during the development of the two Canadian editions of this textbook:

Jean-Louis Castonguay, McGill University
John Cocchio, University of Alberta
Warren J. Fox, British Columbia Institute of Technology
Paul G. Halleran, College of the North Atlantic
Abdul Hameed, Sheridan College
Chun-Yip Hon, Ryerson University
Helen Mersereau, University College of Cape Breton
Paul Phillips, Northern Alberta Institute of Technology
Don Sayers, University of New Brunswick
Julie Aitken Schermer, University of Western Ontario
Gary Stroich, Northern Alberta Institute of Technology
Caroline Wakim, Algonquin College
Moreen Jones Weekes, Centennial College
Kathryn Woodcock, Ryerson University

Part 1
General Principles of Health and Safety

Chapter 1

Health and Safety Movement, Then and Now

MAJOR TOPICS

- Developments before the Industrial Revolution
- Milestones in the Canadian Safety Movement
- Tragedies and Their Impact on Safety in Canada
- Role of Organized Labour
- Role of Specific Health Problems
- Development of Accident Prevention Programs
- Health and Safety Movement Today
- New Materials, New Processes, and New Problems
- Rapid Growth in the Profession
- Return on Investment in Health and Safety Management

safety movement Began during World War II when all of the various practitioners of occupational health and safety began to see the need for cooperative efforts. This movement is very strong today.

accident An unplanned or unexpected event that results in injuries to people or loss of product or process.

The **safety movement** in Canada has developed steadily since the early 1900s. About 90 years ago, at the beginning of the Great Depression, industrial **accidents** were commonplace in this country; for example, in 1930, the number of fatalities due to industrial accidents recorded was 1,607.[1] During this period, legislation, precedent, and public opinion all favoured management. There were few protections for workers' safety. Eighty-five years later in 2015, with the population and the workforce almost four times greater, the number of occupational fatalities in Canada had dropped to 852.[2]

The long-term trend shows a decline in the number of workplace fatalities; however, during the past two decades, this progress has slowed and, in some years, even spiked back over 1,000.[3] As shown in Figure 1–1, the fatality rates are declining very slowly. This equates to approximately 3 worker fatalities each day in Canada. Beyond the statistics, these numbers represent real tragedies for the families whose loved ones are killed on the job. As we will discuss in Chapter 9, fatalities are only the tip of the proverbial iceberg—there are many times greater numbers who lose time from work from debilitating injuries.

Figure 1–1 Fatalities in Canada, 2015.

	2005	2006	2007	2008	2009	2010	2011	2012	2013	2014	2015
Fatalities	1,098	976	1,055	1,035	939	1,014	919	977	902	919	852

Source: Based on Association of Workers' Compensation Boards of Canada, Key Statistical Measures. Retrieved from http://awcbc.org/?page_id=9759.

Until recently, improvements in safety have been the result of pressure for legislation to promote health and safety, the steadily increasing costs associated with accidents and injuries, and the professionalization of safety as an occupation. Improvements today are driven by a greater awareness of the cost effectiveness and resultant competitiveness gained from a safe and healthy workforce. As the **Information Age** continues to unfold, organizations place a greater value on the overall well-being of their employees and, in particular, protecting mental health. As society and the workplace evolve, we will see increased collaboration between Human Resources and Safety departments as workers' psychological health and safety moves into the spotlight.

This chapter examines the history of the safety movement in Canada and how it has developed over the years. Such a perspective will help practising and prospective safety professionals form a better understanding of both their roots and their future.

DEVELOPMENTS BEFORE THE INDUSTRIAL REVOLUTION

It is important for students of industrial health and safety to first study the past. Understanding the past can help health and safety professionals examine the present and future with a sense of perspective and continuity. Modern developments in health and safety are neither isolated nor independent. Rather, they are part of the long continuum of developments in the health and safety movement.

The continuum begins with the days of the ancient Babylonians. During that time, circa 1780 B.C., their ruler Hammurabi developed his **Code of Hammurabi**. The code encompassed all of the laws of the land at that time, showed Hammurabi to be a just ruler, and set a precedent followed by other Mesopotamian kings. The significance of the code from the perspective of health and safety is that it contained clauses dealing with injuries, allowable fees for physicians, and monetary damages assessed against those who injured others.[4] This clause from the code illustrates Hammurabi's concern for the proper handling of injuries: "If a man has caused the loss of a gentleman's eye, his own eye shall be caused to be lost."[5]

This movement continued and emerged in later Egyptian civilization. As evidenced by the temples and pyramids that still remain, the Egyptians were an industrious people. Much of their labour was provided by slaves, and there is ample evidence that slaves were not treated well—that is, unless it suited the needs of the Egyptian taskmasters.

One such case occurred during the reign of Ramses II (circa 1200 B.C.), who undertook a major construction project, the Ramesseum. To ensure the maintenance of a workforce sufficient to build this huge temple bearing his name, Ramses created an industrial medical service to care for the workers. They were required to bathe daily in the Nile and were given regular medical examinations. Sick workers were isolated.[6]

The Romans also were vitally concerned with health and safety, as can be seen from the remains of their construction projects. The Romans built aqueducts, sewerage systems, public baths, latrines, and well-ventilated houses.[7]

As civilization progressed, so did health and safety developments. Philippus Aureolus produced a treatise on the pulmonary diseases of miners, which was not published until 26 years after his death in 1567. Titled *On the Miners' Sickness and Other Diseases of Miners,*

Information Age The current period of our history brought on by computers and digital technology. The proliferation of microcomputers and these technologies fostered by the enhancement of the global economy.

Code of Hammurabi Developed by the ruler Hammurabi around 1780 B.C. during the time of the Babylonians, this code encompassed all of the laws of the land at that time. The significant aspect for our purposes is that it contained clauses dealing with injuries, allowable fees for physicians, and monetary damages assessed against those who injured others.

the treatise covered diseases of smelter workers and metallurgists and diseases associated with the handling of and exposure to mercury. Around the same time, Georgius Agricola published his treatise *De Re Metallica*, emphasizing the need for ventilation in mines and illustrating various devices that could be used to introduce fresh air into mines.[8]

The eighteenth century saw the contributions of Bernardino Ramazzini, who wrote *Discourse on the Diseases of Workers*. Ramazzini drew conclusive parallels between diseases suffered by workers and their occupations. He related occupational diseases to the handling of harmful materials and to irregular or unnatural movements of the body. Much of what Ramazzini wrote is still relevant today.[9]

Later in the same century, the start of the Industrial Revolution changed forever the methods of producing goods. According to Joseph LaDou, the changes in production brought about by the Industrial Revolution can be summarized as follows:

inanimate power Power that is lacking life or spirit. During the Industrial Revolution, humans and animals were replaced with inanimate power (e.g., steam power).

- the introduction of **inanimate power** (e.g., steam power) to replace people and animal power,
- the substitution of machines for people,
- the introduction of new methods for converting raw materials, and
- the organization and specialization of work, resulting in a division of labour.[10]

These changes necessitated a greater focus of attention on the health and safety of workers. Steam power increased markedly the potential for life-threatening injuries, as did machines. The new methods used for converting raw materials also introduced new risks of injuries and diseases. Specialization, by increasing the likelihood of boredom and inattentiveness, also made the workplace a more dangerous environment.

MILESTONES IN THE CANADIAN SAFETY MOVEMENT

The safety movement in this country traces its roots to England. During the Industrial Revolution, child labour in factories was common. The hours were long, the work hard, and the conditions often unhealthy and unsafe. Following an outbreak of fever among the children working in their cotton mills, the people of Manchester, England, began demanding better working conditions in the factories. Public pressure eventually forced a government response, and in 1802 the Health and Morals of Apprentices Act was passed. This was a milestone piece of legislation: It marked the beginning of governmental involvement in workplace safety.

In the 1880s when the industrial sector was booming and the Industrial Revolution in full swing, hazardous working conditions were commonplace, especially in the factories of the larger urban centres such as Montreal and Toronto, where children were exploited. The public outcry against these conditions led to the birth of occupational health and safety legislation in Canada. In 1884 the Ontario Factories Act was passed. Its main purpose was to stop child labour and establish some basic rules of conduct for factory owners. The act limited working days to 10 hours and set a minimum age limit of 12 years for boys and 14 for girls.[11] However, the rules were vague and difficult to enforce and ultimately did very little to limit injuries or accidents in the factories.

Common law precedents established in England in the early 1800s were adopted by Canadian courts in the later part of the century when dealing with employer/worker disputes regarding injuries. Workers who were injured on the job had the right to sue their employer, but the cost of such a suit was in itself an adequate deterrent for most low-paid workers. Those who did make it to court had the cards stacked against them because the **employer-biased laws** that existed at the time provided three lines of defence to employers:

employer-biased laws A collection of laws that favoured employers over employees in establishing a responsibility for workplace safety.

Contributory Negligence If a worker's action, in any way contributed to the injury or accident, then the worker would be deemed fully responsible, no damages would be paid, and the full blame would be placed upon the employee.

Fellow Servant Rule An employer could not be held liable for any injury to a worker if any other worker was negligent in his duties. This essentially meant that in order for employers to be held liable, they would have to have been personally involved in the accident.

Assumption of Risk Another defence used by employers at the time was that the worker accepted the risks and inherent dangers when employment was accepted. (Today's thrill-seekers may be familiar with the phrase because signature of an "assumption of risk" release waiver is often required before embarking on many dangerous activities.)

One of the most important developments in the history of the safety movement in Canada occurred in 1914 when **workers' compensation** was introduced. Workers' compensation actually had its beginnings in Germany in 1884, and the practice soon spread throughout the rest of Europe. The Ontario government began studying the German program in 1900 but didn't develop much momentum for change until 1910, under pressure from both labour and industry.[12] Ontario Premier James Whitney then appointed Sir William Meredith to investigate the options for a workers' compensation program for Ontario. Through intense research and travel throughout Europe, Meredith was able to draft his own set of rules, which became the Ontario Workmen's Compensation Act of 1914.

The delay in including the provision for compensating injured workers into Canadian law (30 years after the passage of similar legislation in Germany) was largely due to a difference in workplace safety priorities: The focus in Germany had been on the provision of compensation for injured workers, whereas the main objective in Canada was to improve working conditions through labour laws, with the aim of reducing the number of workplace injuries.

Each provincial and territorial jurisdiction subsequently enacted its own legislation, all based on the basic principles that Sir William Meredith put forth in Ontario in 1914. Workers' compensation is examined in more depth in Chapter 5.

The next significant development in the history of Canada's health and safety movement came with the passage of Industrial Standards acts in Ontario, Alberta, and Quebec in 1935. These acts were intended to parallel the Wagner Act (more correctly known as the National Labor Relations Act) in the United States. Although the Wagner Act dealt with the workers' right to form and participate in labour unions and to engage in collective bargaining with employers, the Canadian acts confined themselves mainly to setting out rules for employers regarding pay and hours of work—particularly in the construction, clothing, and furniture industries. In Ontario, the act gave the provincial government the power to set wages and hours of work in some sectors. Unlike the American Wagner Act, although they legalized collective bargaining, the Canadian acts did not encourage the formation of unions.

World War II affected every aspect of life for most Canadians, whether at home or fighting overseas. Of those who did remain, most were called upon to support the war effort. Factories mobilized around the clock to produce the supplies and hardware required for the war. Since most of the reasonably fit men were off fighting, the factories were staffed by a large number of women as well as by older men. This precious (because scarce) labour force was trained well, and the best equipment and resources were provided. Productivity and safety were a very high priority, and accident rates fell. Ergonomic studies by the military were applied to civilian factory workers to enhance productivity and reduce accidents and injuries.

The next significant advance in occupational health and safety was made in Saskatchewan with the passing of the **Occupational Health and Safety Act** in 1972. The first such legislation of its kind in North America, this act provided for the establishment of occupational health and safety committees in the workplace. Often referred to as "joint

contributory negligence An injured worker's own negligence contributed to the accident. If the actions of employees contributed to their own injuries, the employer is absolved of any liability.

fellow servant rule Employers are not liable for workplace injuries that result from negligence of other employees.

assumption of risk Based on the theory that people who accept a job assume the risks that go with it. It says employees who work voluntarily should accept the consequences of their actions on the job rather than blaming the employer.

workers' compensation A no-fault, employer-paid, insurance program developed to allow injured employees to be compensated appropriately without having to take their employers to court.

Occupational Health and Safety Act Legislation that sets out the rights and duties of all parties in the workplace for the protection of workers against hazards on the job.

right to participate Workers' basic right to participate in their own safety (e.g., via committees).

right to know Workers' basic right to be informed of any hazards that exist in the workplace.

right to refuse Workers' basic right to refuse work that they believe is unsafe.

Ham Commission Royal commission headed by Dr. James Ham in 1975, dealing with miners' illnesses, laid the foundation for Ontario's first Occupational Health and Safety Act.

internal responsibility system A mechanism to allow employers, supervisors, and workers to monitor one another's actions and ensure compliance with legislation.

WHMIS Workplace Hazardous Materials Information System. A national communication system implemented on October 31, 1988, that provides the worker with information on the production, use, storage, and safe handling of hazardous materials in the workplace. The program was updated to WHMIS 2015, to align with the Globally Harmonized System of Classification and Labelling of Chemicals (GHS).

presumptive legislation Presumptive legislation links a particular occupation with a disease or condition that has been shown to be a hazard associated with that occupation. As a result of this linkage, if an individual employed in the occupation covered by the presumption contracts a disease or condition that is specified in the presumptive law, then that disease or condition is presumed to have come from that occupation. In this case, the burden of proof shifts from the employee to the employer to demonstrate that the condition was not in fact associated with the occupation but with another cause.

post-traumatic stress disorder (PTSD) Post-traumatic stress disorder (PTSD) is a serious condition that can develop after a person has experienced or witnessed a traumatic or terrifying event in which serious harm occurred or was threatened. While PTSD is most often linked with military personnel or first responders, it may also be linked to ongoing emotional trauma, such as exposure to chronic bullying, harassment, or an abusive relationship at work.

occupational health and safety" committees, these groups consisted of both management and workers. The birth of these joint committees provided the foundation for two of the three fundamental rights that all Canadians now exercise: the **right to participate** and the **right to know**. The following year the Act was amended to include the third basic right we have as workers in Canada: the **right to refuse**.

The Royal Commission on the Health and Safety of Workers in Mines in Ontario represents another major milestone in the safety movement in Canada. Prompted by the Elliott Lake miners' strike in 1974 (see more below) and chaired by Dr. James Ham, what became known as the **Ham Commission** first presented the philosophy of an **internal responsibility system**. This system gives responsibility to both employers and workers to cooperate to control occupational health and safety hazards. By its nature, this system is self-regulating, with minimal interference or enforcement from outside agencies. The system assigns specific duties to both workers and management, and it is in the best interest of both parties to fulfill their assigned roles. The taxpayer also saves because fewer safety officers are required to monitor each workplace. The recommendations of the Ham Commission form the basis of Ontario's Occupational Health and Safety Act, passed in 1978.

Another significant development, specifically in the protection of workers who handle or are exposed to hazardous materials, **WHMIS** (Workplace Hazardous Materials Information System) legislation became law when the federal government passed Bill C-70 in 1987. This bill established the criteria for identifying hazardous materials and defined the format and content of labels for containers of hazardous materials and their safety data sheets. WHMIS provides the information to back up the workers' right to know about hazards in the workplace, which was enshrined in earlier legislation. Each province and territory has incorporated WHMIS into its own health and safety legislation. Canada has aligned WHMIS with the Globally Harmonized System of Classification and Labelling of Chemicals (GHS). More on WHMIS can be found in Chapter 12.

In 2002, Manitoba passed **presumptive legislation** for firefighters. Due to the prevalence of certain diseases and conditions in particular occupations, these diseases or conditions are presumed to have come from that occupation. This legislation shifts the burden of proof from the employee to the employer to demonstrate that the condition was not in fact associated with the occupation. Most other jurisdictions soon followed with similar legislation for firefighters.

The Manitoba government also led the way in 2015, by introducing amendments to the Workers' Compensation Act that would recognize **post-traumatic stress disorder (PTSD)** as a work-related occupational disease. These changes impacted how employers consider the overall well-being of their employees and also clearly reflected the evolution of workplace safety's shift toward wellness of the worker.

In response to reports by Dr. Martin Shain, in which he stated that there are seven areas of law trending toward holding employers increasingly responsible for providing a psychologically safe workplace, the Mental Health Commission of Canada (MHCC) took up the cause and championed the development of a national standard for Psychological Health and Safety in the Workplace. In early 2011, an agreement was reached among the Government of Canada, the Mental Health Commission of Canada, the CSA Group (CSA), and the Bureau de Normalisation du Quebec (BNQ) to begin the process of developing a national standard.

In 2013, the *CAN/CSA-Z1003-13/BNQ 9700-803/2013* standard was released with a complementary implementation guide. The movement to bring mental health into the light by celebrity endorsements and major Canadian corporations further supports the converging role of the human resources and safety professions. The needle is moving from doing no harm to the worker to enhancing their overall well-being. Addressing mental health goes beyond the bottom line: It speaks to the changing workplace, worker demands, and societal norms. More information on psychological health and safety in the workplace can be found in Chapter 23.

Figure 1–2 summarizes these and other significant milestones in the development of the safety movement in Canada.

Figure 1–2 Milestones in the safety movement.

B.C.	
1780	Code of Hammurabi
1200s	Ramses's maintenance of the workforce
370	Hippocrates observes colic in lead mine workers
A.D.	
1	Pliny identifies lead, mercury, sulphur, and zinc as occupational hazards
1500s	Philippus Aureolus, miners' sickness and disease from metal vapour
1556	Agricola, *De Re Metallica*, mine ventilation requirements
1600s	French hatmakers suffer dementia from mercury exposure
1700s	Ramazzini, father of occupational medicine
1760	The Industrial Revolution
1788	Chimney Sweeps Act passed in England
1800s	Common law, anti-labour laws
1884	First workers' compensation program (Germany)
1914	Canada's first workers' compensation program (Ontario)
1926	Heinrich, development of several accident theories and models
1929	The Great Depression
1935	Industrial Standards Act
1939	World War II
1972	Canada's first Occupational Health and Safety Act (Saskatchewan)
1974	Elliot Lake miners' strike
1975	Ham Commission
1987	WHMIS introduced
2002	Presumptive Legislation
2003	Bill C-45, the Westray Bill
2013	Psychological Health and Safety standard

TRAGEDIES AND THEIR IMPACT ON SAFETY IN CANADA

Health and safety tragedies in the workplace have greatly accelerated the pace of the safety movement in Canada. On a global scale, stories in the news about devastating workplace disasters are frequent, but in Canada they are fewer. However, occasionally some region is faced with the consequences of a major workplace accident. Three significant disasters to occur in Canadian workplaces were the Elliot Lake miners' strike in Ontario, the sinking of the *Ocean Ranger* drilling rig off the Newfoundland coast, and the Westray Mine explosion in Nova Scotia. This section briefly explains these three tragedies and looks at a few others to illustrate their lasting effects on the health and safety movement in Canada.

Elliot Lake Miners' Strike

In 1974, Elliot Lake uranium miners went on strike to protest deplorable health and safety conditions in their industry, which had led to very high rates of lung cancer. Although no single event at the mine may be considered a tragedy, the collective effects of the mining conditions at the time were indeed tragic. In 1969, 5 years before the strike, the Ontario Workman's Compensation Board stated that 16 out of 20 deaths of Elliot Lake miners were the result of lung cancer.[13]

The strike at Elliot Lake in 1974 would turn out to be the catalyst for the creation of Ontario's Occupational Health and Safety Act. The Ham Commission's 1976 report made over 100 recommendations for the mining industry and for workplaces in general. These recommendations not only provided the basis for the Ontario Occupational Health and Safety Act, passed in 1978, but also enhanced safety regulations in most other industries throughout Canada.

Sinking of the *Ocean Ranger*

On Valentine's Day in 1982, as the *Ocean Ranger* sat 175 nautical miles off the Newfoundland and Labrador coasts, anchored to the ocean floor, a violent storm raged. The storm caused a window to smash in the ballast control room, and from that point on a tragic chain of events caused the world's largest offshore drilling rig to capsize. Given the brutal weather conditions and the distance from land, any attempts to rescue survivors from the icy waters were fruitless: 84 people, including 56 Newfoundlanders, perished that stormy night in the cold Atlantic.

Because the rig was registered in the United States but had a Canadian crew and was in Canadian waters, both the Canadian and American governments ran their own inquiries. The Canadian inquiry was called the Royal Commission on the *Ocean Ranger* Marine Disaster, while the American investigation was a joint inquiry of the US Coast Guard and the National Transportation Safety Board. As a result of the Royal Commission on the *Ocean Ranger* Marine Disaster, several safety systems were developed and installed on offshore oil rigs. Other changes resulting from the inquiry were engineering changes to the ballast control system to improve rig stability, improved training for rig personnel, better survival suit access, and regular engineering inspections. The recommendations resulting from both inquiries have made offshore oil exploration much safer. However, the power of the ocean can exceed any safety system. The *Ocean Ranger*, like the *Titanic*, was said to be "unsinkable."

Westray Mine Disaster

Like most workplace disasters, the Westray mine explosion was the result of "actions, omissions, mistakes, incompetence, apathy, cynicism, stupidity and neglect," said Mr. Justice Peter Richard in his report on the tragedy.[14] On May 9, 1992, at 5:18 a.m., a little less than 2 months after the mine's official opening in Plymouth, Nova Scotia, methane gas in the mine ignited, causing an explosion so large that it was felt in two nearby communities. The blast trapped and killed 26 miners. The community was devastated, even though they were all too familiar with loss of life in the mines.

An inquiry into the accident took 5 years and cost nearly $5 million. The report's title, *The Westray Story: A Predictable Path to Disaster*, foreshadows the tone of the document. It points out a lengthy list of shortcomings and makes several recommendations for improving coal mine safety. Charges laid against two managers were eventually dropped because there were no laws at the time that held company senior officers liable in such cases. Although laws ensuring **employer liability** have existed throughout the world for over 100 years, gaps in Canadian law provided employers with immunity from responsibility for their workers' safety. Finally in November 2003, after years of lobbying by the United Steel Workers Union, Bill C-45—or the Westray Bill—became law. These amendments to the Criminal Code now hold corporations and their senior officers accountable for criminal negligence in the workplace.

employer liability In 1877, the Employer's Liability Law was passed and established the potential for employers to be liable for accidents that occurred in the workplace.

Other Notable Workplace Disasters

On January 23, 2014, at the Résidence du Havre nursing home in L'Isle-Verte, Quebec, a fire broke out around 12:35 a.m., killing 32 people and injuring 15. Because the fire spread so rapidly through the all-wooden building, rescuers were unable to evacuate many residents, who were in wheelchairs and walkers. The subsequent investigation resulted in a re-evaluation of sprinkler systems and building requirements for similar facilities throughout Quebec.

In November 2012, a garment-factory fire in Bangladesh killed 112 employees. The magnitude of the tragedy was enhanced when it was discovered that the factory produced garments for sale in several major retail outlets in North America. Fire inspectors suspected that an electrical short-circuit caused the blaze, which spread quickly because of the flammable nature of the material used to produce T-shirts in the factory. There were complaints that well-known retailers in the Western world were partially culpable in the tragedy because there was evidence that they knew of the unsafe conditions beforehand. The garment factory in question had a functioning fire alarm and the alarm did go off properly. Unfortunately, supervisors demanded that workers go back to their sewing machines and even blocked an exit door that workers could have used to escape the conflagration. It was learned in the subsequent investigation that the factory's fire extinguishers did not work and were displayed only to fool inspectors. A follow-up investigation revealed that 100 workers had been burned to death inside the factory, while another 12 jumped to their deaths to escape the flames. This tragedy added to the mounting pressure for companies that contract with offshore manufacturers to pressure those manufacturers to implement safe and healthy work practices.

A collision that killed six people occurred between a OC Transpo double-decker bus and a Via Rail train in the Ottawa suburb of Barrhaven on September 18, 2013. Two years later the Transportation Safety Board (TSB) report found that the driver of the bus was most likely distracted by the video screens that he was required to monitor as part of his job. The TSB made recommendations to Transport Canada to develop guidelines for the use of in-vehicle video screens to reduce distraction, to develop crashworthiness standards for passenger buses, and to equip passenger buses with crashworthy event data recorders.

While the lessons learned from investigating these workplace tragedies is invaluable, the devastation from the loss of lives and property is incalculable. For example, the Lac-Mégantic rail disaster in July 2013 killed 47 people and decimated the downtown area. Whether it is these spectacular events or the more subtle epidemic of psychological injuries, the safety professional and organizational leaders have a role to play in gleaning lessons from these tragic events and creating safer and healthier workplaces.

ROLE OF ORGANIZED LABOUR

Organized labour has played a crucial role in the development of the safety movement in Canada. From the outset of the Industrial Revolution in this country, organized labour has fought for safer working conditions and appropriate compensation for workers injured on the job. Many of the earliest developments in the safety movement were the result of long and hard-fought battles by organized labour.

The Trade Union Act of 1872, which legalized unions in Canada, was the first big step in Canadian industrial labour relations. Later, in 1919, the general strike in Winnipeg, which was Western Canada's largest city at the time, established unions as a significant force for workers' interests. During the strike, 30,000 workers joined forces, bringing the city to a standstill for 42 days. The strike ended on "Bloody Saturday" when two civilian demonstrators were killed and several labour leaders were arrested.

In the 1920s, reflecting the advances in automation, many of the old craft unions were replaced by industrial unions. And in 1956, in the course of uniting several Canadian

organized labour A group of employees who join together to fight for the rights of all employees (i.e., unions).

unions, the Canadian Labour Congress (CLC) was formed. In 1961, with support from the CLC, the New Democratic Party (NDP) was formed.

Although the role of unions in promoting safety is generally acknowledged, one school of thought takes the opposite view, holding that union involvement actually slowed the development of the safety movement. Proponents of this view maintain that unions allowed their demands for safer working conditions to become entangled with their demands for better wages and, as a result, they met with resistance from management. Regardless of the point of view, however, there is no question that working conditions in the earliest years of the safety movement often reflected management's insensitivity to safety concerns.

anti-labour laws Nineteenth-century laws that strongly favoured employers.

Among the most important contributions of organized labour to the safety movement in Canada was their work to overturn **anti-labour laws** relating to safety in the workplace. These laws, as mentioned above, were the fellow servant rule, the statutes defining contributory negligence, and the concept of assumption of risk.[15]

Because the overwhelming majority of industrial accidents involved negligence on the part of one or more workers, historically employers had little to worry about. Therefore, they had little incentive to promote a safe work environment. Organized labour played a significant role in bringing unsafe working conditions to the attention of the general public. Public awareness—and, in some cases, outrage—eventually led to these employer-biased laws being overturned.

The Ontario Workplace Health and Safety Agency, in a report published in 2004, "found that 78–79 percent of unionized workplaces reported high compliance with health and safety legislation, while only 54–61 percent of non-unionized workplaces reported such compliance."[16] This would indicate that pressure from unions still plays an important part in workplace health and safety.

>>> **DISCUSSION CASE** | What Is Your Opinion?

Two health and safety students are debating the issue of corporate responsibility. Tom thinks that over the years industry has clearly demonstrated its unwillingness to provide a safe and healthy work environment for employees. He offers examples such as the Westray and Elliot Lake mines as evidence. Janet agrees that industry does, indeed, have a checkered past on health and safety, but she thinks employers have learned that their workforce is a valuable asset that should be protected. Tom's response is, "Take away federal and provincial regulations, and industry would return to their old ways in less than a year." Join this debate. What is your opinion?

ROLE OF SPECIFIC HEALTH PROBLEMS

Specific health problems linked to workplace hazards have played a significant role in the development of the modern health and safety movement. These health problems contributed to public awareness of dangerous and unhealthy working conditions, which, in turn, led to legislation, regulations, better work procedures, and better working conditions.

Lung disease in coal miners was a major problem in the 1800s, particularly in Great Britain, where much of the Western world's coal was mined at the time. Frequent contact with coal dust led to a widespread outbreak of anthracosis among Great Britain's coal miners. Also known as the *black spit,* this disease persisted from the early 1800s, when it was first identified, until around 1875, when it was finally eliminated by such health and safety measures as ventilation and decreased work hours.

In the 1930s, Great Britain saw a resurgence of lung problems among coal miners. By the early 1940s, British scientists were using the term *coal-miner's pneumoconiosis,* or CMP (now more usually known as *coal workers' pneumoconiosis,* or CWP), to describe a disease from which many miners suffered. Great Britain designated CMP, also known as black lung, a separate and compensable disease in 1943. Health problems, however, were not limited to coal miners. Other types of miners developed a variety of diseases, the most common of which was silicosis. Again, it took a huge outcry from those affected—like the Elliot Lake miners discussed earlier, for example—to focus attention on a serious workplace problem.

Mercury poisoning is another health problem that has contributed to the evolution of the health and safety movement by focusing public attention on unsafe conditions in the workplace. The disease was first noticed among the citizens of a Japanese fishing village in the early 1930s. This disease, with symptoms such as convulsions, loss of vision and hearing, and in extreme cases paralysis or death, was common in Minamata, but extremely rare throughout the rest of Japan. After investigation of the situation, it was discovered that a nearby chemical plant periodically dumped methyl mercury into the bay that was the village's primary source of food. Consequently, the citizens of this small village ingested hazardous doses of mercury every time they ate fish from the bay.

Mercury poisoning also became an issue in Canada after the Ojibwa families on the English-Wabigoon River discovered that their main source of food was severely contaminated in 1970. From 1962 up to that point, Dryden Chemicals had dumped 10 tonnes of mercury (used in the pulp-bleaching process for the paper industry) into the river. In 1985, the people of Grassy Narrows and White Dog reserves received close to $17 million in compensation. Great Lakes Forest Products Ltd., which bought Dryden Chemicals Ltd. in 1979, contributed $6 million; the previous owner, Reed Inc., paid $5.75 million; and the federal and provincial governments paid the rest.

The legacy of such disregard for public health and safety is still evident today, however. A study of the people of Grassy Narrows and White Dog in 2004 found many of the classic long-term symptoms of mercury poisoning—numbness in the hands, upper body, and legs; pain in the joints; loss of skin sensation; impaired balance; and poor muscle coordination— in a number of people ranging in age from teens to some in their seventies. As well, "mercury poisoning can lead to a weakening of the immune system and therefore high levels of other illnesses in these communities may be related to mercury."[17]

Today, mercury is considered a "designated" substance and its use and handling is strictly regulated in each province and territory. Canada-wide standards are also enforced by Environment Canada to ensure that unified environmental protection goals are met. (A distinguishing factor between occupational health and safety issues and environmental issues is often whether exposure to harmful substances spreads beyond the workplace. When harmful products are used in the workplace, the problem is with occupational health and safety. When the public is exposed to these products, the concern is environmental.)

As with other substances that cause various forms of lung cancer, asbestos is another important substance in the evolution of the modern health and safety movement. By the time it was determined that asbestos was a hazardous material, the fibres of which can cause asbestosis or lung cancer (mesothelioma), thousands of buildings contained the substance. As these buildings began to age, the asbestos that was used to insulate pipes began to break down. And as asbestos breaks down, it releases dangerous microscopic fibres into the air. These fibres are so hazardous that removing asbestos from old buildings has become a highly specialized task requiring special equipment and training.

occupational accidents
Unplanned events that cause injury to a worker.

With so many health issues developing in various workplaces throughout the world, the focus for many occupational health and safety professionals has gradually shifted from **occupational accidents** to **occupational diseases**. Illnesses caused by many workplace products may not begin to show up in the worker for several years—or even decades— after exposure. Because of this **latency period**, the correlation between the diseases and the workplace can easily go unnoticed, which is why, historically, occupational health and safety practitioners have been more concerned with injuries and other immediate effects of accidents.

occupational diseases
Pathological conditions brought about by workplace conditions or factors.

latency period Time after exposure to a hazardous product before symptoms appear.

DEVELOPMENT OF ACCIDENT PREVENTION PROGRAMS

accident prevention The act of preventing a happening that may cause loss or injury to a person.

In the modern workplace there are many different types of **accident prevention** programs, ranging from the simple to the complex. Widely used accident prevention techniques include failure minimization, fail-safe designs, isolation, lockouts, screening, personal protective equipment, redundancy, timed replacements, and many others. These techniques are individual components of broader safety programs. Such programs have evolved since the late 1800s.

In the early 1800s, employers had little concern for the safety of workers and little incentive to be concerned. Consequently, organized safety programs were nonexistent, a situation that continued for many years. However, between World War I and World War II, industry discovered the connection between quality and safety. Then, during World War II, troop call-ups and deployments created severe labour shortages. Faced with these shortages, employers could not afford to lose workers to accidents or for any other reason. This realization created a greater openness toward giving safety the serious consideration it deserved. For example, according to the Society of Manufacturing Engineers, around this time industry began to realize the following:

- Improved engineering could prevent accidents.
- Employees were willing to learn and adhere to safety rules.
- Safety rules could be established and enforced.
- Financial savings from safety improvement could be reaped by savings in compensation and medical bills.[18]

With these realizations came the long-needed incentive for employers to begin playing an active role in creating and maintaining a safe workplace. This, in turn, led to the development of organized safety programs sponsored by management. Early safety programs were based on what is known as the **three E's of safety**: engineering, education, and enforcement (see Figure 1–3). The engineering aspects of a safety program involve making design improvements to both product and process. By altering the design of a product, the processes used to manufacture it can be simplified and, as a result, made less dangerous. In addition, the manufacturing processes for products can be engineered in ways that decrease potential hazards associated with the processes.

three E's of safety Engineering, education, and enforcement.

Figure 1–3 Three E's of safety.

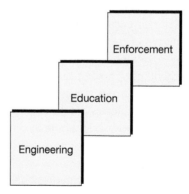

The education aspect of a safety program ensures that employees know how to work safely, why it is important to do so, and that safety is expected by management. Safety education typically covers the what, when, where, why, and how of safety.

The enforcement aspect of a safety program involves making sure that employees abide by safety policies, rules, regulations, practices, and procedures. Supervisors and fellow employees play a key role in the enforcement aspects of modern safety programs.

HEALTH AND SAFETY MOVEMENT TODAY

The health and safety movement has come a long way since the Industrial Revolution. Today there is widespread understanding of the importance of providing a safe and healthy workplace. The tone was set during and after World War II when all of the various practitioners of occupational health and safety began to see the need for cooperative efforts. These practitioners included safety engineers, safety managers, industrial hygienists, occupational health nurses, and physicians.

One of the earliest and most vocal proponents of the cooperative, or integrated, approach was H. G. Dyktor. He proposed the following objectives of integration:

- Learn more through sharing knowledge about health problems in the workplace, particularly those caused by toxic substances.
- Provide a greater level of expertise in evaluating health and safety problems.
- Provide a broad database that can be used to compare health and safety problems experienced by different companies in the same industry.
- Encourage accident prevention.
- Make employee health and safety a high priority.[19]

> ⟫⟫ **SAFETY FACT** | Safety Movement and War
>
> World War II actually had a positive effect on the modern health and safety movement. During the war, there was a shortage of able-bodied, skilled workers in factories supporting the war effort because most of these workers were in the armed services. Consequently, preserving the health and safety of the relatively few skilled workers still available was paramount. The law of supply and demand suddenly made workplace safety a significant issue, which it still is today. The military war is over, but the economic war still rages. To be competitive in this international conflict, employers today must follow the lead of their predecessors during World War II and protect their employees.

NEW MATERIALS, NEW PROCESSES, AND NEW PROBLEMS

The job of the health and safety professional is more complex than it has ever been. The materials from which products are made have become increasingly complex and exotic. Engineering metals now include carbon steels; alloy steels; high-strength, low-alloy steels; stainless steels; managing steels; cast steels; cast irons; tungsten; molybdenum; titanium; aluminum; copper; magnesium; lead; tin; zinc; and powdered metals. Each of these metals requires its own specialized process.

Nonmetals are more numerous and have also become more complex. Plastics, plastic alloys and blends, advanced composites, fibrous materials, elastomers, and ceramics also bring their own potential hazards to the workplace.

In addition to the more complex materials being used in modern industry and the new health and safety concerns associated with them, modern industrial processes are also becoming more complex. As these processes become automated, the potential hazards associated with them often increase. Computers; lasers; industrial robots; nontraditional processes such as explosive welding, photochemical machining, laser-beam machining, ultrasonic machining, and chemical milling; automated material handling; water-jet-cutting expert systems; flexible manufacturing cells; and computer-integrated manufacturing have all introduced new health and safety problems in the workplace and new challenges for the health and safety professional.

Chapter 25 is devoted to coverage of the special health and safety problems associated with computers, robots, and automation. In addition, coverage of specific aspects of these problems is provided in different chapters throughout this book.

RAPID GROWTH IN THE PROFESSION

The complexities of the modern workplace have made health and safety a growing profession. Diploma and degree programs in industrial technology typically include industrial safety courses. Some engineering degree programs have health and safety tracks. Several colleges and universities offer full degrees in occupational health and safety.

The inevitable result of the increased attention given to industrial health and safety is that more large companies are employing health and safety professionals and more small companies are assigning these duties to existing employees. This trend is likely to continue as employers see their responsibilities for health and safety spread beyond the workplace to the environment, the community, the users of their products, and the recipients of their by-products and waste. Support for employing health and safety professionals in the workplace also comes from the corporate financial departments, who see the increasing value of such employees.

RETURN ON INVESTMENT IN HEALTH AND SAFETY MANAGEMENT

Businesses tend to focus on the bottom line. Consequently, executives constantly pressure managers in their organizations—including health and safety professionals—to document their department's return on investment, or ROI. In other words, executives want to know that safety is not just about preventing losses, it can also make money for their organizations.

The Foster Wheeler Study

Foster Wheeler, a large construction firm in the United Kingdom, conducted a comprehensive 17-year study to determine if a link exists between workplace safety and productivity. Productivity, of course, is the key ingredient in the formula for profitability and competitiveness. Consequently, a demonstrable link between investing in workplace safety and an increase in productivity would show that safety produces a positive ROI. The **Foster Wheeler (FW) study** showed a very high correlation (63 percent) between safety and productivity.[20]

Foster Wheeler (FW) study Seventeen-year study conducted by Foster Wheeler, a large United Kingdom construction company, to determine if a link exists between workplace safety and productivity.

This study analyzed safety- and performance-related data from 19 construction projects that were completed over a 17-year period. The analysis was based on the following four indicators:

- Cost ratio (budgeted costs versus actual costs)
- Schedule ratio (planned schedule versus actual schedule)
- Safety (total hours of worker exposure versus time lost to injuries)
- Productivity ratio (budgeted man-hours versus actual man-hours)

By grouping these four indicators into six pairs, FW was able to use a technique called regression analysis to determine if an association existed between them. The key result was a 63 percent degree of overlap between safety and productivity. Best of all, the FW study showed that cutting the frequency of injury in half resulted in a 10 percent increase in productivity.[21]

This study, because of its length and comprehensive nature, pushed the health and safety movement into a new era. Along with other studies that have shown similar results, the Foster Wheeler study gives health and safety professionals the hard data they need to demonstrate the ROI of providing a safe and healthy work environment.

SUMMARY

1. Health and safety awareness has a long history. There is evidence of occupational health and safety efforts as far back as the time of the Egyptian pharaohs. The Code of Hammurabi, circa 1780 B.C., contained clauses that could be interpreted as early attempts at workers' compensation. There is also evidence of concern for health and safety during the time of the Romans.

2. Milestones in the development of the safety movement in Canada include the following: first workers' compensation programs in 1914, first health and safety act in 1972, Elliott Lake miners' strike in 1974, the Ham Commission Report in 1976, WHMIS in 1987, the Westray Bill in 2003, and the CSA standard for Psychological Health and Safety in the Workplace in 2013.

3. Organized labour has played a crucial role in the development of the safety movement in Canada. Particularly important was the work of unions to overturn anti-labour laws inhibiting safety in the workplace.

4. Specific health problems associated with the workplace have contributed to the development of the modern health and safety movement. These problems include lung diseases in miners, mercury poisoning, and lung cancer tied to asbestos, silica, and coal.

5. Tragedies such as the Elliot Lake miners' strike in Ontario, the sinking of the *Ocean Ranger* drilling rig off the Newfoundland and Labrador coast, and the Westray Mine explosion in Nova Scotia have changed the face of the safety movement in Canada.

6. As new products, procedures, and technology enter the workplace, the breadth of the occupational health and safety (OHS) professional's knowledge must increase to address these new hazards. By learning from past events and implementing a sound safety management system, these risks can be minimized.

7. The Foster Wheeler study has shown that investing in safety devices, tools, or training will show a very favourable return on investment.

Key Terms and Concepts

Accident	Ham Commission	Post-traumatic stress
Accident prevention	Inanimate power	disorder (PTSD)
Anti-labour laws	Information Age	Presumptive legislation
Assumption of risk	Internal responsibility system	Right to know
Code of Hammurabi	Latency period	Right to participate
Contributory negligence	Occupational accidents	Right to refuse
Employer-biased laws	Occupational diseases	Safety movement
Employer liability	Occupational Health and	Three E's of safety
Fellow servant rule	Safety Act	WHMIS
Foster Wheeler (FW) Study	Organized labour	Workers' compensation

Review Questions

1. To what cause(s) can the improvements in workplace safety made to date be attributed?

2. Explain the significance of the Code of Hammurabi in terms of the safety movement.

3. What significance has the mining industry had on the development of occupational health and safety throughout history?

4. Explain how major events in at least three provinces contributed to the development of occupational health and safety in Canada.

5. What contribution to the Canadian workplace was made by Sir William Meredith?

6. What are the three fundamental rights enjoyed by all Canadian workers?

7. What impact did labour shortages in World War II have on the safety movement?

8. Explain how workplace tragedies have affected the safety movement. Give examples.

9. Summarize briefly the role that organized labour has played in the advancement of the safety movement.

10. Define the following terms: fellow servant rule, contributory negligence, assumption of risk.

11. What are the key findings of the Forest Wheeler study?

Weblinks

Canadian Auto Workers

www.caw.ca/index.asp

The CAW is the largest private-sector union in Canada, with a long and rich history that has had a major impact on Canadian labour, reaching well beyond the automotive industry. Throughout the website, there is evidence of their significant role in advancing health and safety awareness.

Canadian Occupational Safety Magazine

http://www.cos-mag.com/

Your gateway to a world of online industrial and safety information. This online magazine has hundreds of interesting articles and safety resources, such as product reviews and links to other resources.

Employment and Social Development Canada

http://www.esdc.gc.ca/eng/home.shtml

The Department of Employment and Social Development (ESDC) is responsible for providing all Canadians with the tools they need to thrive and prosper in the workplace and community.

International Labour Organization

www.ilo.org

The International Labour Organization is the UN-specialized agency that seeks the promotion of social justice and internationally-recognized human and labour rights. It was founded in 1919 and is the only surviving major creation of the Treaty of Versailles, which brought the League of Nations into being; it became the first specialized agency of the UN in 1946.

Endnotes

[1] "Fatal Industrial Accidents in Canada in 1930." *The Labour Gazette* (March 1931), 365–373. [Online]. Available: http://socserv.mcmaster.ca/oldlabourstudies/onlinelearning/article.php?id=24. (Retrieved November 11, 2016).

[2] Association of Workers' Compensation Boards of Canada. *Canadian Workers' Compensation System—Year at a Glance*. (2013). [Online]. Available: http://awcbc.org/?page_id=11803. (Retrieved November 26, 2016).

[3] Ibid.

[4] J. LaDou, ed. *Introduction to Occupational Health and Safety*. (Chicago: National Safety Council, 1986), 28.

[5] Ibid., 28.

[6] A. Soubiran. "Medical Services under the Pharaohs." *Abbottempo* 1 (1963): 19–23.

[7] J. LaDou. *Occupational Health and Safety*, 31.

[8] Ibid., 34.

[9] Ibid., 35.

[10] Ibid., 37.

[11] D. W. Martyn Bone. "Historical Summary: Ontario in the 1880s." (November 2003). [Online]. Available: http://xenon.xe.com/~mbone/webtree/1880. (Retrieved June 20, 2004).

[12] Wally Fox-Decent. "A Look Way, Way Back at Our Compensation History." *Canadian Occupational Safety* (April 2003). [Online]. Available: http://www.industrialsourcebook.com/cgi-bin/archivef.pl?id=477. (Retrieved June 20, 2004).

[13] Roger Moody. "The Gulliver File—Mines, People and Land: A Global Battleground." *The Gulliver Rio Algom Dossier*. (1992). [Online]. Available: http://www.sea-us.org.au/gulliver/rioalgom.html. (Retrieved June 20, 2004).

[14] Martyn O'Malley. The Horror of Westray. *CBC News Online* (May 9, 2002). [Online]. Available: http://www.cbc.ca/news/features/westray.html. (Retrieved June 20, 2004).

[15] S. Minter and V. Sutcliff. "Fighting Two Wars." *Occupational Hazards* (July 1998): 41.

[16] Rory O'Neill. "When It Comes to Health and Safety, Your Life Should Be in Union Hands." *Labour Education* 1, no. 126 (2002). [Online]. Available: http://www.ilo.org/public/english/dialogue/actrav/publ/126/neill.pdf. (Retrieved June 20, 2004).

[17] Minter and Sutcliff. "Fighting Two Wars," 41.

[18] Julie Fine. "Communities Still Affected Decades Later: Mercury Poisoning at White Dog." Manitoba Eco-Network. *Eco-Journal* 14, no. 5 (November/December 2004). [Online]. Available: http://www.mbeconetwork.org/archives/eco-j-14(5).asp#WhiteDog. (Retrieved April 20, 2005).

[19] H. G. Dyktor. "Integration of Industrial Hygiene with Industrial Medicine." *Industrial Medicine* 9, no. 4 (1940): 193.

[20] A. Hamilton and H. Hardy. Industrial Toxicology (Boston: John Wright, 1983), 2.

[21] Ibid.

Chapter 2
Safety Motivation and Culture in Organizations

One of the best ways to promote safety is to design it into the tools, machines, and technologies with which people interact in the workplace. Safety analysis can also be effective by eliminating hazards before they cause accidents and illnesses. Kim Laing, of St. John Ambulance said that safety is best when built into the system and not viewed as a separate add-on. "The best programs are those that are not even seen—safe practices are just how we do business here."[1] When we learn to drive, ski, or perform numerous activities, we are taught the safe way to do each task—safety is not presented as an add-on. A job done correctly is a job done safely.

However, even the best design or analysis cannot completely eliminate the potential for accidents. Employee engagement in the process is a critical element for success; therefore persistent promotion and continuous improvement is needed for optimum workplace health and safety. Motivating employees is one of the fundamental roles of leaders at all levels and continues to be a challenge for organizations.

SAFETY STARTS WITH LEADERSHIP

The strategies and activities employed to improve safety or effect change in the organization will reflect the leadership philosophy of the company. One common classification of leadership style is to label the leader as either *transformational* or *transactional*.

Renowned organizational behaviour experts James M. Kouzes and Barry Z. Posner define **transformational leadership** as "the kind of leadership that gets people to infuse their energies into strategies."[2]

Transformational leadership is about encouraging others to first visualize and then bring about a new order. "The essence of transformational leadership appears to be inspiring, developing and empowering followers."[3]

Transactional leadership, on the other hand, promotes compliance of its followers through both rewards and punishments. This bureaucratic approach to safety is seen through prescriptive rules and regimented procedures. Among the strongest criticism of transactional leadership is that it does not foster **employee engagement**.

While both styles have their place in the promotion of health and safety in the workplace, caution must be exercised to ensure that the strategies used align with workplace needs and culture. A parallel comparison between transactional leaders and transformational leaders may be made to "managers" versus "leaders."

transformational leadership A leadership style that engages employees by inspiring, developing, and empowering them. Transformational leadership motivates followers by creating a vision of an ideal future state.

transactional leadership A leadership style that focuses on the role of supervision, organization, compliance with rules, and group performance.

employee engagement The positive relationship the employee has with their organization. Highly engaged employees have an interest in the organization's success and will exert more discretionary effort into their assigned tasks.

safety policy A written description of an organization's commitment to maintaining a safe and healthy workplace.

COMPANY SAFETY POLICY

Promoting safety begins with having a published company **safety policy**. The policy should make it clear that safe work practices are expected of all employees at all levels at all times. The safety policy serves as the foundation upon which all other promotional efforts are built.

Figure 2–1 is an example of a company safety policy. This policy briefly and succinctly expresses the company's commitment to safety. It also indicates clearly that employees are expected to perform their duties with safety foremost in their minds. With such a policy in place and clearly communicated to all employees, other efforts to promote safety will have solid backing.

Figure 2–1 Sample company safety policy.

Bridge Creek Forestry, Inc.

Grovedale, Alberta

Safety Policy

Bridge Creek Forestry is committed to protecting the health and safety of its employees, customers, and community. BCF will provide all employees with the tools and training required and will take every reasonable step to ensure the workplace is free from physical and psychological harm.

Managers and supervisors are responsible and accountable for providing a safe workplace and ensuring that employees are aware of their health and safety rights and responsibilities. All employees are responsible and accountable for working safely and not putting their coworkers, clients, or visitors at risk.

Chief Executive Officer,

K. D. Boucher

A company's safety policy need not be long. In fact, a short and simple policy is better. Regardless of its length or format, a safety policy should convey at least the following messages:

- The company and its top managers are committed to health and safety.
- Employees are expected to perform their duties in a safe and healthy manner.
- The company's commitment extends beyond the walls of its plant to include customers and the community.

MOTIVATING SAFE WORK PRACTICES

Employee Participation in Promoting Safety

One of the keys to promoting safety successfully is to involve employees. They usually know better than anyone where hazards exist. In addition, they are the ones who must follow safety rules. A fundamental rule of management is, *If you want employees to make a commitment, involve them from the start*. One of the most effective strategies for getting employees to commit to the safety program is to involve them in the development of it. Employees should also be involved in the implementation, monitoring, and follow-up. In all phases, employees should be empowered to take action to improve safety. The most effective safety program is one that employees view as *their* program.

The *internal responsibility system* and the *right to participate* that we employ in Canada lend themselves very well to employee empowerment. Through joint occupational health and safety committees, which are a major component of employees' right to participate, both workers and management are provided with the tools to reach agreements on safety issues, and the employee is given the power to influence the safety measures taken by the company.

Another excellent way to promote safety is to secure the cooperation of management and labour. For a company's safety program to succeed, employee–management participation and support is critical. Fortunately, employee–management agreement on workplace safety is commonplace.

When disagreement over a safety procedure does surface, the issue at the heart is usually money. Employees are likely to favour procedures that enhance workplace safety regardless of cost. Management, on the other hand, is likely to want to weigh the cost versus the benefit of safety improvement strategies. However, sometimes it is employees rather than managers who question safety strategies.

Gaining a Personal Commitment

If every employee is committed to working safely every day, workplace safety will be dramatically improved. But how does a company gain this type of personal commitment from its employees? One way is to have employees commit themselves to safety by signing on the dotted line. Art Fettig, professional speaker, 35-year veteran of the railroad industry, and safety professional who investigated thousands of accidents, is a strong believer in the value of a signature to foster a commitment to safety.

Fettig's approach to gaining a personal commitment from employees has merit. Ours is a society that revolves around the written signature. We sign countless documents in our lives, from credit statements to bank loans to home mortgages to college registration forms. In each of these cases, our signature is a written pledge of our commitment to meet certain responsibilities.

According to Fettig, companies gain the following three advantages from making signing on the dotted line part of their program to promote safety:

- By their signature, employees make a personal commitment.

- By their signature, employees promise to interact positively with fellow workers when they see other workers ignoring safety precautions.

- By their signature, employees give fellow workers permission to correct them when they ignore safety precautions.[4]

Motivation theorists often refer to *intrinsic* and *extrinsic motivators*. Intrinsic motivators are "a person's internal desire to do something, due to such things as interest,

The table below is a brief summary of the popular "needs" theories presented by four esteemed psychologists. These models are often used by human resources experts to help explain and enhance organizational behaviour. Are you able to provide examples of how each theory could be applied toward safety motivation in the workplace?

Theory	Maslow	Alderfer	Herzberg	McClelland
Is there a hierarchy of needs?	The theory argues that lower-order needs must be satisfied before one progresses to higher-order needs.	More than one need can be important at the same time. If a higher-order need is not being met, the desire to satisfy a lower-level need increases.	Hygiene factors must be met if a person is not to be dissatisfied. They will not lead to satisfaction, however. Motivators lead to satisfaction.	People vary in the types of needs they have. Their motivation and how well they perform in a work situation are related to whether they have a need for achievement, power, or affiliation.
What is the theory's impact/contribution?	The theory enjoys wide recognition among practising managers. Most managers are familiar with it.	The theory is seen as a more valid version of the need hierarchy. It tells us that achievers will be motivated by jobs that offer personal responsibility, feedback, and moderate risks.	The popularity of giving workers greater responsibility for planning and controlling their work can be attributed to his findings. It shows that more than one need may operate at the same time.	The theory tells us that high-need achievers do not necessarily make good managers, since high achievers are more interested in how they do personally.
What empirical support/criticisms exist?	Research does not generally validate the theory. In particular, there is little support for the hierarchical nature of needs. The theory is criticized for how data were collected and interpreted.	It ignores situational variables.	It is not really a *theory* of motivation: It assumes a link between satisfaction and productivity that was not measured or demonstrated.	It has mixed empirical support, but the theory is consistent with our knowledge of individual differences among people. Good empirical support exists on needs achievement in particular.

Source: Langton, Nancy, et al., *Fundamentals of Organizational Behaviour*, 5Ce (updated edition), © 2010, pg. 120. Reprinted with permission by Pearson Canada Inc.

challenge and personal satisfaction."[5] Stated another way, it is "a process of arousal and satisfaction in which the rewards come from carrying out an activity rather [than] from a result of the activity."[6] Extrinsic motivation, on the other hand, is defined as "motivation that comes from outside the person and include such things as pay, bonuses and other tangible rewards."[7] "Extrinsic rewards have been found to reduce intrinsic motivation"[8]

Organizational leaders/supervisors are responsible for motivating employees. SeaBright Insurance Company has excellent resources available on their website for motivating employees to perform their jobs safely. However, they note that there could be a substantial difference in what workers value and what supervisors believe they value. Their findings are summarized in Figure 2–2.

Figure 2–2 What workers value most.

WHAT WORKERS VALUE MOST

	Worker's Ranking	Supervisor Ranking
Credit for their work	1	7
Interest in their work	2	3
Fair pay, with increases	3	1
Understanding & appreciation	4	5
Promotion on merit	5	4
Counsel on personal problems	6	8
Good working conditions	7	6
Job security	8	2

Source: SeaBright Insurance Company. "Motivating Safety Performance." April, 2007.

COMMON TOOLS FOR PROMOTING SAFETY

We have identified the critical role played by management and employees in promoting safety in the workplace. Whatever the leadership style, the corporate culture that exists, or the size of the business, the OHS program will likely use some of the tools discussed below. Anyone who has attended an OHS conference or trade show can tell you that there are scores of vendors with an app, a program, a tool, or some solution to any imaginable OHS challenge. The programs commonly seen in workplaces may not be suitable for some organizations, while others may use any combination of those discussed.

>>> **DISCUSSION CASE** | What Is Your Opinion?

"I want our management team to develop a program to promote better safety practices in this company," said the CEO. "If we develop the program, it will show employees that we are committed to safety."

"I like the idea of showing executive-level commitment," said the vice president for engineering. "But the program may be more readily accepted if we involve employees in developing it."

Executive commitment with or without employee involvement. Which is the better approach? What is your opinion?

Suggestion Programs

Suggestion programs, if properly handled, promote health and safety. Well-run suggestion programs offer two advantages: (1) They solicit input from the people most likely to know where hazards exist, and (2) they involve and empower employees, which, in turn, gives employees ownership of the safety program.

Suggestion programs must meet certain criteria to be effective:

- All suggestions must receive a formal response.

- All suggestions must be answered immediately.

- Management must monitor the performance of each department in generating and responding to suggestions.

- System costs and savings must be reported.

- Recognition and awards must be handled promptly.

- Good ideas must be implemented.

- Personality conflicts must be minimized.[9]

Suggestion programs that meet these criteria are more likely to be successful than those that don't. Figure 2–3 is an example of a suggestion form that may be used as part of a company's safety program. Note that all of the following must be recorded: the date that the suggestion was submitted, the date that the suggestion was logged in, and the date that the employee received a response.

Figure 2–3   Sample safety suggestion form.

Jones Petroleum Products, Inc.
5113 Crowchild Trail SW
Calgary, AB T3E 1T9

Suggestion Form

Name of employee: _____   Date of suggestion: _____

Department: _____

Suggested improvement: _____

_____

_____

_____

Date logged in: _____   Time: _____

Logged in by: _____

Action taken: _____

_____

Current status: _____

Date of response to employee: _____

Person responding: _____

(Signature)

This form satisfies the formal response and immediate response criteria. It also makes it easier to monitor responses. Jones Petroleum Products (the company whose suggestion form we are looking at in Figure 2–3) also publishes system costs and savings in its monthly newsletter for employees, implements good ideas, and recognizes employees with a variety of awards ranging from certificates to cash at a monthly recognition ceremony. This company's suggestion program is an example of one that promotes not just safety but continual improvements in quality, productivity, and competitiveness.

Visual Awareness

We tend to be a visual society. This is why television and billboards are so effective in marketing promotions. Making a health and safety message *visual* can be an effective way to get the message across. Figure 2–4 is a sign that gives machine operators a visual reminder to use the appropriate machine guards.

Figure 2–4   Sample safety reminder sign.

Such a sign is placed on or near the machine in question. If operators cannot activate their machines without first seeing this sign, they will be reminded to use the safe way every time they operate the machine.

Figure 2–5 may be placed on the door leading into the hard-hat area or on a stand placed prominently at the main point of entry if there is no door. Such a sign helps prevent inadvertent slip-ups when employees are in a hurry or are thinking about something else. Figures 2–6, 2–7, and 2–8 are additional examples of signs and posters that make a safety message visual.

Figure 2–5   Sample safety reminder sign.

Figure 2–6   Sample safety reminder sign.

Figure 2–7   Sample safety reminder sign.

Figure 2–8 Sample safety reminder sign.

NOTICE
SAFETY SHOES ARE REQUIRED IN THIS AREA

Several rules of thumb can help ensure the effectiveness of efforts to make safety visual:

- Change signs, posters, and other visual aids periodically. Visual aids left up too long begin to blend into the background and are no longer noticed.

- Involve employees in developing the messages that are displayed on signs and posters. Employees are more likely to notice and heed their own messages than those of others.

- Keep visual aids simple and the messages brief.

- Make visual aids large enough to be seen easily from a reasonable distance.

- Locate visual aids for maximum effect. For example, the sign in Figure 2–4 should be located on the machine in question, preferably near the on/off switch so that the operator cannot activate the machine without seeing it.

- Use colour whenever possible to attract attention to the visual aid.

▶▶▶ SAFETY FACT   Supervisor's Role in Safety

Research and experience show that the first-line supervisor plays a critical role in promoting safe and healthy work practices. The supervisor has the most frequent face-to-face contact with employees and provides the example employees are most likely to follow. If supervisors are committed to safety, those who report directly to them will probably be equally committed. Therefore, time spent by health and safety professionals gaining the support, cooperation, and commitment of supervisors is time well spent.

Incentives

If properly used, **incentives** can help promote safety. However, the proper use of incentives is a widely misunderstood concept. Tim Puffer has this to say about the use of incentives in the modern workplace:

> Most companies have no problem developing incentive programs for their sales forces. . . . But with the shift toward a service economy, a growing number of companies are becoming just as concerned with non-sales performance issues such as productivity and customer service.[10]

To promote safety effectively, incentives must be properly structured. Puffer recommends the following strategies for enhancing the effectiveness of incentive programs:

1. **Define objectives.** Begin by deciding what is supposed to be accomplished by the incentive program.

2. **Develop specific criteria.** On what basis will the incentives be awarded? This question should be answered during the development of the program. Specific criteria define the

incentives Rewards for desirable performance.

type of behaviour and level of performance that is to be rewarded as well as guidelines for measuring success.

3. **Make rewards meaningful.** For an incentive program to be effective, the rewards must be meaningful to the recipients. Giving an employee a reward that he or she does not value will not produce the desired results. To determine what types of rewards will be meaningful, it is necessary to involve employees.

4. **Recognize that only employees who will participate in an incentive program know what incentives will motivate them.** In addition, employees must feel it is *their* program. This means that employees should be involved in the planning, implementation, and evaluation of the incentive program.

5. **Keep communications clear.** It is important for employees to understand fully the incentive program and all of its aspects. Communicate with employees about the program, ask for continual feedback, listen to the feedback, and act on it.

6. **Reward teams.** Rewarding teams can be more effective than rewarding individuals. This is because work in the modern industrial setting is more likely to be accomplished by a team than an individual. When this is the case, other team members may resent the recognition given to an individual member. Such a situation can cause the incentive program to backfire.[11]

Effectiveness of Incentive Programs How effective are incentive programs? The answer to this question is: *It depends.* According to Sandy Smith, the following statistics show the effectiveness of incentive programs on workplace safety in selected circumstances:

1. Incentive programs that target individuals improve performance by 27 percent.

2. Incentive programs that target teams improve performance by 45 percent.

3. Incentive programs have an equally positive effect on both the quality and quantity of employee performance.

4. Incentive programs work best when they are structured with employee input.

5. Long-term incentives are more effective than short-term (44 percent improvement in performance compared with 20 percent, respectively).[12]

Potential Problems with Incentive Programs Clearly, incentive programs are an excellent way to promote safety in the workplace. However, there are potential problems that, if ignored, can undermine the effectiveness of the programs. Bill Sims states these problems as follows:

1. *Employee taxes.* Taxes must be paid on incentives provided to employees. This means either the employer pays or the employee will be stuck with an added tax bill. In either case, taxes increase the cost of cash incentives to employers and decrease the net amount for employees.

2. *Injury hiding.* Incentive programs that are based on statistics can undermine the real effectiveness of the safety program as opposed to the apparent effectiveness. When departments and units hide (fail to report) injuries to win incentive rewards, the integrity of the safety program is at risk. The US Occupational Safety and Health Administration (OSHA) frowns on statistics-based programs because the agency thinks they cause organizations to cheat on reporting requirements.

3. *Unfair programs.* Programs that award incentives based on yearly or quarterly improvements can undermine employee morale and support of the safety program when an accident occurs the day before the end of the period. Employees can maintain

a safe working record for 364 days only to lose out on incentives when an accident occurs on day 365. It is better to base incentives on daily observation of safe behaviour and work practices.

4. **Insufficient budget.** Companies typically budget too little for safety incentives. A realistic budget would be in the range of $100 per employee per year. Less will have insufficient impact to be worth the time and effort an incentive program requires.[13]

Employer Incentive Programs   Most workers' compensation boards in Canada offer some form of reduced premium for those employers who keep accident rates and their associated costs low. Commonly referred to as **experience rating**, these programs that reward good safety performance are one very effective tool used by these agencies to increase workplace safety. Workplace compensation boards across the country offer various incentives to large and small employers to reduce accidents, increase worker awareness, and expedite injured workers' return to work.

experience rating The recent safety performance of the company is rated and reflected in the premiums charged.

Competition

Competition is another strategy that can be used to promote safety. However, if this approach is not used wisely, it can backfire and do more harm than good. To a degree, most people are competitive. A child's competitive instinct is nurtured through play and reinforced by sports and school activities. Health and safety professionals can use the adult's competitive instinct when trying to motivate employees, but competition on the job should be carefully organized, closely monitored, and strictly controlled. Competition that is allowed to get out of hand can lead to cheating and hard feelings among coworkers.

Competition can be organized between teams, shifts, divisions, or even plants. Here are some tips that will help health and safety professionals use competition in a positive way:

- Involve the employees who will compete in planning programs of competition.

- Where possible, encourage competition among groups rather than individuals, while simultaneously promoting individual initiative within groups.

- Make sure that the competition is fair by ensuring that the resources available to competing teams are equitably distributed and that human talent is as appropriately spread among the teams as possible.

The main problem with using competition to promote safety is that it can induce competing teams to cover up or fail to report accidents just to win. Health and safety professionals should be particularly attentive to this situation and watch carefully for evidence that accidents are going unreported. If this occurs, the best approach is to confront the situation openly and frankly. Employees should be reminded that improved safety is the first priority and winning the competition is second. Failing to report an accident should be grounds for eliminating a team from competition.

Orient Personnel to the Desired Safety-Related Behaviours and Attitudes

Organizations often miss out on an excellent opportunity to get employees started off on the right foot after they are hired. This opportunity is the organization's orientation for new employees. Too often orientations for new employees are little more than filling out forms, choosing insurance program options, and learning how to navigate the facility successfully. This is unfortunate because the only time the organization can make a first impression on new employees is during their orientation.

Anything and everything that is relevant to the organization's corporate culture should be introduced and explained during the new-employee orientation sessions—including expectations relating to health and safety. Human resources personnel who conduct the orientation sessions should be encouraged to emphasize that in this organization the right way is the safe way. In addition, a representative of the organization's health and safety department should participate in the sessions. More on this topic is covered in the next chapter on training.

ESTABLISHING A SAFETY-FIRST CORPORATE CULTURE

safety culture The collective beliefs, values, attitudes, and perceptions toward safety in the workplace.

Safety-related disasters that have occurred over time, such as the Chernobyl nuclear power plant meltdown, the explosion of the space shuttle *Challenger* on takeoff, and the Westray mine disaster, have given rise to the term **safety culture**. This term is often heard when something major goes wrong relating to occupational health and safety. Organizations that experience major health or safety failures that lead to accidents or disasters are sometimes said to be lacking a safety culture.

In reality the term *safety culture* is a misnomer in that it implies that safety is a stand-alone, nonintegrated concept that can occur in a vacuum—that it is not part of a larger corporate culture. This is not the case. An organization's safety culture or lack of it is an important part of the larger corporate culture. For this reason, this chapter introduces the term *safety-first corporate culture*.

Safety-First Corporate Culture Defined

The concept can be defined as follows:

> A safety-first corporate culture exists when the *tacit assumptions*, *beliefs*, *values*, *attitudes*, *expectations*, and *behaviours* that are widely shared and accepted in an organization support the establishment and maintenance of a safe and healthy work environment for all personnel at all levels.

Evidence of an organization's corporate culture includes the following:

1. **Its priorities.** Are health and safety top priorities in the organization?
2. **How people in the organization succeed.** Are personnel recognized and rewarded for working safely?
3. **How decisions are made in the organization.** Is safety a major consideration when decisions are made?
4. **Expectations management has of employees.** Do executives and management personnel make it clear that safe behaviour is the expected behaviour in all cases?
5. **Expectations employees have of management.** Are employees encouraged to make their views known about the quality of the work environment?
6. **Effects of internal peer pressure on safety.** Does peer pressure among workers support or undermine safety?
7. **Unwritten rules that are widely accepted.** Do the organization's unwritten rules support or undermine safety?
8. **How conflict about safety is handled.** When conflicts arise between productivity and safety, are they settled in favor of safety?

These questions make the critical point that the cultural elements of health and safety are part of an organization's larger corporate culture, not some separate and distinct component that stands alone. Health and safety should be so fully integrated into an organization's culture that they are seen to be critical elements in the organization's ability to compete in the global marketplace.

Importance of Having a Safety-First Corporate Culture

If asked to summarize in just one word why it is so important for organizations to establish and maintain a safety-first corporate culture, the appropriate word would be *competition*. The market force behind the need for a safety-first corporate culture is competition. There is also the **moral obligation** for employers to provide a safe and healthy work environment for workers and the **legal obligation** that grows out of regulatory compliance, but competition is the foundational driver behind the need. From a business perspective, competition is the key driver because to survive in the global marketplace businesses must be competitive. A business that fails to provide a work environment that is conducive to peak performance and continual improvement will not—in the long run—compete, and if it cannot compete it will fail.

moral obligation A duty to which one is bound by one's values, but not legally.

legal obligation A duty to which one is bound by law.

When the work environment is not safe, organizations begin to experience problems that sap their financial and intellectual strength, making them less able to compete in the global marketplace. These problems include accidents and injuries that erode the organization's talent pool, poor morale among employees, regulatory penalties, negative publicity, increased medical costs, increased workers' compensation costs, and lawsuits.

The competitive value of a safe and healthy workplace is an important concept for modern health and safety professionals to understand and articulate because it is often the pressures of competition that cause organizations to cut corners when it comes to health and safety concerns. Such an approach is shortsighted, ill-advised, and costly in the long run.

HOW CORPORATE CULTURES ARE CREATED

Many factors contribute to the creation of an organization's corporate culture, and typically play a major role in the establishment and perpetuation of it. All these factors can either help or hurt an organization:

- The value systems of executive-level decision-makers
- How managers treat employees and how employees at all levels interact
- What management expects of employees and what employees in turn expect of management
- The stories passed along from employee to employee

If supervisors push workers to take shortcuts on safety procedures when management personnel are not looking, it is not likely that there will be a safety-first corporate culture. On the other hand, if supervisors insist on the safe and healthy approach in all cases regardless of who is watching, it is more likely that there will be a safety-first corporate culture. If none of the organization's corporate heroes are people who build a reputation for safety, it is not likely that there will be a safety-first corporate culture. On the other hand, if the stories that are passed down through generations of workers about the organization's corporate heroes include stories about managers, supervisors, or employees who earned a reputation for safety, it is more likely that there will be a safety-first corporate culture.

Corporate cultures in organizations are established based on what is expected, modeled, passed on during orientation, taught by mentors, included in training, monitored and evaluated, and reinforced through recognition and rewards. If safety is expected by management personnel and individual workers, if it is modeled by people in positions of authority, if it is stressed during the worker's initial orientation to the organization, if it is taught as the right way to do things by mentors, if it is stressed through training, if it is monitored and evaluated by supervisors, and if it is reinforced by management personnel through recognition and rewards, safety will become a fully integrated part of the organization's corporate culture.

WHAT A SAFETY-FIRST CORPORATE CULTURE LOOKS LIKE

Part of the process of establishing a safety-first corporate culture is developing an understanding of what one looks like. This is a lot like a person who wants to lose weight taping a picture of a role model to the bathroom mirror. The picture serves not only as a constant reminder of the desired goal, but also as a measurement device that indicates when a goal has been met. If a picture of an organization with a safety-first corporate culture could be taped to an organization's wall for all employees to see, it would have the following characteristics:

- Widely shared agreement among key decision-makers that providing a safe and healthy work environment is an essential competitive strategy.
- Emphasis on the importance of human resources to the organization and the corresponding need to protect them from hazards.
- Ceremonies to celebrate safety- and health-related successes.
- Widely shared agreement that the work environment that is most conducive to peak performance and continual improvement is a safe and healthy work environment.
- Recognition and rewards given to high-performing workers and teams that include safety- and health-related performance on the job.
- Strong customer focus that includes product safety as a critical concern.
- Insistence on health and safety as part of supplier relations.
- Effective internal network for communicating health and safety information and expectations.
- Informal rules of behaviour that promote safe and healthy work practices.
- Strong pro-safety corporate value system set forth in the strategic plan.
- High expectations and standards for performance relating to health and safety.
- Employee behaviour that promotes safe and healthy work practices.

TEN STEPS FOR ESTABLISHING A SAFETY-FIRST CORPORATE CULTURE

The process for establishing a safety-first corporate culture in an organization consists of ten broad steps. Those steps are as follows:

1. *Understand* the need for a safety-first corporate culture.
2. *Assess* the current corporate culture as it relates to health and safety.
3. *Plan* for a safety-first corporate culture.
4. *Expect* appropriate safety-related behaviours and attitudes.
5. *Model* the desired safety-related behaviours and attitudes.
6. *Orient* personnel to the desired safety-first corporate culture.
7. *Mentor* personnel in the desired safety-related behaviours and attitudes.
8. *Train* personnel in the desired safety-related behaviours and attitudes.
9. *Monitor and evaluate* safety-related behaviour and attitudes at all levels.
10. *Reinforce and maintain* the desired safety-first corporate culture.

Understand the Need for a Safety-First Corporate Culture

Personnel at all levels need to be shown that providing a safe and healthy work environment is an important responsibility of management. Everyone, from the CEO of the organization to the newest employee, should understand and be able to articulate the following factors that support the need for a safety-first corporate culture.

- An organization's corporate culture determines the normal and accepted way things are done in the organization. Consequently, if the normal and accepted way is to be the safe and healthy way, the organization must have a safety-first corporate culture.

- In the same way that the work practices of individuals become habitual, the work practices of organizations become cultural; that is, they become ingrained and codified in the organization's unwritten rules. They become the way things are done when "the boss isn't looking." In order for the way people work when not closely supervised to be the safe and healthy way, an organization must establish and maintain a safety-first corporate culture.

Assess the Current Corporate Culture as It Relates to Health and Safety

Does an organization have a safety-first corporate culture? This is a good question to ask and the answer should never be assumed—either yes or no. The answer to this question, no matter how good or bad the organization's health and safety record might be, should be the result of a thorough assessment. Figure 2–9 is an example of an assessment instrument that can be used as is or modified to fit the specific needs of an individual organization in conducting an assessment of the safety component of its corporate culture.

An instrument such as the one in Figure 2–9 should be widely distributed among personnel at all levels of the organization. Although management personnel should complete the instrument, do not make the mistake of having *only* management personnel complete it. All personnel should be given the opportunity to complete the instrument anonymously to ensure truthful answers.

The organization's chief health and safety professional should be the facilitator of the assessment process. It is a good idea to ask respondents to indicate whether they are a manager, supervisor, or employee so that the perceptions of the various employment categories can be compared. It is not uncommon for management to view things one way and employees to view them quite another. Larger organizations might want to take the time to create an electronic distribution, collection, and tabulation system for conducting the assessment.

Plan for a Safety-First Corporate Culture

The plan for establishing a safety-first corporate culture or for enhancing one that has weaknesses should be based on the results of a comprehensive and thorough assessment.

Once the organization's chief health and safety professional has collected and tabulated the results of the assessment shown in Figure 2–9, the results should be used as the basis for planning for the establishment of a safety-first corporate culture or for enhancing one that already exists but has weaknesses. For example, assume that the results of the assessment show that employees are not recognized and rewarded for working safely. A planning goal to correct this deficiency might read as follows:

> Revise the organization's employee recognition and reward system to include health and safety criteria as part of the selection process.

Figure 2–9 Always assess the existing culture—never presume to know what it is.

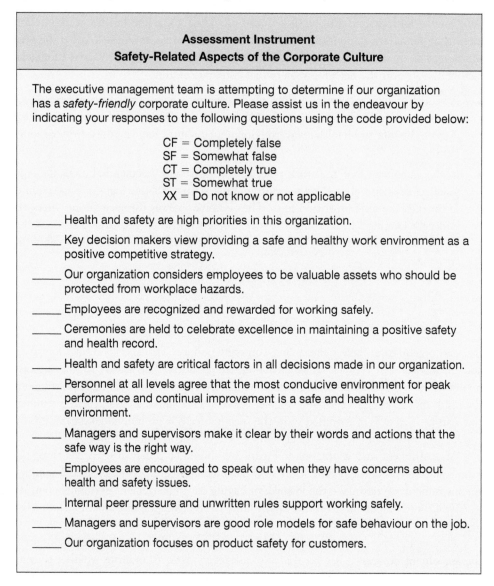

Assessment Instrument
Safety-Related Aspects of the Corporate Culture

The executive management team is attempting to determine if our organization has a *safety-friendly* corporate culture. Please assist us in the endeavour by indicating your responses to the following questions using the code provided below:

CF = Completely false
SF = Somewhat false
CT = Completely true
ST = Somewhat true
XX = Do not know or not applicable

_____ Health and safety are high priorities in this organization.

_____ Key decision makers view providing a safe and healthy work environment as a positive competitive strategy.

_____ Our organization considers employees to be valuable assets who should be protected from workplace hazards.

_____ Employees are recognized and rewarded for working safely.

_____ Ceremonies are held to celebrate excellence in maintaining a positive safety and health record.

_____ Health and safety are critical factors in all decisions made in our organization.

_____ Personnel at all levels agree that the most conducive environment for peak performance and continual improvement is a safe and healthy work environment.

_____ Managers and supervisors make it clear by their words and actions that the safe way is the right way.

_____ Employees are encouraged to speak out when they have concerns about health and safety issues.

_____ Internal peer pressure and unwritten rules support working safely.

_____ Managers and supervisors are good role models for safe behaviour on the job.

_____ Our organization focuses on product safety for customers.

Expect Appropriate Safety-Related Behaviours and Attitudes

If you want people to perform well, you must first have high expectations. It is the same with safety-related behaviours and attitudes. If you want people to work safely, you must let them know that safety is expected. There are several ways that organizations can let employees know what is expected of them, including safety-related expectations. These include job descriptions, team charters, and the examples set by supervisors and managers.

Job descriptions should contain at least one statement that clearly shows that the employees are expected to work safely and to help the team as well as the larger organization maintain a safe and healthy work environment. Such a statement might read as follows:

> Employees in this position are expected to (1) comply with all applicable safety- and health-related rules, regulations, and procedures; (2) work safely themselves and help their teammates work safely; (3) assist supervisors and managers in identifying and mitigating potentially hazardous conditions; and (4) help the organization maintain a safe and healthy work environment.

Team charters also are an excellent way to show employees that safe and healthy work practices are expected. Not all organizations use team charters, but all should. A team charter explains the mission of the team in question, enumerates its overall goals, and lists the expectations of team members. For example, Figure 2–10 illustrates a team charter for the Health and Safety Department of a private sector company that competes in the global marketplace.

Figure 2–10 Sample team charter.

Team Charter
Health and Safety Department

Mission
The mission of the Health and Safety Department at ABC, Inc. is to assist our company in achieving its vision of global market dominance by assisting management in providing a safe and healthy workplace that promotes peak performance and continual improvement.

Overall Team Goals
1. Prevent work-related accidents, injuries, and illnesses.
2. Minimize the costs of workers' compensation.
3. Provide workstations and conditions that are ergonomically sound.
4. Provide a workplace that is as stress free as possible.
5. Ensure that management personnel consider the safety and health ramifications of policies, procedures, processes, and decisions before implementing them.
6. Ensure that all employees understand how to perform their jobs in a safe and healthy manner.
7. Ensure that supervisors know how to monitor daily work practices from the perspective of health and safety and that they follow through and consistently monitor these practices.
8. Ensure that all personnel know how to do their part in accident prevention and hazard management.

Expectations of Team Members
1. All team members are expected to interact with each other in mutually supportive ways that promote peak performance and continual improvement.
2. All team members are expected to be role models whose behaviour on the job is an exemplary role model of safe and healthy work practices.
3. All team members are expected to be critical thinkers.
4. All team members are expected to ensure that when they disagree with others on the job, they do not become disagreeable.
5. All team members are expected to be able to articulate in all cases why the safe way is the productive, competitive way to perform job tasks.

You can see that any new employee assigned to this company's health and safety department (team) would understand from the outset the team's mission, overall goals, and expectations. Under "Expectations of Team Members" you can see that team members are not only expected to work safely themselves, but also to be role models of safe work behaviour.

Model the Desired Safety-Related Behaviours and Attitudes

After a safety policy has been implemented, its credibility with employees will be determined by the example set by management, from supervisors through executives. It is critical that managers follow the company safety policy in both letter and spirit. Nothing speaks louder to employees than the examples—good or bad—set by supervisors and managers. Consequently, if people in positions of authority want employees to work safely, they must set a consistently positive model for doing so themselves. In addition, they must set an example of making decisions, expending resources, and managing the organization in ways that clearly say "Safety is a priority here."

Mentor Personnel in the Desired Safety-Related Behaviours and Attitudes

Once personnel have completed a comprehensive orientation, the next step is to assign them an experienced mentor who exemplifies the desired safety-related behaviours and attitudes. Mentors help guide inexperienced personnel until they gain the experience necessary to work safely without assistance, but even more important, they also help them develop a safety-first attitude. Mentors answer questions, make suggestions, and provide guidance, but the most important responsibility of mentors is to set a positive example that includes a safety-first approach.

Train Personnel in the Desired Safety-Related Behaviours and Attitudes

There are two fundamental principles of good management that apply when trying to establish a safety-first corporate culture. The first is that you should never expect employees to do anything they have not been trained to do. The second is that you should never assume that employees know how to do anything without having been trained. If you want employees to work safely, teach them how. If you want employees to have the right attitudes toward health and safety, teach them what such an attitude looks like and the practical applications of such an attitude. Do not assume that employees know how to work safely—teach them how.

Monitor and Evaluate Safety-Related Behaviours and Attitudes at All Levels

A principle of effective supervision is "You get the behaviour you accept." Supervisors and managers who allow their direct reports to get away with unsafe work practices are saying "Your unsafe behaviour is acceptable to me." Letting unsafe work practices go unchallenged and uncorrected is the same thing as approving of them. Consequently, it is critical that supervisors and managers monitor their direct reports and correct all unsafe work practices immediately. Another reason for monitoring employees and correcting them immediately is that work practices become habitual. Once people become accustomed to doing a task a given way, that way becomes a habit and habits are hard to break. If the habitual way is the unsafe way, the employee in question is heading down a one-way street to disaster.

In addition to monitoring on a daily basis, it is important to make safety- and health-related behaviours part of formal performance evaluations. The performance appraisal instrument should have at least one criterion about health and safety such as the one shown in Figure 2–11.

Figure 2–11   Sample safety-related criterion for a performance appraisal instrument.

This employee exemplifies our organization's
motto that "the safe way is the right way."

___ Always

___ Usually

___ Seldom

___ Never

There is a management principle that says "If you want performance to improve, measure it." This is why it is important to evaluate the safety- and health-related performance of workers. By measuring how well they work in terms of health and safety, supervisors and managers have the hard data needed in order to make improvements.

Reinforce and Maintain the Safety-First Corporate Culture

Just as employees should never stop working safely no matter how good their team's safety record might be, organizations should never stop doing what is necessary to maintain a safety-first corporate culture. Such a culture is not a goal an organization achieves and then moves on to other matters. It is a state of being that must be reinforced constantly or it will be lost. What follows are some strategies organizations can use to reinforce and maintain their safety-first corporate culture once it has been established:

1. Reward safe work behaviour by making it an important factor when promoting workers to higher positions.

2. Reward safe work behaviour by making it an important factor when giving workers wage increases.

3. Reward safe work behaviour by making it an important factor when giving performance incentive awards to workers.

4. Recognize safe work behaviour by making it an important criterion when singling out workers or teams for recognition awards.

5. Encourage supervisors to verbally and publicly recognize workers who are doing their jobs safely every day as they monitor work performance.

SUMMARY

1. Organizational leaders have a critical role in promoting health and safety.

2. Transformational leadership is often preferred over transactional; however, we see many programs using the "safety rule" or compliance strategy to drive safety.

3. A company's safety policy should convey the following messages: (a) a companywide commitment; (b) the expectation that employees will perform their duties in a safe manner; and (c) the inclusion of customers and the community in the company's safety commitment.

4. A fundamental rule of management is, *If you want employees to make a commitment, involve them from the start.* This is especially important when formulating safety rules.

5. Well-run suggestion programs promote safety by (a) soliciting input from the people who are most likely to know where hazards exist, and (b) involving employees in a way that lets them feel ownership in the safety program.

6. Employee–management agreement is important in promoting safety. Fortunately, safety is an issue on which employees and management can usually agree.

7. Incentives can promote safety if they are properly applied. To enhance the effectiveness of incentives, the following steps should be followed: (a) define objectives, (b) develop specific criteria, (c) make rewards meaningful, (d) involve employees in

planning the incentives, (e) keep communications clear, and (f) reward teams. However, cash incentives can create tax problems, and poorly designed incentives can lead to injury hiding, unfair circumstances, and morale problems.

8. Competition can promote safety, but it can also get out of hand and do more harm than good. To keep competition positive, involve employees in planning programs of competition and encourage competition between teams rather than individuals.

9. A safety-first corporate culture is one in which the tacit assumptions, beliefs, values, attitudes, expectations, and behaviours that are widely shared and accepted in an organization support the establishment and maintenance of a safe and healthy work environment for all personnel at all levels.

10. Evidence of a safety-first corporate culture exists in an organization's priorities, how people in the organization succeed, how decisions are made, expectations management has of employees, expectations employees have of management, effects of internal peer pressure, unwritten rules that are widely accepted, and how conflict about safety is handled.

11. Having a safety-first corporate culture is important to organizations because it is the right thing to do and because it contributes to more effective regulatory compliance. However, the most fundamental reason for having a safety-first corporate culture is competition. The most effective way for an organization to succeed in the global marketplace is to consistently provide superior value to its customers. This is achieved by consistently providing superior quality, cost, and service. All three of these critical elements of superior value require a safe and healthy work environment and cannot be achieved in the long run without such an environment.

12. Corporate cultures are established in organizations based on what is expected, modeled, passed on during orientation, taught by mentors, included in training, monitored and evaluated, and reinforced through recognition and rewards.

13. When a safety-first corporate culture exists in an organization, there is widely shared agreement among decision-makers that a safe and healthy work environment is essential to success; an emphasis on protecting valuable human resources from on-the-job hazards; ceremonies to celebrate safety- and health-related successes; widely shared agreement that a safe and healthy work environment is conducive to peak performance and continual improvement; recognition of safe work behaviour; rewards for safe work behaviour; a strong customer focus that includes product safety as a critical concern; insistence on safety as part of supplier relations; an effective internal network for communicating health and safety information and expectations; informal rules of behaviour that promote safe and healthy work practices; a strong pro-safety value system set forth in the strategic plan; high expectations and high standards for performance relating to health and safety; and employee behaviour that promotes safe and healthy work practices.

14. The 10 steps for establishing a safety-first corporate culture are understand, assess, plan, expect, model, orient, mentor, train, monitor and evaluate, and reinforce and maintain.

Key Terms and Concepts

Employee engagement	Legal obligation	Safety policy
Experience rating	Moral obligation	Transactional leadership
Incentives	Safety culture	Transformational leadership

Review Questions

1. What messages should a company's safety policy convey?
2. Explain why promoting safety by example is so important.
3. Why is employee participation and involvement so critical in the promotion of safety?
4. List three benefits that companies gain from asking employees to sign a declaration of safety.
5. What are the steps for ensuring that incentives actually promote safety?
6. What problems can be caused by poorly designed incentives?
7. Define the concept of the safety-first corporate culture.
8. Why is the term *safety culture* a misnomer?
9. List at least five ways (evidence) to tell if an organization has a safety-first corporate culture.
10. Why is it important for organizations to have a safety-first corporate culture?
11. Describe how corporate cultures are established.
12. What does a safety-first corporate culture look like?
13. List and explain each of the ten steps for establishing a safety-first corporate culture.

Weblinks

Canada's National Workplace Health and Safety Website

www.canoshweb.org

This website has links to health and safety agencies and resources from all Canadian jurisdictions.

Canadian Centre for Occupational Health and Safety (CCOHS)

www.ccohs.ca

An essential health and safety resource for Canadians.

Institute for Work & Health (IWH)

www.iwh.on.ca

The Institute for Work & Health provides information and conducts scientific research on the cause, cure, and prevention of soft-tissue injuries.

The Changing Minds website has a number of valuable resources geared toward (as the name implies) getting people to alter their thoughts and behaviour.

http://changingminds.org/explanations/motivation/motivation.htm

The following link elaborates on Leadership vs. Management.

http://changingminds.org/disciplines/leadership/articles/manager_leader.htm

SeaBright Insurance Company.

http://www.sbic.com

American insurance company with a lot of useful resources.

OHS Magazine has an online link to different areas, including articles on incentives: the pros, the cons, and their effective use.

http://ohsonline.com/portals/incentives.aspx

Endnotes

[1] Kim Laing. "Building an Effective Health and Safety Plan for Your Organization." St. John Ambulance. Presentation during the 10th Annual Health and Safety Conference, Calgary Alberta, October 24, 2011.

[2] James M. Kouzes and Barry Z. Posner. *The Leadership Challenge*, 4th ed. (San Francisco: Jossey-Bass, 2007), 122.

[3] G. Yukl. *Leadership in Organizations*, 3rd custom ed. Royal Roads University. (Englewood Cliffs, NJ: Prentice-Hall, 2002), 153.

[4] A. Fettig. "Sign Up for Safety." *Safety + Health* 144, no. 1: 26.

[5] Nancy Langton, Stephen E. Robbins, and Timothy A. Judge. *Organizational Behaviour*, 5th Canadian ed. (Pearson Canada: Toronto, 2010), 130.

[6] David Beswick. *Management Implications of the Interaction Between Intrinsic Motivation and Extrinsic Rewards*. University of Melbourne. [Online]. Available: http://www.beswick.info/psychres/management.htm. (Retrieved October 23, 2016).

[7] Langton, et al., 130.

[8] Beswick. (Retrieved October 23, 2016).

[9] B. McDermott. "Employees Are Best Source of Ideas for Constant Improvement." *Total Quality Newsletter* 1, no. 4: 5.

[10] T. Puffer. "Eight Ways to Construct Effective Service Reward Systems." *Reward & Recognition Supplement, Training* (August 1990): 8–12.

[11] Ibid.

[12] S. Smith. "Safety Incentives: It's Not Just a Breakfast Anymore." *Occupational Hazards* 64, no. 6 (June 2002): 58.

[13] B. Smith, as quoted in Smith. "Safety Incentives," 58.

Chapter 3
Health and Safety Training and Certification

Education and training have been recognized as important components of organized safety programs for many years. In today's rapidly changing high-tech workplace, they are more important than ever. Modern health and safety professionals have a key role to play in ensuring that all employees at all levels receive the appropriate types and amounts of training. They must also be prepared to play an active role in preparing, presenting, arranging for the application of, and evaluating health and safety training.

Initial safety training should be part of the orientation process for new employees. Subsequent safety training should be aimed at developing new, more specific, and more in-depth knowledge, and at renewing and updating existing knowledge. Training serves a dual purpose in the promotion of safety. First, it ensures that employees know how to work safely and why doing so is important. Second, it shows that management is committed to safety.

Providing safety training provides numerous opportunities as well as challenges for the human resources and safety professional. As health and safety training becomes more integral with policies and procedures throughout the workplace, there are countless opportunities to incorporate it into the workers' professional development. On the other hand, addressing the demographic differences in today's workplaces is seen as a challenge in many organizations. In an *EHS Today* magazine article by Anthony Geise, it is suggested that "one of the most significant barriers that safety educators face today is teaching different generations of workers."[1]

RATIONALE FOR HEALTH AND SAFETY TRAINING

Workers who have not been trained to perform their jobs safely are more likely to have accidents, and accidents are costly in terms of money, morale, quality, productivity, and competitiveness. According to the US National Safety Council (NSC):

> Many studies have been made to determine why people fail to follow safety procedures or to take reasonable precautions on the job. Some of the reasons are that workers have:
>
> - Not been given specific instructions in the operation
> - Misunderstood the instructions
> - Not listened to the instructions
> - Considered the instructions either unimportant or unnecessary
> - Disregarded the instructions
>
> Any of the above lapses can result in an accident. To prevent such an occurrence, it is essential that safety training work be conducted efficiently.[2]

Legal and Ethical Reasons for Training

The Occupational Health and Safety legislation for each jurisdiction mandates that employers provide health and safety training for their workers. Although the various statutes throughout Canada present these training requirements in different formats, the general requirements include the following:

- Workers must be informed of any hazards in the workplace.
- Workers must be trained in safe procedure and proper use of any safety devices used on the job.
- Workers must be trained in the safe handling of any "controlled products" used on the job.

Because of the important role of Joint Occupational Health and Safety Committees, certification training is required in most jurisdictions. For example, in Ontario, where joint health and safety committees are required, certification training is mandatory. Part one of the training provides overall knowledge of health and safety, while part two focuses on hazards specific to the member's workplace.[3] Newfoundland and Labrador have similar requirements for their OHS committee members and representatives. More information on OHS committees is provided in Chapter 4.

Beyond the legal reasons for providing health and safety training, there are also ethical reasons. No amount of legislation can properly regulate every hazardous substance or every potentially hazardous situation. Chemicals and technologies are developed and put in place much more rapidly than is legislation. Clearly, the only way to guarantee that employees are well informed about the health and safety aspects of their jobs is for companies to fulfill their moral obligations along these lines. According to Spencer and Simonowitz,

> If the sick person has rights to information and determination regarding his or her body, should the well, healthy employee or working person have any less right to the same consideration when there are health implications of exposure on the job? If the sick person is entitled to know about procedures and prognosis, discomforts and inconveniences, risk, and experience of proposed treatment, surely working persons should have similar rights to information about the nature and toxicity of

the substances with which they work, controls and their effectiveness, personal discomforts and inconvenience of both hazards and controls, morbidity and mortality data, and the relative risk.[4]

HEALTH AND SAFETY TRAINING RESOURCES

The safety practitioner should be aware of the numerous health and safety resources that are available for workers and employers. Regardless of the size or type of business being conducted, training is available through private trainers, industry associations, and various government agencies. The Internet offers thousands of helpful sites, ranging from free information to complete online courses. While various resources may help fill some technical or legal training requirements, they will be more effective when used to supplement the **safety management system** of the workplace. Some of these useful resource websites are listed at the end of this chapter.

safety management system A business tool that provides a comprehensive and structured approach to identifying hazards and controlling risks in the workplace.

Safety training is a key element in any safety management system – the effectiveness of it needs to be considered. For many safety and other professionals, safety training is offered as a tool to affect behaviour and ultimately to reduce the number and severity of injuries. The effectiveness of safety training by itself is questioned by Peterson, who says that "training does not beget performance at any level."[5] *The International Journal of Human Resource Management* agrees in an article by Ford and Tetrick: "According to Behaviourist approaches, conveying information during training about risk is insufficient in changing behaviour; there must be subsequent management reinforcement."[6]

Role of Supervisors and Managers

Supervisors and managers play a key role in the maintenance of a safe and healthy workplace. Consequently, health and safety professionals need to ensure that supervisors have had the training they need to be positive participants in the process. A *Safety + Health* survey revealed that only 53 percent of the companies that responded provided health and safety training for their supervisors.[7] This is an unfortunate statistic because supervisors are the health and safety professional's link with employees. In the words of Peter Minetos, "Supervisors . . . are the ones who have to teach employees the safe way to conduct their jobs. With proper training, they can spot and eliminate risks that are waiting to create havoc for their workers."[8]

According to the NSC, the objectives of supervisor safety training are to:

- Involve supervisors in the company's accident-prevention programs.
- Establish the supervisor as the key person in preventing accidents.
- Get supervisors to understand their safety responsibilities.
- Provide supervisors with information on causes of accidents and occupational health hazards and methods of prevention.

- Give supervisors an opportunity to consider current problems of accident prevention and develop solutions based on their own and others' experience.
- Help supervisors gain skill in accident prevention activities.
- Help supervisors keep their own departments safe.[9]

Orientation

Perhaps the most important aspect of safety training is orientation for new and transferred employees. Consider the following quote from *Today's Supervisor*:

> The confusion and stress that accompany the first day of any job are often the reasons that new employees are more than twice as likely to have accidents as experienced workers. A lack of experience, a strong desire to please and a hesitation to ask for help all cause one in eight new employees to be involved in some type of accident the first year on the job. The first month is the most critical.[10]

The early training provided for new and transferred employees should have at least the following components: orientation, job-specific procedures, and follow-up. These components are discussed in the following paragraphs.

orientation The process of introducing new employees to the organization, its rules, culture, and expectations.

Orientation is critical. Too often, companies hand over new employees to an experienced employee who is supposed to "show them the ropes." This is a dangerous practice that can have the effect of minimizing, rather than emphasizing, the importance of safety. Orientation should be structured, and it should involve the new worker's supervisor as well as other personnel as appropriate. A good orientation program should teach the following at a minimum:

- Management is sincerely interested in preventing accidents.
- Accidents may occur, but it is possible to prevent them.
- Safeguarding equipment and the workplace has been done, and management is willing to go further as needs and methods are discovered.
- Each employee is expected to report to the supervisor any unsafe conditions encountered at work.
- The supervisor will give job instructions. No employee is expected to undertake a job before learning how to do it and being authorized to do it by a supervisor.
- The employee should contact the supervisor for guidance before undertaking a job that appears to be unsafe.
- If an employee suffers an injury, even a slight one, it must be reported at once.

In addition to these points, any safety rules that are a condition of employment, such as wearing eye protection or safety hats, should be understood and enforced from the first day of employment.[11]

⟫⟫ DISCUSSION CASE | What Is Your Opinion?

Richard Branson, business magnate and founder of Virgin Group said, "Train people well enough so they can leave, treat them well enough so they don't want to."

Unfortunately this same view on training is missing in many organizations. The cliché used in business settings is:

CFO: "What happens if we train them and they leave?"

CEO: "What happens if we don't – and they stay?"

This also speaks to the need to train employees. One may argue that this would apply to technical training, but not necessarily to safety training. What is your opinion?

Job-Specific Procedures

Before a new employee is allowed to begin work, he or she should be given instruction in safe operation procedures, the use of personal protective equipment, and any other procedures that promote a safe and healthy work environment.

Follow-Up

After a new employee has worked for three days to a week, a follow-up meeting should be called. This meeting should be led by the worker's supervisor. It should answer the following questions: Was the initial training effective? Does the new employee have questions or concerns? Does the new employee have suggestions for improving the health and safety of his or her work environment? It can also be a good idea to ask the employee to verify that he or she has been adequately and properly oriented by signing a checklist such as the one in Figure 3–1.

Figure 3–1   Sample employee orientation checklist.

Orientation Verification Checklist

Please review this checklist and indicate which topics were covered during your orientation by initialling the entry.

Reporting/Authority

☐ Your immediate supervisor
☐ Midmanagers, managers, and executives in your chain of command
☐ Safety and health manager
☐ Human resources manager

Job Requirements

☐ Job description
☐ Responsibility
☐ Authority
☐ Performance standards
☐ Evaluation system

Pay/Benefits

☐ Wages
☐ Pay days
☐ Payroll deduction options
☐ Medical benefits
☐ Life insurance
☐ Disability coverage
☐ Annuity opportunities
☐ Saving deductions
☐ Retirement

Rules/Regulations

☐ Company rules/regulations
☐ Department rules/regulations
☐ Unit rules/regulations
☐ General safety rules
☐ Job-specific safety rules
☐ Consequences of breaking rules

Tools/Equipment

☐ Check-out/check-in procedures
☐ Maintenance procedures
☐ Orientation to use
☐ Emergency shut-down
☐ Personal protective equipment

Work Hours

☐ Workdays
☐ Work hours
☐ Overtime compensation
☐ Holidays/down days
☐ Vacation
☐ Sick leave
☐ Nontraditional scheduling opportunities

Employee signature: _____   Date: _____

Principles of Learning

The principles of learning summarize what is known and widely accepted about how people learn. Trainers can do a better job of facilitating learning if they understand the following principles:

1. **People learn best when they are ready to learn.** You cannot *make* employees learn anything. You can only make them *want* to learn. Explain why employees need to learn and how they will benefit personally from having done so.

2. **People learn more easily when what they are learning can be related to something they already know.** Build today's learning on what was learned yesterday and tomorrow's learning on what was learned today.

3. **People learn best in a step-by-step manner.** Learning should be organized into logically sequenced steps that proceed from the concrete to the abstract, from the simple to the complex, and from the known to the unknown.

4. **People learn by doing.** Inexperienced trainers tend to confuse talking (i.e., lecturing or demonstrating) with teaching. Explanations can be part of the teaching process but are useful only if they are followed by application activities that require the learner to *do* something.

5. **The more often people use what they are learning, the better they will remember and understand it.** How many things have you learned in your life that you can no longer remember? People forget what they do not use. It means that repetition and application should be built into the learning process.

6. **Success in learning tends to stimulate additional learning.** Organize training into long enough segments to allow learners to see progress, but not so long that they become bored.

7. **People need immediate and continual feedback to know if they have learned.** People who are learning want to know immediately and continually how they are doing. Feedback can be as simple as a nod, a pat on the back, or a comment such as "Good job!" It can also be more formal, such as a progress report or a graded activity.

LITERACY AND SAFETY

While Canadian organizations invest heavily in occupational health and safety training and new equipment to protect employees, they spend little on upgrading the basic skills and literacy of their workers, according to a Conference Board of Canada report examining literacy's impact on workplace health and safety.[12] The Conference Board's survey research also reveals an inverse relationship between industries requiring a high level of health and safety and investment in literacy skills.[13] For instance, employers in the construction industry, which is inherently hazardous, are likely to spend less on literacy training than those in technology or business.

literacy Knowledge of a particular area, usually referring to one's ability to read and write.

Low **literacy** in the workplace can impact more than the organization's productivity and competitiveness—it also put workers' health and safety at risk. The fact that illiteracy on the job increases the likelihood of accidents should be of concern to health and safety professionals. For example, an illiterate employee would not be able to read or understand a safety data sheet explaining the safe handling procedures for a given chemical or toxic material.[14] Written notification of health and safety hazards and written instruction for minimizing those hazards are of little use if the workforce or any part of it is illiterate.[15] "If workers can't understand health and safety regulations provided to them, or if they can't understand their rights to a safe workplace, there is an increased risk of incidents and injury."[16]

The basic skills necessary to be productive in a modern industrial setting are increasing steadily. Canadians, in general, are gradually becoming more literate and more educated (see Figure 3–2). More Canadians are currently completing secondary school than in 1990; during the same period the percentage of Canadians with college or trade certification or a university degree also increased. Although Canadians are now more literate in an absolute sense, it is not known if they keep pace with the demand in new literacy skills, because little work has been done in tracking the changing levels of literacy needed for full participation in society.[17]

Figure 3–2 Literacy levels of Canadians aged 16 to 65.

Level 1—14.6% of Canadians
This level comprises persons with very poor skills. Individuals may, for example, be unable to determine the correct amount of medicine to give to a child from information printed on a label.

Level 2—27.3% of Canadians
Persons at this level can deal only with material that is simple and clearly laid out, and where the tasks involved are not too complex. These people can read but test poorly. Their lack of skill may be less obvious than that at level 1, since they may have developed coping skills to manage everyday literacy demands. However, their low level of proficiency makes it difficult for them to face novel demands, such as learning new job skills.

Level 3—38.6% of Canadians
Level 3 is considered a suitable minimum for coping with the demands of everyday life and work in a complex, advanced society. It approximates the skill level required for successful secondary school completion and college entry. Like higher levels, it requires the ability to integrate several sources of information and solve more complex problems.

Levels 4 and 5—19.5% of Canadians
These levels describe people who demonstrate command of higher-order information-processing skills.

Results are for the Prose Scale, one of three measures of literacy used in the International Adult Literacy Survey.

Source: OECD and Statistics Canada. *Learning a Living:* 50. [Online]. Available: http://www.statcan.gc.ca/access_acces/alternative_alternatif.action?l=eng&loc=pdf/4200878-eng.pdf. (Retrieved November 6, 2016).

Literacy in the broadest sense is the ability to read, write, compute, solve problems, and communicate. Functionally illiterate people read at the fourth-grade level or below. Marginally literate people read at the fifth- through eighth-grade levels. Functionally literate people read at the ninth-grade level or above. This is the literacy continuum as it now exists. However, technological developments are having the effect of shifting these levels up the continuum. As a result, what constitutes functional or marginal literacy now will have to be redefined periodically.

International survey results show that more than 4 in 10 Canadians in the working-age population do not have the literacy skills needed to perform most jobs well.[18] Problem-solving skills are becoming critical as companies implement quality-management programs. Such programs involve all employees in identifying and correcting problems that negatively affect quality or do not add value to the company's products. As industrial companies continue to enhance their technological capabilities, and health and safety concerns increase correspondingly, the literacy levels of the workforce will also have to increase.

TRAINING ISSUES WITH ENGLISH AND FRENCH AS A SECOND LANGUAGE

To enjoy the gains that come with a safe and healthy workplace, organizations that have employees who speak only limited English or French, or for whom English or French is a second language, must take steps to accommodate these workers' special needs in terms of both training and cultural perspectives. There is little question that a language barrier can magnify the potential for accidents and injuries in the workplace. In addition to increasing the likelihood of accidents, language problems can also result in lower productivity and higher turnover.[19]

Methods for Training Across Language Barriers

Traditional training methods—videos, lectures, handouts, and other *classroom*-oriented methods—will not work well with employees who do not speak English or French as their principal language. *Hands-on* training that requires more doing and less listening, reading, and writing is the better approach with limited-English/French-speaking audiences. In other words, when working with a diverse group of employees in which language might be a barrier, don't use training methods that rely heavily on understanding the language. Instead of *telling* employees how to work safely, *show* them. Set up demonstrations that replicate the actual situation in question and let employees do what they are supposed to do on the job rather than just watching a video of someone else doing it.

According to Halcarz, the best way to overcome language, culture, and literacy barriers is to provide safety training programs that have the following attributes:

1. Bilingual training materials that address cultural issues.

2. Training materials that recognize the dignity of all employees regardless of their backgrounds.

3. Training materials that minimize literacy requirements.[20]

Considering Cultural Concerns

We tend to think of cultural issues in terms of language and national origin. However, even people who speak the same language and come from the same country can have cultural differences. An employee's attitude toward reporting an injury can have cultural roots. For example, an employee from one culture might be quick to report an injury, whereas an employee from another culture might see filing a report as making trouble or showing weakness.

cultural barriers Rules, expectations, or norms of a culture that often impede full participation in a new setting. Language and religion are common cultural barriers.

An effective way to identify the various **cultural barriers** that might have a negative effect on an employee's ability to fully grasp the training provided is to arrange facilitated brainstorming sessions. In these sessions, a third-party facilitator helps employees discuss freely, openly, and without attribution any concerns they might have about the training they need and any barriers that might inhibit their progress in completing the training. A third-party facilitator, especially one who speaks the principal language of the employees in question, is more likely to bring out employee concerns than their supervisor or manager.

>>> **SAFETY FACT** Safety Training is Not Only About Dollars and Cents

Too many business executives take the MBA (management by accounting) approach to their jobs. They will accept only dollars on the bottom line as proof of the value of an activity or function. Although the value of safety training can be shown in dollars and cents, the ubiquitous MBA mentality that persists in business and industry can sometimes get in the way of training programs.

The same executives who question the value of safety training have no problem understanding that professional football teams train all week to play just one game. Military units train constantly for the eventuality of a deployment. Training is fundamental to most professions and occupations. It should be fundamental to all.

THE ROLE AND CERTIFICATION OF MODERN HEALTH AND SAFETY PROFESSIONALS

It would be unreasonable to expect one person to be an expert in all of the many complex and diverse issues faced in the modern workplace. For this reason, the management and promotion of health and safety in the age of high technology has become a team sport. Figure 3–3 illustrates the types of positions that may comprise a health and safety team. The various professions are discussed below.

Figure 3–3 A modern health and safety team.

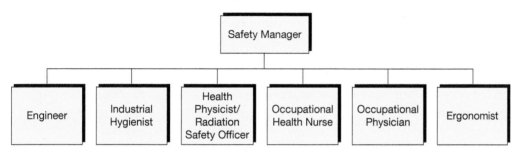

Professional **certification** is an excellent way to establish credentials in the health and safety profession. Some of the most widely pursued Canadian accreditations are:

- Certified Registered Safety Professional (CRSP)
- Certified Industrial Hygienist (CIH)
- Certified Canadian Professional Ergonomist (CCPE)
- Certified Health and Safety Consultant (CHSC)
- Certified Occupational Health Nurse (COHN)

certification A designation or acknowledgment from an accrediting body that a person is qualified to conduct work in a particular field.

Safety Manager

Often part of or closely tied to the human resources department, the job of the health and safety manager is complex and diverse. Figure 3–4 is an example of a job description for such a position. The description attests to the diverse nature of the job. Duties range from hazard analysis to accident reporting to standards and compliance to record keeping to training to emergency planning to policy development and implementation, and so on. Many safety managers have certification in one of the specific technical areas described below, or may have a professional safety designation, or both.

Engineer

Engineers can make a significant contribution to safety. Correspondingly, they can also cause, inadvertently or through incompetence, accidents that result in serious injury and property damage. The engineer has more potential to affect safety in the workplace than any other person.

The engineer's greatest opportunity to impact safety comes during the design process. The process is basically the same regardless of whether the product being designed is a small toy, an industrial machine, an automobile, a nuclear power plant, a ship, a jumbo jetliner, or a space vehicle. Health and safety professionals should be familiar with the design process so that they can more fully understand the role of engineers in regard to workplace safety.

Not all engineers are design engineers. Other engineers who have a broad knowledge of their respective fields are an invaluable resource to individual organizations. Engineers provide rigorous scrutiny to health and safety policy and legislation to ensure accuracy and that the desired systems will function as planned.

Figure 3–4 Health and safety manager job description.

POULTRY PROCESSING, INC.
2306 Industrial Avenue
Toronto, ON M4W 1L5
Vacancy Announcement

Position Title: Health and Safety Manager

Position Description: The Health and Safety Manager for PPI is responsible for establishing, implementing, and managing the company's overall health and safety program. The position reports to the local plant manager. Specific duties include the following:

- Establish and maintain a comprehensive companywide health and safety program.
- Assess and analyze all departments, processes, and materials for potential hazards.
- Work with appropriate personnel to develop, implement, monitor, and evaluate accident prevention and hazard control strategies.
- Ensure companywide compliance with all applicable laws, standards, and codes.
- Coordinate the activities of all members of the company's health and safety program.
- Plan, implement, and broker, as appropriate, health and safety–related training.
- Maintain all required health and safety–related records and reports.
- Conduct accident investigations as necessary.
- Develop and maintain a companywide emergency action plan (EAP).
- Establish and maintain an ongoing safety promotion effort.
- Analyze the company's products from the perspectives of safety, health, and liability.

Qualifications Required: The following qualifications have been established by the PPI management team with input from all levels and all departments.

- *Minimum Education.* Applicants must have at least a one-year community college certificate or an associate of science or applied science degree in industrial safety or a closely related degree (A.S. holders will begin work at a salary 15 percent higher than a certificate graduate).
- *Preferred Education.* Applicants with a baccalaureate degree in any of the following major fields of study will be given first priority: industrial health and safety, industrial technology, industrial management, manufacturing technology, engineering technology, and related. Degree programs in these fields must include at least one three-semester or five-quarter-hour course in industrial or occupational health and safety.

Canadian professional engineering associations regulate every aspect of the engineering profession in Canada. To be a professional engineer (P.Eng.) and to practise in Canada, you need to become licensed by a Canadian provincial or territorial engineering association. The engineering associations for each jurisdiction are listed in Figure 3–5. You must apply for your P.Eng. licence with the professional engineering association in the province or territory where you want to work.[21]

Figure 3–5 Provincial and territorial professional engineering associations.

Engineers PEI
Engineers Nova Scotia
Engineers & Geoscientists New Brunswick
Ordre des ingénieurs du Québec (OIQ)
Professional Engineers Ontario (PEO)
Engineers Geoscientists Manitoba
Association of Professional Engineers & Geoscientists of Saskatchewan (APEGS)
Association of Professional Engineers and Geoscientists of Alberta (APEGA)
Association of Professional Engineers and Geoscientists of British Columbia (APEGBC)
Engineers Yukon
Northwest Territories and Nunavut Association of Professional Engineers and Geoscientists (NAPEG)

Industrial Hygienist

Industrial hygienists, or occupational hygienists, are highly trained professionals dedicated to the health, well-being, and productivity of the worker and the community through anticipation, recognition, evaluation, and control of occupational and environmental hazards.

Industrial **hygiene** is the science of the recognition, evaluation, and control of those environmental factors or stressors, arising in and from the workplace, that may cause sickness, impaired health and well-being, or significant discomfort and inefficiency among workers or among citizens of the community.[22] Industrial hygienists are primarily concerned about the following types of hazards: solvents, particulates, noise, dermatoses, radiation, temperature, ergonomics, toxic substances, biological substances, ventilation, gas, and vapors.

The Canadian Registration Board of Occupational Hygienists (CRBOH) is a national organization that sets standards of professional competence for occupational hygienists and occupational hygiene technologists in Canada and around the world. Registration with the CRBOH confers the right to use the title Registered Occupational Hygienist (ROH) or Registered Occupational Hygiene Technologist (ROHT), and indicates the attainment and maintenance of a high standard of professionalism.[24]

hygiene According to the World Health Organization (WHO), "Hygiene refers to conditions and practices that help to maintain health and prevent the spread of diseases."[23]

Health Physicist / Radiation Safety Officer

Health physicists are concerned primarily with radiation in the workplace. Their duties include the following: monitoring radiation inside and outside the facility, measuring the radioactivity levels of biological samples, developing the radiation components of the company's emergency action plan, and supervising the decontamination of workers and the workplace when necessary.

The Canadian Association of Medical Radiation Technologists (CAMRT) is the national professional association and certifying body for radiological technologists, nuclear medicine and magnetic resonance imaging technologists and radiation therapists. Related programs across Canada are accredited by the Canadian Medical Association (CMA) and include the following disciplines:

- Magnetic Resonance
- Nuclear Medicine
- Radiation Therapy
- Radiological Technology

There must be a health physicist or radiation safety officer (RSO) to act as an advisor on all radiation protection aspects during the initial stages of construction of the facility, installation of the equipment, and during subsequent operations. Health physicists are health care professionals with specialized training in the medical applications of physics. A radiation safety officer is the title commonly assigned to a radiation safety specialist who routinely manages a facilities radiation protection program. A designated RSO must be appointed to oversee and implement the radiation safety program at each facility in which industrial **radiography** is carried out.

radiography A form of imaging using small doses of ionizing radiation, as opposed to visual light. X-rays are used in medical radiology to view the internal body systems and in industrial radiography to see internal structures or defects in mechanical parts.

Occupational Health Nurse

Occupational health nurses have long been important members of corporate health and safety programs. Occupational health nurses are registered nurses employed by organizations to promote employee health and wellness, increase compliance with occupational health and safety legislation, provide emergency response and first-aid training, and facilitate the rehabilitation of sick or injured employees. Occupational health nurses are registered nurses who may have additional education in the field of occupational health. The Canadian designation for certification in Occupational Health Nursing is *COHN(C)*—Canadian Occupational Health Nurse (Certified).

Employers generally prefer to hire registered nurses who have:

- at least five years of nursing experience,

- job-related certification (for example, instructor certification to teach first aid, audiometric certification, spirometry certification, advanced cardiac life support certification),

- a certificate in occupational health nursing from a post-secondary education institution,

- successfully passed the Canadian Nurses Association national occupational nursing certification exam,

- continued related post-secondary education (for example, courses in management, research, toxicology, disability management, audiometry, or spirometry), and

- used computer software for data management, presentations, communications, or medical testing.[25]

Like occupational physicians, today's occupational health nurses have seen their profession evolve over the years. The shift in emphasis is away from after-the-fact treatment to prevention-related activities such as analysis, monitoring, counseling, and education.

Occupational Physician

Bernardino Ramazzini is widely thought of as being the first occupational physician. This reputation is primarily the result of his study of the work-related problems of workers in Modena, Italy, and a subsequent book he authored titled *The Diseases of Workers* (1700). Occupational medicine as a specialized field dates back to World War II, when production of manufactured goods skyrocketed and workplace-related medical needs followed suit.

Occupational physicians are fully degreed and licensed medical doctors. In addition they must have completed postgraduate work in the following areas of safety:

> biostatistics and epidemiology, industrial toxicology, work physiology, radiation (ionizing and nonionizing), noise and hearing conservation, effects of certain environmental conditions such as high altitude and high pressures (hyperbaric and hypobaric factors), principles of occupational safety, fundamentals of industrial hygiene, occupational aspects of dermatology, psychiatric and psychological factors, occupational respiratory diseases, biological monitoring, ergonomics, basic personnel management functions, record and data collection, governmental regulations, general environmental health (air, water, ground pollution, and waste management control).[26]

The Royal College of Physicians and Surgeons of Canada established the specialty of occupational medicine some thirty years ago. Occupational medicine is a subspecialty of internal medicine, and training is done during the internal medicine training as with any other internal medicine subspecialty. Both the University of Alberta and the University of Toronto offer residency programs. Graduates become Fellows of the Royal College of Physicians of Canada (FRCPC). The Colleges of Physicians and Surgeons in each province or territory determines whether physicians will be recognized as specialists; the FRCPC (Occ Med) is the usual requirement for recognition as a specialist in occupational medicine.[27]

Ergonomist

Ergonomists are an important element of the safety team. Ergonomics is the study of the relationship between humans and their interaction with the work environment and its objects. The role of ergonomists is to apply their broad knowledge to the workplace to ensure that the machines, tools, facilities, and environment are efficient, comfortable, and safe for the worker.

The CCPE (Certified Canadian Professional Ergonomist) designation through the Canadian College for the Certification of Professional Ergonomists (CCCPE) requires that applicants:

- meet standard competencies in both education and practice,

- have a degree in a related field,

- have a minimum of four years of full-time practice,

- devote the majority of their work time to the application, practice, and/or teaching of ergonomics, and

- maintain their certification through a continuance of certification process.

All members are held to a **code of ethics**.[28]

Many safety practitioners who have the professional designations noted above may also hold a CRSP or CHSC certification. The Board of Canadian Registered Safety Professionals (BCRSP) ensures that members who receive the Canadian Registered Safety Professional (CRSP) designation have met their prescribed standards for OHS experience, *ethics*, and education. Many employers prefer or require applicants for OHS positions to hold the CRSP designation, particularly for midcareer and senior positions.[29]

The Canadian Society of Safety Engineering (CSSE), Certified Health and Safety Consultant (CHSC) designation recognizes and promotes excellence in professional occupational health and safety consulting. It shows clients that the holder has taken the time and made the investment necessary to learn the essentials of being a professional occupational health and safety consultant. To obtain the CHSC designation, the consultant must meet specific criteria as well as successfully complete six courses offered by the CSSE—three mandatory courses and three elective courses.[30]

code of ethics A set of rules that govern behaviour or conduct, based on the organization's moral principles.

THE EMERGING ROLE OF SAFETY PROFESSIONALS

As the world gets flatter, as organizations get leaner, and as global competition becomes more intense, the role of safety professionals—whether managers, engineers, technologists, technicians, or health care personnel—is changing. This is the message of Don Groover and Jim Spigener in a series of articles in *Occupational Health & Safety*.[31] According to the authors, the core duty of safety professionals has not changed. They are still responsible for preventing accidents and incidents that lead to injuries to personnel and damage to property or the environment. However, the skills they need to fulfill this duty are changing.

In today's hypercompetitive business climate, fewer people are doing more work with fewer resources, technology continues to change at a rapid pace, employees work with less supervision while being required to make more complex decisions, baby boomers are retiring and being replaced by less experienced personnel, and older people are re-entering the workforce. Add to this that the expectations of a safe and healthy workplace are higher and that society is even more litigious than ever and the challenge of the modern safety professional becomes clear.[32]

According to Groover and Spigener, what all this means is that being an expert in a specific health-and-safety–related discipline—although still necessary and important—is no longer sufficient. Today's safety professionals need to be able to partner with the top leaders in their organizations in ways that promote the establishment and maintenance of a *safety-first corporate culture* that helps enhance the performance of people, processes, and products. To do this, safety professionals have to become change leaders who are able to effectively challenge, engage, inspire, and influence people at all levels. In other words, safety professionals have to become transformational leaders in their organizations.[33]

SUMMARY

1. The rationale for health and safety training is that workers who know how to do their jobs properly are less likely to have accidents.

2. Beyond the legal reasons for providing health and safety training, there are also ethical reasons.

3. Health and safety training is available through private trainers, industry associations, and various government agencies.

4. Supervisors play a key role in the maintenance of a safe and healthy workplace. Consequently, health and safety professionals need to ensure that supervisors have had the training they need to be positive participants in the process.

5. One of the most important aspects of a safety program is the orientation of new employees. It should consist of a general introduction to the workplace, job-specific procedures, and follow-up.

6. Low literacy in the workplace can impact more than the organization's productivity and competitiveness—it also put workers' health and safety at risk.

7. Employers who hire workers with limited English/French-speaking capabilities should use less classroom instruction and more hands-on activities when providing safety training.

8. Traditional training methods—videos, lectures, handouts, and other *classroom*-oriented methods—will not work well with employees who do not speak English or French as their principal language.

9. Modern health and safety teams may consist of a safety manager, engineer, industrial hygienist, health physicist, occupational health nurse, occupational physician, and ergonomist.

10. The job of the health and safety manager is complex and diverse, focusing on analysis, prevention, planning, evaluation, promotion, and compliance. Educational requirements range from technical certificates to graduate degrees.

11. Engineers can have a significant impact on safety in the workplace and the marketplace by designing safety into products.

12. Industrial hygienists are concerned with recognizing the impact of environmental factors on people, evaluating the potential hazards of environmental stressors, and prescribing methods to eliminate stressors.

13. Health physicists are concerned primarily with radiation in the workplace. Their duties include monitoring radiation in the air, measuring radioactivity levels in biological samples, developing the radiation components of a company's emergency action plan, and supervising decontamination activities.

14. Occupational health nurses are concerned with preserving the health of workers through prevention, recognition, and treatment. Like occupational physicians, occupational health nurses now focus more attention on anticipation and prevention than they did in the past.

15. Occupational physicians are medical doctors who specialize in workplace-related health problems and injuries. In the past, occupational physicians treated injuries and illnesses as they occurred. Today's occupational physicians focus more attention on anticipating and preventing problems.

16. Ergonomists specialize in the relationship between humans and their interaction with the work environment and its objects.

Key Terms and Concepts

Certification	Hygiene	Radiograpy
Code of ethics	Literacy	Safety management system
Cultural barriers	Orientation	

Review Questions

1. Explain briefly the rationale for providing safety training.
2. What legal obligations does an employer have to provide health and safety training?
3. Explain the importance of safety training for health and safety managers.
4. List the minimum content of a good orientation program.
5. Describe how low literacy impacts health and safety in the workplace.
6. Explain how an employer can accommodate the training needs of workers with limited English/French-speaking ability.
7. Describe how cultural differences can impact health and safety in the workplace.
8. What are the desired skills and credentials possessed by a safety manager?
9. How do engineers impact safety?

10. Describe the job of the industrial hygienist.

11. What is a health physicist and a radiation safety officer?

12. Describe the job of the occupational health nurse.

13. Describe the job of the occupational physician.

14. Explain the role of the ergonomist.

15. What factors are influencing the changing role of the safety professional? What changes to this profession are required to be effective?

Endnotes

[1] Anthony Giese. Barriers to Effective Safety Training: Finding Safety Training Techniques that Bridge the Generation Gap. *EHS Today*. (October 10, 2011). [Online]. Available: http://ehstoday.com/training/barriers-effective-finding-training-tech-generation-gaps-102011/. (Retrieved November 5, 2016).

[2] P. M. Laing, ed. *Supervisor's Safety Manual* (Chicago: National Safety Council, 2009), 35.

[3] Ontario, Ministry of Labour. (July 2016). "Joint Health and Safety Committees." [Online]. Available: https://www.labour.gov.on.ca/english/hs/topics/certification.php. (Retrieved November 5, 2016).

[4] J. A. Spencer and J. A. Simonowitz. "Employee Education," in *Introduction to Occupational Health and Safety*. Joseph LaDon, ed. (Chicago: National Safety Council, 1986), 277–278.

[5] Dan Petersen. "Techniques of Safety Management Systems: A Systems Approach, 4th ed. (Dan Peterson, 2003), 97.

[6] Michael T. Ford and Lois E. Tetrick. "Safety Motivation and Human Resource Management in North America." *International Journal of Human Resource Management* 19, no. 8 (August 2008): 1472–1485. Business Source Elite, EBSCOhost. (Retrieved November 2, 2011).

[7] P. Minetos. "Supervisors: Teach Them Well." *Safety + Health* 140, no. 4: 64.

[8] Ibid.

[9] National Safety Council. *Accident Prevention Manual*, 186.

[10] K. Knowles, ed. "Start Safety Training Early." *Today's Supervisor* 55, no. 7: 4.

[11] G. LaBar. "Worker Training: An Investment in Safety." *Occupational Hazards* (August 1991): 25.

[12] The Conference Board of Canada. Alison Campbell. *All Signs Point to Yes: Literacy's Impact on Workplace Health and Safety*. Publication 08-279 (September 2008).

[13] Ibid.

[14] M. Kutner, E. Greenberg, and J. Baer. *A First Look at the Literacy of America's Adults in the 21st Century* (Washington, DC: National Center for Education Statistics, 2009), 8. [Online]. Available: nces.ed.gov/pubsearch/pubsinfo.asp?pubid=2006470. (Retrieved July 1, 2013).

[15] Ibid. 14.

[16] Ibid.

[17] *The Canadian Encyclopedia*. [Online]. Available: http://www.thecanadianencyclopedia.ca/en/article/literacy/. (Retrieved November 5, 2016).

[18] Ibid.

[19] Joseph E. Halcarz. "Safety Training for Diverse Worker Population." *Occupational Hazards* 65, no. 2 (February 2003): 26–28.

[20] Ibid.

[21] Engineers Canada. [Online]. Available: https://newcomers.engineerscanada.ca/licensing-canada. (Retrieved December 4, 2016).

[22] American Industrial Hygiene Association (AIHA). *Engineering Field Reference Manual*. [Online]. Available: aiha.org. (Retrieved April 4, 2006).

[23] World Health Organization. *Health Topics, Hygiene*. [Online]. Available: http://www.who.int/topics/hygiene/en/ . (Retrieved December 13, 2016).

[24] Canadian Registration Board of Occupational Hygienists. [Online]. Available: http://www.crboh.ca/default.htm. (Retrieved December 4, 2016).

[25] Alberta Learning Information Service (ALIS). [Online]. Available: http://occinfo.alis.alberta.ca/occinfopreview/info/browse-occupations/occupation-profile.html?id=71017913. (Retrieved December 4, 2016).

[26] C. Zenz. "The Occupational Physician," in *Fundamentals of Industrial Hygiene* (Chicago: National Safety Council, 1988), 607.

[27] Canadian Board of Occupational Medicine. *Training and Credentials in Occupational Medicine*. [Online]. Available: http://www.cbom.ca/about-cbom/training-and-credentials-in-occupational-medicine/. (Retrieved December 13, 2016).

[28] Association of Canadian Ergonomists. [Online]. Available: https://www.ace-ergocanada.ca/about/certification.html. (Retrieved December 4, 2016).

[29] The Board of Canadian Registered Safety Professionals (BCRSP). [Online]. Available: http://bcrsp.ca/prospective-certificants/faq. (Retrieved December 4, 2016).

[30] Canadian Society of Safety Engineers. *Certified Health & Safety Consultant*. [Online]. Available: http://www.csse.org/chsc_designation. (Retrieved December 12, 2016).

[31] D. Groover and J. Spigener. "The Emerging Role of the Safety Professional, Part 1." *Occupational Health & Safety* 77, no. 4 (2005): 24.

[32] Ibid., no. 7: 38.

[33] Ibid.

Chapter 4
Occupational Health and Safety Legislation in Canada

MAJOR TOPICS

- The Canadian Legal System
- Acts and Regulations
- Standards and Codes
- Occupational Health and Safety Jurisdictions
- How Workers Are Protected
- The Role of Key Players
- Joint Occupational Health and Safety Committees
- Internal Responsibility System

laws Rules that limit behaviour.

For society to function in a safe and productive manner, the activities of each member are governed by rules of conduct. These **laws** may restrict the activities of some while providing certain privileges for others. For laws to be effective, they must benefit society as a whole, be enforced, and have a component that deters deviation from those rules. This chapter describes how health and safety **legislation** is made and enforced in Canada, the role of the key players, and to which jurisdiction different legislation applies.

legislation Laws brought into force by a legislative body.

THE CANADIAN LEGAL SYSTEM

Magna Carta Charter enacted in 1215 that limited the power of King John of England.

To fully appreciate the scope of our health and safety legislation, it is necessary to take a brief look at how our legal system has evolved to the point where it is today. The Canadian legal system is based largely on the English system. A major development in the British system was the signing of the **Magna Carta** (Great Charter) by King John of England in 1215. The significance of the Magna Carta was that for the first time the king's power could be limited and his subjects protected from arbitrary rule. Although King John was forced to agree to the terms of the Magna Carta in order to maintain power, the powerful barons renewed their allegiance to the king. As a result an important constitutional principle was established—**consent of the governed**.

consent of the governed The phrase is most commonly cited from the American Declaration of Independence. It refers to a government's just right to exercise power only when it is validated by the consent of those governed.

When Canada won its independence from Britain in 1867, the **British North America (BNA) Act** laid out the terms of reference for the new country, including the dividing up of power between the provinces and the federal government. Federal responsibility would include areas such as commerce, currency, the military, postal service, and criminal law. The provinces were given jurisdiction over the areas of marriage, shops, local taxation, maintenance of local resources, hospitals, and workplace conditions, including occupational health and safety.

The **Constitution Act, 1982**, maintained the contents of the BNA Act, but also included a "charter of rights and freedoms," which guarantees all Canadian citizens the rights and freedoms that are often taken for granted by Canadians but are the envy of most other countries. The charter also affords workers protection beyond traditional safety laws when legislation within OHS acts or regulations leave gaps or ambiguity. Meanwhile, Canadian jurisdictions continue to create more comprehensive health and safety legislation to address psychological well-being and the protection of workers' rights and freedoms, as well as physical safety.

British North America (BNA) Act, 1867 Established the constitutional layout of the new country, Canada, including the powers of the provincial and federal governments.

Constitution Act, 1982 Provided Canada with a new constitution that included the charter of rights and freedoms.

ACTS AND REGULATIONS

Canada has a parliamentary system of government with each province being governed by a legislature. When a cabinet minister responsible for an area such as occupational health and safety decides that a new **statute** or **act** is needed or an existing one needs to be amended, the ministry staff drafts a new law. After an internal review by the department or ministry, the minister will receive approval from the cabinet to introduce the new law in the legislature or parliament in the form of a **bill**. After the bill has been debated and amendments made, it will get three readings in the legislature. After the third reading the bill is given "royal assent" and then becomes an "act."[1]

Acts or statutes are the framework around which **regulations** are built. Many statutes consist largely of a list of powers to make regulations.[2] Regulations specify how the act is intended to be applied to each situation. For example, the act may require workers to use the correct procedures or equipment, but the details of those prescribed procedures or equipment are found in the related regulations. Several sets of regulations made under the occupational act cover various workplace sectors. For example, in Ontario, separate regulations are in place for construction projects, mines, industrial establishments, teachers, health care, and WHMIS for designated substances, such as lead and mercury.

statute Law made by provincial legislature or federal parliament.

act Document containing laws made by provincial legislature or federal parliament.

bill Law in draft form.

regulations Specific rules that support other legislation.

STANDARDS AND CODES

A **standard** is an operational principle, criterion, or requirement—or a combination of these. A **code** is a set of standards, rules, or regulations relating to a specific area. Standards and codes play an important role in modern health and safety management and engineering. These written procedures detail the safe and healthy way to perform job tasks and, consequently, to make the workplace safer and healthier.

Having written standards and codes that employees carefully follow can also decrease a company's exposure to costly litigation. Courts tend to hand down harsher rulings to companies that fail to develop, adapt, implement, and enforce appropriate standards and codes. Because of this, health and safety professionals should be familiar with the standards and codes relating to their company.

Numerous organizations develop standards for different industries. These organizations can be categorized broadly as follows: government, professional organizations, and technical/trade associations.

Organizations that fall within these broad categories develop standards and codes in a wide variety of areas including, but not limited to, the following: fire protection, hazardous chemicals, instrumentation, insulation, lighting, lubrication, materials, noise/vibration,

standard An operational principle, criterion, or requirement pertaining to working conditions, methods, equipment, or materials in the workplace.

code A set of standards, rules, or regulations relating to a specific area.

power, wiring, pressure relief, piping materials, piping systems, radiation exposure, safety equipment, shutdown systems, and ventilation.

Following are some examples of the three types of organizations involved in developing standards. The widely accepted standards for many consumer products are those set by **CSA Group** (formerly the Canadian Standards Association). **ACGIH** (American Conference of Governmental Industrial Hygienists), which develops and publishes recommended exposure limits for chemical and physical agents, is a *professional association*. (The ACGIH limits are the standard to which most jurisdictions refer when developing their own standards.) And the HRAI (Heating, Refrigeration and Air Conditioning Institute of Canada), which sets standards and provides certification to members of the heating and refrigeration field, is a *trade association*.

CSA Group Formerly, the Canadian Standards Association. Independent agency that develops standards for the performance of many products inside and outside of the workplace.

ACGIH American Conference of Governmental Industrial Hygienists. A professional association that develops and publishes recommended exposure limits for chemical and physical agents.

OCCUPATIONAL HEALTH AND SAFETY JURISDICTIONS

Workers in Canada are covered by occupational health and safety legislation under one of two jurisdictions. Most workers are covered by health and safety laws of their province or territory, while about 10 percent of workers are covered by federal legislation. Each province or territory has its own version of an occupational health and safety act and corresponding regulations for various sectors. Figure 4–1 lists the legislation and who administers it in each jurisdiction. The format and content of the acts are very similar for each province and territory.

Figure 4–1 Health and safety jurisdictions in Canada.

Jurisdiction/Website	Legislation	Administration
Newfoundland and Labrador www.servicenl.gov.nl.ca/ohs	Occupational Health and Safety Act	Service NL
Prince Edward Island www.wcb.pe.ca	Occupational Health and Safety Act	Workers Compensation Board of Prince Edward Island
Nova Scotia www.workplaceinitiatives.novascotia.ca/nshr toolkit/links/ohs.asp	Occupational Health and Safety Act	Department of Labour and Education, Occupational Health and Safety Division
New Brunswick www.worksafenb.ca	Occupational Health and Safety Act	WorkSafe NB
Quebec www.csst.qc.ca/en	Occupational Health and Safety Act	Commission des normes, de l'équité, de la santé et de la sécurité du travail
Ontario www.labour.gov.on.ca/english/hs	Occupational Health and Safety Act	Ministry of Labour
Manitoba www.gov.mb.ca/labour/safety/index.html	Manitoba Workplace Safety and Health Act and Regulation	Department of Labour and Immigration
Saskatchewan www.worksafesask.ca	The Saskatchewan Employment Act	Ministry of Labour Relations and Workplace Safety
Alberta www.work.alberta.ca/occupational-health-safety.html	Occupational Health and Safety Act and OHS Code	Ministry of Labour
British Columbia www.worksafebc.com	Workers Compensation Act and Regulation	WorkSafeBC
Yukon Territory www.wcb.yk.ca	Occupational Health and Safety Act	Yukon Workers' Compensation Health and Safety Board
Northwest Territories and Nunavut www.wscc.nt.ca	Safety Act	Workers' Safety and Compensation Commission
Canada www.labour.gc.ca	Canada Labour Code Part II	Human Resources and Skills Development Canada

Workers employed directly by the federal government or by the following employers are covered by the **Canada Labour Code**. Part I addresses labour relations; Part II covers occupational health and safety; and Part III deals with standard hours, wages, vacations, and holidays. Examples of workers covered by the Canada Labour Code include the following:

Canada Labour Code Legislation that sets out the rights and duties of federal employees who work under federal jurisdiction. About 10 percent of the Canadian workforce is covered by the Canada Labour Code.

- Federal crown corporations
- Interprovincial trucking, shipping, and bridges
- Airlines and airports
- Railways
- Telephone, television, and radio broadcasters
- Banks
- Grain elevators
- Other specific employers, as prescribed in Section 2 of the Code

HOW WORKERS ARE PROTECTED

The federal legislation is very similar in format and content to that of the provinces and territories. The occupational health and safety acts for the provinces and territories are divided into sections that are, in turn, often divided into subsections to expand on a particular area of concern. For example, section 5 of the Safety Act for the Northwest Territories states the duty of workers in the following format:

5. Every worker employed on or in connection with an establishment shall, within the course of his or her employment,

   (a) take all reasonable precautions to ensure his or her own safety and the safety of other persons in the establishment; and

   (b) as the circumstances require, use devices or articles of clothing or equipment that are intended for his or her protection and provided to the worker by his or her employer, or required pursuant to the regulations to be used or worn by the worker.[3]

As shown below, in section 28 of Ontario's Occupational Health and Safety Act, the duties of workers are presented in greater detail, but the basic principle and the format are very similar.

28. (1) A worker shall,

   (a) work in compliance with the provisions of this Act and the regulations;

   (b) use or wear the equipment, protective devices or clothing that the worker's employer requires to be used or worn;

   (c) report to his or her employer or supervisor the absence of or defect in any equipment or protective device of which the worker is aware and which may endanger himself, herself or another worker; and

   (d) report to his or her employer or supervisor any contravention of this Act or the regulations or the existence of any hazard of which he or she knows.

Idem

   (2) No worker shall,

   (a) remove or make ineffective any protective device required by the regulations or by his or her employer, without providing an adequate temporary protective device and when the need for removing or making ineffective the protective device has ceased, the protective device shall be replaced immediately;

   (b) use or operate any equipment, machine, device or thing or work in a manner that may endanger himself, herself or any other worker; or

(c) engage in any prank, contest, feat of strength, unnecessary running or rough and boisterous conduct.[4]

Section 126.(1) from the Canada Labour Code shown below also reveals the similarities in the presentation of the federal legislation to that of the provinces and territories:

Duties of Employees 126. (1) While at work, every employee shall

(a) use any safety materials, equipment, devices and clothing that are intended for the employee's protection and furnished to the employee by the employer or that are prescribed;

(b) follow prescribed procedures with respect to the health and safety of employees;

(c) take all reasonable and necessary precautions to ensure the health and safety of the employee, the other employees and any person likely to be affected by the employee's acts or omissions;

(d) comply with all instructions from the employer concerning the health and safety of employees;

(e) cooperate with any person carrying out a duty imposed under this Part;

(f) cooperate with the policy and work place committees or the health and safety representative;

(g) report to the employer any thing or circumstance in a work place that is likely to be hazardous to the health or safety of the employee, or that of the other employees or other persons granted access to the work place by the employer;

(h) report in the prescribed manner every accident or other occurrence arising in the course of or in connection with the employee's work that has caused injury to the employee or to any other person;

(i) comply with every oral or written direction of a health and safety officer and appeals officer concerning the health and safety of employees.

(j) report to the employer any situation that the employee believes to be a contravention of this Part by the employer, another employee or any other person.[5]

Regardless of the jurisdiction, all workers are granted the three basic rights explained in Chapter 1, either directly or indirectly: the right to know, the right to participate, and the right to refuse.

The right for a worker to "know," refers to the worker's right to be informed of both any potential hazard they may face and of the means to protect themselves from it. For example, the general duties of employers or supervisors in each jurisdiction require that the worker is made aware of any hazards. The Workplace Hazardous Materials Information System (WHMIS) is an important component in the workers' right to know. WHMIS, which will be covered in more depth in Chapter 12, provides the worker with information on the hazards, use, storage, and safe handling of chemicals in the workplace.

objectivity Rules are enforced equally, regardless of employee or management status, within the company.

The "right to participate" refers to the right each worker has to be involved in safety issues at work. This right can be granted directly, through representation on joint health and safety committees (JHSCs), or indirectly, through the worker's duty to inform others of hazards in the workplace. Later in the chapter we will take a closer look at joint occupational health and safety committees and their role in the workplace.

The right to refuse is granted to all Canadian workers and is dealt with at length in the statutes of most jurisdictions. Workers have the right to refuse to do work that they believe may harm them or another worker. The specific procedure for workers to follow and the steps taken in the event of a work refusal may be detailed in the act for that jurisdiction.

In most areas the basic procedure requires that a refusal be investigated by a supervisor and a worker representative to decide the validity of the refusal. If the situation is deemed to be unsafe, the problem is rectified, but if no agreement can be reached between the two parties, a government inspector or officer may be called in to assess the matter. While waiting for a conclusion to the complaint, the worker who refused may be assigned alternate work but not dismissed. Workers are also protected from reprisal by the employer for refusing work in good faith or for abiding by any of the requirements of the act.

The right to refuse may be limited in some occupations that have obvious inherent danger or in which the public safety is concerned. For example, a police officer cannot refuse to respond to a domestic dispute because of fear of getting hurt, but refusing to use a vehicle that has loose steering or faulty brakes for a regular street patrol would be very well justified. A similar case can be made for firefighters, workers in correctional institutes, and some health care workers. Although these occupations often involve high risk, these workers can expect to be provided with reasonable means of protection, whether performing routine tasks or responding to an emergency.

⟫⟫ DISCUSSION CASE | What Is Your Opinion?

Between 30 and 40 employees work at Corona Solar, in Edmonton, manufacturing and installing commercial solar panels. Zainab was asked by her supervisor, Mark, to use the new industrial table saw to cut 60 triangular mounting blocks for a large installation that was overdue. Zainab noticed that the factory-installed guard had been removed from the saw and felt it was now unsafe as a result. After asking her coworkers about the guard, it was discovered that it had been thrown out because one senior employee felt that it was not necessary and slowed production. Zainab decided to refuse to perform the assigned task, believing that it was unsafe to operate the saw without the guard in place. Using the health and safety act for your jurisdiction, describe the proper steps required to take this matter to its proper conclusion. Would it be acceptable for another worker to cut the blocks on that saw while the parties involved dealt with the matter?

THE ROLE OF KEY PLAYERS

All workers have a moral and legal responsibility to protect themselves and their coworkers from hazards on the job; however, some workers play an even greater role in making the workplace safe. In some jurisdictions, added responsibilities, such as workplace inspections and accident investigation, are given to worker representatives or health and safety committee members. All workers are obligated to learn about the hazards in the workplace and take the steps necessary to protect themselves and their coworkers by employing whatever means are available, such using the proper **personal protective equipment (PPE)** provided by the employer.

The employer is required by law to provide a safe workplace for its employees, but as we will explore in Chapter 7, the cost of accidents, along with the legal and moral obligation, provides significant motivation to ensure workers' safety. Huge fines and even

personal protective equipment (PPE) Any type of clothing or device that puts a barrier between the worker and the hazard (e.g., safety goggles, gloves, hard hats, and so on).

imprisonment also provide a substantial deterrent to neglecting workplace safety. An employer is also required to exercise **due diligence** with regard to employee safety. The duties of employers are listed in Sec. 25 of the Ontario Occupational Health and Safety Act. The definition of due diligence may be found in Sec. 25 (2)(h):

> **Sec. 25 (2)(h)** An employer shall take every precaution reasonable in the circumstances for the protection of a worker.[6]

due diligence A measure of prudence and care that a reasonable person would exercise under the circumstances.

This **general duty clause** is employed in each province and territory and serves to provide an expectation that all workplace parties make a reasonable and practicable effort to protect the health and safety of workers. Even when the "letter of the law" is met, there is an obligation to address and mitigate any known or foreseeable hazards.

general duty clause Legislation found in each Canadian jurisdiction to ensure that OHS obligations, which are not explicitly stated, are met.

The supervisor plays a crucial role in maintaining a safe workplace. The specific duties of the supervisor are spelled out in varying detail among the jurisdictions. When a worker is injured, one could ask the following questions: Was the worker informed of the hazards, was the worker trained to do the job properly, and was the worker provided with the equipment, tools, or facilities to protect themselves? Shortcomings in each case can be traced back to the supervisor. It should be noted that a job done "properly" is one that is done safely.

Governments have a social obligation to reduce workplace accidents. The government has a responsibility to ensure that the best policies and programs are in place to protect the well-being of its citizens. Unfortunately, government safety campaigns, advertisements, and changes to legislation are often noticed only after some catastrophe or sensational workplace issue is publicized by the media. As with workers and employers, it is in the government's financial interest to promote occupational health and safety, because the cost of accidents through increased health care costs and lost productivity can be enormous.

The government must use its resources to establish guidelines and standards. Information from outside agencies, such as the ACGIH's exposure limits for chemicals, is often used as a source for standards. Governments may also choose to establish their own agencies for research or enforcement. **The Canadian Centre for Occupational Health and Safety (CCOHS)**, for example, was created by the federal government to research and provide safety information resources to all Canadian workers.

Canadian Centre for Occupational Health and Safety (CCOHS) A federal government agency established to research and provide safety information resources to all Canadian workers.

Collection and sharing of data on occupational accidents and illness provides health and safety practitioners with the resources to see trends and locate areas of concern. When this data is collected by a central agency, such as CCOHS or the Association of Workers' Compensation Boards of Canada (AWCBC) or other similar agencies, comparisons can be made among various occupations, employers, age groups, locations, etc. Long-term trends help expose problems, such as industrial disease and illness in specific industries or locations. Historically, high rates of cancer or respiratory diseases would have been attributed to other causes, such as lifestyle, geographic location, or demographics. But with this huge database available, a correlation between certain diseases and occupations becomes more pronounced.

JOINT OCCUPATIONAL HEALTH AND SAFETY COMMITTEES

The joint occupational health and safety committee is a partnership between workers and employer representatives, whose collective goal is to identify and solve health and safety problems in the workplace. The health and safety committee also ensures that the workers' right to know and right to participate are fulfilled. Workplace committees are mandatory in most workplaces within most jurisdictions in Canada, but the prescribed duties may vary for each area. In any workplace, the minister responsible may require that a health and safety committee be established if it is felt that the workers' safety would be improved. In smaller workplaces, where a committee may not be practical, a single safety representative is often required.

Depending on the jurisdiction, health and safety committees may be referred to as occupational health committees, workplace health and safety committees, or joint worksite health and safety committees. This section describes the general makeup of and duties for health and safety committees in the workplace. For specific information in a particular jurisdiction, the relevant local legislation should be consulted. Figure 4–2 summarizes the requirements for health and safety committees, as of 2017.

Figure 4–2 Health and safety committee requirements.

	Legislation Requirements for Health and Safety Committees		
	When Do I Need One?	Size of Committee	Representation
Canada	Mandatory when 20 or more employees	At least 2	At least half to represent employees
British Columbia	Mandatory when 20 or more employees or when "required by order"	Not less than 4	At least half must be worker representatives
Alberta	Mandatory when 20 or more employees	Not less than 4	At least half to represent workers
Saskatchewan	Mandatory when 10 employees or more	At least 2 but not more than 12	At least half to represent employees
Manitoba	Mandatory when 20 or more employees	At least 4 but not more than 12	At least half to represent employees
Ontario	Mandatory when 20 or more employees, when ordered by the minister, or where a designated substance is in use (no minimum number of employees in that case)	At least 2 (when fewer than 50 employees); at least 4 (when 50 or more employees)	At least half to represent employees
Quebec	Mandatory when 20 or more employees and where regulated	At least 4	At least half to represent employees
New Brunswick	Mandatory when 20 or more employees	As agreed upon by employees and employer	Equal representation
Nova Scotia	Mandatory when 20 or more employees	As agreed upon by employees and employer	At least half to represent employees
PEI	Mandatory when 20 or more employees	Not specified	At least half to represent employees
Newfoundland	Discretionary when 10 or more employees	At least 2 but not more than 12	At least half to represent employees
Yukon	Mandatory when 20 or more employees	At least 4 but not more than 12	At least half to represent employees
Northwest Territories and Nunavut	All workplaces require committee or representative	Not specified	Equal representation

The employer is responsible for establishing a health and safety committee in the workplace. Although legislation outlines the conduct and duties of the health and safety committee in most areas, this represents only the minimum requirements and is often superseded by the committees' own **terms of reference**. The initial terms of reference for

terms of reference A set of rules under which the health and safety committee is to operate.

the committee are also established by the employer, but are usually tailored by the present committee to suit the particular workplace requirements. The terms of reference normally include items such as the number of committee members, the number of committee members required for a quorum, the term of office for members, the frequency of meetings and inspections, and other rules that are deemed to be necessary by the committee.

The health and safety committee members' activities should be performed with the support of management, and the members are to be paid as if they are performing their normal jobs. Committee members who occasionally have access to confidential information about the company or its employees are required to honour the confidentiality of that information as required by the relevant federal, provincial, or territorial act. While exact roles may vary by jurisdiction, in general, the committee assists the employer in:

- recognizing workplace hazards,

- evaluating the risk of accidents/incidents, injuries and illness,

- participating in developing and implementing programs to protect employees' health and safety,

- responding to employee complaints and suggestions concerning health and safety,

- ensuring the maintenance and monitoring of injury and work hazard records,

- monitoring and following up on hazard reports and recommending action,

- setting up and promoting programs to improve employee training and education,

- participating in all health and safety inquiries and investigations,

- consulting with professional and technical experts,

- participating in resolving workplace refusals and work stoppages,

- making recommendations to management for accident prevention and safety program activities, and

- monitoring the effectiveness of safety programs and procedures.[7]

INTERNAL RESPONSIBILITY SYSTEM

internal responsibility system
A mechanism to allow employers, supervisors, and workers to monitor one another's actions and ensure compliance with legislation.

Health and safety legislation in Canada is based on the **internal responsibility system** (IRS). The concept was introduced by Dr. James Ham, who led a Royal Commission to study the health and safety of mine workers after the famous Elliott Lake miners' strike in 1974. In 1978, Ontario passed its first Health and Safety Act, incorporating the IRS, which was primarily founded on the recommendations from the Ham Report.

The health and safety legislation for each jurisdiction lays out the rights and responsibilities for each of the parties within the workplace. The IRS provides a mechanism to allow employers, supervisors, and workers to monitor one another's actions and ensure compliance with the act. Rather than relying on an outside agency to enforce health and safety rules in the workplace, the IRS gives everyone a contributing role in workplace health and safety. It is in the best interest of all parties to strive for a safe and healthy workplace. When all parties work toward a common goal, the spirit of cooperation is fostered and the cost of administering and enforcing safety legislation is reduced significantly.

It is also helpful to have those who are most familiar with their particular workplace play an active role in their own health and safety. Workers play a frontline role in identifying hazards in the workplace and have a sense of personal responsibility. The financial benefits, along with moral and legal obligations, usually ensure that the supervisor and employer diligently promote health and safety with the least amount of involvement by government enforcement agencies.

SUMMARY

1. The Canadian legal system is based largely on the English system.

2. Health and safety legislation in most situations falls under provincial or territorial jurisdiction. Federal employees, which represent about 10 percent of Canadian workers, are covered by the Canada Labour Code.

3. Acts or statutes are the framework around which supporting regulations and codes are built.

4. Acts, regulations, standards, and codes are used to govern people's behaviour. These rules may be restrictive in some situations, but are meant to protect society as a whole.

5. The American Conference of Governmental Industrial Hygienists (ACGIH) and the Canadian Standards Association (CSA) are two agencies whose standards are widely accepted by most Canadian jurisdictions.

6. Health and safety legislation in Canada is based on the internal responsibility system. The internal responsibility system requires less government interference, thus reducing paperwork and cost.

7. The key players in health and safety are workers, supervisors, and employers. Government inspectors are also a key component in enforcement of the statutes for each jurisdiction.

Key Terms and Concepts

ACGIH	Code	Legislation
Act	Consent of the governed	Magna Carta
Bill	Constitution Act, 1982	Objectivity
British North America Act (BNA Act, 1876)	CSA Group	Personal protective equipment (PPE)
Canada Labour Code	Due diligence	Regulations
Canadian Centre for Occupational Health and Safety (CCOHS)	General duty clause	Standard
	Internal responsibility system	Statute
	Laws	Terms of reference

Review Questions

1. A provincial or federal politician sees that new legislation is required to address a serious occupational health and safety issue. Explain what steps are required for that elected member to take the issue from a concern expressed by a group of citizens or special interest group and transform it into an enforceable law.

2. Referring to local provincial or territorial legislation, what is the maximum penalty for an individual who is in breach of health and safety laws? What would be the maximum penalty for a corporation?

3. Define due diligence and describe how an employer's obligation to exercise due diligence ensures that health and safety concerns will not be overlooked.

4. With reference to local provincial or territorial legislation, describe the main duties that employers, supervisors, and workers must undertake to promote a safe workplace.

5. What role does the media play in occupational health and safety?

6. List at least one moral, legal, and economic obligation that each of the following has to invest in workplace safety: worker, employer, supervisor, and government.

7. In your province or territory's legislation, provide specific examples of how the three basic OHS rights are supported.

8. Describe the composition of the health and safety committee and its key duties for your local jurisdiction.

9. What are the benefits of the internal responsibility system? Can you think of any possible shortcomings of this system?

Weblinks

Figure 4–1 contains the website URLs for all the government agencies responsible for health and safety in each Canadian jurisdiction. Note that while ministries and departments responsible for OHS often change names and their website address, the previous URL usually remains active for years.

Endnotes

[1] D. Estrin and J. Swaigen. *Environment on Trial: A Guide to Ontario Environmental Law and Policy*, 3rd ed. (Toronto: Emond Montgomery Publications Limited, 1993), 10.

[2] Ibid., 11.

[3] Safety Act, Northwest Territories. Safety Act R.S.N.W.T. 1988, cS-1. Section 5.

[4] Occupational Health and Safety Act. RSO 1990. Section 28 (1)(2). Queen's Printer for Ontario.

[5] Canada Labour Code (R.S. 1985, c. L-2) Part II. Section 126.

[6] Occupational Health and Safety Act. RSO 1990. Section 25 (2)(h). Queen's Printer for Ontario.

[7] Canadian Centre for Occupational Health and Safety. (December 14, 1999). "OHS Answers." [Online]. Available: http://www.ccohs.ca/oshanswers/hsprograms/hscommittees/whatisa.html. (Retrieved November 27, 2016).

Chapter 5
Workers' Compensation, Disability Management, and Return to Work

MAJOR TOPICS

- Overview of Workers' Compensation
- Objectives of Workers' Compensation
- Historical Perspective
- Modern Workers' Compensation
- Injured Worker Benefits
- Harmful Environments
- Presumptive Legislation
- Disability Management and Return to Work

OVERVIEW OF WORKERS' COMPENSATION

The concept of workers' compensation developed as a way to allow injured employees to be compensated appropriately without having to take their employers to court. The underlying rationale for workers' compensation had two aspects: (1) fairness to injured employees, especially those without the resources to undertake legal actions that are often long, drawn out, and expensive; and (2) reduction of the costs to employers associated with workplace injuries (e.g., legal, image, and morale costs). Workers' compensation is intended to be a no-fault approach to resolving workplace accidents by rehabilitating injured employees and minimizing their personal losses resulting from their reduced ability to perform and compete in the labour market.[1] Since its inception as a concept, workers' compensation in Canada has evolved into a system that pays out over $6 billion per year. In Ontario alone, the cost of benefits paid or provided directly to injured workers was over $2.3 billion in 2015, which is down from almost $2.7 billion a decade earlier.[2]

Workers' compensation represents a compromise between the needs of employees and the needs of employers. Employees give up their right to seek unlimited compensation for pain and suffering through legal action. Employers award the prescribed compensation (typically through insurance premiums) regardless of the employee's negligence.

The theory is that, in the long run, both employees and employers will benefit more than either would through legal action. Although workers' compensation has reduced the amount of legal action arising out of workplace accidents, it has not been completely eliminated.

OBJECTIVES OF WORKERS' COMPENSATION

Workers' compensation laws vary from jurisdiction to jurisdiction. However, regardless of the language contained in the enabling legislation in a specific jurisdiction, workers' compensation as a concept has several widely accepted objectives:

- Replacement of income
- Rehabilitation of the injured employee
- Accident prevention
- Cost allocation

Replacement of Income

income replacement Replacement of current and future income, based on 90 percent of net pay for most jurisdictions.

Employees injured on the job lose income if they are unable to work. For this reason, workers' compensation is intended to replace the lost income adequately and promptly. Adequate **income replacement** is viewed as replacement of both current and future income. The amount of compensation awarded is based on a percentage of net income in all jurisdictions except Yukon. For Alberta, British Columbia, Manitoba, Northwest Territories and Nunavut, Quebec, and Saskatchewan, compensation is based on 90 percent of net earnings, with the remaining provinces replacing income at rates from 75 percent to 85 percent. The rates for Yukon are derived from 75 percent of gross income. Workers' compensation benefits continue even if the employer goes out of business.

Rehabilitation of the Injured Employee

A basic premise of workers' compensation is that the injured worker will return to work in every case possible, although not necessarily in the same job or career field. For this reason, a major objective of workers' compensation is to rehabilitate the injured employee. Occasionally an injured worker will need rehabilitation before they can return to work. There are two types of rehabilitation: medical and vocational. Both are available to workers whose ability to make a living is inhibited by physical and/or mental work-related problems.

medical rehabilitation Designed to provide the needed medical care to the injured employee until he or she is pronounced fit to return to work.

vocational rehabilitation Involves providing the education and training needed to prepare the worker for a new occupation.

Medical rehabilitation consists of providing whatever treatment is required to restore any lost ability to function to the extent that such restoration is possible. This may include such services as physical therapy or the provision of prosthetic devices. The rehabilitation program is to provide the needed medical care at no cost to the injured employee until he or she is pronounced fit to return to work. **Vocational rehabilitation** involves providing the education and training needed to prepare the worker for a new occupation if it is determined that she or he will not be able to return to the previous job. Whether the rehabilitation services are medical or vocational in nature, or both, the goal is to restore the injured worker's capabilities to the level that existed before the accident. Both components seek to motivate the employee to return to the labour force as soon as possible.

A major portion of our social interaction and our self-image is provided by the workplace and by coworkers. Accordingly, workers are required in some and encouraged in other jurisdictions to maintain contact with their employer throughout their rehabilitation from a workplace illness or injury. Several programs are in place to assist the worker's return to work, sometimes in a new position or at a reduced capacity. The longer a worker is away from the workplace, the less likely it is that rehabilitation will be successful.

Accident Prevention

Preventing future accidents is a major objective of workers' compensation. The theory underlying this objective is that employers will invest in **accident prevention** programs in order to hold down compensation costs. Canadian compensation boards offer incentives for employers to reduce accidents and their associated costs, through various programs including premium discounts for those businesses that perform well and surcharges for those that perform poorly. Educational programs may be mandatory for businesses with high accident costs, while others may be rewarded with premium discounts for voluntarily participating in training.

accident prevention The act of preventing a happening that may cause loss or injury to a person.

Cost Allocation

Workers' compensation is an expensive concept. From the outset, one of the basic principles has been **cost allocation**. The costs associated with workers' compensation must be borne by employers as part of their overhead. Cost allocation is the process of spreading the cost of workers' compensation across an industry so that no individual company is overly burdened. The cost of workers' compensation includes the costs of premiums, benefits, and administration, which have risen steadily over the years. Cost allocation is based on the **experience rating** of the industry. In addition to being a fair method of allocating costs, this approach is also intended to give employers an incentive to proactively implement and participate in safety programs.

cost allocation Spreading the cost of workers' compensation appropriately and proportionately among industries, ranging from the most to the least hazardous.

experience rating The recent safety performance of the company is reflected in the premiums charged.

The potential risks associated with different occupations vary. For example, working as a miner is generally considered more hazardous than working as an architect. The underlying principle of cost allocation is to spread the cost of workers' compensation appropriately and proportionately among industries, ranging from the most to the least hazardous. The costs of accidents should be allocated in accordance with the accident history of the industry so that high-risk industries pay higher workers' compensation insurance premiums than do low-risk industries.

HISTORICAL PERSPECTIVE

Before workers' compensation laws were enacted in Canada, injured employees had no way to obtain compensation for their injuries except to take their employer to court. Although common law did require employers to provide a safe and healthy work environment, injured employees bore the burden of proof that negligence in the form of unsafe conditions contributed to these injuries. Prior to passage of workers' compensation legislation, employees often had to sue their employer to receive compensation for injuries resulting from a workplace accident or **occupational diseases**.

Proving that an injury was the result of employer negligence was typically too costly, too difficult, and too time-consuming to be a realistic avenue of redress for most injured employees. Typically, injured workers, having lost their ability to generate income, could barely afford to get by, much less pay medical expenses, legal fees, and court costs. Another inhibitor was the *fear factor*. Injured employees who hoped to return to work after recovering were often afraid to file suit because they feared retribution by their employer. Employers might not only refuse to give them their jobs back but might also **blackball** them with

occupational diseases Pathological conditions brought about by workplace conditions or factors.

blackball To ostracize an employee.

other employers. Add to this that fellow employees were often afraid to testify to the negligence of the employer and it is easy to see why few injured workers elected to take their employers to court.

Even with all of these inhibitors, some injured employees still chose to seek redress through the courts in the days before workers' compensation. Those who did faced a difficult challenge because the laws at that time made it easy for employers to defend themselves successfully. As explained in Chapter 1, all an employer had to do to win a decision denying the injured plaintiff compensation was show that at least one of the following conditions existed at the time of the accident:

employee negligence Condition that exists when an employee fails to take necessary and prudent precautions.

1. The injured worker's **employee negligence** was a factor that contributed to the accident.
2. There was negligence on the part of a fellow worker.
3. There was assumption of risk on the part of the injured employee.

Because the majority of workplace accidents involve at least some degree of negligence on the part of the injured worker or fellow employees, employers typically won these cases. Because it required little more than a verbal warning by the employer to establish grounds for assumption of risk, the odds were clearly against an injured employee being awarded compensation.

As discussed in Chapter 1, workers' compensation had its beginning in Canada when it was introduced in Ontario in 1914 and became law on January 1, 1915. The five principles upon which Canada's first workers' compensation legislation were founded still underpin the philosophy of today's workers' compensation programs.

1. **Collective liability.** The cost of the program is shared by all employers. (This protected individual employers from financial ruin—in contrast to some other early systems in which individual liability required the employer to provide compensation on their own.)
2. **No fault.** Blame is not assigned to the worker or the employer, and the injured worker is compensated without either party able to sue the other.
3. **Security of payment.** Injured workers are ensured payment regardless of the financial condition of the employer—or even if the employer has ceased to operate.
4. **Exclusive jurisdiction.** The board is the final authority for all claims and may judge any case independently, based on its individual merits.
5. **Independent boards.** The workers' compensation boards operate independently of any political party's influence.[3]

Within 15 years the rest of Canada was covered by some form of workers' compensation. These early plans provided for some wage replacement and were a vast improvement for injured workers over previous conditions. Through its evolution, workers' compensation now covers a far greater number of illnesses and injuries than it initially did, at an increased compensation level. These escalating expenses have given rise to the need for compensation boards and for employers to curb workers' compensation costs through various incentive programs that reduce accident costs and encourage workers' quick return to normal employment.

MODERN WORKERS' COMPENSATION

The role of workers' compensation boards (WCBs) today goes far beyond simply doling out compensation payments to injured workers. WCBs have developed into a full-service occupational health and safety resource in most jurisdictions. They provide training and certification for various workplace sectors, along with developing and administering several programs that are designed to reduce costs by reducing the number and severity of accidents and expediting injured workers' return to the workplace.

Workers' compensation is a form of insurance whose premiums reflect the risk being covered, much like automobile insurance plans. Two key factors are used to determine how much the employer will pay in premiums: One is the relative risk to the worker in performing their normal duties, and the other is how well the worker does compared to their peers. A young male driver in a sports car, for example, would represent a greater risk to the insurance company than a middle-aged female driving a sedan, so the premiums would be significantly higher for the young male. Similarly, we would expect that compensation premiums would be much greater for a roofer than for a clerical office worker.

WCB Insurance Premiums

All covered occupations are assigned a rate code to determine the base premium amount. Premiums are based on $100 of payroll. For example in Saskatchewan, which has some of the lowest base rates in the country, the logging industry pays $17.62 per $100 of payroll, while banks and financial institutions pay only 18 cents per $100. If one logging company or financial institution had frequent and/or costly accident experiences, it would have to pay a surcharge on its base assessment until its performance improved. Conversely, companies that exceed the safety performance of others in the same rate group will get a discount on their premiums. These surcharges and discounts, which are usually based on the previous 3 years, provide an incentive for employers to reduce the number and severity of accidents in the workplace.

INJURED WORKER BENEFITS

Workers who miss work due to a work-related injury may be eligible to receive compensation to help replace lost income. The amount the injured worker receives is usually between 75 percent and 90 percent of their average net income before their loss. As seen in Figure 5–1, a maximum amount of earnings is used in each province or territory to determine the maximum possible compensation. For 2017, the greatest maximum compensable income was $127,000 in Manitoba, while the lowest was $52,800 in Prince Edward Island.

Figure 5–1 Maximum compensable earnings, 2017.

Province or Territory	Maximum Compensable Earnings
British Columbia	$81,900
Alberta	$98,700 (cap removed in 2017)
Saskatchewan	$76,086
Manitoba	$127,000
Ontario	$88,500
Quebec	$72,500
New Brunswick	$62,700
Nova Scotia	$59,300
Prince Edward Island	$52,800
Newfoundland and Labrador	$63,420
Yukon Territory	$85,601
Northwest Territories	$90,600
Nunavut	$90,600

Health care, prescription drugs, and therapy costs are covered by the compensation board. In most jurisdictions, once the recovery from the injury is expected to proceed no further, benefits may be paid to compensate the worker for non-economic loss (the permanent physical, functional, or psychological loss the impairment causes that affects the worker's life outside of work as well as her or his ability to work). The amount of compensation is based on the level of impairment, the worker's age, and the number of his or her dependents. The spouse or dependent of a worker who dies because of a workplace accident or illness may be eligible for survivor benefits. Benefits may be paid by regular monthly installments or in a lump sum and include funeral expenses.

DISCUSSION CASE | What Is Your Opinion?

Dejan and Lindsay are discussing compensation benefits awarded to injured workers. Dejan states that he believes the generous benefits granted by most Canadian compensation boards encourage workers to stay off work longer than needed and that the workers would be more anxious to get back to work if the amount of compensation was reduced. Lindsay counters by saying that it is the liberal payments and a compassionate system that allow workers to recover completely from their injuries before returning to work. Do you agree with Dejan or Lindsay? Should rates be increased or decreased?

HARMFUL ENVIRONMENTS

harmful environment A work environment in which physical or psychological factors exist that are potentially hazardous.

A **harmful environment** is often pictured as one in which being struck, overexertion, or falls result in a workers' compensation claim. Occupational diseases, however, have also become a huge part of workers' compensation boards' caseloads. One problem with determining the validity of compensation claims for occupational diseases is that a link between the disease and the workplace has to be made. Cancer may be caused by many sources, so one may ask if the miner's lung cancer is due to exposure to silica dust or caused by decades of cigarette smoking. Another problem with assessing some industrial diseases is that the latency period of exposure to some workplace products may be decades.

A harmful environment does not have to be limited to its physical components either. Psychological factors (such as stress) can also be considered. In fact, the highest rate of growth in workers' compensation claims over the past two decades has been in the area of stress-related injuries. As we shall see in Chapter 23 the effects of workplace stress can be far reaching.

PRESUMPTIVE LEGISLATION

Due to the prevalence of certain diseases and conditions in particular occupations, the disease or condition is presumed to have come from that occupation. One of the first examples of presumptive legislation appeared in Nova Scotia in January 2000. Section 35 of their Workers' Compensation Act sets out the principle of "automatic assumption." This section allows for disability benefits for a coal miner who has worked at the face of a mine or in similar conditions for 20 years or more and suffers from a loss of lung function.

In 2002, Manitoba passed presumptive legislation for firefighters. This legislation shifts the burden of proof from the employee to the employer to demonstrate that the condition was not in fact associated with the occupation. As of January 2017, all other jurisdictions except Quebec and Prince Edward Island followed with similar legislation for firefighters. The diseases and conditions covered are constantly expanding and vary among the jurisdictions.

The Alberta government led the way in December 2012 by introducing amendments to the Workers Compensation Act to create a presumption that a diagnosis of PTSD is work-related, but only for emergency medical technicians, firefighters, peace officers, and police officers. Many provinces soon followed with similar legislation for first responders, while others have introduced bills that are pending at the time of this publication. Manitoba's presumptive legislation became law on January 1, 2016, and recognizes PTSD as a work-related occupational disease for all workers, not just first responders.

DISABILITY MANAGEMENT AND RETURN TO WORK

Human resources practitioners are being challenged with increasing workplace absences. The impact on the workplace goes beyond the obvious loss of productivity for the business, but also has far reaching effects on the organization and the economy in general. At any given time, 8 to 12 percent of Canada's workforce is absent due to illness or injury, costing the Canadian economy an estimated $16.6 billion in 2012.[4]

Some of the factors contributing to this growing trend include stress related to technological change and organizational restructuring, an aging workforce that is more susceptible to long-term illness, and difficulties balancing work and family responsibilities.[5] **Disability management** programs take these factors into account and attempt to proactively prevent injuries and illness, provide effective and prompt interventions in the event of injury or illness, and offer support for rehabilitation and a quick return to work.

disability management A set of practices intended to reduce the human and financial cost that workplace injuries and illness have on the worker and workplace.

Injuries that are compensable typically fall into one of four categories: (1) temporary partial disability, (2) temporary total disability, (3) permanent partial disability, and (4) permanent total disability (Figure 5–2). Determining the extent of disability is sometimes a contentious issue and usually requires substantial coordination and administration by the employer.

Figure 5–2 Types of disabilities.

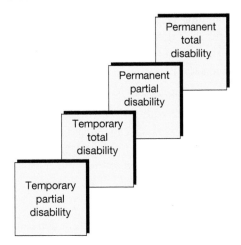

Temporary Disability

Temporary disability is the state that exists when it is probable that an injured worker who is currently unable to work will be able to resume gainful employment with no or only partial disability. Temporary disability assumes that the employee's condition will substantially improve. Determining whether an employee is temporarily disabled is not normally difficult. Competent professionals can usually determine the extent of the employee's injuries, prescribe the appropriate treatment, and establish a timeline for recovery. They can then determine if the employee will be able to return to work and when the return might take place.

Temporary disability can be classified as either temporary total disability or temporary partial disability. A temporary total disability classification means the injured worker is incapable of any work for a period of time but is expected to recover fully. Most workers' compensation cases fall under this classification. A temporary partial disability means the injured worker is capable of light or part-time duties. Depending on the extent of the injury, employers are encouraged to exercise this option to hold down the cost of their workers' compensation premium.

Permanent Partial Disability

Permanent partial disability is the condition that exists when an injured employee is not expected to recover fully. In such cases, the employee will be able to work again but not at full capacity. Often employees who are partially disabled must be retrained for another occupation.

Permanent partial disabilities can be classified as schedule or nonschedule disabilities. Schedule disabilities are typically the result of nonambiguous injuries such as the loss of a critical but duplicated body part (for example, arm, ear, hand, finger, or toe). Because such injuries are relatively straightforward, the amount of compensation that they generate and the period of time that it will be paid can be set forth in a standard schedule.

Nonschedule injuries are less straightforward and must be dealt with on a case-by-case basis. Disabilities in this category tend to be the result of head injuries, the effects of which can be more difficult to determine. The amount of compensation awarded and the period over which it is awarded must be determined by studying the evidence. Awards are typically made based on a determination of disability percentage. For example, if it is determined that an employee has a 25 percent disability, the employee might be entitled to 25 percent of the income he or she could have earned before the injury with normal career progression factored in.

Four approaches to handling permanent partial disability cases have evolved. Three are based on specific theories, and the fourth is based on a combination of two or more of these theories. The three theories are (1) whole-person theory, (2) wage-loss theory, and (3) loss-of-wage-earning-capacity theory.

Whole-Person Theory   The whole-person theory is the simplest and most straight-forward of the theories for dealing with permanent partial disability cases. Once it has been determined that an injured worker's capabilities have been permanently impaired to some extent, this theory is applied like a subtraction problem. What the worker can do after recuperating from the injury is determined and subtracted from what he or she could do before the accident. Factors such as age, education, and occupation are not considered.

Wage-Loss Theory   The wage-loss theory requires a determination of how much the employee could have earned had the injury not occurred. The wages actually being earned are subtracted from what could have been earned, and the employee is awarded a percentage of the difference. No consideration is given to the extent or degree of disability. The only consideration is loss of actual wages.

Loss-of-Wage-Earning-Capacity Theory   The most complex of the theories for handling permanent partial disability cases is the loss-of-wage-earning-capacity theory, because it is based not just on what the employee earned at the time of the accident, but also on what he or she might have earned in the future. Making such a determination is obviously a subjective undertaking. Factors considered include past job performance, education, age, gender, and advancement potential at the time of the accident, among others. Once future earning capacity has been determined, the extent to which it has been impaired is estimated, and the employee is awarded a percentage of the difference.

Permanent Total Disability

A permanent total disability exists when an injured employee's disability is such that he or she cannot compete in the job market. This does not necessarily mean that the employee is helpless. Rather, it means an inability to compete reasonably. Handling permanent total disability cases is similar to handling permanent partial disability cases except that certain injuries simplify the process.

Beyond the financial and moral reasons for developing a disability management program, there are legal obligations as well. In general terms, the **Canadian Human Rights Act** is designed to extend legislation to ensure that all people are afforded an equal opportunity to live with dignity and respect, and free of discrimination by race, national or ethnic origin, colour, religion, age, sex (including pregnancy and childbirth), sexual orientation, marital status, family status, mental or physical disability (including previous or present drug or alcohol dependence), or pardoned conviction.

Employers have a **duty to accommodate** the specific needs of employees who are returning from an absence. Although the employee's particular needs should be met so that they can perform their work to the best of their potential, the worker's right to equality must be balanced with the employer's right to run a productive workplace. The circumstances of each accommodation or return to work will determine the extent to which the employer is expected to meet the specific needs for the situation or worker.[6]

Employers are obligated to provide accommodation "up to the point of **undue hardship.**" This means an employer is not expected to provide accommodation if doing so would bring about unreasonable difficulties for the organization. There is no defined legal definition, nor is there a formula to determine the point at which an accommodation results in undue hardship. Therefore each case has to be examined in its own context.[7] The main factors to be considered to determine when this threshold is met, include:

- **Cost:** The cost to the organization, must be substantial, with regard to the resources available.

- **Health and safety:** Consideration must be given to the impact the accommodation will have on the worker, coworkers, the public, and the employer.

- **Conflicting rights:** The duty to accommodate must not discriminate against the rights of others.[8]

Canadian Human Rights Act Legislation passed by the Parliament of Canada in 1977, to protect the basic human rights of all Canadians.

duty to accommodate A set of practices intended to reduce the human and financial cost that workplace injuries and illness have on the worker and workplace.

undue hardship Worker accommodation beyond the point of incurring reasonable difficulty in terms of health and safety or financial hardship on the organization.

⟫⟫⟫ SAFETY FACT   Where You Work Can Affect How Often You Are Absent

Workers in Saskatchewan have the highest absentee rates (11 days per year) versus Alberta, their neighbour, with the lowest (7.9 days).

Larger organizations have more absenteeism than smaller businesses:

    Fewer than 20 employees, 7.5 days

    20–99 employees, 9.3 days

    100–500 employees, 10.6 days

    More than 500 employees, 11.1 days

The industry in which you work also has a distinct correlation to the number of days that workers are absent. It may seem ironic or counterintuitive that the health care and social assistance sector has the greatest number of lost days. However, chronic exposure to ill clients and the prevalence of shift work and overtime, which interferes with rest, are significant contributing factors.

Source: Based on Nicole Stewart. *Missing in Action: Absenteeism Trends in Canadian Organizations.* (Ottawa: The Conference Board of Canada, 2013).

SUMMARY

1. Workers' compensation was developed to allow injured employees to be compensated without the need for litigation. It has four main objectives: replacement of income, rehabilitation, accident prevention, and cost allocation.

2. Prior to the enactment of workers' compensation laws, employees' only recourse when injured was through the courts, and the prevailing laws favoured employers.

3. Workers' compensation benefits accrue to the families and dependents of workers who are fatally injured.

4. All workers' compensation laws provide for payment of medical expenses.

5. Cost allocation is the process of attempting to spread the cost of workers' compensation across an industry so that no individual company is overly burdened. The cost of workers' compensation includes the cost of premiums, benefits, and administration.

6. The premiums charged to employers may be higher or lower than the base rate for a particular industry. This "experience rating" provides an incentive for employers to reduce the number and severity of workplace accidents.

7. Presumptive legislation is in place for numerous diseases and conditions. By default, the disease or condition is assumed to be caused by the workplace.

8. Employers have moral, financial, and legal reasons for accommodating workers' prompt return to work.

9. The legal obligation for employers duty to accommodate is founded in human rights legislation.

Key Terms and Concepts

Accident prevention
Blackball
Canadian Human Rights
    Act
Cost allocation

Disability management
Duty to accommodate
Employee negligence
Experience rating
Harmful environment

Income replacement
Medical rehabilitation
Occupational diseases
Undue hardship
Vocational rehabilitation

Review Questions

1. Explain the underlying rationale of the concept of workers' compensation.

2. List four objectives of workers' compensation.

3. How does experience rating benefit companies with good safety records and create a liability for those with a poor history?

4. Explain the reasons for the unprecedented increases in workers' compensation costs in Canada in recent decades.

5. Distinguish between medical and vocational rehabilitation.

6. Explain the most common workers' compensation cost-reduction strategies.

7. What benefits can injured workers or their families expect from the workers' compensation board?

8. Provide a brief overview of the presumptive legislation for your jurisdiction.
9. What limitations are there on an employers' duty to accommodate?
10. What three considerations are to be made in determining whether a worker accommodation constitutes undue hardship?

Weblinks

Following are the websites for each of the Workers' Compensation Boards in each Canadian jurisdiction:

Workers' Compensation Board of British Columbia
www.worksafebc.com

Workers' Compensation Board of Alberta
www.wcb.ab.ca

Saskatchewan Workers' Compensation Board
www.wcbsask.com

Workers Compensation Board of Manitoba
www.wcb.mb.ca

Workplace Safety and Insurance Board of Ontario
www.wsib.on.ca

Commission des normes, de l'équité, de la santé et de la sécurité du travail
www.csst.qc.ca

Workplace Health, Safety and Compensation Commission of New Brunswick
www.worksafenb.ca

Workers' Compensation Board of Nova Scotia
www.wcb.ns.ca

Workers Compensation Board of Prince Edward Island
www.wcb.pe.ca

WorkplaceNL
www.workplacenl.ca

Yukon Workers' Compensation Health and Safety Board
www.wcb.yk.ca

Workers' Safety and Compensation Commission, Northwest Territories and Nunavut
www.wscc.nt.ca

Other useful web resources:

National Institute of Disability Management and Research
www.nidmar.ca

Canadian Human Rights Commission
www.chrc-ccdp.gc.ca/eng

Endnotes

[1] "Workers' Comp Update." *Occupational Hazards* 61, no. 10 (October 1999): 51.

[2] Workplace Safety & Insurance Board. Annual Report 2015. [Online]. Available: http://www.wsib.on.ca/WSIBPortal/faces/WSIBDetailPage?cGUID=WSIB015387&rDef=WSIB_RD_ARTICLE&_afrLoop=1906649644887000&_afrWindowMode=0&_afrWindowId=2jjkahrrz_26#%40%3FcGUID%3DWSIB015387%26_afrWindowId%3D2jjkahrrz_26%26_afrLoop%3D1906649644887000%26rDef%3DWSIB_RD_ARTICLE%26_afrWindowMode%3D0%26_adf.ctrl-state%3D2jjkahrrz_96.

[3] Workers' Compensation Board of Saskatchewan. (2016). [Online]. Available: https://www.wcbsask.com/about-wcb/who-we-are/.

[4] Nicole Stewart. *Missing in Action: Absenteeism Trends in Canadian Organizations.* (Ottawa: The Conference Board of Canada, 2013), 1.

[5] Canadian Human Rights Commission. *A Guide for Managing the Return to Work.* [Online]. Available: http://www.chrc-ccdp.gc.ca/eng/content/guide-managing-return-work. (Retrieved January 8, 2017).

[6] Ibid.

[7] Ibid.

[8] Laura Barnett, Julia Nicol, and Julian Walker. Library of Parliament. Parliamentary Information and Research Service. *An Examination of the Duty to Accommodate in the Canadian Human Rights Context.* (January 10, 2012). [Online]. Available: http://publications.gc.ca/site/eng/421155/publication.html.

Part 2
Management of Occupational Health and Safety

Chapter 6
Accidents and Their Effects

workplace accidents Unplanned events at an employee's place of work that result in injury or loss.

accident prevention The act of preventing a happening that may cause loss or injury to a person.

There is a long history of debate in this country concerning the effect of **workplace accidents**[†] on industry and the cost of preventing accidents. Historically, the prevailing view was that **accident prevention** programs were too costly. The more contemporary view is that accidents themselves are too costly and that accident prevention makes sense economically. As a result, accident prevention, which had previously been advocated on a moral and legal basis, is now also justified in economic terms.

ACCIDENTS AND FATALITIES IN THE WORKPLACE

Accidents are the fifth leading cause of death in this country after cancer, heart disease, stroke, and lung disease. This ranking is based on all types of accidents, including motor vehicle accidents, drowning, fires, falls, and natural disasters as well as work-related accidents. Although there are more deaths every year from natural causes than from accidents, they tend to be concentrated among people at or near retirement age. Among people 44 years of age or younger—prime working years—accidents are the number one cause of death.

[†]See Preface on p. xix for discussion of the term "accident."

Accidents represent a serious detriment to productivity, quality, and competitiveness in today's workplace. Yet accidents are the one cause of injury and death that companies can most easily control. Although it is true that companies may have some success in decreasing the incidence of heart disease and stroke among their employees through such activities as corporate wellness programs, their impact in this regard is limited. However, employers can have a significant impact on preventing accidents.

While deaths from murder tend to be more newsworthy than workplace deaths, murders occur far less frequently. For example, there were 604 murders in Canada in 2015. Workplace accidents, on the other hand, cause about 900 deaths annually in Canada. The following compelling statistics from 2015 should help place workplace accidents and deaths in the proper perspective, notwithstanding their apparent lack of newsworthiness:

- 756,544 workplace accidents were reported in Canada; 232,629 resulted in lost work time.

- 852 people lost their lives as a result of workplace accidents (including disease).

- 1 in 25 workers reported an injury at work, representing 1 injury every 9 seconds.

- A lost time injury occurred in Canada every 135 seconds.

- WCBs paid out over $7.1 billion in 2015; that is, $326,712.33/day, $ 3,613.03/minute, or $226.88/second.[1]

This chapter provides the student and the practising **health and safety professional** with the information needed to have a full understanding of workplace accidents and their effect on workers and industry in Canada. A snapshot of the number of injuries and fatalities is captured in Figure 6–1 below, and a further breakdown of the data is presented throughout the chapter. This understanding will help both workers and management to ensure that health and safety in the workplace remain a top priority.

> **health and safety professional**
> An individual whose profession (job) is to be concerned with health and safety measures in the workforce.

Figure 6–1 Injuries and fatalities by province, 2015.

	CAN	AB	BC	MB	NB	NL	NS	NT/NU	ON	PE	QC	SK	YT
Lost Time Claims	232,629	26,325	49,956	14,570	3,861	3,598	6,056	835	51,570	904	65,859	8,669	426
Injury Frequency	1.51	1.25	2.22	2.99	1.15	1.7	1.94	2.02	0.85	1.3	1.74	2.04	2
Fatalities	852	125	123	19	19	24	28	3	281	1	196	32	1

Source: Association of Workers' Compensation Boards of Canada, Key Statistical Measures. Available: http://awcbc.org/?page_id=9759.

⟫⟫ SAFETY FACT   The North American Industry Classification System

Due to different coding, naming, and classification protocols among the various jurisdictions, there may be slight discrepancies in the data presented. The industries discussed throughout this text are most often classified according to the North American Industry Classification System (NAICS), Canada. The aggregate data cited by Statistics Canada or Association of Workers' Compensation Boards of Canada (AWCBC) uses this industry classification, which may be different from classifications used in provincial or territorial jurisdictions that are also cited throughout this text.

NAICS was jointly adopted in 1997 by Canada, Mexico, and the United States to align with the needs of NAFTA. The classification system, updated in 2012 and 2017, was designed to provide common definitions of the industrial structure of the three countries and a common statistical framework. Its hierarchical structure is composed of sectors (two-digit code), subsectors (three-digit code), industry groups (four-digit code), and industries (five-digit code). NAICS Canada 2012 consists of 20 sectors, 102 sub-sectors, 323 industry groups, 711 industries, and 922 Canadian industries.

For more information on NAICS, visit the Government of Canada, Innovation, Science and Economic Development Canada website shown in the links at the end of this chapter.

LOST TIME INJURIES

lost time The amount of time that an employee is unable to work due to an injury.

workplace injuries Injuries that occur while an employee is at work.

An important consideration when assessing the effect of accidents on industry and workers is the amount of **lost time** due to **workplace injuries**. Statistics Canada and AWCBC have collected immense amounts of data related to the Canadian workforce. Much of the information in this chapter is from AWCBC, provided to them by workers' compensation boards from across the country. The reader should consider that, as compelling as the numbers may be, these statistics and figures do not include the thousands of injuries that are not reported or that are compensated directly by the employer. In addition to these figures, the Mental Health Commission of Canada states that "on any given week, more than 500,000 Canadians will not go to work because of mental illness."[2] See Chapter 23 for detailed information on workplace psychological health and safety.

The lost time claim rate has shown an overall general decline for the past decade; however, there have been exceptions in some industries and the reduction in the numbers lags behind the projected levels of some jurisdictions. Figure 6–2 shows the gradual decline in the number of lost time claims since 2005. Due to an increasing number in the workforce, the lost time claim rate, shown in Figure 6–3, more accurately reflects the improvements in workplace safety.

Figure 6–2 Number of lost time claims, 2005–2015.

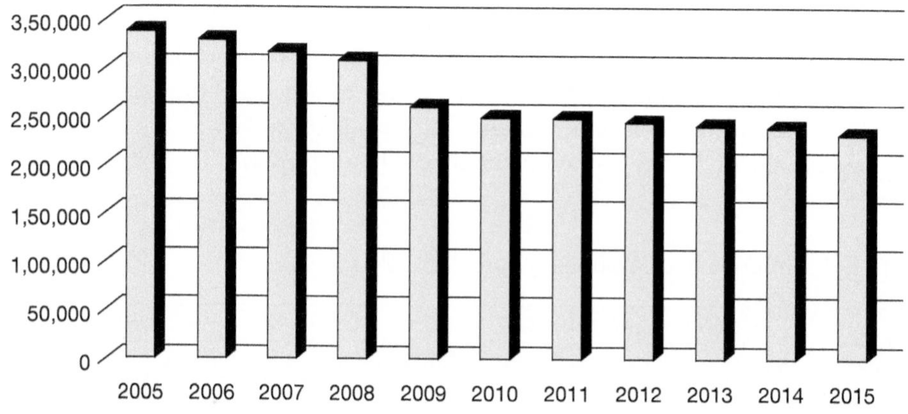

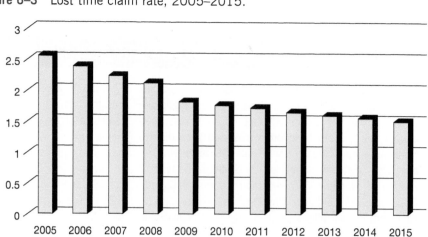

Source: Association of Workers' Compensation Boards of Canada, Key Statistical Measures. Available: http://awcbc .org/?page_id=9759.

Figure 6–3 Lost time claim rate, 2005–2015.

Source: Association of Workers' Compensation Boards of Canada, Key Statistical Measures. Available: http://awcbc .org/?page_id=9759.

LOST TIME INJURIES BY INDUSTRY

By monitoring the number of **lost time injuries** in each industry, comparisons can be made to other occupations and businesses within the same industrial category. One primary use of this data is to establish workers' compensation premium rates. As with any type of insurance, the premiums will be higher if the inherent risk of injury or loss is greater. When lost time accidents are disproportionately high in a particular industry, this serves as a warning to a variety of agencies and organizations that these sectors need greater attention. The relative risk involved in a particular industry may also be reflected in its **disabling injury rate**. The disabling injury rate is similar to the **lost time rate** although it covers a broader range of injuries, including those that are less severe in nature. Not all workplace injuries require time away from work, but may require a change to the workers' normal tasks or **modified work**.

Figure 6–4, comparing lost time injuries by industry, shows that the health and social services industries have the greatest number of injuries recorded. This sector has the highest number of workers and represents 17.67 percent of total injuries of all sectors combined, even though only 15.21 percent of workers are employed in this industry. When the percentage of total injuries exceeds the percentage of the combined workforce, a disproportionately high lost time injury rate is indicated. Manufacturing, for example, shows an even greater proportional lost time injury rate. The 33,013 workers represent 11.36 percent of the workforce, but contribute to 14.19 percent of the injuries. Business services, on the other hand, is shown to have relatively few lost time injuries, with 5.05 percent of the workforce contributing to only 2.72 percent of the incidents recorded.

lost time injuries Injuries or illnesses due to a work-related accident or exposure to a noxious substance that results in an employee missing work and for which the employee receives compensation for lost income.

disabling injury rate The disabling injury rate represents the probability or risk of a disabling injury or disease to a worker. The disabling injury rate is similar to the lost time rate although it covers a broader range of injuries, including those that are less severe in nature (do not require time away from work). The rate represents the number of claims per 100 people per year.

lost time rate Indicates the probability of lost time for each 100 person-years worked. The lost-time rate is calculated by dividing the number of lost-time claims by the person-years worked estimate, and multiplying the result by 100.

modified work Altered duties after an injury or disease to accommodate the workers' limitations or rehabilitation while permitting the worker to avoid losing time from work.

Figure 6–4 Lost time injuries by industry, 2015.

Industry	Number of Lost Time Injuries	Percentage of Total Injuries	Number of Total Workers x1,000	Percentage of Total Workforce
Health and social services industries	41,111	17.67%	2,292.3	15.21%
Wholesale and retail trade	36,590	15.73%	2,732.7	18.14%
Manufacturing	33,013	14.19%	1,712.4	11.36%
Construction	26,015	11.18%	1,371.2	9.10%
Transportation and storage	15,538	6.68%	917.2	6.09%
Government services	15,229	6.55%	907.4	6.02%
Accommodation, food and beverage	14,776	6.35%	1,210.6	8.03%
Educational services	6,556	2.82%	1,274.1	8.46%
Business services	6,306	2.71%	760.6	5.05%
Communications and utilities	4,146	1.78%	137	0.91%
Mining, quarrying, and oil wells	3,504	0.73%	354.9	2.36%
Agriculture and related services	3,331	1.43%	294.9	1.96%
Finance, insurance, real estate, rental and leasing	2,002	0.86%	1,102.9	7.32%
Other	24,512	10.54%	2,878.2	19.10%
Total	208,117	100%	15,068.2	100.00%

Source: Association of Workers' Compensation Boards of Canada, Key Statistical Measures. Available: http://awcbc.org/?page_id=9759.

For an accurate comparison of various industries, local, provincial, or territorial statistics would be viewed. For example, national figures for forestry, fishing, or mining would not reflect the local incident numbers of Prince Edward Island or Alberta, where certain industries may be more prevalent or do not exist. The inherent hazardous nature of some industries and their prominence in each jurisdiction could have a significant impact on the provincial or territorial lost time claim rate as well. There are numerous factors that can affect the lost time claim rate, such as reporting and tracking requirements. The dramatic difference among jurisdictions can be seen in Figure 6–5.

Figure 6–5 Lost time claim rates by province, 2015.

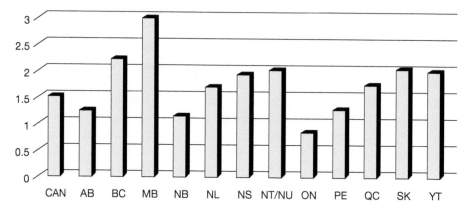

Source: Association of Workers' Compensation Boards of Canada, Key Statistical Measures. Available: http://awcbc.org/?page_id=9759.

LOST TIME INJURIES BY TYPE (NATURE) OF INJURY

To effectively direct their efforts toward reducing lost time from work due to accidents, managers and health and safety practitioners must know which injuries result in the greatest amount of lost time. The sample data from Alberta clearly show that **sprains** and **strains** are by far the most common type of injury. In 2015, the 12,108 strains and sprains reported accounted for 47.5 percent of all lost time occupational injuries.[3] Figure 6–6 shows that strains and sprains were approximately five times as frequent as the second most common types of disabling injuries: superficial wounds, which include **contusions**, crushing, and bruises.

Further down the list, the frequency with which injuries occur drops dramatically. However, some industries and occupations have a very high incident rate for some types of injury. Comprehensive record keeping by employers is vital to identifying which types of injuries are of most concern.

LOST TIME INJURIES BY BODY PART

Back injuries are by far the most concerning injuries in the workplace. Canadian workers' compensation boards accepted 55,237 back injury claims in 2015.[4] The lower back (lumbar, sacral, coccygeal regions), in particular, represented most of those claims. Almost one quarter of all occupational injuries were to the back. The frequency of back injuries is a concern, but so is the potential severity and the far-reaching effects of these injuries on the workers and their families. Reducing the number and severity of back injuries often involves ergonomic factors such as changing the manner in which a certain task is performed or altering workstation design.

sprains The result of torn ligaments.

strains The result of overstretched or torn muscles.

contusions Bruises resulting from a blow.

Figure 6–6 Lost time by nature of injury or disease, Alberta, 2015.

Nature of Injury	Lost Time Claims	Percentage of All Lost Time Claims	Disabling Injury Claims	Percentage of All Disabling Injury Claims
Traumatic Injuries and Disorders	23,733	93.2%	45,465	94.8%
Sprains/Strains	12,108	47.5%	24,562	51.2%
Superficial Wounds	2,425	9.5%	5,016	10.5%
Fractures and Dislocations	2,598	10.2%	3,843	8.0%
Open Wounds	2,046	8.0%	4,586	9.6%
Burns	648	2.5%	945	2.0%
Other Traumatic Injuries and Disorders	3,908	15.3%	6,513	13.6%
Systemic Diseases and Disorders	1,073	4.2%	1,734	3.6%
Infectious and Parasitic Disorders	179	0.7%	180	0.4%
Neoplasms, Tumors, and Cancer	16	0.1%	16	0.0%
Abnormal Symptoms/ Conditions	127	0.5%	184	0.4%
Multiple Diseases, Conditions, and Disorders	7	0.06%	7	0.04%
Other Diseases, Conditions, and Disorders	298	1.2%	317	0.7%
Nature of Injury - Unknown	32	0.1%	68	0.1%
Total	25,465	100.0%	47,971	100.0%

Source: Alberta Labour. *2015 Workplace Injury, Disease and Fatality Statistics: Provincial Summary.* [Online]. Available: https://work.alberta.ca/documents/2015-ohs-data.pdf.

Upper extremities, especially finger injuries ranked as the second most common lost time occupational injury. The back, fingers, legs, and shoulders are the parts of the body where workers were most often injured in 2015, accounting for more than half of all lost time occupational injuries.

The effects of injuries to some parts of the body are often more serious than statistics reveal. Disabilities and impairments resulting from injuries to eyes, ears, and brain, for example, can dramatically influence not only working ability but the quality of life outside work for those people affected. Various means of protecting the worker from injury are available, such as using **personal protective equipment**, changing the products or materials used, providing machine guarding, and using ergonomic design.

personal protective equipment (PPE) Any type of clothing or device that puts a barrier between the worker and the hazard (e.g., safety goggles, gloves, hard hats, and so on).

LOST TIME INJURIES BY SOURCE

What action, product, material, tool, or item caused injury to the worker? Dangerous machinery, chemicals, or tools cause many injuries, but by far the most common cause is bodily motion. The movement of the worker or someone else is the prevailing source of injuries in the workplace. Even when tool and equipment design, workplace setup and ergonomics, and other diligent measures are in place, the workers themselves can factor into injuries on the job. Protecting the worker not only involves providing the proper tools, equipment, and workstation design, but must also incorporate training the worker in safe procedures. As we have seen in the previous section, incorrect procedures frequently result in injury to the back.

In 2015, the source of the injury was deemed to be bodily motion of the injured worker in 40,426 incidents and bodily motion from other people in 18,226 other incidents. This is about four times greater than injuries caused by hand tools. Interestingly, non-powered hand tools contributed to injuries significantly more often than powered hand tools, at 8,131 versus 2,261, respectively. Other notable sources of injuries reported in 2015 include floors, walkways, and ground surfaces at 37,193 incidents reported. Another 8,428 were attributed to highway motor vehicles.[5]

OTHER FACTORS AFFECTING LOST TIME INJURIES

overexertion The result of employees working beyond their physical limits.

Overexertion, the result of employees working beyond their physical limits, accounted for nearly 25 percent of all reported injuries in 1998.

Lost time injury statistics also reveal that gender, age, and even the time of year, week, or day can be a factor in workplace injuries. Men in the workforce were responsible for 143,478 lost time claims, while women accounted for 89,123. The statistics show us that baby boomers, near the end of their careers, are showing a spike in the number of injuries, as shown in Figure 6–7. Two factors contributing to this trend are the number of workers in that demographic and that these aging workers are more prone to injuries because their physical ability wanes more than they realize. Among various notable facts regarding younger workers is that the body part injured most frequently in this group (15 to 29 years old) is the hands—as opposed to the back for all workers.

Figure 6–7 Lost time claims by age, 2015.

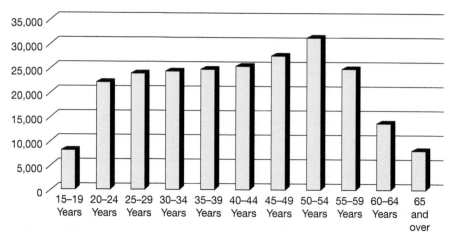

Source: Association of Workers' Compensation Boards of Canada, Key Statistical Measures. Available: http://awcbc.org/?page_id=9759.

》》》 DISCUSSION CASE | What Is Your Opinion?

Lisa has been a safety engineer at Crumb Manufacturing, Inc. for over twenty years. Danny, her protegé, started at Crumb only 1 week ago after graduating from a safety diploma program. Over lunch, they had a discussion about lost time workplace injuries. During the discussion, Lisa said she thought back injuries were still the problem that safety professionals should worry about the most. Danny disagreed. He said strains and sprains were the most common type of injury in the workplace. What is your opinion?

COSTS OF ACCIDENTS

At the beginning of this chapter we provided the cost incurred by WCBs for workplace accidents. The cost and impact of these workplace injuries go well beyond the $7.1 billion paid out in 2015. Clearly, accidents are expensive. Throughout the text we discuss the non-financial impact on the organization and workers. As workplaces and the expectation of workers evolve, the "cost" of injured or ill workers continues to rise.

The **direct costs** of workplace accidents are those that are easily identified and quantified. The expenses incurred by the employer, such as wages paid to an injured worker and damaged goods and equipment, are obvious, but the costs borne by the state and outside institutions should also be considered.

direct costs Identifiable costs incurred as a result of an accident.

There is a tendency for most companies to disregard the significance of the cost of accidents. Major accident damage costs are usually covered by some form of insurance. Minor damage is often considered as a "cost of doing business" and is written off as maintenance. And injured workers are covered by workers' compensation. The uninsured costs of accidents, however, can add up to quite a significant amount. These less obvious expenses, which can be described as hidden or **indirect costs**, could include:

indirect costs Uninsured costs that are not directly identifiable with workplace accidents.

- **Time lost by uninjured workers.** Many workers lose time because they watched or assisted the injured party.

- **Production slowdowns.** Productivity may suffer if equipment or facilities are damaged.

- **Non-compensated time lost by injured workers.** Wages may be paid while waiting for workers' compensation. In most jurisdictions, the employer is required to pay the wages for the injured worker for the remainder of the day in which the injury occurred.

- **Cost of overtime.** Overtime at a premium rate is often required by other workers to cover the lost output of the injured worker.

- **Reduced output of replacement workers.** It is very likely that the replacement worker will not be as productive as the regular employee.

- **Reduced output of the injured worker after return to work.** Most workers will take some time to resume normal productivity after an injury.

- **Supervisors' activities.** Supervisors may spend time addressing issues related to the accident instead of performing their normal duties, which would include enhancing productivity.

- **Accident investigation, record keeping, and claims processing.** Personnel from upper management to clerical staff will spend time away from their normal duties, filing reports, filling out forms, etc.

- **Damage to equipment or machinery.** Costs such as repairs, rentals, or replacement of equipment are often incurred because of an accident.

Another cost associated with workplace accidents is a tarnished corporate image resulting from repeated reports of accidents and injuries taking place at a particular business. Companies that are viewed by the public or their customers as having little regard for their employees' health and safety will lose business to those that actively promote workplace safety.

Clearly, accidents on and off the job cost Canadian industry dearly. Every dollar that is spent responding to accidents is a dollar that could have been reinvested in modernization, research and development, facility upgrades, and other competitiveness-enhancing activities.

Estimating the Costs (and Hidden Costs) of Accidents

Even decision makers who support accident prevention must consider the relative costs of such efforts. Clearly, accidents are expensive. However, to be successful, health and safety professionals must be able to show that accidents are more expensive than prevention. To do this, they must be able to estimate the cost of accidents. This section will explore various cost-estimating methods from pioneers in the field such as Heinrich and Simonds to more contemporary models used by Hansen and the Manitoba Heavy Construction Association.

Safety professionals often use the *iceberg analogy* when talking about the real costs of accidents. Accident costs are like an iceberg in that their greatest portion is hidden from view.[6] In the case of icebergs, the larger part is hidden beneath the surface of the water. In the case of an accident, the larger part of the actual cost is also hidden beneath the surface. Figure 6–8 illustrates how the hidden cost can far exceed the direct cost of an accident. The same analogy may also be used to compare insured versus uninsured accident costs.

Figure 6–8 The direct costs represent only the tip of the iceberg.

According to Daniel Corcoran,

> When a serious accident occurs, there is usually a great deal of activity associated with the accident. There may be a slowdown in production near the site of the accident, for instance. There also will be a need to replace the injured worker, at least temporarily, and there will be costs associated with the learning curve of the replacement worker.
>
> The supervisor and the accident investigation team probably will need to spend time conducting an investigation, and there will be a lot of time spent on the administration of paperwork related to the accident.[7]

There are many different models that can be used for estimating both the direct and indirect costs of accidents. Some of these models are so complex that their usefulness is questionable. The ratio of direct to indirect cost can vary greatly depending on the model used. For instance, while numerous models suggest that indirect costs are 50 to 300 percent greater than direct costs, the federal government has conducted studies that conclude that the ratio of direct to indirect cost is approximately 1:1.[8] The checklist in Figure 6–9 is a simple and straightforward tool that can be used for consideration when estimating the hidden costs of accidents.

Figure 6–9 Some accident costs that might be overlooked.

<table>
<tr>
<td colspan="2" style="text-align:center">Checklist for
Estimating the Hidden Costs of Accidents</td>
</tr>
<tr>
<td>✓</td>
<td>Paid time to the injured employee on the day of the accident.</td>
</tr>
<tr>
<td>✓</td>
<td>Paid time of any emergency-responder personnel involved (including ambulance driver).</td>
</tr>
<tr>
<td>✓</td>
<td>Paid time of all employees who were interviewed as part of the accident investigation.</td>
</tr>
<tr>
<td>✓</td>
<td>Paid time of the safety personnel who conducted the accident investigation.</td>
</tr>
<tr>
<td>✓</td>
<td>Paid time of the Human Resources personnel who handled the workers' compensation and medical aspects of the accident.</td>
</tr>
<tr>
<td>✓</td>
<td>Paid time of the supervisor involved in the accident investigation and accident response.</td>
</tr>
<tr>
<td>✓</td>
<td>Paid time to employees near the accident who stopped working (or slowed down) temporarily as a result of the accident.</td>
</tr>
<tr>
<td>✓</td>
<td>Paid time to employees who spent time talking about the accident as news of it spread through the company's grapevine.</td>
</tr>
</table>

The ratio of direct cost to indirect cost not only varies from model to model, it also changes from workplace to workplace. Over 50 years ago, W. H. Heinrich introduced a 4:1 ratio to compare direct cost to indirect cost. Although others performing similar studies showed ratios ranging from 2.3:1 to 101:1, they all reached the same conclusion: that the hidden costs far exceeded the direct or indirect costs.[9]

Another early health and safety practitioner to develop a procedure for estimating accident costs was an American professor, Rollin H. Simonds. Professor Simonds stated that in order to have value, a cost estimate must relate directly to the specific company in question. Applying broad industry cost factors will not suffice. To arrive at company-specific figures, Simonds recommended that costs associated with an accident be divided into *insured* and *uninsured* costs.[10]

Determining the insured costs of accidents is a simple matter of examining accounting records. The next step involves calculating the uninsured costs. Simonds recommended that accidents be divided into the following four classes:

- **Class 1 accidents.** Lost workdays, permanent partial disabilities, and temporary total disabilities.
- **Class 2 accidents.** Treatment by a physician outside the company's facility.

- **Class 3 accidents.** Locally provided first aid, property damage of less than $100, or the loss of fewer than eight hours of work time.
- **Class 4 accidents.** Injuries that are so minor they do not require the attention of a physician, result in property damage of less than $100 and fewer than eight work hours lost.[11]

Average uninsured costs for each class of accident can be determined by pulling the records of all accidents that occurred during a specified period and sorting the records according to class. For each accident in each class, record every cost that was not covered by insurance. Compute the total of these costs by class of accident and divide by the total number of accidents in that class to determine an average uninsured cost for each class, specific to the particular company.

Figure 6–10 is an example of how the average cost of a selected sample of Class 1 accidents can be determined. In this example, there were four Class 1 accidents in the pilot test. These four accidents cost the company a total of $554.23 in uninsured costs, or an average of $138.56 per accident. Using this information, accurate cost estimates of an accident can be figured, as can accurate predictions.

Figure 6–10 Uninsured costs worksheet.

Class of Accident	Accident Number							
Class 1	1	2	3	4	5	6	7	8
Cost A	16.00	6.95	15.17	3.26				
Cost B	72.00	103.15	97.06	51.52				
Cost C	26.73	12.62	—	36.94				
Cost D	—	51.36	—	38.76				
Cost E	—	11.17	—	24.95				
Cost F	—	—	—	13.41				
Cost G	—	—	—	—				
Total	114.73	185.25	112.23	142.02				

Grand Total: $554.23

Average Cost per Accident: $138.56 (grand total ÷ number of accidents)

Signature: _____   Date: _____

In estimating the cost of accidents, James Hansen, a research strategist with the Industrial Accident Prevention Association (IAPA; now known as Workplace Safety & Prevention Services (WSPS)), suggests that the costs involved in industrial accidents be divided into two categories: *subjective* and *objective*. Subjective costs, like hidden or uninsured costs, may be very difficult to quantify and may include lost sales or customers due to damaged corporate image, or the effect of degraded worker morale or concern for safety could have on productivity.

Objective costs are those that can be measured and for which a specific dollar value can be assigned. These measurable costs include pay for the worker while not at work, replacement workers, overtime, increased benefit or WCB premiums, legal expenses, damage to property or equipment, and other direct costs incurred.

To compete in today's global market, many companies are operating at a very narrow profit margin. When an accident takes place, the money lost can be very difficult to recover. Figure 6–11 shows, for example, that a $1,000 loss incurred from an accident would require $12,500 in additional sales to recoup if the company was operating at an 8 percent profit margin. As the profit margin goes down, the additional sales required to get the money back will increase.

Figure 6–11   Additional sales required to recover the cost of an accident.

Accident Cost:	Additional Sales Required to Recover the Cost at 2%–10% Profit Margins				
	2%	4%	6%	8%	10%
$50	$2,500	$1,250	$833	$625	$500
$500	$25,000	$12,500	$8,333	$6,250	$5,000
$1,000	$50,000	$25,000	$16,667	$12,500	$10,000
$10,000	$500,000	$250,000	$166,667	$125,000	$100,000
$25,000	$1,250,000	$625,000	$416,667	$312,000	$500,000
$500,000	$25,000,000	$12,000,000	$8,333,333	$6,250,000	$5,000,000

SUMMARY

1. Accidents are the fifth leading cause of death in this country after cancer, heart disease, stroke, and lung disease.

2. In 2015, workers' compensation payments to injured workers cost the Canadian economy $3613.03/minute.

3. In 2015, a lost time injury occurred in Canada every 135 seconds.

4. Manitoba has the highest injury rate at 2.99, in 2015, while Ontario had the lowest at 0.85.

5. On average, two people die from workplace injuries each day in Canada.

6. The health and social services industries have the greatest number of lost time injuries.

7. Sprains and strains are by far the most common type of injury.

8. In 2015, back problems were the most common type of lost time injury in Canada.

9. The most common source of injury in 2015 was bodily motion.

10. The cost of accidents is comprised of direct costs and the indirect costs.

11. As the profit margin goes down, the additional sales required to recover money that was lost due to accidents increases.

Key Terms and Concepts

Accident prevention
Contusions
Direct costs
Disabling injury rate
Health and safety
   professional

Indirect costs
Lost time
Lost time rate
Lost time injuries
Modified work
Overexertion

Personal protective
   equipment
Sprains
Strains
Workplace injuries
Workplace accidents

Review Questions

1. What are the leading causes of death in Canada?

2. When the overall cost of an accident is calculated, what elements make up the cost?

3. Which industry has the greatest number of lost time injuries?

4. Lost time injuries to which body part are most common among all workers?

5. Explain the difference between the rate of accidents and the number of accidents. Which term best describes the relative risk involved with a particular occupation or industry?

6. What are the direct costs associated with an accident? List five indirect costs associated with accidents.

7. Using a workplace with which you are familiar, provide an example of accidents that would fall under each class of accident as outlined by Simonds.

Weblinks

Association of Workers' Compensation Boards of Canada
www.awcbc.org

The Association of Workers' Compensation Boards of Canada provides data compiled from the provincial and territorial workers' compensation boards.

Innovation, Science and Economic Development Canada
https://www.ic.gc.ca/eic/site/icgc.nsf/eng/home

ISEDC has industries, statistics, and innovation initiatives.

The Workers' Compensation Board of British Columbia
https://www.worksafebc.com/en/resources/health-safety/interactive-tools/workplace-incident-cost-calculator?lang=en

The Workers' Compensation Board of British Columbia's website provides an easy-to-use tool for calculating the costs of accidents.

Endnotes

[1] Association of Workers' Compensation Boards. *Detailed Key Statistical Measures (KSM) Report—2015*. [Online]. Available: http://awcbc.org/?page_id=9759. (Retrieved January 21, 2017).

[2] Mental Health Commission of Canada. National Standard. (2017). [Online]. Available: http://www.mentalhealthcommission.ca/English/national-standard. (Retrieved January 12, 2017).

[3] Alberta Labour. *2015 Workplace Injury, Disease and Fatality Statistics: Provincial Summary*. [Online]. Available: https://work.alberta.ca/documents/2015-ohs-data.pdf.

[4] Association of Workers' Compensation Boards. *Detailed Key Statistical Measures (KSM) Report—2015*. [Online]. Available: http://awcbc.org/?page_id=9759. (Retrieved January 21, 2017).

[5] Ibid.

[6] Daniel Corcoran. "The Hidden Value of Safety." *Occupational Health and Safety* 71, no. 6 (June 2002): 20–22.

[7] Ibid. 22.

[8] Human Resources and Skills Development Canada. (April 28, 2003). "General Statistics on Occupational Injuries and Fatalities, 1994 -1998." [Online]. Available: http://www.hrsdc .gc.ca/asp/gateway.asp?hr=/en/lp/lo/ohs/statistics/naosh/2.shtml&hs=oxs#2.3. (Retrieved February 27, 2005).

[9] John A. Fletcher and Hugh M. Douglas. *Total Environmental Control* (National Profile Limited, 1986), 35.

[10] National Safety Council. *Accident Prevention Manual for Business and Industry*, 13th ed. (Chicago: National Safety Council, 2009), 158.

[11] Ibid.

Chapter 7
Hazard Analysis: Recognition, Assessment, and Control of Hazards

MAJOR TOPICS

- Overview of Hazard Analysis
- Hazard Recognition
- Hazard Assessment
- Controlling Hazards
- Leading Indicators
- Formal Hazard Assessment Process
- Cost–Benefit Factors in Hazard Analysis

There is a saying that an ounce of prevention is worth a pound of cure. This is certainly the case with workplace health and safety. Every hazard that can be identified should be corrected or at least minimized through the introduction of appropriate safeguards. Careful analysis of potential hazards in the workplace has led to many of today's widely used safety measures and practices.

hazard A condition with the potential of causing injury to personnel, damage to equipment or structures, loss of material, or lessening of the ability to perform a prescribed function.

The key to preventing accidents is identifying and eliminating hazards. A **hazard** is a condition or combination of conditions that, if left uncorrected, may lead to an accident, illness, or property damage.

risk The likelihood and severity of harm from exposure to a hazard.

This chapter provides prospective and practising health and safety professionals with the information they need to identify hazards that exist in the workplace, determine the level of **risk** associated with each, and develop preventive measures necessary to neutralize the hazards.

OVERVIEW OF HAZARD ANALYSIS

hazard analysis A systematic process for identifying hazards and recommending corrective action.

Hazard analysis is a core part of occupational health and safety management systems. It helps employers focus their efforts in the right areas and develop worker training, inspections, emergency response plans, etc. specific to the hazards on their work site.[1] If a hazard is a condition that could lead to an injury or illness, hazard analysis or safety analysis is a systematic process for identifying hazards and recommending corrective action. The obligation for employers to ensure that hazards are identified and eliminated or controlled exists in the legislation of each jurisdiction. The process is often referred to as recognition, assessment, and control (RAC) of hazards.

The obvious benefit of the hazard identification, assessment, and control process is that hazards are identified and eliminated or controlled before a worker is injured or becomes ill. The additional benefits include the following:

- Operational efficiency from improved processes and proactively addressing items such as training, housekeeping, and workflow.

- Improvement of worker morale when they are provided with a safe workplace, resulting in fewer sick days and lower turnover.

- Demonstration of management's commitment to safety by their participating in the process and creating the expectation that all workers will, as well.

- Maintenance of the positive public image of an organization which is important to its success but can be easily tarnished by workplace accidents.

- Substantial reduction of the debilitating direct and indirect costs of workplace accidents through proactive measures resulting from the safety analysis process.

There are numerous models used for safety analysis and just as many terms are used to describe them, however the common purpose among them is to proactively identify and mitigate hazards in the workplace. Safety professionals will hear the terms *job safety analysis* (JSA), *job safety assessment* (JSA), *job hazard analysis* (JHA), *hazard assessment*, and so on to describe the hazard recognition, assessment, and control process.

HAZARD RECOGNITION

There are countless hazards in our workplaces that may be classified as health or safety hazards. Exposure to many substances, such as lead, asbestos, and benzene, can be serious health hazards that can harm one's health, either immediately after exposure or over time. Safety hazards, such as working from heights or around moving equipment, can result in immediate injuries like cuts, contusions, or broken bones. In the following sections we will provide a brief overview of the four categories of workplace hazards; physical, chemical, biological, and psychosocial. Each of these hazards is detailed in later chapters.

Physical Hazards

Physical hazards are those substances, tools, equipment, activities, and forms of energy that can cause injury or illness to exposed workers. Noise, vibration, radiation, and temperature are forms of energy that can be hazardous if not controlled. Working around moving machinery, working from heights, lifting heavy loads, or working on poor surfaces where slips or trips could result, are further examples. **Ergonomic hazards** are sometimes categorized separately but are most often physical hazards as well—these hazards include noise, lighting, room temperature, workstation design, and repetitive motion.

physical hazards Substances, tools, equipment, activities, and forms of energy that can cause injury or illness to exposed workers.

ergonomic hazards Factors within the workplace environment that can harm the musculoskeletal system.

Chemical Hazards

Chemical hazards are those caused by exposure to harmful chemical substances. While we tend to think of highly caustic or acidic chemicals in a lab or industrial setting, many common products in an office or home environment contain chemicals that can impact our health and safety if not used properly. Examples of these potentially harmful chemicals that can be found in your office or home may include common cleaning supplies, garage products such as degreasers and solvents, paints and thinners, and photocopy toners. These harmful chemicals, which may be in liquid, solid, or gaseous states, can enter the body through different routes and their effects may be acute, or they may potentially lie dormant for many years before any effects are seen.

chemical hazards Hazards that are caused by exposure to harmful chemical substances.

Biological Hazards

Biological hazards are living things, or products of living things, that can cause illness and disease in humans. Biological agents include viruses, bacteria, and fungi, as well as parasites and some plants. Like chemical agents, these can enter the body through ingestion, through the skin, or through inhalation. Biological hazards are most often associated with health care workers and those who work with animals; however, exposure can come from a variety of sources, such as food and utensils, insects, pet waste, sewage, and people coughing or sneezing. When these **pathogens** enter the body, their effect may be immediate, or they could lie dormant. They might have little or no effect, or cause acute sickness to death.

Psychosocial Hazards

Psychosocial hazards are any hazards that affect the mental well-being or mental health of the worker. The prevalence of this hazard is being acknowledged across Canada in safety legislation addressing bullying, harassment, violence, and post-traumatic stress disorder (PTSD). The psychological harm from this hazard may be very gradual, which can make it difficult for health care providers and those who are exposed to make the connection to the workplace. Examples of psychosocial hazards include stress, fatigue, harassment, and bullying. The sources and effects of stress in the workplace will be examined in detail in Chapter 23.

Contributing Factors

With an understanding of the source and effect of the hazards in the workplace, we also have to consider how other factors may impact the worker. The four factors to consider are people, equipment, materials, and environment. The people factor looks at the worker and asks how their level of training, coaching, communication skills, or even their hygiene practices could affect exposure levels to these hazards. Equipment factors include the equipment being suitable for the job and the level of maintenance and operating procedures being followed. The materials being used may be contributing to the hazard if they are not used and stored properly. The environment in which the work is being carried out can have a huge impact on what hazards are present and how they impact the worker. For example, noise, temperature, air quality, and lighting could contribute differently for workers in an office, a shop, a construction site, or in a vehicle.

HAZARD ASSESSMENT

The next step in the RAC process is the hazard assessment phase where we determine the relative risk associated with each hazard and prioritize the hazards according to a combination of factors including the (1) likelihood of an accident or injury being caused by the hazard; (2) severity of injury, illness, or property damage that could result if the hazard caused an accident; (3) consequences of exposure to the hazard; and (4) frequency of potential exposure. These factors are combined, quantified, and then used in risk matrices and formulas to determine the overall risk.

Preliminary Hazard Analysis

It is not always feasible to wait until all the data are compiled from a detailed analysis before taking steps to identify and eliminate hazards. For example, when a new system or piece of equipment is installed, management probably wants to bring it on line as soon as possible. In such cases, a **preliminary hazard analysis (PHA)** is in order. The PHA evaluates the likelihood of an accident or injury being caused by the hazard and the severity of injury, illness, or property damage that could result if the hazard caused an accident. The

PHA can serve two purposes: (1) It can expedite bringing the new system on line, but at a substantially reduced risk of injuring workers, and (2) it can serve as a guide for a future detailed analysis.

The Society of Manufacturing Engineers (SME) has this to say about preliminary hazard analysis:

> Each hazard should be ranked according to its probability to cause an accident and the severity of that accident. The ranking here is relative. Some hazards identified might be placed into a category for further analysis. A useful practice for early sorting is to place catastrophic severities together, followed by critical, marginal, and nuisance hazards, respectively. Then, with each item, indicate the probability of occurrence—considerable, probable, or unlikely. Rate the correction of these hazards next by cost.[2]

Key terms in this quote are those that describe the likelihood of an accident occurring (*considerable*, *probable*, or *unlikely*) and those that rate the probable level of injuries that could occur (*catastrophic*, *critical*, *marginal*, and *nuisance*). A key step is rating the cost of correcting hazards. All of these concepts are covered later in this chapter.

Preliminary hazard analysis amounts to forming an ad hoc team of experienced personnel who are familiar with the equipment, material, substance, or process being analyzed. Experience and related expertise are important factors in conducting a preliminary review. For example, say a new piece of equipment, such as a computer numerically controlled (CNC) machining centre, is installed. The health and safety professional could form a team that includes an experienced machinist, an electrician, a materials expert, and a computer control specialist.

All members of the team are asked to look over the machining centre for obvious hazards relating to their respective areas of expertise. Then they work together as a group to play devil's advocate. Each team member asks the others a series of "what if" questions: What if a cutting bit breaks? What if the wrong command is entered? What if the material stock is too long? Depending on the nature of the process being analyzed, personnel from adjacent or related processes should be added to the team.

Figure 7–1 is an example of a job hazard analysis survey adapted from one developed by the National Institute for Occupational Safety and Health (NIOSH). A preliminary

Figure 7–1 Sample job hazard analysis survey.

Operation:												Date:					
Number of Employees	Job Title	Exposure Substance	Form (Type of hazard)						Route of Entry		Control Methods					
			Dust	Liquid	Vapour	Gas	Fume	Mist	Skin	Inhaled	Local Ventilation	General Ventilation	Respirator	Gloves	Face Protection	Other Protection

Source: Adapted from Survey Instrument in NIOSH. Safety Guide for Textile Machinery Manufacturers (Cincinnati, OH: US Department of Health, Education, and Welfare, January 1978), 11.

analysis team would use this form to identify potential hazards associated with a spray-painting process. Key elements include the substances to which workers will be exposed, the form that those substances will take, the probable route of entry, and recommended hazard control strategies. A similar form can be developed for any process or operation that could be the focus of a preliminary hazard analysis.

Whereas a preliminary analysis might involve just observation or pilot testing of new equipment and systems, the *detailed hazard analysis* involves the application of analytical, inductive, and deductive methods. However, other common methods of detailed hazard analysis that may be used in various settings would include the following:

- Failure mode and effects of analysis (FMEA)
- Hazard and operability review (HAZOP)
- Technic of operations review (TOR)
- Human error analysis (HEA)
- Fault tree analysis (FTA)

Risk Analysis

risk analysis An analytical methodology normally associated with insurance and investments.

There are times when a preliminary hazard analysis is sufficient. However, in cases where the potential exists for serious injury, multiple injuries, or catastrophic illness, a detailed hazard analysis is conducted. A number of different methods can be used for conducting detailed analyses. The **risk analysis** method is a simple and effective method of detailed hazard analysis. The risk analysis method will be explained below.

Where are we at risk? Where are we at greatest risk? These are important questions for health and safety professionals involved in analyzing the workplace for the purpose of identifying and overcoming hazards. Risk analysis is an analytical methodology normally associated with insurance and investments. However, risk analysis can be used to analyze the workplace, identify hazards, and develop strategies for overcoming these hazards. The risk analysis process focuses on two key questions:

- How *frequently* does a given event occur?
- How *severe* are the consequences of a given event? The fundamental rule of thumb of risk analysis is that risk is decreased by decreasing the frequency and severity of hazard-related events.

frequency The number of events in a given time; the number of cycles per second in hertz (Hz).

severity The magnitude of the results of an event or action.

Health and safety professionals should understand the relationship that exists between the **frequency** and **severity** factors relating to accidents. Historical data on accidents, injuries, and illness show that the less severe an injury or illness, the more frequently it is likely to occur. Correspondingly, the more severe an injury or illness, the less frequently it is likely to occur. For example, there are many more minor scrapes, bumps, and abrasions experienced in the workplace than major debilitating injuries such as amputations or broken bones.

probability The statistical likelihood of an action or event taking place.

impact The consequences of an action or event.

A number of different approaches can be used in conducting a risk analysis. One of the most effective is that developed by Chapanis.[3] Chapanis's approach to risk analysis considers both **probability** and **impact**.

Probability levels and corresponding frequency of occurrence ratings are as follows: 1 = Impossible (frequency of occurrence: 10^{-8}/day); 2 = Extremely unlikely (frequency of occurrence: 10^{-6}/day); 3 = Remote (frequency of occurrence: 10^{-5}/day); 4 = Occasional (frequency of occurrence: 10^{-4}/day); 5 = Reasonably probable (frequency of occurrence: 10^{-3}/day); 6 = Frequent (frequency of occurrence: 10^{-2}/day).[4]

The lowest rating (1) means it is impossible that a given error will be committed or a given failure will occur. The highest rating (6) means it is very likely that a given error will be committed frequently or a given failure will occur frequently. Notice the quantification of frequency levels for each level of probability. For example, the expected frequency of occurrence for a probability level of "remote" is 10 to the negative fifth power per day.

Severity levels can also be rated according to the likely consequence of an accident or failure event. The least severe incidents (1) are not likely to cause an injury or damage property. The most severe incidents (4) are almost certain to cause death or serious property damage. Critical accidents (3) may cause severe injury or major loss. Marginal accidents (2) may cause minor injury, minor occupational illness, or minor damage.[5]

Risk Assessment

Risk assessment in this context is the process of quantifying the level of risk associated with the operation of a given machine.[6] It should be a structured and systematic process that answers the following four specific questions:

risk assessment The process of quantifying the level of risk.

- How *severe* are potential injuries?
- How *frequently* are employees exposed to the potential hazards?
- What is the *possibility* of avoiding the hazard if it does occur?
- What is the *likelihood* of an injury should a safety control system fail?

The most widely used risk assessment technique is the decision tree, coupled with codes representing these four questions and defined levels of risk.

⟩⟩⟩ SAFETY FACT | What to Include in a Hazards Inventory

An excellent tool for getting the work of health and safety personnel organized, prioritized, and properly focused is the hazards inventory. Such an inventory is a comprehensive list of all hazards associated with all processes and work tasks in a company. A hazards inventory should include at least the following information:

- Process descriptions.
- Associated hazards.

- Controls relating to the hazards.
- Department location of each process.
- Names of supervisors of all personnel who work on each process (including contact information).
- Number of employees who work on each process.
- Medical information relating to the hazards.
- Historical information about the process and related hazards.

Figure 7–2 is an example of a risk assessment decision tree. In this example, the codes and their associated levels of risk are as follows:

S = Severity

Question 1: Severity of potential injuries

S1   Slight injury (bruise, abrasion)

S2   Severe injury (amputation or death)

F = Frequency

Question 2: Frequency of exposure to potential hazards

F1   Infrequent exposure

F2   From frequent to continuous exposure

P = Possibility

Question 3: Possibility of avoiding the hazard if it does occur

P1   Possible

P2   Less possible to not impossible

L = Likelihood

Question 4: Likelihood that the hazard will occur

L1   Highly unlikely

L2   Unlikely

L3   Highly likely

Risk Levels

Associated risk factors ranging from lowest (B) to highest (4)

By applying the decision tree in Figure 7–2 or a similar device, the risk associated with the operation of a given machine can be quantified. This allows safety personnel to assign logical priorities for machine safeguarding and hazard prevention.

Figure 7–2 Risk assessment decision tree.

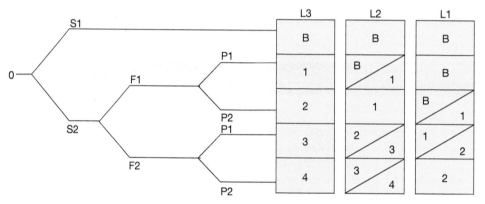

Source: Based on Alberta Government. Hazard Assessment and Control: A Handbook for Alberta Employers and Workers. (March 2015). https://work.alberta.ca/documents/ohs-best-practices-BP018.pdf. (Retrieved February 2, 2017).

Hazard Assessment Risk Matrix

A risk matrix tool provided by Alberta Labour is a simple and easy-to-use method to rank the hazards identified in the previous step. The tool used to rank the hazards does not have to be complicated. It is important, however, that the same method is used consistently throughout the organization. The two factors being used in this model are *severity* (How serious could the consequences be?) and *likelihood* (How likely is it to happen?). See Figure 7–3.

Assign each hazard a number from 1 to 3 to describe severity, where:

    3   It could kill you or cause a permanent disability, today or over time.

    2   It could send you to the hospital.

    1   It could make you uncomfortable.

Then…

Assign each hazard a number from 1 to 3 to describe likelihood, where:

    3   It is highly likely.

    2   It might happen.

    1   It is unlikely.

Figure 7-3 Risk matrix.

	Severity		
	Make you uncomfortable 1	Send you to the hospital 2	Kill you/cause a permanent disability 3
Unlikely 1	1	2	3
Might happen 2	2	4	6
Highly likely 3	3	6	9

(Likelihood is the vertical axis label at the left of the matrix.)

Multiply the score of severity and likelihood for each hazard. The hazards with the highest scores pose the greatest risk to workplace health and safety.

Using the above risk matrix, a hazard that ranks a 3 for severity and a 3 for likelihood would score a 9 ($3 \times 3 = 9$). A hazard with a 1 severity and a 3 likelihood would score a 3 ($1 \times 3 = 3$). The hazard that scored 9 in the matrix should be addressed first.[7]

Source: Alberta Government. *Hazard Assessment and Control: A Handbook for Alberta Employers and Workers.* (March 2015). [Online]. Available: https://work.alberta.ca/documents/ohs-best-practices-BP018.pdf. (Retrieved February 2, 2017).

CONTROLLING HAZARDS

Throughout the hazard recognition and assessment stages, some of the identified hazards may already have some form of controls in place. The goal of the health and safety professional is to implement measures that will reduce the workers' potential of exposure to the hazard. Controlling the hazard at the earliest stage of the process will provide the greatest level of protection. Figure 7-4 illustrates how the placement of these controls can be *at the source*, along the *path*, or at the *worker*.

Figure 7-4 Controlling hazards at the source, along the path, or at the worker.

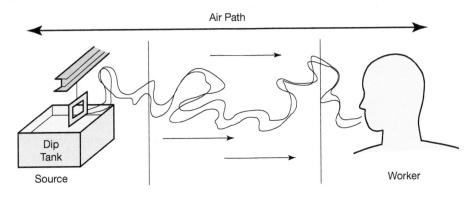

Source: Used with the permission of Canadian Centre for Occupational Health and Safety.

Whatever the type of hazard, the first choice would be eliminating it at the source. For example, a noisy machine or process can be replaced with one less noisy, or toxic chemicals can be replaced with less harmful products. If that option is not feasible or practical, then some form of control along the path may be used. Barriers for noise, heat, and dust, or ventilation systems are considered controls along the path that separates the worker from the hazard. If the hazard is still not eliminated or controlled to an acceptable level, then we place the control at the worker with the use of personal protective equipment (PPE).

Hierarchy of Controls

hierarchy of controls A system of hazard control methods ranging from most effective (elimination) to least effective (personal protective equipment).

Another method of determining the order in which the controls are implemented is through the **hierarchy of controls**. This approach starts with the most effective controls for a particular hazard and continues with a logical progression through the options to the least desirable. In Figure 7–5, you will see that the most effective controls are at the top and offer the broadest level of protection for workers, while personal protective equipment is considered a last resort. Each level of control is explained below.

Figure 7–5 Hierarchy of controls.

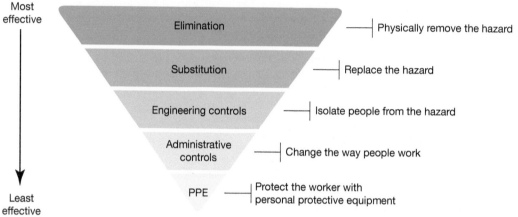

Source: Used with the permission of WorkSafeBC (Workers' Compensation Board).

Elimination By completely eliminating the hazard the risk of worker exposure is eliminated. One approach to eliminating hazards at the source would be to ask if the process or procedure is necessary. For example, construction workers, especially roofers, are often exposed to hazards from working at heights. By constructing the roof units on the ground and hoisting them into place after they are assembled, the hazard is virtually eliminated. Another means of eliminating a hazard could be through automation or using robots for some tasks.

Substitution Substituting the hazardous product, equipment, or procedure may remove some of the hazards associated with the process or activity. Many industrial processes using toxic solvents have found alternate agents to accomplish the same task. The substitute product may result in additional cost, longer soak times, or changes to the process, or could result in improvements in those areas. When substitutions are made, the health and safety professional has to be aware of any potential new hazards that are introduced.

Engineering controls Engineering controls involve redesigning equipment or workspace to separate the worker from the hazard. Machine guarding, extraction or ventilation systems, robotics and automation, and tool design with reduced noise, weight, or vibration are all examples of engineering controls. These are often more expensive and may not be practical for temporary situations, but they should be considered when new processes, facilities, equipment and systems are being implemented.

Administrative controls   Administrative controls are aimed at influencing the worker's behaviour. These controls include best practice or standard operating procedures, providing worker training, or sharing information that is created to limit exposure to the hazard. Another administrative control to limit exposure to a hazard is to use scheduling and job rotation.

Personal protective equipment   Personal protective equipment (PPE) is a form of protection at the worker level and is least desirable. PPE is often used in conjunction with one or more of the other controls. Examples of PPE used to control worker exposure to various hazards include gloves, glasses, face shields, earplugs, earmuffs, aprons, safety footwear, respirators, and dust masks.

Society of Manufacturing Engineers Model

The different methods and procedures discussed in this chapter concerned with controlling hazards have a number of similarities. The safety student will see similarities in the Society of Manufacturing Engineers (SME) model, which contains many of these elements in its hazard control method:

- Eliminate the source of the hazards.
- Substitute a less hazardous equivalent.
- Reduce the hazards at the source.
- Remove the employee from the hazard (e.g., substitute a robot or other automated system).
- Isolate the hazards (e.g., enclose them in barriers).
- Dilute the hazards (e.g., ventilate the hazardous substances).
- Apply appropriate management strategies.
- Use appropriate personal protective equipment.
- Provide employee training.
- Practise good housekeeping.[8]

For every hazard identified during the analysis process, one or more of these hazard control methods will apply. Figure 7–6 shows the steps involved in implementing hazard control methods. The first step involves selecting the method or methods that are most likely to produce the desired results. Once selected, the method is applied and monitored to determine if the expected results are being achieved.

Monitoring and observing are informal procedures. They should be followed by a more formal, more structured assessment of the effectiveness of the method. If the method selected is not producing the desired results, adjustments should be made. This may mean changing the way in which the method is applied or dropping it and trying another.

The example of Crestview Container Corporation's (CCC) problems with toxic paint illustrates how the process works: CCC produces airtight aluminum containers for transporting electromechanical devices. The containers must be painted as the last step in the production process. Although the specified paint was supposed to be only slightly toxic—a problem that should have been resolved by using personal protective equipment—paint station operators complained frequently of various negative side effects.

The CCC health and safety professional, working with management, solved the problem by applying the following steps:

1. **Select a method.** Of the various methods available, the one selected involved eliminating the source of the hazard (the toxic paint). CCC personnel were tasked with

Figure 7–6 Steps for implementing hazard control measures.

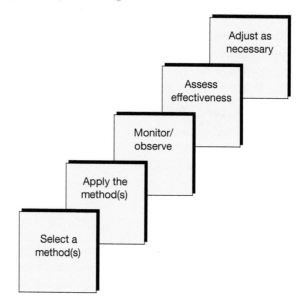

testing various nontoxic paints until one was found that could match the problem paint in all categories (e.g., ease of application, drying time, quality of surface finish, etc.). After forty different paints were tested, a nontoxic substitute was found.

2. **Apply the method.** The new paint was ordered and used on a partial shipment of containers.

3. **Monitor/observe.** The health and safety professional, along with CCC's painting supervisors, monitored both employee performance and employee complaints concerning the paint.

4. **Assess effectiveness.** To assess effectiveness, employee complaints were tabulated. The number of complaints was down to a negligible amount and not serious in nature. Productivity was also assessed. It was found that the new paint had no noticeable effect on productivity, negative or positive.

5. **Adjust as necessary.** CCC found that no adjustments were necessary.

LEADING INDICATORS

Health and safety texts necessarily focus on what can go wrong and cause accidents and injuries in the workplace. This is because health and safety professionals must be able to identify hazardous conditions and take the appropriate steps to keep them from harming people. The success of these OHS processes, policies, and procedures are then measured using **lagging indicators**, such as numbers of incidents reported or injury rates, or WCB premium rates. However, it is also helpful for health and safety personnel to study the other side of the coin—outstanding practices that make the workplace safer. Each provincial and territorial jurisdiction produces and shares numerous best practice OHS resources and many that address hazards in specific industries.

While lagging indicators can provide valuable information on past trends and provide a sense of how well the organization's OHS system has worked, **leading indicators** focus on the future outcomes by implementing policies, procedures, and practices to achieve the desired outcomes. Leading indicators measure the inputs that people are making to the OHS management process. They measure the presence of safety as opposed to the absence of injury.[9] Having standard operating procedures created, the number of workers trained,

lagging indicators A record of incidents that already happened. A reactive measure of OHS program success.

leading indicators A record of systems or measures in place. A proactive measure of OHS program success.

housekeeping, equipment maintenance, and the number of workers engaged in health and safety committees are all signals of future OHS success. Among the most important leading indicators are hazard assessments and hazard reporting. As discussed throughout this chapter, the main purpose of hazard analysis is to proactively identify and mitigate hazards before an accident occurs.

>>> DISCUSSION CASE | What Is Your Opinion?

Mike Chinchar is the new safety director at MicroTel Corporation. He completed his college degree just 6 weeks ago. At the moment, he is wishing he could transport himself back in time and be a college student again. He is on the hot seat. "Chinchar, you seem to think that this company should simply stop functioning every time you identify a hazard. This situation you are proposing will be expensive! Isn't there some other way to solve the problem? Did you do a cost–benefit analysis before arriving at this recommendation?" What types of factors should Chinchar have considered before recommending a solution to a hazardous situation? What is your opinion?

FORMAL HAZARD ASSESSMENT PROCESS

When all the pieces are put together to create a comprehensive hazard control program, the process used in most organizations will look quite similar. The listed steps may range from simple recognition, assessment, and control, to a detailed nine-step process, such as Alberta Labour's formal hazard assessment process, shown in the Figure 7–7 below.

Figure 7–7 Formal hazard assessment process.

1. Figure out what people do.
2. List all work tasks/activities.
3. Identify hazards of each task.
4. Rank the hazards according to risk.
5. Find ways to eliminate or control the hazards.
6. Implement the selected controls.
7. Communicate the hazards and follow the controls.
8. Monitor the controls for effectiveness.
9. Review and revise hazard assessment as needed.

Using this model, the process begins with conducting an inventory of all the jobs in the organization. This is further broken down into the tasks performed by each position. Depending on the type of organization, there will be similar tasks conducted by people from different parts of the organization. For example, most office work, which is usually conducted by members throughout the organization, will have common hazards. The workers whose hazards are being assessed should be involved in the assessment process to ensure that no steps or hazards are overlooked. Be sure to look for health hazards as well as safety.

The next steps are to rate the hazards, using the same tool or method across the organization. A hazard assessment template, similar to the sample in Figure 7–8, should be used to record the assessment process. Starting with the highest risk tasks, determine the controls to be used for each hazard. Apply the hierarchy of control and start with elimination of the hazard and then progress to personal protective equipment, if needed. One level of control may not adequately address the hazard, therefore a combination of controls may be needed. For example, noise hazards may be reduced with improved equipment, sound-absorbing panels, or barriers, but the worker may still need earmuffs or earplugs for optimum protection.

Figure 7–8 Sample hazard assessment template.

Job/position/work type:							
Assessment performed by: (names)							**Date of assessment:**
Tasks (List all tasks/ activities of the job/position)	**Hazards** (List all existing and potential health and safety hazards)	**Severity**	**Likelihood**	**Risk**	**Controls** (List the controls for each hazard: Elimination, Substitution, Engineering, Administrative, Personal Protective Equipment)		**Date implemented**
					S × L = R		
Severity: How serious could the consequences be? 3 – It could kill you or cause a permanent disability, today or over time. 2 – It could send you to the hospital. 1 – It could make you uncomfortable.		**Likelihood**: How likely is it to happen? 3 – It's highly likely. 2 – It might happen. 1 – It's unlikely.			**Risk**: Calculate the risk of hazards to prioritize preventative actions. Severity × Likelihood = Risk		

Source: Alberta Government. *Hazard Assessment and Control: A Handbook for Alberta Employers and Workers.* (March 2015). [Online]. Available: https://work.alberta.ca/documents/ohs-best-practices-BP018.pdf. (Retrieved February 2, 2017).

Now that the control methods have been determined, they have to be put into action. The implementation has to be monitored closely and adjustments or temporary measures may be needed. PPE, such as hearing protection or respirators, may be needed until the permanent solutions, such as sound barriers or exhaust extraction systems, are in place. Communication with workers is important to inform them of both the hazards and the controls. The last steps are to continuously monitor the controls for effectiveness and to ensure that new hazards have not been created. Finally, review existing hazard assessment and revise accordingly when a new task, work process, or equipment is introduced, or when there are any significant changes to a work site.

COST–BENEFIT FACTORS IN HAZARD ANALYSIS

cost–benefit The relationship between the cost of a remedy and the benefit it produces.

Every hazard typically has several different remedies. Every remedy has a corresponding **cost** and corresponding **benefit**. Management is not likely to want to apply $10 solutions to $1 problems. Therefore, it is important to factor in cost when recommending corrective action regarding hazards. This amounts to listing all of the potential remedies along with their respective costs and then estimating the extent to which each will reduce the hazard (its benefit).

Going back to the earlier example of the CNC machining centre, assume that the analysis team identified the following potential hazards:

- Lubricants sprayed on the machine operator or floor.
- Flying metal chips hitting the operator or other workers.
- Jammed metal stock kicking back into the operator.

Figure 7–9 is a matrix that can be developed by the analysis team to illustrate the cost of each hazard versus the benefit of each remedy. After examining this matrix, the remedy

Figure 7-9 Sample cost–benefit analysis matrix.

Cost–Benefit Analysis Matrix				
		Impact on Hazard		
Possible Remedy	**Estimated Cost**	**Spraying Lubricants**	**Metal Chips**	**Jammed Stock**
Plexiglas™ door	$250	E	E	R
Flexible curtain	75	R	R	N
Acme chip/jam guard	260	N	E	E
Acme spray guard	260	N	E	E

R = Reduces the hazard

E = Eliminates the hazard

N = No effect on the hazard

I = Increases the hazard

C = Creates new hazard

that makes the most sense from the perspective of both cost and impact on the hazards is the Plexiglas™ door. It eliminates two of the hazards and reduces the third. The flexible curtain costs less but does not have a sufficient impact on the hazards. The third and fourth options cost more and have less impact on the hazards.

SUMMARY

1. A hazard is a condition or combination of conditions that, if left uncorrected, may lead to an accident, illness, or property damage.

2. Hazard analysis is a systematic process for identifying hazards and recommending corrective action.

3. Secondary benefits of a hazard analysis include operational efficiencies, improved corporate image, and improved worker morale with less employee turnover.

4. Hazards may be classified as health hazards or safety hazards.

5. There are four categories of hazards: physical, chemical, biological, and psychosocial.

6. Four factors that contribute to workplace hazards are people, equipment, materials, and environment.

7. Hazard assessment is the second step in the hazard recognition, assessment, and control process.

8. A preliminary hazard analysis involves forming an ad hoc team of experienced personnel who are familiar with the equipment, material substance, and process being analyzed. Experience and related expertise are critical in conducting a preliminary hazard analysis.

9. The risk analysis process revolves around answering two questions: How frequently does a given event occur? How severe are the consequences of a given event? The fundamental rule of thumb of risk analysis is that risk is decreased by decreasing the frequency and severity of hazard-related events.

10. Risk assessment model answers four questions: (1) How severe are potential injuries? (2) How frequently are employees exposed to potential hazards? (3) What is the possibility of avoiding the hazard if it does occur? (4) What is the likelihood of an injury if a safety control system fails?

11. The hazard assessment risk matrix uses severity and likelihood to rank risk.

12. The Society of Manufacturing Engineers (SME) model contains ten elements in its hazard control. The fundamentals of its hazard prevention and deterrence include the following strategies: eliminate the source of the hazard, substitute a less hazardous substance, reduce the hazard at the source, remove the employee from the hazard, isolate the hazard, dilute the hazard, apply appropriate management strategies, use personal protective equipment, provide employee training, and practise good housekeeping.

13. Hazards can be controlled at the source, along the path, or at the worker.

14. The hierarchy of controls is a system of hazard control methods ranging from most effective (elimination) to least effective (personal protective equipment).

15. Lagging indicators are a reactive record of incidents that happened. Leading indicators are proactive measures in place to prevent accidents.

16. The formal hazard assessment process is a nine-step comprehensive hazard control system.

17. The cost-benefit ratio relationship is considered when proposing solutions.

Key Terms and Concepts

Biological hazards
Chemical hazards
Cost–benefit
Ergonomic hazards
Frequency
Hazard
Hazard analysis
Hierarchy of controls

Impact
Lagging indicators
Leading indicators
Pathogens
Physical Hazards
Preliminary hazard analysis
   (PHA)
Probability

Psychosocial hazards
Risk
Risk analysis
Risk assessment
Severity

Review Questions

1. Define the term *hazard*.
2. What legislation in your area obligates the employer to conduct hazard assessments?
3. What are the primary and secondary benefits of hazard analysis?
4. What is the purpose of preliminary hazard analysis?
5. Explain the difference between health and safety hazards.
6. What are the four categories of hazards? Provide at least one example for each.
7. Explain why experience and related expertise are so important when conducting a preliminary hazard analysis.
8. Provide examples of hazard control, at the source, along the path, and at the worker.
9. Describe how hazards are controlled using the hierarchy of control system.
10. Why is cost–benefit analysis such a critical part of hazard analysis and prevention?

Weblinks

Alberta Labour

https://work.alberta.ca/documents/ohs-best-practices-BP018.pdf

The OHS resource page has links to practical resources for employers and workers, including bulletins, fact sheets, manuals, and other health and safety documents.

Association of Workers' Compensation Boards of Canada

www.awcbc.org

The Association of Workers' Compensation Boards of Canada provides links to the WCB agency for each jurisdiction, each having numerous publications on hazard awareness and prevention.

Canadian Centre for Occupational Health and Safety (CCOHS)

http://www.ccohs.ca/topics/hazards/

The CCOHS hazards page contains extensive information on hazard recognition, assessment, and control.

Endnotes

[1] Alberta Government. *Hazard Assessment and Control: A Handbook for Alberta Employers and Workers*. (March 2015). [Online]. Available: https://work.alberta.ca/documents/ohs-best-practices-BP018.pdf. (Retrieved February 2, 2017).

[2] Society of Manufacturing Engineers (SME). *Tool and Manufacturing Engineers Handbook* 6 (Dearborn, MI: Society of Manufacturing Engineers, 1998), 12–17.

[3] A. Chapanis. "To Err Is Human, to Forgive, Design." Proceedings of the ASSE Annual Professional Development Conference, New Orleans, 1986, 6.

[4] Ibid.

[5] Ibid.

[6] "Safety of Machinery—Principles of Safety Related to Control Systems," EN 954, Part I, European Union (1997).

[7] Alberta Government. *Hazard Assessment and Control: A Handbook for Alberta Employers and Workers*. (March 2015). [Online]. Available: https://work.alberta.ca/documents/ohs-best-practices-BP018.pdf. (Retrieved February 2, 2017).

[8] Society of Manufacturing Engineers (SME). *Tool and Manufacturing Engineers Handbook* 6 (Dearborn, MI: Society of Manufacturing Engineers, 1998), 12–17.

[9] Alberta Government. *Leading Indicators for Workplace Health and Safety: A User Guide*. (2015). [Online]. Available: http://work.alberta.ca/documents/ohs-best-practices-BP019.pdf. (Retrieved July 18, 2017).

Chapter 8
Theories of Accident Causation

MAJOR TOPICS

- Domino Theory of Accident Causation

- Human Factors Theory of Accident Causation

- Accident/Incident Theory of Accident Causation

- Epidemiological Theory of Accident Causation

- Limitations of Event-Chain Accident Causation Theories

- Systems Theory of Accident Causation

- Combination Theory of Accident Causation

- Behavioural Theory of Accident Causation

Each year, work-related accidents take an enormous toll on Canadian workers and the economy. The very compelling statistics put forth in earlier chapters demonstrate the magnitude of the problem. These workplace accidents degrade both the economic stability of many businesses and the quality of life for those injured and their families. The first step in preventing accidents is to identify their cause.

Why do accidents happen? This question has concerned health and safety decision makers for decades because in order to prevent accidents we must know why they happen. Over the years, several theories of accident causation have evolved that attempt to explain why accidents occur. Models based on these theories are used to predict and prevent accidents.

The most widely known theories of accident causation are the domino theory, the human factors theory, the accident/incident theory, the epidemiological theory, the systems theory, the combination theory, and the behavioural theory. This chapter provides practising and prospective health and safety professionals with the information they need to understand fully and apply these theories.

DOMINO THEORY OF ACCIDENT CAUSATION

An early pioneer of accident prevention and industrial safety was Herbert W. Heinrich, an official with the Travelers Insurance Company. In the late 1920s, after studying the reports of 75,000 industrial accidents, Heinrich concluded that:

- 88 percent of industrial accidents are caused by unsafe acts committed by fellow workers.
- 10 percent of industrial accidents are caused by unsafe conditions.
- 2 percent of industrial accidents are unavoidable.[1]

Heinrich's study laid the foundation for his Axioms of Industrial Safety and his theory of accident causation, which came to be known as the **domino theory**. So much of Heinrich's theory has been discounted by more contemporary research that it is now considered outdated. However, because some of today's more widely accepted theories can be traced back to Heinrich's theory, students of industrial safety should be familiar with his work.

domino theory Injuries are caused by the action of preceding factors. Removal of the central factor negates the action of the preceding factors and, in so doing, prevents accidents and injuries.

Heinrich's Axioms of Industrial Safety

Heinrich summarized what he thought health and safety decision makers should know about industrial accidents in ten statements he called Axioms of Industrial Safety. These axioms can be paraphrased as follows:

1. Injuries result from a completed series of factors, one of which is the accident itself.
2. An accident can occur only as the result of an unsafe act by a person and/or a physical or mechanical hazard.
3. Most accidents are the result of unsafe behaviour by people.
4. An unsafe act by a person or an unsafe condition does not always immediately result in an accident/injury.
5. The reasons that people commit unsafe acts can serve as helpful guides in selecting corrective actions.
6. The severity of an accident is largely fortuitous, and its cause is largely preventable.
7. The best accident prevention techniques are analogous with the best quality and productivity techniques.
8. Management should assume responsibility for safety because it is in the best position to get results.
9. The supervisor is the key person in the prevention of industrial accidents.
10. In addition to the direct costs of an accident (e.g., compensation, liability claims, medical costs, and hospital expenses), there are also hidden or indirect costs.[2]

According to Heinrich, these axioms encompass the fundamental body of knowledge that must be understood by decision makers interested in preventing accidents. Any accident prevention program that takes all ten axioms into account is more likely to be effective than a program that leaves out one or more axioms.

Heinrich's Domino Theory

Perhaps you have stood up a row of dominoes, tipped the first one over, and watched as each successive domino topples the one next to it. This is how Heinrich's theory of accident causation works. According to Heinrich, there are five factors in the consecutive sequence of events leading up to and including an accident. These factors can be summarized as follows:

1. **Ancestry and social environment.** Negative character traits that may lead people to behave in an unsafe manner can be inherited (**ancestry**) or acquired as a result of the **social environment**.

ancestry A person's line of descent.

social environment The general value system of the society in which an individual lives, works, grows up, and so on.

unsafe act An act that is not
safe for an employee.

2. **Fault of person.** Negative character traits, whether inherited or acquired, are why people behave in an unsafe manner and why hazardous conditions exist.

3. **Unsafe act/mechanical or physical hazard. Unsafe acts** committed by people and mechanical or physical hazards are the direct causes of accidents.

4. **Accident.** Typically, accidents that result in injury are caused by falling or being hit by moving objects.

5. **Injury.** Typical injuries resulting from accidents include lacerations and fractures.[3]

preceding factors Factors that
led up to an accident.

central factor The main issue or
factor in a problem or act.

hazardous condition A condition
that exposes a person to risks.

Heinrich's theory has two central points: (1) Injuries are caused by the action of **preceding factors** and (2) removal of the **central factor** (unsafe act/**hazardous condition**) negates the action of the preceding factors and, in so doing, prevents accidents and injuries.

Domino Theory in Practice

Construction Products Company (CPC) is a distributor of lumber, pipe, and concrete products. Its customers are typically small building contractors. CPC's facility consists of an office in which orders are placed and several large warehouses. Contractors place their orders in the office. They then drive their trucks through the appropriate warehouses to be loaded by CPC personnel.

Because the contractors are small operations, most of their orders are also relatively small and can be loaded by hand. Warehouse personnel go to the appropriate bins, pull out the materials needed to fill their orders, and load the materials on customers' trucks. Even though most orders are small enough to be loaded by hand, many of the materials purchased are bulky and cumbersome to handle. Because of this, CPC's loaders are required to wear such personal protection gear as hard hats, padded gloves, and steel-toed boots.

For years CPC's management team had noticed an increase in minor injuries to warehouse personnel during the summer months. Typically, these injuries consisted of nothing worse than minor cuts, scrapes, and bruises. However, this past summer had been different. Two warehouse workers had sustained serious back injuries. These injuries have been costly to CPC both financially and in terms of employee morale.

An investigation of these accidents quickly identified a series of events and a central causal behaviour that set up a domino effect that, in turn, resulted in the injuries. The investigation revealed that CPC's warehouses became so hot during the summer months that personal protection gear was uncomfortable. As a result, warehouse personnel simply discarded it. Failure to use appropriate personal protection gear in the summer months had always led to an increase in injuries. However, because the injuries were minor in nature, management had never paid much attention to the situation. It was probably inevitable that more serious injuries would occur eventually.

To prevent a recurrence of the summer-injury epidemic, CPC's management team decided to remove the causal factor—failure of warehouse personnel to use their personal protection gear during the summer months. To facilitate the removal of this factor, CPC's management team formed a committee consisting of one executive manager, one warehouse supervisor, and three warehouse employees.

The committee made the following recommendations: (1) Provide all warehouse personnel with training on the importance and proper use of personal protection gear; (2) require warehouse supervisors to monitor the use of personal protection gear more closely; (3) establish a company policy that contains specific and progressive disciplinary measures for failure to use required personal protection gear; and (4) implement several heat reduction measures to make warehouses cooler during the summer months.

CPC's management team adopted all of the committee's recommendations. In doing so, it removed the central causal factor that had historically led to an increase in injuries during the summer months.

HUMAN FACTORS THEORY OF ACCIDENT CAUSATION

The **human factors theory** of accident causation attributes accidents to a chain of events ultimately caused by **human error**. It consists of the following three broad factors that lead to human error: overload, inappropriate response and workstation incompatibility, and inappropriate activities (see Figure 8–1).

human factors theory Attributes accidents to a chain of events ultimately caused by human error.

human error A mistake that is made by a human, not a machine.

Figure 8–1 Factors that cause human errors.

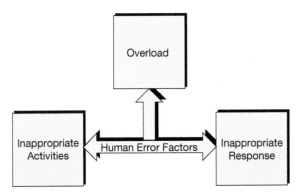

Overload

Overload amounts to an imbalance between a person's capacity at any given time and the load that person is carrying in a given state. A person's capacity is the product of such factors as his or her natural ability, training, state of mind, fatigue, stress, and physical condition. The load that a person is carrying consists of tasks for which he or she is responsible and added burdens resulting from **environmental factors** (noise, distractions, and so on), **internal factors** (personal problems, emotional stress, and worry), and **situational factors** (level of risk, unclear instructions, and so on). The state in which a person is acting is the product of his or her motivational and arousal levels.

overload An imbalance between a person's capacity at any given time and the load that person is carrying in a given state.

environmental factors Characteristics of the environment in which an employee works that can affect his or her state of mind or physical conditions, such as noise or distractions.

internal factors Factors that can add a burden on a person and interfere with his or her work, such as personal problems.

Inappropriate Response and Workstation Incompatibility

How a person responds in a given situation can cause or prevent an accident. If a person detects a hazardous condition but does nothing to correct it, he or she has responded inappropriately. If a person removes a safeguard from a machine in an effort to increase output, he or she has responded inappropriately. If a person disregards an established safety procedure, he or she has responded inappropriately. Such responses can lead to accidents. In addition to **inappropriate responses**, this component includes workstation incompatibility. The incompatibility of a person's workstation with regard to size, force, reach, feel, and similar factors can lead to accidents and injuries.

situational factors Environmental factors that can affect an employee's safety and that can differ from situation to situation.

inappropriate response A response in which a person disregards an established safety procedure.

Inappropriate Activities

Human error can be the result of **inappropriate activities**. An example of an inappropriate activity is a person who undertakes a task that he or she doesn't know how to do. Another example is a person who misjudges the degree of risk involved in a given task and proceeds based on that misjudgment. Such inappropriate activities can lead to accidents and injuries. Figure 8–2 summarizes the various components of the human factors theory.[4]

inappropriate activities Activities undertaken with disregard for established safety procedures.

Figure 8–2 Human factors theory.

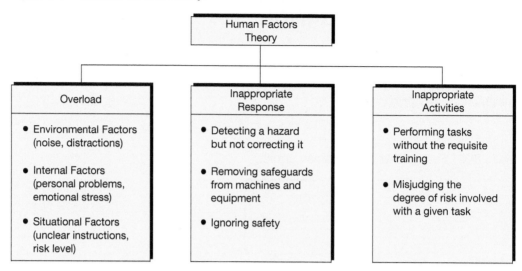

Strenuous physical work and pregnancy can be a dangerous combination. Too much strenuous labour can result in a miscarriage. The types of work to be avoided by pregnant employees include the following:

- Standing for more than three hours per day.
- Operating machinery that vibrates.

- Lifting heavy loads.
- Working in extremes of hot or cold.

Shift work and workstations that require awkward postures can also put pregnant employees at risk. The third trimester is the most risk-intensive time during pregnancy.

Human Factors Theory in Practice

Kitchenware Manufacturing Incorporated (KMI) produces aluminum kitchenware for commercial settings. After ten years of steady, respectable growth, KMI suddenly saw its sales triple in less than six months. This rapid growth was the result of KMI's successful entry into European and Asian markets.

The growth in sales, although welcomed by both management and employees, quickly overloaded and, before long, overwhelmed the company's production facility. KMI responded by adding a second shift of production personnel and approving unlimited overtime for highly skilled personnel. Shortly after the upturn in production, KMI began to experience a disturbing increase in accidents and injuries. During his accident investigations, KMI's safety manager noticed that human error figured prominently in the accidents. He grouped all of the human errors identified into three categories: (1) overload, (2) inappropriate response, and (3) inappropriate activities.

In the category of *overload*, he found that the rush to fill orders was pushing production personnel beyond their personal limits in some cases, and beyond their capabilities in others. Stress, insufficient training of new employees, and fatigue all contributed to the overload. In the category of *inappropriate response*, the safety manager determined that many of KMI's production personnel had removed safeguards from their machines in an attempt to speed up production. All of the machines involved in accidents had had safeguards removed.

In the category of *inappropriate activities*, the safety manager found that new employees were being assigned duties for which they weren't yet fully trained. As a result, they often misjudged the amount of risk associated with their work tasks.

With enough accident investigations completed to identify a pattern of human error, the safety manager prepared a presentation containing a set of recommendations for corrective measures for KMI's executive management team. His recommendations were designed to prevent human-error-oriented accidents without slowing production.

ACCIDENT/INCIDENT THEORY OF ACCIDENT CAUSATION

The **accident/incident theory** is an extension of the human factors theory. It was developed by Dan Petersen and is sometimes referred to as the Petersen accident/incident theory.[5] Petersen introduced such new elements as **ergonomic traps**, the decision to err, and systems failures, while retaining much of the human factors theory. A model based on his theory is shown in Figure 8–3.

accident/incident theory Theory of accident causation in which overload, ergonomic traps, or a decision to err lead to human error.

ergonomic traps Unsafe conditions unintentionally designed into a workstation.

Figure 8–3 Accident/incident theory.

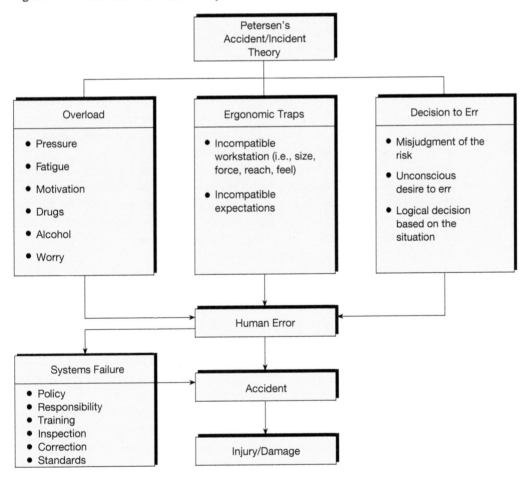

In this model, overload, ergonomic traps, or a decision to err lead to human error. The decision to err may be conscious and based on logic or it may be unconscious. A variety of pressures such as deadlines, peer pressure, and budget factors can lead to **unsafe behaviour**. Another factor that can influence such a decision is the "It won't happen to me" syndrome.

unsafe behaviour The manner in which people conduct themselves that is unsafe to them or to another.

The systems failure component is an important contribution of Petersen's theory. First, it shows the potential for a **causal relationship** between management decisions or management behaviour and safety. Second, it establishes management's role in accident prevention as well as the broader concepts of health and safety in the workplace.

Following are just some of the different ways that systems can fail, according to Petersen's theory:

- Management does not establish a comprehensive safety policy.
- Responsibility and authority with regard to safety are not clearly defined.
- Safety procedures such as measurement, inspection, correction, and investigation are ignored or given insufficient attention.
- Employees do not receive proper orientation.
- Employees are not given sufficient safety training.

Accident/Incident Theory in Practice

Poultry Processing Corporation (PPC) processes chickens and turkeys for grocery chains. Poultry processing is a labour-intensive enterprise involving a great deal of handwork. A variety of different knives, shears, and cleavers are used. Much of the work is monotonous and repetitive. Selected parts of the overall process must be done in cold conditions.

PPC has gone to great lengths to ensure that workstations are ergonomically sound, that personal protection gear is used as appropriate, and that adequate precautions are taken to prevent illness and injuries. As a result, PPC is an award-winning company in the area of workplace health and safety.

Consequently, the poultry-processing industry was shocked when a class action lawsuit was filed against PPC on behalf of over fifty employees, all of whom claimed to be suffering from carpal tunnel syndrome. Because of PPC's excellent health and safety record, most observers felt sure that the company would be vindicated in the end.

The company's policies and procedures relating to health and safety were investigated thoroughly by consultants brought in by both PPC and the attorney for the plaintiffs. Over 100 witnesses gave depositions, and several preliminary hearings were held. By the time the trial finally rolled around, both sides had accumulated mountains of paper and filing cabinets full of evidence. Then, suddenly and without advance notice, PPC offered a substantial financial settlement, which the plaintiffs accepted.

It was one of PPC's outside consultants who discovered what had caused the increased incidence of carpal tunnel syndrome. The company had always used a centralized approach to managing health and safety. Responsibility for such tasks as measurement, inspection, correction, and investigation was assigned to the safety manager, Joe Don Huttle. Huttle had an excellent record during his twenty years in the poultry-processing industry, with the last five spent at PPC. In fact, he was so well respected in the industry that his peers had elected him president of a statewide safety organization. This, as it turned out, is where PPC's troubles began.

When Huttle took it over, the safety organization had experienced a 3-year decline in membership and was struggling to stay afloat financially. He had been elected as "the man who could save the organization." Intending to do just that, Huttle went right to work. For months at a time he worked 7 days a week, often spending as much as 2 weeks at a time on the road. When he was in his office at PPC, Huttle was either on the telephone or doing paperwork for the safety organization.

Within six months, he had reversed the organization's downhill slide, but not without paying a price at PPC. During the same six-month period, his duties at PPC were badly neglected. Measurement of individual and group safety performance had come to a standstill. The same was true of inspection, correction, investigation, and reporting.

It was during this time of neglect that the increased incidence of carpal tunnel syndrome occurred. Safety precautions that Huttle had instituted to guard against this particular problem were no longer observed properly once the workers realized that he had stopped observing and correcting them. Measurement and inspection might also have prevented the injuries had Huttle maintained his normal schedule of these activities.

PPC's consultant, in a confidential report to executive managers, cited the accident/incident theory in explaining his view of why the injuries occurred. In this report, the consultant said that Huttle was guilty of applying "It won't happen here" logic when he made a conscious decision to neglect his duties at PPC in favour of his duties with the professional organization. Of course, the employees themselves were guilty of not following clearly established procedures. However, because Huttle's neglect was also a major contributing factor, PPC decided to settle out of court.

EPIDEMIOLOGICAL THEORY OF ACCIDENT CAUSATION

Traditionally, safety theories and programs have focused on accidents and the resulting injuries. However, the current trend is toward a broader perspective that also encompasses the issue of industrial hygiene. **Industrial hygiene** concerns environmental factors that can lead to sickness, disease, or other forms of impaired health.

This trend has, in turn, led to the development of an epidemiological theory of accident causation. Epidemiology is the study of causal relationships between environmental factors and disease. The **epidemiological theory** holds that the models used for studying and determining these relationships can also be used to study causal relationships between environmental factors and accidents or diseases.[6]

Figure 8–4 illustrates the epidemiological theory of accident causation. The key components are **predispositional characteristics** and **situational characteristics**. These characteristics, taken together, can either result in or prevent conditions that may result in an accident. For example, if an employee who is particularly susceptible to peer pressure

industrial hygiene An area of specialization in the field of industrial health and safety that is concerned with predicting, recognizing, assessing, controlling, and preventing environmental stressors in the workplace that can cause sickness or serious discomfort.

epidemiological theory Theory that the models used for studying and determining epidemiological relationships can also be used to study causal relationships between environmental factors and accidents or diseases.

predispositional characteristics Human personality characteristics that can have a catalytic effect in causing an accident.

situational characteristics Factors that can change from setting to setting and have a catalytic effect in causing an accident.

Figure 8–4 Epidemiological theory.

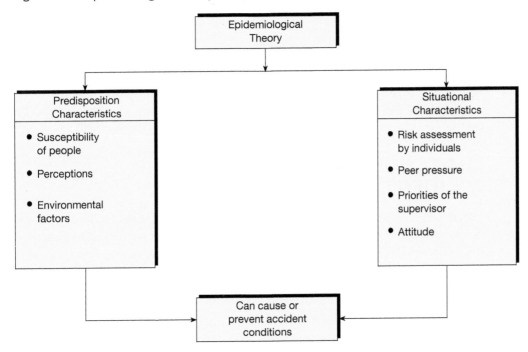

(predisposition characteristic) is pressured by his co-workers (situational characteristic) to speed up his operation, the result will be an increased probability of an accident.

Epidemiological Theory in Practice

Jane Andrews was the newest member of the loading unit for Parcel Delivery Service (PDS). She and the other members of her unit were responsible for loading fifty trucks every morning. It was physically demanding work, and she was the first woman ever selected by PDS to work in the loading unit. She had gotten the job as part of the company's upward mobility program. She was excited about her new position, because within PDS the loading unit was considered a springboard to advancement. Consequently, she was eager to do well. The responsibility she felt toward other female employees at PDS only intensified her anxiety. Andrews felt that if she failed, other women might not get a chance to try in the future.

Before beginning work in the loading unit, employees must complete two days of training on proper lifting techniques. Consequently, Andrews became concerned when the supervisor called her aside on her first day in the unit and told her to forget what she had learned in training. He said, "Jane, nobody wants a back injury, so be careful. But the key to success in this unit is speed. The lifting techniques they teach in that workshop will just slow you down. You've got the job, and I'm glad you're here. But you won't last long if you can't keep up."

Andrews was torn between following safety procedures and making a good impression on her new supervisor. At first, she made an effort to use proper lifting techniques. However, when several of her coworkers complained that she wasn't keeping up, the supervisor told Andrews to "keep up or get out of the way." Feeling the pressure, she started taking the same shortcuts she had seen her coworkers use. Positive results were immediate, and Andrews received several nods of approval from fellow workers and a "good job" from the supervisor. Before long, Andrews had won the approval and respect of her colleagues.

However, after two months of working in the loading unit, she began to experience persistent lower back pain. Andrews felt sure that her hurried lifting techniques were to blame, but she valued the approval of her supervisor and fellow workers too much to do anything that might slow her down. Finally, one day while loading a truck, Andrews fell to the pavement in pain and could not get up. Her back throbbed with intense pain, and her legs were numb. She had to be rushed to the emergency room of the local hospital. By the time Andrews checked out of the hospital a week later, she had undergone major surgery to repair two ruptured discs.

Jane Andrews's situation can be explained by the epidemiological theory of accident causation. The predisposition factor was her susceptibility to peer pressure from her coworkers and supervisor. The applicable situational factors were peer pressure and the priorities of the supervisor. These factors, taken together, caused the accident.

LIMITATIONS OF EVENT-CHAIN ACCIDENT CAUSATION THEORIES

The accident causation theories presented up to this point—Heinrich's domino, human factors, accident/incident, and epidemiological theories—all fall into the broad category of event-chain theories. Event-chain theories explain accident causation in terms of:

- Multiple events that occur in a sequence.
- Events that are linked by direct relationships between and among causal factors but ignore indirect relationships.
- Events that involve human error, component failure, and/or energy-related factors.

All of these event-chain theories have value, but they also have shortcomings that health and safety professionals should be aware of. These shortcomings include the following:

- Neglect of the broader social and organizational factors.
- Inadequate accounting for physical context, social context, personal values, or the dynamics of work processes when assessing human error.
- Neglect of the human adaptation (the tendency of more experienced workers to behave in ways that involve higher levels of risk).

The shortcomings of event-chain theories of accident causation led to the development of additional theories that attempt to take a more holistic approach to the analysis of accident causation. These additional theories are explained in the remainder of this chapter.

SYSTEMS THEORY OF ACCIDENT CAUSATION

A system is a group of regularly interacting and interrelated components that together form a unified whole. This definition is the basis for the **systems theory** of accident causation. This theory views a situation in which an accident may occur as a system comprising the following elements: person (host), machine (agency), and **environment**.[7] The likelihood of an accident occurring is determined by how these components interact. Changes in the patterns of interaction can increase or reduce the probability of an accident.

For example, an experienced employee who operates a numerically controlled five-axis machining centre in a shop environment may take a 2-week vacation. Her temporary replacement may be less experienced. This change in one component of the system (person/host) increases the probability of an accident. Such a simple example is easily understood. However, not all changes in patterns of interaction are this simple. Some are so subtle that their analysis may require a team of people, each with a different type of expertise.

The primary components of the systems model are the person-machine-environment chain, information, decisions, risks, and the task to be performed.[8] Each of the components has a bearing on the probability that an accident will occur. The systems model is illustrated in Figure 8–5.

systems theory Views a situation in which an accident may occur as a system comprising the following elements: person (host), machine (agency), and environment.

environment The aggregate of social and cultural conditions that influence the life of an individual.

Figure 8–5 Systems theory.

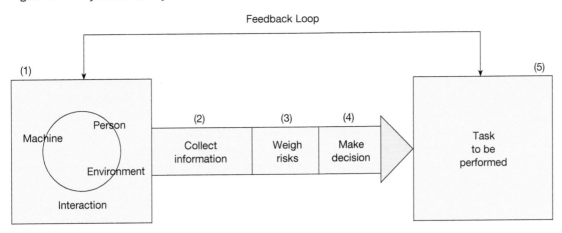

As this model shows, even as a person interacts with a machine within an environment, three activities take place between the system and the task to be performed. Every time a task must be performed, there is the risk that an accident may occur. Sometimes the risks are great; at other times, they are small. This is where information collection and decision-making come in.

Based on the information that has been collected by observing and mentally noting the current circumstances, the person weighs the risks and decides whether to perform the task under existing circumstances. For example, say a machine operator is working on a rush order that is behind schedule. An important safety device has malfunctioned on his machine. Simply taking it off will interrupt work for only five minutes, but it will also increase the probability of an accident. However, replacing it could take up to an hour. Should the operator remove the safety guard and proceed with the task or take the time to replace it? The operator and his supervisor may assess the situation (collect information), weigh the risks, and make a decision to proceed. If their information is right and their assessment of the risks accurate, the task will probably be accomplished without an accident.

However, the environment in which the machine operator is working is unusually hectic, and the pressure to complete an order that is already behind schedule is intense. These factors are **stressors** that can cloud the judgment of those collecting information, weighing risks, and making the decision. When stressors are introduced between points 1 and 3 in Figure 8–5, the likelihood of an accident increases.

For this reason, Firenzie recommends that five factors be considered before beginning the process of collecting information, weighing risks, and making a decision:

stressors Stimuli that cause stress.

- The job requirements.
- The workers' abilities and limitations.
- The gain if the task is successfully accomplished.
- The loss if the task is attempted but fails.
- The loss if the task is not attempted.[9]

These factors can help a person achieve the proper perspective before collecting information, weighing risks, and making a decision. It is particularly important to consider these factors when stressors such as noise, time constraints, or pressure from a supervisor may tend to cloud one's judgment.

Systems Theory in Practice

Precision Tooling Company (PTC) specializes in difficult orders that are produced in small lots, and in making corrections to parts that otherwise would wind up as expensive rejects in the scrap bin. In short, PTC specializes in doing the types of work that other companies cannot, or will not, do. Most of PTC's work comes in the form of subcontracts from larger manufacturing companies. Consequently, living up to its reputation as a high-performance, on-time company is important to PTC.

Because much of its work consists of small batches of parts to be reworked, PTC still uses several manually operated machines. The least experienced machinists operate these machines. This causes two problems. The first problem is that it is difficult for even a master machinist to hold to modern tolerance levels on these old machines. Consequently, apprentice machinists find holding to precise tolerances quite a challenge. The second problem is that the machines are so old that they frequently break down.

Complaints from apprentice machinists about the old machines are frequent. However, their supervisors consider time on the old "ulcer makers" to be one of the rites of passage that upstart machinists must endure. Their attitude is, "We had to do it, so why shouldn't you?" This was where things stood at PTC when the company won the Johnson contract.

PTC had been trying for years to become a preferred supplier for H. R. Johnson Company. PTC's big chance finally came when Johnson's manufacturing division incorrectly produced 10,000 copies of a critical part before noticing the problem. Simply scrapping the part and starting over was an expensive solution. Johnson's vice president for manufacturing decided to give PTC a chance.

PTC's management team was ecstatic! Finally, they had an opportunity to partner with H. R. Johnson Company. If PTC could perform well on this one, even more lucrative contracts were sure to follow. The top managers called a companywide meeting of all employees. Attendance was mandatory. The CEO explained the situation as follows:

> Ladies and gentlemen, we are faced with a great opportunity. I've just signed a contract with H. R. Johnson Company to rework 10,000 parts that their manufacturing folks produced improperly. The rework tasks are not that complicated, but every part has got to go through several manual operations at the front end of the rework process. This means our manual machining unit is going to have to supply the heroes on this job. I've promised the manufacturing VP at Johnson that we would have his parts ready in ninety days. I know that's a lot to do in so short a period of time, but Johnson is in a real bind here. If we can produce on this one, they won't forget us in the future.

This put PTC's apprentice machinists on the spot. If PTC didn't perform on this contract, it would be their fault. They cursed their old machines and got to work. The CEO had said the rework tasks would not be "that complicated," but, as it turned out, the processes weren't that simple either. The problem was tolerances. Holding to the tolerances specified in the Johnson contract took extra time and a special effort on every single part. Before long, the manual machining unit was behind schedule, and management was getting nervous. The situation was made even worse by the continual breakdowns and equipment failures experienced. The harder the unit supervisor pushed, the more stressed the employees and machines became.

Predictably, it wasn't long before safety procedures were forgotten and unreasonable risks were being taken. The pressure from management, the inexperience of the apprentice machinists, and the constant equipment failures finally took their toll. In a hurry to get back on schedule, and fearing that his machine would break down again, one machinist got careless and ran his hand into the cutter on his milling machine. By the time the machine had been shut down, his hand was badly mutilated. In the aftershock of this accident, PTC was unable to meet the agreed-upon completion schedule. Unfortunately, PTC did not make the kind of impression on H. R. Johnson's management team that it had hoped.

This accident can be explained by the systems theory. The person-machine-environment chain has a direct application in this case. The person involved was relatively inexperienced. The machine involved was old and prone to breakdowns. The environment was especially stressful and pressure-packed. These three factors, taken together, resulted in this serious and tragic accident.

COMBINATION THEORY OF ACCIDENT CAUSATION

There is often a degree of difference between any theory of accident causation and reality. The various models presented with their corresponding theories in this chapter attempt to explain why accidents occur. For some accidents, a given model may be very accurate. For others, it may be less so. Often the cause of an accident cannot be adequately explained by just one model or theory. Thus, according to the **combination theory**, the actual cause may combine parts of several different models. Safety personnel should use these theories as appropriate both for accident prevention and accident investigation. However, they should avoid the tendency to try to apply one model to all accidents.

combination theory The actual cause of an accident is best explained by combining many models.

Combination Theory in Practice

Crestview Grain Corporation (CGC) maintains ten large silos for storing corn, rice, wheat, barley, and various other grains. Because stored grain generates fine dust and gases, ventilation of the silos is important. Consequently, all of CGC's silos have several large vents. Each of these vents uses a filter, similar to the type used in home air conditioners, that must be changed periodically.

There is an element of risk involved in changing the vent filters because of two potential hazards. The first hazard comes from unvented dust and gases that can make breathing difficult, or even dangerous. The second hazard is the silo itself. Each silo has a catwalk that runs around its inside circumference near the top. These catwalks give employees access to the vents that are also near the top of each silo. The catwalks are almost 30 metres (100 feet) above ground level, they are narrow, and the guardrails on them are only knee high. A fall from a catwalk into the grain below would probably be fatal.

Consequently, CGC has well-defined rules that employees are to follow when changing filters. Because these rules are strictly enforced, there had never been an accident in one of CGC's silos—that is, not until the Juan Perez tragedy occurred. Perez was not new to the company. At the time of his accident, he had worked at CGC for over five years. However, he was new to the job of silo maintenance. His inexperience, as it turned out, would prove fatal.

It was time to change the vent filters in silo number 4. Perez had never changed vent filters himself. He hadn't been in the job long enough. However, he had served as the required "second man" when his supervisor, Bao Chu Lai, had changed the filters in silos 1, 2, and 3. Because Chu Lai was at home recuperating from heart surgery and would be out for another 4 weeks, Perez decided to change the filters himself. Changing the filters was a simple enough task, and Perez had always thought the second-man concept was overdoing it a little. He believed in taking reasonable precautions as much as the next person, but in his opinion, CGC was paranoid about safety.

Perez collected his safety harness, respirator, and four new vent filters. Then he climbed the external ladder to the entrance-exit platform near the top of silo number 4. Before going in, Perez donned his respirator and strapped on his safety harness. Opening the hatch cover, he stepped inside the silo onto the catwalk. Following procedure, Perez attached a lifeline to his safety harness, picked up the new vent filters, and headed for the first vent. He changed the first two filters without incident. It was while he was changing the third filter that tragedy struck.

The filter in the third vent was wedged in tightly. After several attempts to pull it out, Perez became frustrated and gave the filter a good jerk. When the filter suddenly broke loose, the momentum propelled Perez backward and he toppled off the catwalk. At first it appeared that his lifeline would hold, but without a second person to pull him up or call for help, Perez was suspended by only the lifeline for over twenty minutes. He finally panicked, and in his struggle to pull himself up, knocked open the buckle of his safety harness. The buckle gave way, and Perez fell over 15 metres (50 feet) into the grain below. The impact knocked off his respirator, the grain quickly enveloped him, and Perez was asphyxiated.

The accident investigation that followed revealed that several factors combined to cause the fatal accident. The factors that contributed to the silo number 4 accident may be identified by applying any of the previously discussed causation theories, hence the combination theory. The most critical of these factors were as follows:

- Absence of the supervisor.
- Inexperience of Perez.
- A conscious decision by Perez to disregard CGC's safety procedures.
- A faulty buckling mechanism on the safety harness.
- An unsafe design (only a knee-high guardrail on the catwalk).

"All accidents, one way or another, are the result of human error."

"No, accidents are the result of a combination of things. I like the combination theory."

"You're both wrong. Accidents are best explained by the domino theory."

So the debate went in Dr. Jameson's class at Burton University. What is your opinion concerning the various theories of accident causation?

BEHAVIOURAL THEORY OF ACCIDENT CAUSATION

The behavioural theory of accident causation and prevention is often referred to as *behaviour-based safety* (BBS). BBS has both proponents and critics. One of the most prominent proponents of BBS is E. Scott Geller, a senior partner of Safety Performance Solutions, Inc. and a professor of psychology.

According to Geller, there are seven basic principles of BBS:

1. Intervention that is focused on employee behaviour.

2. Identification of external factors that will help understand and improve employee behaviour (from the perspective of safety in the workplace).

3. Direction of behaviour with activators or events antecedent to the desired behaviour, and motivation of the employee to behave as desired with incentives and rewards that will follow the desired behaviour.

4. Focus on the positive consequences that will result from the desired behaviour as a way to motivate employees.

5. Application of the scientific method to improve attempts at behavioural interventions.

6. Use of theory to integrate information rather than to limit possibilities.

7. Planned interventions designed with the feelings and attitudes of the individual employee in mind.[10]

Those who have studied psychology will recognize BBS as an innovative and practical application of standard behavioural theory to the field of occupational safety. These theories are relevant in any situation in which certain types of human behaviours are desired while others are to be avoided. Positive reinforcement in the form of incentives and rewards is used to promote the desired (safe) behaviours.

Behavioural Theory in Practice

Mark Potter is the safety manager for Excello Corporation. Several months ago, he became concerned because employees seemed to have developed a lax attitude toward wearing hard hats. What troubled Potter was that there is more than the usual potential for head injuries because of the type of work done in Excello's plant, and he had personally witnessed two near misses in less than a week. An advocate of behaviour-based safety (BBS), he decided to apply this model in turning this unsafe behaviour pattern around.

His first step was to remove all of the old "Hard Hat Area" signs from the plant and replace them with newer, more noticeable signs. Then he scheduled a brief seminar on head injuries and cycled all employees through it over a 2-week period. The seminar took an unusual approach. It told a story of two employees. One was in a hospital bed surrounded by family members he did not even recognize. The other was shown enjoying a family outing with happy family members. The clear message of the video was "the difference between these two employees is a hard hat." These two activities were the antecedents to the behaviour he hoped to produce (all employees wearing hard hats when in a hard hat area).

The video contained a powerful message and it had the desired effect. Within days, employees were once again disciplining themselves to wear their hard hats (the desired behaviour). The consequence was that near misses stopped and no head injuries have occurred at Excello in months. The outcome of this is that Excello's employees have been able to continue enjoying the fruits of their labour and the company of loved ones.

SUMMARY

1. The domino theory of accident causation was one of the earliest developed. The theory posits that injuries result from a series of consecutive factors, one of which is an accident. The theory is operationalized in ten statements called the Axioms of Industrial Safety. According to this theory, there are five factors in the sequence of events leading to an accident: ancestry and social environment, fault of person, unsafe act/mechanical or physical hazard, accident, and injury.

2. The human factors theory of accident causation attributes accidents to a chain of events ultimately caused by human error. It consists of three broad factors that lead to human error: overload, inappropriate response, and inappropriate activities.

3. The accident/incident theory of accident causation is an extension of the human factors theory. It introduces such new elements as ergonomic traps, the decision to err, and systems failures.

4. The epidemiological theory of accident causation holds that the models used for studying and determining the relationships between environmental factors and disease can be used to study the causal relationships between environmental factors and accidents.

5. The systems theory of accident causation views any situation in which an accident may occur as a system with three components: person (host), machine (agency), and environment.

6. The combination theory of accident causation posits that no one model or theory can explain all accidents. Factors from two or more models may be part of the cause.

7. There are seven principles of behaviour-based safety: intervention; identification of external factors; motivation to behave in the desired manner; focus on the positive consequences of appropriate behaviour; application of the scientific method; integration of information; and planned interventions.

Key Terms and Concepts

Accident/incident theory	Environment	Inappropriate activities
Ancestry	Environmental factors	Inappropriate response
Causal relationship	Epidemiological theory	Industrial hygiene
Central factor	Ergonomic traps	Internal factors
Combination theory	Hazardous condition	Overload
Domino theory	Human error	Preceding factors
	Human factors theory	

Predispositional	Situational factors	Systems theory
characteristics	Social environment	Unsafe act
Situational characteristics	Stressors	Unsafe behaviour

Review Questions

1. Explain the domino theory of accident causation, including its origin and its impact on more modern theories.

2. What were the findings of Herbert W. Heinrich's 1920s study of the causes of industrial accidents?

3. List five of Heinrich's Axioms of Industrial Safety.

4. Explain the following concepts in the domino theory: preceding factor, central factor.

5. What are the three broad factors that lead to human error in the human factors theory? Briefly explain each.

6. Explain the systems failure component of the accident/incident theory.

7. What are the key components of the epidemiological theory? How does their interaction affect accident causation?

8. Explain the systems theory of accident causation.

9. What impact do stressors have in the systems theory?

10. List five factors to consider before making workplace decisions that involve risk.

11. Explain the principles of behaviour-based safety.

Weblinks

Workplace Safety & Prevention Services (WSPS)

http://www.wsps.ca

Industrial Accident Prevention Association (IAPA), Farm Safety Association (FSA), and Ontario Service Safety Alliance (OSSA), amalgamated on January 1, 2010, into a new health and safety organization, Workplace Safety & Prevention Services (WSPS). The site contains numerous safety resources and links for members and the public.

Institute for Work & Health

www.iwh.on.ca/about/who.php

The Institute for Work & Health is an independent, not-for-profit organization whose mission is to conduct and share research with workers, labour organizations, employers, clinicians, and policy makers to promote, protect, and improve the health of working people.

NASA

www.hq.nasa.gov/office/codeq/accident/accident.pdf

This NASA website gives the viewer a lighthearted look at accidents and their cause.

Endnotes

[1] H. W. Heinrich, D. Petersen, and N. Roos. *Industrial Accident Prevention*, 5th ed. (New York: McGraw-Hill, 1980).

[2] Ibid.

[3] Ibid.

[4] Ibid.

[5] Ibid.

[6] M. A. Topf. "Chicken/Egg/Chegg!" *Occupational Health and Safety* 68, no. 6 (June 1999): 60–66.

[7] D. L. Goetsch. *Implementing Total Safety Management* (Upper Saddle River, NJ: Prentice Hall, 1998), 227.

[8] Ibid.

[9] Ibid.

[10] E. S. Geller. "Behavior-Based Safety: Confusion, Controversy, and Clarification." *Occupational Health and Safety* 68, no. 1 (January 1999): 40–49.

Chapter 9
Accident Investigation and Reporting

Dan Hartshorn defines an accident as "any unplanned event that causes injury, illness, property damage or harmful disruption of work process."[1]

When an accident occurs, it is important that it be investigated thoroughly. The results of a comprehensive accident report can help health and safety professionals pinpoint the cause of the accident. This information can then be used to prevent future accidents, which is the primary purpose of accident investigation.

The Society of Manufacturing Engineers describes the importance of thoroughly investigating accidents:

> The primary reason for investigating an accident is not to identify a scapegoat, but to determine the cause of the accident. The investigation concentrates on gathering factual information about the details that led to the accident. If investigations are conducted properly, there is the added benefit of uncovering problems that did not directly lead to the accident. This information benefits the ongoing effort of reducing the likelihood of accidents. As problems are revealed during the investigation, action items and improvements that can prevent similar accidents from happening in the future will be easier to identify than at any time.[2]

This chapter gives prospective and practising health and safety professionals the information they need to conduct thorough, effective accident investigations and prepare comprehensive accident reports.

TYPES OF ACCIDENT INVESTIGATIONS

There are *accident reports* and there are *accident-analysis reports*. An **accident report** is completed when the accident in question represents only a minor incident. It answers the following questions: *who, what, where,* and *when.* However, it does not answer the *why* question.[3] An accident report can be completed by a person with very little formal investigation and reporting training or experience. Supervisors often complete accident reports that, in turn, might be used later as part one of a more in-depth accident report.

An **accident-analysis report** is completed when the accident in question is serious. This level of report should answer the same questions as the regular accident report plus one more—*why.* Consequently, it involves a formal accident analysis. The analysis is undertaken for the purpose of determining the root cause of the accident. Accident analysis requires special skills and should be undertaken only by an individual with those skills. There are two reasons for this: First, the accident analysis must identify the actual root cause or the company will expend resources treating only symptoms or, even worse, solving the wrong problem. Second, serious accidents are always accompanied by the potential for litigation. If there might be legal action as a result of an accident, it is important to have a professional conduct the investigation, even if it means bringing in an outside consultant.

How can health and safety professionals determine when an accident report is sufficient and when an accident-analysis report is called for?

Accident reports are called for when the accident in question is a minor incident that did *not* result in any of the following circumstances: death, loss of consciousness, medical treatment beyond first aid, more than one additional day of lost work beyond the day of the accident, or any kind of modifications to the injured employee's work duties beyond those that might occur on the day of the accident.

Accident-analysis reports are called for when any of the following circumstances result from the accident in question: death, loss of consciousness, professional medical treatment beyond first aid, one or more days of lost work beyond the day of the accident, or any modifications to the injured employee's work duties beyond those that might occur on the day of the injury.

WHEN TO INVESTIGATE

Of course, the first thing to do when an accident takes place is to implement emergency procedures. This involves bringing the situation under control and caring for the injured worker. As soon as all emergency procedures have been accomplished, the accident investigation should begin. Waiting too long to complete an investigation can harm the results. This is an important rule of thumb to remember. Another is that *all* accidents, no matter how small, should be investigated. Evidence suggests that the same factors that cause minor accidents cause major accidents.[4] Further, a near miss should be treated like an accident and investigated thoroughly.

There are several reasons why it is important to conduct investigations immediately. First, immediate investigations are more likely to produce accurate information. Conversely, the longer the time span between an accident and an investigation, the greater the likelihood of important facts becoming blurred as memories fade. Second, it is important to collect information before the accident scene is changed and before witnesses begin comparing notes. Human nature encourages people to change their stories to agree with those of other witnesses.[5] Finally, an immediate investigation is evidence of management's commitment to preventing future accidents. An immediate response shows that management cares.[6]

WHAT TO INVESTIGATE

The purpose of an **accident investigation** is to collect facts. It is not to find fault. It is important that health and safety professionals make this distinction known to all involved. Fault-finding can cause reticence among witnesses who have valuable information to share. Causes of the accident should be the primary focus. The investigation should be guided by the following words: *who, what, when, where, why,* and *how.*

accident investigation The process of collecting facts to determine the cause of an accident.

This does not mean that mistakes and breaches of precautionary procedures by workers are not noted. Rather, when these things are noted, they are recorded as facts instead of faults. CCOHS takes this approach:

> A difficulty that has bothered many investigators is the idea that one does not want to lay blame. However, when a thorough worksite accident investigation reveals that some person or persons among management, supervisor, and the workers were apparently at fault, then this fact should be pointed out. The intention here is to remedy the situation, not to discipline an individual.
>
> Failing to point out human failings that contributed to an accident will not only downgrade the quality of the investigation. Furthermore, it will also allow future accidents to happen from similar causes because they have not been addressed.[7]

In attempting to find the facts and identify causes, certain questions should be asked regardless of the nature of the accident. The Society of Manufacturing Engineers recommends using the following questions when conducting accident investigations:

- What type of work was the injured person doing?
- Exactly what was the injured person doing or trying to do at the time of the accident?
- Was the injured person proficient in the task being performed at the time of the accident? Had the worker received proper training?
- Was the injured person authorized to use the equipment or perform the process involved in the accident?
- Were there other workers present at the time of the accident? If so, who are they, and what were they doing?
- Was the task in question being performed according to properly approved procedures?
- Was the proper equipment being used, including personal protective equipment?
- Was the injured employee new to the job?
- Was the process, equipment, or system involved new?
- Was the injured person being supervised at the time of the accident?
- Are there any established safety rules or procedures that were clearly not being followed?
- Where did the accident take place?
- What was the condition of the accident site at the time of the accident?
- Has a similar accident occurred before? If so, were corrective measures recommended? Were they implemented?
- Are there obvious solutions that would have prevented the accident?[8]

The answers to these questions should be carefully and copiously recorded. You may find it helpful to dictate your findings into a digital recorder. This approach allows you to focus more time and energy on investigating and less on taking written notes.

Regardless of how the findings are recorded, it is important to be thorough. What may seem like a minor unrelated fact at the moment could turn out to be a valuable fact later when all of the evidence has been collected and is being analyzed.

Common Causes of Accidents

Hartshorn places many of the common causes of accidents in the following categories: personal beliefs and feelings, decision to work unsafely, mismatch or overload, systems failures, traps, unsafe conditions, and unsafe acts.[9] The common causes in each of these categories can help investigators determine the root cause of an accident.

1. *Personal beliefs and feelings.* Causes in this category include the following: individual did not believe the accident would happen to him or her; individual was working too fast, showing off, or being a know-it-all; individual ignored the rules out of contempt for authority and rules in general; individual gave in to peer pressure; and individual had personal problems that clouded his or her judgment.

2. *Decision to work unsafely.* Some people, for a variety of reasons, feel it is in their best interests or to their benefit to work unsafely. Hence, they make a conscious decision to do so.

3. *Mismatch or overload.* Causes in this category include the following: individual is in poor physical condition; individual is fatigued; individual has a high stress level; individual is mentally unfocused or distracted; the task required is too complex or difficult; the task required is boring; the physical environment is stressful (e.g., excessive noise, heat, dust, or other factors); the work in question is very demanding—even for an individual in good physical condition; and individual has a negative attitude (e.g., hostile, uncooperative, apathetic, etc.).

4. *Systems failure.* Causes in this category consist of the various errors management makes that are not grossly negligent or serious and willful. Common causes in this category include lack of a clear policy; lack of rules, regulations, and procedures; poor hiring procedures; inadequate monitoring and inspections; failure to correct known hazards; insufficient training for employees; rules that are in place but are not enforced; no rewarding or reinforcement of safe behaviour; inadequate tools and equipment provided; production requirements set too high; inadequate communication to employees of safety concerns, statistics, and rules; poor safety management; no or insufficient job safety analysis; and insufficient management support for safety.

5. *Traps.* Poor design of workstations and processes can create traps that, in turn, lead to unsafe behaviour. Common causes in this category include defective equipment; failure to provide, maintain, and replace proper personal protective equipment; failure to train employees in the proper use of their personal protective equipment; overly complicated and confusing controls; poorly laid-out work area; mechanical lifting equipment that is inadequate for the jobs required of it; uncontrolled hazards that might lead to slips and falls; excessive reaching, bending, stooping, and twisting; excessive contact pressure, vibration, or force; awkward postures that result from poor workstation or tool design; excessive temperature extremes; insufficient lighting; and insufficient ventilation.

6. *Unsafe conditions.* Common causes in this category include the following: unsafe condition created by the person injured in the accident; unsafe condition created by a fellow employee; unsafe condition created by a third party; unsafe condition created by management; unsafe condition knowingly overlooked by management; and unsafe condition created by the elements (e.g., rain, sun, snow, ice, wind, darkness, etc.).

7. *Unsafe acts.* Common causes in this category include the following: individual chooses to ignore the rules; people are involved in horseplay or fighting; individual uses drugs or alcohol; individual uses unauthorized tools or equipment; individual chooses an improper work method; individual fails to ask for information or other resources needed to do the job safely; individual forgets a rule, regulation, or procedure; individual does not pay proper attention; and individual uses improper body mechanics.

WHO SHOULD INVESTIGATE

Who should conduct the accident investigation? Should it be the immediate supervisor? The health and safety professional? A higher-level manager? An outside specialist? There is no simple answer to this question, and there is disagreement among professional people of goodwill.

The legal requirements for participation in an accident investigation vary slightly throughout each jurisdiction. Ontario, for example, requires that a designated committee member or worker representative investigate all accidents that result in a **critical injury** or fatality. In some companies, the supervisor of the injured worker conducts the investigation. In others, a health and safety professional performs the job. Some companies form an investigative team; others bring in outside specialists. There are several reasons for the various approaches used. Factors considered in deciding how to approach accident investigations include:

critical injury Injury in which a specified degree of seriousness has been reached. The specific requirements for classifying an injury as "critical" are provided in the statutes of some jurisdictions.

- Size of the company.
- Structure of the company's health and safety program.
- Type of accident.
- Seriousness of the accident.
- Technical complexity.
- Number of times that similar accidents have occurred.
- Company's management philosophy.
- Company's commitment to health and safety.

CONDUCTING THE INVESTIGATION

The questions in the previous section summarize what to look for when conducting accident investigations. Figure 9–1 lists five steps to follow in conducting an accident investigation.[10] These steps are explained in the following paragraphs.

Figure 9–1 Steps in conducting an accident investigation.

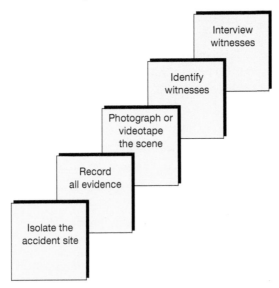

Isolate the Accident Scene

You may have seen a crime scene that was sealed off by the police. The entire area surrounding such a scene is typically blocked off by barriers or yellow tape. This is done to keep curious onlookers from removing, disturbing, or unknowingly destroying vital evidence.

This same approach should be used when conducting an accident investigation. As soon as emergency procedures have been completed and the injured worker has been removed, the accident scene should be isolated until all pertinent evidence has been collected or observed and recorded. Further, nothing but the injured worker should be removed from the scene. If necessary, a security guard should be posted to maintain the integrity of the **accident scene**. The purpose of isolating the scene is to maintain, as closely as, possible the conditions that existed at the time of the accident.

accident scene   The area where an accident occurred.

Record All Evidence

It is important to make a permanent record of all pertinent evidence as quickly as possible. There are three reasons for this: (1) Certain types of evidence may be perishable; (2) the longer an accident scene must be isolated, the more likely it is that evidence will be disturbed, knowingly or unknowingly; and (3) if the isolated scene contains a critical piece of equipment or a critical component in a larger process, pressure will quickly mount to get it back in operation. Evidence can be recorded in a variety of ways, including written notes, sketches, photography, videotape, dictated observations, and diagrams. In deciding what to record, a good rule of thumb is *if in doubt, record it.* It is better to record too much than to skip evidence that may be needed later after the accident scene has been disturbed.

Photograph or Record Video of the Scene

This step is actually an extension of the previous step. Health and safety professionals should be proficient in the operation of any photography or video recording equipment being used. Most cell phones have high resolution cameras that will be adequate and allow the images to be transmitted immediately if needed for review in or from remote locations. It is important to provide context to the scene or item being captured. It is a good practice to take photographs and video at different angles and use a common item in the photo, such as coins, a ruler, or a hand, for scale. As with the previous step, a good rule of thumb in photographing and video recording is *if in doubt, shoot it.* When recording evidence, it is better to have more shots than necessary than to risk missing a vital piece of evidence.

primary witness   An eyewitness to an accident.

secondary witness   Someone who was present at the scene of an accident but did not actually see the accident.

tertiary witness   Someone who may have information that is relevant to an accident investigation although they were not present when the accident happened.

Identify Witnesses

In identifying witnesses, it is important to compile a witness list. Names on the list should be recorded in three categories: (1) **primary witnesses,** (2) **secondary witnesses,** and (3) **tertiary witnesses** (Figure 9–2). When compiling the witness list, ask employees to provide names of all three types of witnesses.

Figure 9–2   Categories of accident witnesses.

- Primary witnesses are eyewitnesses to the accident.
- Secondary witnesses are witnesses who did not actually see the accident happen but were in the vicinity and arrived on the scene immediately or very shortly after the accident.
- Tertiary witnesses are witnesses who were not present at the time of the accident or afterward but may still have relevant evidence to present (e.g., an employee who had complained earlier about a problem with the machine involved in the accident).

Interview Witnesses

Every witness on the list should be interviewed, preferably in the following order: primary witnesses first, secondary next, and tertiary last. After all witnesses have been interviewed, it may be necessary to re-interview witnesses for clarification or corroboration. Interviewing witnesses is such a specialized process that the next section is devoted to it.

INTERVIEWING WITNESSES

The techniques used for interviewing accident witnesses are designed to ensure that the information is objective, accurate, as untainted by the personal opinions and feelings of witnesses as possible, and able to be corroborated. For this reason, it is important to understand the *when, where,* and *how* of interviewing the accident witnesses.

When to Interview

Immediacy is important. Interviews should begin as soon as the witness list has been compiled and, once begun, should proceed expeditiously. There are two main reasons for this. First, a witness's recollections will be best right after the accident. The more time that elapses between the accident and the interview, the more blurred the witness's memory will become. Second, immediacy avoids the possibility of witnesses comparing notes and, as a result, changing their stories. This is just human nature, but it is a tendency that can undermine the value of testimony given and, in turn, the facts collected. Recommendations based on questionable facts are not likely to be valid. Also, witnesses should be interviewed individually and privately, preferably before they have talked to one another.

Where to Interview

The best place to interview is at the accident scene. If this is not possible, interviews should take place in a private setting elsewhere. It is important to ensure that all distractions are removed, interruptions are guarded against, and the witness is not accompanied by other witnesses. All persons interviewed should be allowed to relate their recollections without fear of contradiction or influence by other witnesses or employees. It is also important to select a neutral location in which witnesses will feel comfortable. Avoid the **principal's office syndrome** by selecting a location that is not likely to be intimidating to witnesses.

principal's office syndrome When an accident witness is unable to communicate freely about what they saw because he or she is intimidated or uncomfortable in the interview situation.

How to Interview

The key to getting at the facts is to put the witness at ease and to listen. Listen to what is said, how it is said, and what is not said. Ask questions that will get at the information listed earlier in this chapter, but phrase them in an **open-ended** format. For example, instead of asking, "Did you see the victim pull the red lever?" phrase your question as follows: "Tell me what you saw." Don't lead witnesses with your questions or influence them with gestures, facial expressions, tone of voice, or any other form of nonverbal communication. Interrupt only if absolutely necessary to seek clarification on a critical point. Remain nonjudgmental and objective.

open-ended Questions that do not lead the witness to give certain answers or suggest any prejudgment of the answers.

>>> **SAFETY FACT** | Where to Conduct Accident Interviews

To ensure that employees are willing to give accurate information, health and safety professionals should conduct accident interviews in the privacy of their office. Right? Not necessarily. Experience has shown that the best way to promote accuracy is to interview witnesses at the site of the accident. This puts the accident interview in context in a setting that will help stimulate the memory. To ensure privacy and confidentiality, interview witnesses one at a time at the accident site.

The information being sought in an accident investigation can be summarized as *who*, *what*, *when*, *where*, *why*, and *how* (Figure 9–3). As information is given, it may be necessary to take notes. If you can keep your note-taking to a minimum during the interview, your chances of getting uninhibited information are increased. Note-taking can distract and even frighten a witness.

Figure 9–3 Questions to ask when interviewing witnesses.

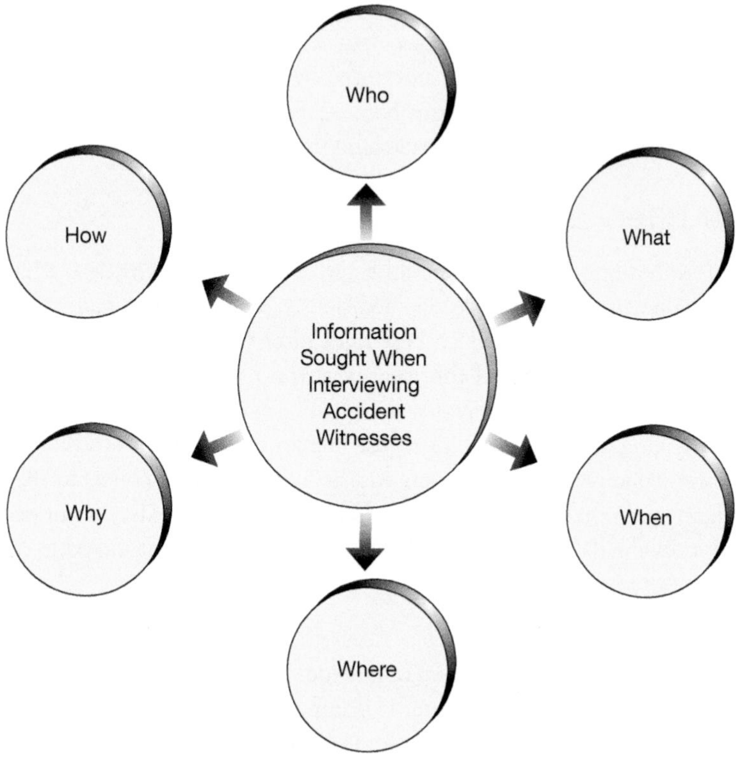

An effective technique is to listen during the interview and make mental notes of critical information. At the end of the interview, summarize what you have heard and have the witness verify your summary. After the witness leaves, develop your notes immediately.

A question that sometimes arises is, "Why not record the interview?" Health and safety professionals disagree on the effectiveness and advisability of taping. Those who favour recording claim it allows the interviewer to concentrate on listening without having to worry about forgetting a key point or having to interrupt the witnesses to jot down critical information. It also preserves everything that is said for the record, as well as the tone of voice in which it is said. A complete transcript of the interview also ensures that information is not taken out of context.

Those opposed say that recording devices tend to inhibit witnesses so that they are not as forthcoming as they would be without recording. Recording also slows down the investigation while the recorded interview is transcribed and the interviewer wades through voluminous testimony trying to separate critical information from irrelevant information.

In any case, if the interview is to be recorded, the following rules should be applied:

- Use the smallest, most unobtrusive recording device available, such as digital recorder or cell phone.

- Inform the witness that the interview will be recorded.

- Make sure the recording device is working properly and has enough storage for the interview.

- Take time at the beginning of the interview to discuss unrelated matters long enough to put the witness at ease and overcome the presence of the recording device.
- Make sure that personnel are available to transcribe the recording immediately.
- Read the transcripts as soon as they are available and highlight critical information.

An effective technique to use with eyewitnesses is to ask them to re-enact the accident for you. Of course, the effectiveness of this technique is enhanced if the re-enactment can take place at the accident site. However, even when this is not possible, an eyewitness re-enactment can yield valuable information.

In using the **re-enactment** technique, a word of caution is in order. If an eyewitness does exactly what the victim did, there may be another accident. Have the eyewitnesses explain what they are going to do before letting them do it. Then, have them *simulate* rather than actually *perform* the steps that led up to the accident.

re-enactment A technique in which a witness to an accident goes through the same set of actions as the accident victim in order to demonstrate what happened. The witness should simulate the actions rather than actually performing them or there may be another accident.

REPORTING ACCIDENTS

An accident investigation should culminate in a comprehensive accident report. The purpose of the report is to record the findings of the accident investigation, the cause or causes of the accident, and recommendations for corrective action.

>>> SAFETY FACT Management Is the Cause

One of the most difficult situations that a health and safety professional will face is when an investigation reveals that management—through action or inaction—is the root cause of an accident. How does the health and safety professional look management in the eye and say, "You are at fault"? Remember two things when facing such a situation. First, focus on the *condition* that led to the accident rather than whose action or inaction caused the condition. You want the condition corrected, and you don't want a higher manager wasting time and effort covering up. Second, be tactful. Remember, tact means "driving in the nail without breaking the board." By handling such situations in this way, you may achieve two good things: (1) A hazardous condition will be corrected, and (2) you will win an important ally.

Reporting requirements vary among the Canadian jurisdictions; however, there are similarities and common principles applied throughout. The most important step is to get first aid or medical treatment. Complete the reporting forms required by your employer and notify the treating physician, if you see one, that the injury was work-related. Each jurisdiction has prescribed reporting requirements and definitions of "serious" or reportable injuries and incidents. The employer is usually required to notify the WCB and/or the government ministry responsible within 2 or 3 days if a "serious injury" has occurred. All injuries and illnesses should be recorded, regardless of severity, if they result in the worker seeking medical help, sustaining a lost time injury, or being unable to perform their usual work. Check the local reporting requirements for your jurisdiction.

Accident report forms vary from company to company. However, the information contained in them is fairly standard. Regardless of the type of form used, an accident report should contain at least the information needed to meet the record-keeping requirements set forth by the local statutes.

In addition to these items, you may want to record such additional information as the list of witnesses; dates, times, and places of interviews; historical data relating to similar accidents; information about related corrective actions that were made previously but had not yet been followed up on; and any other information that might be relevant. Figure 9–4 is an example of a generic accident report form from the Industrial Accident Prevention Association (IAPA).

Figure 9–4 Accident investigation report form.

Accident / Incident Investigation Report

Identification

Name: _____ Department: _____ Position: _____

Address: _____

Description of Accident

Date of Incident: _____ Time of incident: _____ Location of Incident: _____.

Classification of Injury: ___ Hazard Only ___ No Injury ___ First Aid ___ Health Care ___ Lost Time

Type of Accident: 1. ___ Struck Against 2. ___ Struck By 3. ___ Caught In, On or Between 4. ___ Slip, Trip or Fall

  5. ___ Strain / Sprain 6. ___ Exposure 7. ___ Explosion 8. ___ Other _____

Describe the Event: _____

_____

_____

_____

_____

_____

_____

_____

Employee's Signature _____ Supervisor's Signature _____

Cause Analysis

Describe the immediate cause of the accident. E.g., what actions or conditions caused the accident?

_____

_____

Describe the root cause of the accident. E.g., what personal, environmental, personal or job factors contributed to the accident?

_____

_____

_____

Corrective Action

What remedial actions are required to control the conditions listed above, and to prevent similar events from occurring?

_____

_____

_____

"Find out who is at fault and get rid of him," demanded the CEO. "I'm not going to have a careless employee running up our health care costs. It's tough enough trying to make a profit without some careless employee causing accidents. There will be a lawsuit, just you wait and see. We are going to be sued!" Travis Boucher, Penson Processing Company's safety director, bit his tongue and just listened. He had learned to let his boss vent before making a counterproposal. When the time seemed right, Boucher said, "Sir, if we focus on finding an employee to blame, it's just going to make matters worse. I'll never get to the root of it that way." Whose approach is best in this case? What is your opinion?

Why Some Accidents Are Not Reported

In spite of the legal requirements and the benefits of statistical data that is accumulated, there are several reasons why some accidents go unreported. Be familiar with these reasons so that you can do your part to overcome them. Cunningham and Kane list the main reasons as follows:

1. **Red tape.** Some people see the paperwork involved in accident reporting as red tape and, therefore, don't report accidents just to avoid paperwork.

2. **Ignorance.** Not all managers and supervisors are as knowledgeable as they should be about the reasons for accident reporting.

3. **Embarrassment.** Occasionally, people do not report an accident because they are embarrassed by their part in it. A supervisor who did not properly supervise or a manager who has not provided the proper training for employees may be embarrassed to file a report.

4. **Record-spoiling.** Some accidents go unreported just to preserve a safety record, such as the record for days worked without an accident.

5. **Fear of repercussions.** Some accidents go unreported because the people involved are afraid of being found at fault, being labelled accident prone, or being subjected to other negative repercussions.

6. **No feedback.** Some accidents go unreported because those involved feel that filing a report is a waste of time. This typically happens when management does not respond to recommendations made in earlier accident reports.[11]

Clearly, these reasons for not reporting accidents present health and safety professionals with a challenge. To overcome these inhibitors, it is necessary to develop a simple reporting system that will not be viewed as too much bureaucratic paperwork to have to do. Health and safety professionals must educate personnel at all levels concerning the purpose of accident reporting and why it is important. An important step is to communicate that fault-finding is not the purpose. Another important step is to follow up to ensure that recommendations are acted on or that employees are made aware of why they aren't. This helps to ensure the integrity of the process.

Discipline and Accident Reporting

Fault-finding is not the purpose of an accident investigation. However, an investigation sometimes reveals that an employee has violated or simply overlooked safety regulations. Should such violations be condoned? According to Kane and Cunningham,

> Many companies condone nonconformance to safety rules as long as no injury results. However, if the nonconformance results in an accident involving an injury, the disciplinary boom is promptly lowered. This inconsistency inevitably leads to resentment and failure to report accidents and a hiding of accident problems.[12]

There is a built-in dilemma here that modern health and safety professionals must be prepared to handle. On the one hand, it is important that fault-finding not be seen as the purpose of an accident investigation. Such a perception limits the amount of information that can be collected. On the other hand, if those workers whose behaviour leads to accidents are not disciplined, the credibility of the safety program is undermined. Kane and Cunningham recommend the following procedures for handling this dilemma: *Never* discipline an employee because he or she had an accident. *Always* discipline employees for noncompliance with safety regulations.[13]

Such an approach applied with consistency will help maintain the integrity of both the accident investigation process and the overall safety program.

TEN ACCIDENT INVESTIGATION MISTAKES TO AVOID

The amount of information you collect and how you collect it will go a long way toward determining how effective your resultant corrective actions will be after a workplace accident. According to William R. Coffee Jr., health and safety professionals should avoid the following commonly made mistakes when investigating accidents.

1. **Failing to investigate near misses.** A near miss is simply an accident that did not happen because of luck. Consequently, investigating near misses can reveal critical accident prevention information.

2. **Taking ineffective corrective action.** Ineffective corrective action is often the result of a cursory accident investigation. When investigating, look for the root cause, not the symptoms. Corrective action based on symptoms will not prevent future accidents.

3. **Allowing your biases to colour the results of the investigation.** Look for facts and be objective when investigating an accident. Do not make assumptions or jump to conclusions. One of the best ways to eliminate bias in accident investigations is to use a standard, structured routine and to skip no steps in the routine.

4. **Failing to investigate in a timely manner.** Accident investigations should begin as soon as possible after the accident. The longer you wait to begin, the more likely it is that evidence will be lost, corrupted, or compromised. For example, once people start talking to one another about what they saw, invariably their memories will be shaped by the opinions of their fellow workers and witnesses. People walking through an accident scene can compromise the integrity of the scene by unwittingly destroying evidence.

5. **Failing to account for human nature when conducting interviews.** Often what those involved in an accident as well as witnesses to an accident will say during an interview will be shaped by their desire to escape blame, deflect blame to someone else, or protect a friend. This is why it is important to interview witnesses and others involved privately and individually, and to look for corroborating evidence to support (or refute) their input.

6. **Failing to learn investigation techniques.** Before investigating an accident, health and safety professionals should complete specialized training or undertake self-study to learn investigation techniques such as those presented in this chapter. An unskilled investigator is not likely to conduct a valid investigation.

7. **Allowing politics to enter into an investigation.** The goal of an investigation is and must be to identify the root cause so that appropriate corrective action can be taken. Personal likes, dislikes, favoritism, and office politics will corrupt an investigation from the outset.

8. **Failing to conduct an in-depth investigation.** Everyone is in a hurry and investigating an accident was not on your agenda for the day. In addition, there is sometimes pressure from higher management to "get this thing behind us." Such pressures and

circumstances can lead to a rushed investigation in which the goal is to get it over with, not to find the root cause of the accident. Surface-level investigations almost ensure that the same type of accident will happen again.

9. **Allowing conflicting goals to enter into an investigation.** The ultimate goal of an accident investigation is to prevent future accidents and injuries. However, even when that is your goal, there may be other people who have different goals. Some may see the investigation as an opportunity to deflect blame, others may see it as an opportunity to protect the organization from litigation, and some may see it as a way to explain not meeting production quotas or performance standards. Health and safety professionals should be aware that other agendas may be in play every time an accident investigation is conducted. For this reason, objectivity, structure, and routine are critical.

10. **Failing to account for the effects of uncooperative people.** One would think that employees and management personnel would automatically want to cooperate in accident investigation to ensure that similar accidents are prevented in the future. Unfortunately, this is not always the case. People will not always cooperate for a variety of reasons—all growing out of the concept of perceived self-interest. Further, the lack of cooperation will not always be overt. In fact, often it will be covert (for example, a person you need to interview keeps putting you off or cancelling meetings). Health and safety professionals need to understand that self-interest is one of the most powerful motivators of human beings and factor this into their planning for accident investigations.[14]

These ten mistakes will probably never be completely eliminated from every accident investigation. However, if health and safety professionals are aware of them, they can at least ensure that such mistakes are minimized. The fewer of these mistakes that are made during an accident investigation, the better the quality of the investigation and the more likely that it will lead to effective corrective action.

SUMMARY

1. Accidents are investigated for the purpose of identifying causal factors that could lead to other accidents if not corrected. The purpose is not to assign blame.

2. There are accident reports and accident-analysis reports. The latter attempt to determine *why* and should be completed by a professional.

3. It is important to begin an accident investigation as soon as possible after an accident occurs so that evidence and the memories of witnesses are still fresh.

4. Facts to be uncovered in an accident investigation can be summarized as *who*, *what*, *when*, *where*, *why*, and *how*.

5. Common causes of accidents fall into the following categories: personal beliefs and feelings, decision to work unsafely, mismatch or overload, systems failure, traps, unsafe conditions, and unsafe acts.

6. Who conducts the accident investigation can vary according to circumstances. However, regardless of how it is done, the health and safety professional should play an active role in the process.

7. Steps for conducting an accident investigation are as follows: (a) Isolate the accident scene, (b) record all evidence, (c) photograph or record the accident scene, (d) identify witnesses, and (e) interview witnesses.

8. Witnesses to accidents fall into one of three categories: primary (eyewitnesses), secondary (present at the scene, but did not see the accident), and tertiary (not present but have information that may be relevant).

9. Interviews should take place at the accident site whenever possible. When this isn't practical, interviews should take place at a neutral location that is private and where the witness is comfortable.

10. The keys to getting at the facts in an interview are (a) put the witness at ease, (b) ask open-ended questions, and (c) listen. Interrupt only if absolutely necessary.

11. When possible, let eyewitnesses re-enact the accident through simulation at the jobsite. Do not let them actually perform the tasks that led up to the accident.

12. The purpose of an accident report is to record the findings of the accident investigation, the cause or causes of the accident, and recommendations for corrective action.

Key Terms and Concepts

Accident-analysis report	Critical injury	Re-enactment
Accident investigation	Open-ended	Secondary witness
Accident report	Primary witness	Tertiary witness
Accident scene	Principal's office syndrome	

Review Questions

1. Explain the rationale for investigating accidents.
2. Explain the difference between an accident report and an accident-analysis report.
3. List the categories of the most common causes of accidents.
4. What are the terms that should guide the conduct of an accident investigation?
5. What role should the health and safety professional play in the conduct of an accident investigation?
6. List and explain the steps for conducting an accident investigation.
7. Why is it important to record all pertinent evidence relating to an accident immediately after an accident has occurred?
8. List and differentiate among the three categories of witnesses to an accident.
9. Briefly explain the *when* and *where* of interviewing witnesses.
10. Briefly explain the *how* of interviewing witnesses.
11. What is the purpose of an accident report? When should an accident be reported? Why?
12. List common reasons why accidents go unreported.
13. When discussing the ten accident investigation mistakes to avoid, what is meant by "allowing conflicting goals to enter into an investigation"?

Weblinks

Canadian Centre for Occupational Health and Safety

www.ccohs.ca/oshanswers/hsprograms/investig.html

CCOHS's website is an essential resource for health and safety professionals. At this link, common questions and answers on accident investigation can be found.

Workplace Safety & Prevention Services (WSPS)

www.wsps.ca/Home.aspx

Their vision, "the elimination of all work-related injuries, illnesses and fatalities," is supported by a large volume of resources, including those from the Industrial Accident Prevention Association (IAPA), and can be found on this website.

Association of Workers' Compensation Boards of Canada (AWCBC)

http://awcbc.org/?page_id=10

The AWCBC webpage provides links to the WCB injury and illness reporting requirements for each jurisdiction.

Endnotes

[1] D. Hartshorn. "Solving Accident Investigation Problems." *Occupational Hazards* 65, no. 1 (January 2003): 57.

[2] Society of Manufacturing Engineers (SME). *Tool and Manufacturing Engineers Handbook* 6 (Dearborn, MI: Society of Manufacturing Engineers, 1998), 12–21.

[3] Hartshorn. "Solving Problems," 57–58.

[4] SME. *Tool and Manufacturing*, 12–21.

[5] Ibid.

[6] Ibid.

[7] Canadian Centre for Occupational Health and Safety. (April 9, 1998). "OHS Answers, Accident Investigation." [Online]. Available: http://www.ccohs.ca/oshanswers/hsprograms/investig.html. (Retrieved January 23, 2005).

[8] SME. *Tool and Manufacturing*, 12–21.

[9] Hartshorn. "Solving Problems," 58–59.

[10] National Safety Council. *Supervisor's Safety Manual* (Chicago: National Safety Council, 1991), 71.

[11] J. Cunningham and A. Kane. "Accident Reporting—Part I: Key to Prevention." *Safety & Health* 139, no. 4: 70–71.

[12] A. Kane and J. Cunningham. "Accident Reporting—Part II: Consistent Discipline Is Vital." *Safety & Health* 139, no. 5: 78.

[13] Ibid.

[14] W. R. Coffee, Jr. "Avoid These 10 Mistakes." *Occupational Health & Safety* 74, no. 5: 44–47.

Chapter 10
Safety Management in a Global Marketplace

MAJOR TOPICS

- Competing in the Global Marketplace
- Productivity and Competitiveness
- Quality and Competitiveness
- How Health and Safety Can Improve Competitiveness
- Safety Management in a Quality Management Setting
- Total Safety Management (TSM)
- International Safety Standards

competitiveness The ability to succeed and prosper consistently in the marketplace whether it is local, regional, national, or global.

One of the most frequently heard terms in the language of modern business and industry is **competitiveness**. To survive and prosper in today's global marketplace, industrial companies must be competitive. Companies that used to compete only with neighbouring firms now find themselves competing against companies from the United States, Japan, Germany, Taiwan, Korea, Mexico, Great Britain, China, and many other countries throughout the world.

COMPETING IN THE GLOBAL MARKETPLACE

The global marketplace is intensely competitive. It is like a sports contest that never ends. You may win today, but the race begins again tomorrow. Competing in the global marketplace has been described as the equivalent of running in a race that has no finish line.

The need to achieve peak performance levels day after day puts intense pressure on companies, and pressure runs downhill. This means that all employees, from executive-level managers to workers on the shop floor, feel the pressure. It is not uncommon for this pressure to create a harried atmosphere that can increase the likelihood of accidents. It can also lead to shortcuts that increase the potential for health hazards (e.g., improper storage, handling, and use of hazardous materials).

It is unfortunate that some of these organizations perceive addressing hazards as impeding productivity, because the most competitive companies typically are also the safest and healthiest. It is critical that health and safety professionals understand the positive relationship between health and safety and competitiveness. Global competition is enhanced if companies meet established international standards for business management and environmental protection. It is also extremely important that they be able to articulate that connection effectively.

Competitiveness Defined

The Institute for Corporate Competitiveness defines *competitiveness* as "the ability to consistently succeed and prosper in the marketplace whether it is local, regional, national, or global."[1]

The most competitive companies are those that do the following: (1) consistently outperform their competitors in the key areas of quality, productivity, response time, service, cost, and corporate image (Figure 10–1); and (2) continually improve all of these areas. The two key concepts associated with competitiveness are peak performance and continual improvement.

Figure 10–1   Key areas that result in competitiveness.

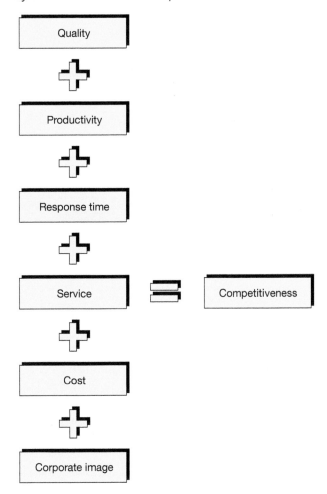

Competing in the **global marketplace** is difficult to do but easy to understand. One need only think of Olympic athletes to gain a perspective on the concept. Olympic athletes train continually to improve their performance to world-class levels. Their goal is to improve steadily in practice so that they can achieve peak performance levels in competition. Those who do this consistently win.

global marketplace   The worldwide economic market in which many companies must compete for business.

Of the various factors influencing a company's competitiveness, the two most important are *productivity* and *quality*. The other factors are, to a large extent, functions of these two. Therefore, health and safety managers should be knowledgeable about these two concepts and be able to discuss them on an equal footing with production managers, supervisors, and representatives of higher management.

PRODUCTIVITY AND COMPETITIVENESS

productivity The concept of comparing output of goods or services to the input of resources needed to produce or deliver them.

value added The difference between what it costs to produce a product and the value the marketplace puts on it (what it costs to purchase it).

Productivity is the concept of comparing output of goods or services to the input of resources needed to produce or deliver them. Productivity is typically expressed as the ratio of output to input in the following manner:

$$Output/Input = Productivity$$

To fully understand productivity, it is necessary to understand the concept of value added. Converting raw materials into useable products adds value to the materials. **Value added** is the difference between what it costs to produce a product and what it costs to purchase it (Figure 10–2). This difference represents the value that has been added to the product by the production process. Value added is increased when productivity is increased.

Figure 10–2 The value added concept.

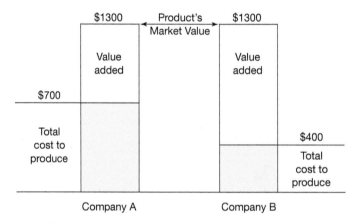

In Figure 10–2, Company A and Company B manufacture the same product. Each is able to sell its product for $1,300. However, Company B can manufacture the product for $400 because it is more productive than Company A, which produces the same product at a cost of $700. The productivity difference gives Company B at least two competitive advantages: (1) It can lower its price for the product below that of Company A and still make a profit; and (2) its greater profit margin gives Company B more capital to reinvest in upgrading its facilities, equipment, and personnel, which will, in turn, improve its competitiveness even more.

This productivity difference is important because all competing companies that produce a given product probably pay approximately the same for the raw materials. Consequently, the winner most likely is the one that adds the most value to the materials, which means the one that is the most productive (produces the most output with the least input).

Following are some rules of thumb that production managers use to monitor productivity in their plants. Health and safety managers should be familiar with these rules.

• Productivity is declining when (1) output declines and input is constant, or (2) output is constant but input increases.

- Productivity is improving when (1) output is constant but input decreases, or (2) output increases and input is constant.

In considering the concept of productivity, remember that it represents only half of the equation. Nothing has been gained if productivity is improved to the detriment of quality. When productivity is improved, quality must also improve or at least remain constant.

In the community of industrialized nations, Canada has historically been among the most productive. While Canadian productivity in the industrial sector has made steady gains since World War II, other industrialized countries, particularly Japan, increased even more during this same period (Figure 10–3).

Figure 10–3 Increases in output per hour of workers (1950–2003).

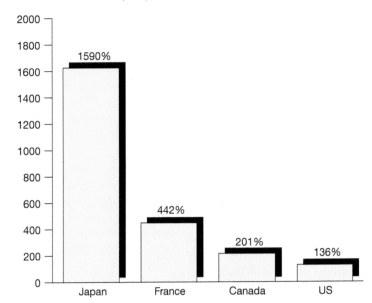

Pressure to increase productivity often results in actions that are detrimental to the health and safety of workers. In their rush to meet deadlines or quotas, workers may disassemble safeguards, stop taking the time to use appropriate personal protective gear, ignore safety rules, neglect equipment maintenance duties, improperly handle or store toxic substances, and take chances that they wouldn't take under normal conditions.

Such efforts occasionally result in short-term productivity improvements, but they invariably do more harm than good in the long run. The inevitable result is that productivity ultimately suffers, and the company finds that it won a battle only to lose the war.

QUALITY AND COMPETITIVENESS

Quality goes hand in hand with productivity in the competitiveness equation. Today's production company must have both. Quality without productivity results in costs that are too high to be competitive. Productivity without quality results in a shabby product that quickly tarnishes the corporate image.

Quality is a measure of the extent to which a product or service meets or exceeds customer expectations. According to Peters, it is important to define quality in terms of customer expectations.[2]

quality A measure of the extent to which a product or service meets or exceeds customer expectations.

Whereas the pressure to increase productivity can be detrimental to health and safety, the pressure to improve quality generally supports health and safety. In the next section, prospective and practising health and safety professionals will see how to use productivity and quality to gain a commitment to health and safety or to increase a commitment that already exists.

HOW HEALTH AND SAFETY CAN IMPROVE COMPETITIVENESS

When the pressures of competing become intense, it is not uncommon for health and safety to be given a lower priority. Not only is this wrong from an ethical standpoint, it is also wrong from the perspective of competitiveness and profitability. In the days when a worker's most important qualifications were physical strength and stamina, there were always plenty of applicants in the labour pool. If a worker was injured, several equally quali-fied applicants were waiting to replace him or her.

However, with the dawning of the age of technology and the advent of global competi-tion, this situation changed. Mental ability became more important than physical ability; suddenly, the number of qualified applicants got smaller. As we discussed in Chapter 3, although the literacy level of the Canadian workforce is increasing, it is not keeping pace with the increasingly technical and complex workplace. While Goetsch refers to the US marketplace, consider the implications of the following statement for Canadian global competitiveness:

> The basic skills necessary to be productive in a modern industrial setting are increasing steadily. At the same time the national high school dropout rate continues to increase as does the number of high school graduates who are functionally illiterate in spite of their diplomas. This means that while the number of high-skill jobs in modern industry is increasing, the number of people able to fill them is on the decline. The impact this will have on industry in the United States can be summarized as follows:
>
> 1. Difficulty in filling high-skill jobs.
> 2. Lower levels of productivity and, as a result, a lower level of competitiveness.
> 3. Higher levels of waste.
> 4. Higher potential for damage to sophisticated technological systems.
> 5. Greater numbers of dissatisfied employees in the workplace.[3]

The illiteracy problem, coupled with rapid and continual technological change, has serious implications for global competitiveness. Modern industrial companies are like modern sports teams. To compete, they must recruit, employ, and develop the best possible personnel. Having done so, they must keep them safe and healthy to derive the benefits of their talents. Talented people working in a safe and healthy environment will be more competitive than equally talented people who are constantly distracted by concerns for their health and safety. In addition, the most talented employees cannot help a company compete if they are slowed by injuries.

The aging workforce also has serious implications for global competitiveness, and there are two sides to the imminent retirement of a huge portion of the baby-boom generation. They bring invaluable experience and a positive work ethic to the job, but they also have special needs and physical limitations that introduce a whole new set of health and safety concerns.

The people side of the competitiveness equation is only part of it. There is also the technology side. With technological change occurring so rapidly, reinvestment in modern equipment is essential. Today's industrial firm must invest a higher percentage of its profits in equipment upgrades and do so more frequently. Money that must be diverted to workers' compensation, medical claims, product liability litigation, and environmental cleanups is money that could have been invested in technological upgrades.

If they are able to convey these facts effectively, health and safety professionals should be able to secure a strong commitment to health and safety in the workplace. Naturally, they should still use the ethics and compliance arguments as well, because these are proper and compelling. However, health and safety professionals must not stop there. They must convince companies that committing to health and safety is not just the right thing to do ethically or the smart thing to do legally, it is also the profitable thing to do in terms of competitiveness.

Health and safety managers can make this point by highlighting the following factors in the competitiveness equation: productivity, cost, quality, response time, service, and corporate image. Each of these ingredients relies directly in some way on having a safe and healthy workplace. Some of the more direct ways are summarized in the following paragraphs.

>>> **SAFETY MYTH** **Safety and Global Competitiveness**

Maintaining a safe and healthy workplace cannot be shown to enhance a company's global competitiveness. Right? Not necessarily. Productivity is a measurement of how well various factors, when taken together, perform. These factors include employees, material, money, and motivation. All four of these factors are affected by the work environment. In fact, more than 90 percent of employees identify quality of the work environment as critical in terms of their motivation and performance.

Source: Institute for Corporate Competition. *Employee Perceptions: Impact of Work Factors on Job Performance,* Report 2003-11 (Niceville, FL: Institute for Corporate Competition, June 2003).

Productivity and Cost

Productivity is a function of people, technology, and management strategies. Health and safety have a direct effect on the first two: people and technology. Companies with a reputation for providing a safe and healthy workplace will find it easier to attract and keep the best people. Correspondingly, these talented employees will be able to focus their skills more intently on being productive rather than worrying about accidents or health problems. On the **cost** side of the issue, companies with a record of safe and healthy practices will be better able to reinvest in equipment upgrades than those who must divert funds into such nonproductive costs as medical claims, environmental cleanups, and health- and safety-related litigation. The more productive a company, the more competitive it can be in setting prices for its products.

cost The amount of money needed to produce a product, not to be confused with "price," which is the amount of money needed to purchase a product after the cost has been marked up.

Quality

Quality is essential to competitiveness. Fortunately, those practices that enhance quality also tend to enhance health and safety. Quality requires strict adherence to established production practices, attention to detail, and a commitment to doing things the right way. So do health and safety. For this reason, health and safety professionals should also be advocates of quality.

Response Time

Response time is like productivity in that it is a function of people, technology, and management strategies. Therefore, the same arguments that apply to productivity apply to response

response time The amount of time between when an order is placed and when the product is delivered.

time. This is particularly important in the age of global competition because response time and quality, taken together, are becoming more important than the old "low bid" approach when it comes to winning contracts. The ability to deliver a quality product on demand is a prerequisite to participating in just-in-time contracts. These are contracts in which suppliers provide their products just in time to be used in the production process. This allows manufacturers to produce their products while carrying little or no inventory, a characteristic of today's most competitive companies.

Service

Service is an important ingredient in competitiveness. With industrial companies, service typically means in-field or after-delivery service. The most common example is service provided to people who purchase an automobile.

Service is important because it can have a significant impact on customer satisfaction and, in turn, on corporate image. Service is not closely associated with health and safety and is, therefore, not a component to be used when trying to gain a commitment to health and safety.

⟫⟫ DISCUSSION CASE | What Is Your Opinion?

"Explain this to me again. You say that making all of these modifications to our workstations and implementing these new procedures will make us more competitive. How? These workstation modifications are expensive, and it seems to me that some of these new procedures will just slow down production."

This wasn't the first time that Garner Baxter, an independent health and safety consultant, had been asked to explain the strategic advantages of a safe and healthy workplace. Can the quality of the work environment really make an organization more competitive? What is your opinion?

Image

corporate image How a company is perceived to interact with its workers, customers, and community.

In a competitive world, industrial companies must be concerned about their **corporate image**. An image of being concerned about employee health and safety will help companies attract and keep the best people. An image of being concerned about product safety will help companies market their products. An image of being concerned about the environment will make a company a welcome neighbour in any community. Correspondingly, a poor image in any of these areas can undermine a company's competitiveness. A product safety problem that becomes a media story can cause a company's sales of a given product to plummet overnight. This happened to a major automobile manufacturer when it was discovered that one of its economy models had a tendency to ignite and explode in rear-end collisions. It also happened to pharmaceutical manufacturers when various headache relief products were tampered with and found to have been laced with poison. Had these manufacturers not shown their concern by immediately recalling all containers that may have been affected and quickly developing tamper-proof substitutes, they could have suffered irreparable damage in the marketplace.

Image problems are not limited to product liability issues. Companies that are not careful about protecting the environment may find themselves the subject of protest demonstrations on the nightly news. Such negative publicity can harm the corporate image and translate very quickly into market losses. As corporate decision makers become more sensitive to these facts, health and safety professionals can use them to gain a commitment to their programs.

Bangladesh's Rana Plaza Collapse (How Not to Compete)

On April 24, 2013, the eight-story Rana Plaza building collapsed, killing more than 1,100 people and injuring thousands. The collapse of the building, which contained clothing factories among other businesses, on the outskirts of Bangladesh's capital, Dhaka, was the worst industrial incident to hit the garment industry. Twenty-nine global brands including Canada-based Joe Fresh and US retailer J.C. Penney were among the apparel companies for which clothing was being supplied.

How do companies compete in the global market? One way is to exploit the cheap labor of offshore countries such as Bangladesh. At the time of the factory collapse, the minimum wage for the millions of factory workers, mostly women, was $37 a month. The scant wages and deplorable working conditions reflected the investment the factory operators put into worker safety.

The immediate fallout after the Rana Plaza collapse included protests and boycotts condemning the exploitation of these workers. To help meet their moral obligations to the affected Bangladeshi workers and to help restore their severely tarnished corporate image, many of the apparel companies contributed millions of dollars to various agencies and funds. While the conditions in these factories are still deplorable by Canadian standards, there have been numerous improvements to the working conditions for many of these workers, including stricter safety and building regulations along with a minimum wage increase to $68 a month.

SAFETY MANAGEMENT IN A QUALITY MANAGEMENT SETTING

Quality management (QM) is an approach to doing business that began to gain wide acceptance in the late 1980s and early 1990s, and was originally called Total Quality Management, or TQM. Various individual components of this concept had been used by forward-looking organizations for years. However, not until the 1990s were these components pulled together into a cohesive philosophy of how to do business in a competitive global environment.

The health and safety professional of today is likely to work in an organization that practises the QM philosophy. Consequently, students of health and safety should understand QM and how to apply its principles to the management of an organization's health and safety programs. **Total safety management (TSM)** is the management of workplace health and safety according to the principles of QM.

quality management (QM) A way of managing a company that revolves around a total and willing commitment of all personnel at all levels to quality.

total safety management (TSM) The principles of quality management (QM) applied to safety management.

What Is QM?

The QM concept goes by several different names. It is has been called TQL for *total quality leadership*, TQC for *total quality control*, TQ for *total quality*, or TQM for *total quality management*. Regardless of the name used, the concept can be defined as *Quality management (QM)* which is an approach to doing business that maximizes the competitiveness of an organization through continuous improvement of its products, services, people, processes, and environments.[4]

How Does QM Relate to Safety?

QM has proven itself to be an effective way to maximize an organization's long-term competitiveness. It is also an excellent approach for maximizing the effectiveness of an organization's health and safety programs. QM can solve the same problem for safety managers that it solves for quality managers—the problem of *isolation*.

Often in a traditionally managed organization, quality is viewed as the sole responsibility of the quality department or the quality manager. The weaknesses of this approach became evident when organizations wedded to it began losing market share to foreign competition in the 1970s and 1980s. QM solved this problem by making quality everybody's job and casting the quality manager in the role of facilitator and catalyst.[5]

The same type of isolation often occurs with health and safety managers. Management and employees sometimes view safety as the responsibility of the safety department or the safety manager. In the case of quality, isolation is a prescription for failure. In the case of safety, it is a prescription for disaster. QM principles can solve the problem of safety isolation by making safety everybody's job and casting the safety manager in the role of facilitator and catalyst.

QM has excellent potential as an approach to health and safety management. In fact, other ties between quality and safety are so close that it can be argued that safety and quality must be improved simultaneously.

》》》 DISCUSSION CASE | What Is Your Opinion?

"QM is a quality initiative. It has nothing to do with safety," said the CEO with a laugh.

"On the contrary," replied the vice president for health and safety, "QM and safety management have a great deal in common. In fact, the two concepts are complementary."

Is there a relationship between QM and safety management? If so, what is it? If not, why not? What is your opinion?

TOTAL SAFETY MANAGEMENT (TSM)

TSM is to health and safety management what QM is to quality management. It is safety management according to the principles of QM. QM has revolutionized the way in which organizations do business and compete in the global marketplace.

Just as QM involves the total organization in continually improving quality, TSM involves the total organization in establishing and maintaining a work environment that is safe and conducive to quality and productivity. Both concepts are rooted firmly in the pressures of the global marketplace.

The origin of TSM can be traced back to the globalization of the marketplace that began after World War II, but really took hold in the 1970s. The need for TSM was created by the need for organizations to be competitive globally. Consequently, TSM is a performance- and process-oriented approach to health and safety management that gives organizations a sustainable competitive advantage in the global marketplace by establishing a safe and healthy work environment that is conducive to consistent peak performance and that is continually improved forever. It involves applying the principles of QM to the management of health and safety.

This definition contains several key elements that must be understood if one is to comprehend TSM fully. These elements are as follows:

1. **Sustainable competitive advantage.** Every organization that competes at any level, but especially those that compete at the global level, must have competitive advantages. These are capabilities or characteristics that allow them to outperform the competition. Traditionally, competitive advantages have been sought in the key areas of quality, productivity, service, and distribution. However, peak-performing organizations have learned that a safe and healthy work environment is essential to gaining competitive advantages in all of these critical areas. In fact, a safe and healthy work environment is itself a competitive advantage. In today's competitive marketplace, high-performance employers are adding one more critical area to the list of those in which competitive advantages are sought. This new addition is the work environment.

Peak-performance organizations are learning that a safe and healthy work environment gives them a doubly effective competitive advantage. First, it ensures that employees work in an environment that allows them to focus all of their attention, energy, and creativity on continually improving performance. Second, it prevents an organization's limited resources from being drained by the non–value added costs associated with accidents and injuries.

2. **Peak performance.** The primary drivers behind TSM performance are organizational, team, and individual. An organization's ability to survive and prosper in the global marketplace is determined largely by the collective performance of individuals and teams. Consistent peak performance by all individuals and teams in an organization is essential to long-term success. The quality of the work environment is a major determinant of the performance levels that individuals, teams, and organizations are able to achieve. A better work environment promotes better performance.

3. **Continual improvement forever.** People work in an environment, and the quality of that environment affects the quality of their work. In the age of global competition, quality is an ever-changing phenomenon. Quality that is competitive today may not be tomorrow. Consequently, continual improvement is essential. If quality must be improved continually, it follows that the work environment must also be improved continually. Quality and safety are more than complementary; they are inseparable.

⟫⟫⟫ SAFETY FACT A Radical Approach

As globalization of the workforce becomes ingrained in the minds of Canadians, it becomes easier to accept new concepts and ideas to manage safety in the workplace. This was not always the case. H. W. Heinrich was thinking "outside the box" in 1931 when he proposed looking at property damage accidents or "near misses" to predict disabling injuries. Known by many safety practitioners as the "father of safety," his ideas opened the door to a host of ideas that at one time may have seemed quite radical, but now form the basis of many safety management principles.

INTERNATIONAL SAFETY STANDARDS

The **International Organization for Standardization (ISO)** is a worldwide organization of national standards bodies (Figure 10–4). The complete membership roster for ISO contains the 3,368 technical bodies of 162 countries. The overall goal of ISO is to promote the development of standardization and related activities in the world with a view to facilitating the international exchange of goods and services and to developing cooperation in the sphere of intellectual, scientific, technological, and economic activity.[6]

Globalization of the marketplace has created a competitive environment that requires peak performance and continual improvement. The unrelenting demands of today's marketplace have given rise to new philosophies for doing business, most of which fall under the broad umbrella of quality management (QM). One of the initiatives under the QM umbrella is the ISO 9000 family of quality standards. These standards contain criteria for promoting effective quality management systems.

The International Organization for Standardization—the same organization that developed the ISO 9000 quality standards—has now developed the ISO 45001 standard. The standard, developed by over 70 countries and led by the British Standards Institute, is an occupational health and safety management system standard designed to meet the global OHS challenges being faced today. This standard factors into other international OHS standards including the OHSAS 18001 and the International Labour Organization's ILO-OHS Guidelines.

International Organization for Standardization (ISO) An independent, non-governmental worldwide organization of 163 national standards bodies that develop voluntary, consensus-based, market relevant international standards.

Figure 10–4 Addresses of Selected ISO members.

Australia

Standards Australia
Level 10, The Exchange Centre
20 Bridge Street
Sydney NSW 2000
Australia
GPO Box 476
Sydney NSW 2001
Australia
Tel: +61 2 9237 6000
E-mail: intsect@standards.org.au
Web: www.standards.org.au/

Canada

Standards Council of Canada
55 Metcalfe Street, Suite 600
Ottawa, Ontario K1P 6L5
Canada
Tel: +1 613 238 3222
E-mail: info@scc.ca
Web: www.scc.ca

France

Association française de normalisation
11 rue Francis de Pressensé
93000 La Plaine St Denis
France
Tel: +33 1 41 62 80 00
E-mail: uari@afnor.org
Web: www.afnor.org

Germany

DIN Deutsches Institut für Normung e.V.
Am DIN-Platz
Burggrafenstrasse 6
10772 Berlin
Germany
Tel: +49 030 2601-0
E-mail: directorate.international@din.de
Web: www.din.de

United Kingdom

British Standards Institution
389 Chiswick High Road
London W4 4AL
United Kingdom
Tel: +44 345 086 9001
E-mail: standards.international@bsigroup.com
Web: www.bsigroup.com
Webstore: shop.bsigroup.com/

United States

American National Standards Institute
1899 L Street NW, 11th Floor
Washington, DC 20036
United States
Operations
25 West 43rd Street, 4th Floor
New York, NY 10036
United States
Tel: +1 212 642 4900 (NY)/+1 202 293 8020 (DC)
E-mail: info@ansi.org
Web: www.ansi.org

 DISCUSSION CASE What Is Your Opinion?

The executive managers of Kendall Manufacturing, Inc. are debating the relative merits of seeking ISO 45001 certification. The managers have polarized around two opinions. The first opinion is that the company should proceed with preparations for certification immediately. In the words of one ISO proponent, "The sooner we get started, the sooner we will realize the benefits of ISO 45001." The second opinion is that any certification that is not required should be ignored. In the words of one ISO opponent, "Certification is time-consuming and expensive. Why bother if we don't have to? We already have to comply with provincial and federal legislation. Isn't that enough?" Where do you stand on this issue? What is your opinion?

SUMMARY

1. Competitiveness is the ability to succeed and prosper in the local, regional, national, and global marketplace. The most competitive companies are those that consistently outperform their competitors in the key areas of quality, productivity, response time, service, cost, and image.

2. Productivity is a measure of output in goods and services compared to input of resources needed to produce or deliver them. Part of productivity is the concept of value added, which is measured as the difference between what it costs a company to produce a product and the competitive market price of that product.

3. Quality is a measure of the extent to which a product meets or exceeds customer expectations. It goes hand in hand with productivity. Quality without productivity results in costs that are too high to be competitive. Productivity without quality results in an unacceptable product.

4. Health and safety contribute to competitiveness in the following ways: (a) by helping companies attract and keep the best people, (b) by allowing employees to focus on peak performance without being distracted by concerns for their health and safety, (c) by freeing money that can be reinvested in technology updates, and (d) by protecting the corporate image.

5. Quality management (QM) is an approach to doing business that maximizes the competitiveness of an organization through continuous improvement of its products, services, people, processes, and environments.

6. QM can solve the same problems for safety managers that it solves for managers concerned about quality. QM makes quality everybody's responsibility, rather than limiting responsibility to quality personnel. It can do the same for safety managers. In addition, a quality product is a safe product, and the best environment in which to produce quality products is a safe and healthy environment.

7. The rationale of TSM can be found in the connection between job performance and the work environment. To compete in the global marketplace, organizations need all employees performing at peak levels on a consistent basis. A safe and healthy workplace promotes peak performance.

8. ISO is the acronym for the International Organization for Standardization, a worldwide consortium of national standards bodies.

Key Terms and Concepts

Competitiveness
Corporate image
Cost
Global marketplace
International Organization
    for Standardization
    (ISO)

Productivity
Quality
Quality management
    (QM)

Response time
Total safety management
    (TSM)
Value added

Review Questions

1. Explain how global competition can have a negative impact on health and safety in the workplace.

2. Define the terms *competitiveness*, *productivity*, and *value added*.

3. What are the common characteristics of the most competitive companies?

4. Explain the relationship between productivity and quality as it relates to competitiveness.

5. Define *QM*.

6. How does QM relate to safety?
7. Define the term *total safety management*.
8. What is the rationale for TSM?
9. What are the roles of the three standards organizations: ISO, ILO, and SCC?
10. Describe the purpose of ISO 45001 and 9000 standards.

Weblinks

International Organization for Standardization (ISO)

www.iso.org

This is a link to information about ISO and the 9000 and 45001 standards.

International Labour Organization

www.ilo.org/safework

The ILO has designed the *Guidelines on Occupational Safety and Health Management Systems (ILO-OSH 2001)* to assist organizations with achieving continual improvement in OHS performance.

The Standards Council of Canada (SCC)

www.scc.ca

The Standards Council of Canada promotes efficient and effective standards for Canada, and is a member of the International Organization for Standardization.

Endnotes

[1] Institute for Corporate Competitiveness. *Manual of Services* (Niceville, FL: Institute for Corporate Competitiveness, 2003), 1.

[2] T. Peters. *Thriving on Chaos* (New York: Harper & Row, 1987), 78.

[3] D. L. Goetsch, *Effective Supervision* (Upper Saddle River, NJ: Prentice Hall, 2002), 210.

[4] David L. Goetsch and Stanley Davis. *Quality Management* (Upper Saddle River, NJ: Prentice Hall, 2003), 6.

[5] Eleanor J. White, "Saturn's Implementation of Deming's Fourteen Points," undated training document, 1.

[6] D. Goetsch and S. Davis. *ISO 14000 Environmental Management* (Upper Saddle River, NJ: Prentice Hall, 2001), 7.

Part 3
Chemical, Biological, and Physical Hazards

Chapter 11
Industrial Hygiene and Chemical Agents

industrial hygiene A profession dedicated to the recognition, assessment, and control of workplace stressors that may cause injuries, illnesses, or discomfort for workers.

Industrial hygiene is an area of specialization within the broader field of industrial health and safety that is concerned with predicting, recognizing, assessing, controlling, and preventing environmental stressors in the workplace that can cause sickness or serious discomfort to workers. This chapter provides prospective and practising health and safety professionals with the information they need to know about this area of specialization. An environmental stressor is any factor in the workplace that can cause enough discomfort to result in lost time or illness. Common stressors include gases, fumes, vapors, dusts, mists, noise, and radiation.

Tens of thousands of **toxic substances** can be found in workplaces, and hundreds more are introduced each year. Many **chemical agents** to which workers are exposed are very toxic; these may be human-made or naturally occurring. Everyone is exposed to toxic substances every day, whether at work or home, but the concentrations we are exposed to are usually so small that our sophisticated bodies have the ability to excrete the poisons or render them nontoxic by altering their chemical makeup. This chapter will look at some of these chemical agents, their effect on the body, and how to limit exposure to them. Other toxic substances such as **biological agents** will be covered in Chapter 13.

toxic substances Substances that have a negative effect on the health of a person or interfere with the normal biological function of a person.

chemical agents Single elements or compounds that may be toxic to humans.

biological agents Living things or substances produced by living things that may cause harm to humans.

TOXIC SUBSTANCES DEFINED

A toxic substance is one that has a negative effect on the health of a person or animal. Toxic effects are a function of several factors, including the following: (1) the properties of the substance, (2) the dose, (3) the level of exposure, (4) the route of entry, and (5) the resistance of the individual to the substance.

ENTRY POINTS FOR TOXIC AGENTS

The development of preventive measures to protect against the hazards associated with industrial exposure requires first knowing how toxic agents enter the body. A toxic substance must first enter the bloodstream to cause health problems. The most common routes of entry for toxic agents are inhalation, absorption, ingestion, and injection (see Figure 11–1). These routes are explained in the following paragraphs.

Figure 11–1   Common routes of entry of toxic substances.

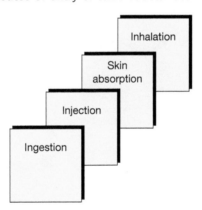

Inhalation

The route of entry about which health and safety professionals should be most concerned is **inhalation**. Airborne toxic substances such as gases, vapours, dust, smoke, fumes, aerosols, and mists can be inhaled and pass through the nose, throat, bronchial tubes, and lungs to enter the bloodstream. The amount of a toxic substance that can be inhaled depends on the following factors: (1) the concentration of the substance, (2) the duration of exposure, and (3) breathing volume.

inhalation Entry of gases, vapours, dust, smoke, fumes, aerosols, or mists into the body by breathing in.

Absorption

The second most common route of entry in an industrial setting is **absorption**, or passage through the skin and into the bloodstream.[1] The human skin is a protective barrier against many hazards. However, certain toxic agents can penetrate this barrier through absorption. Of course, unprotected cuts, sores, and abrasions facilitate the process, but even healthy

absorption Entry through the skin and into the bloodstream.

Most workers who work in dusty environments are concerned about breathing hazardous substances and take measures to limit their exposure by wearing respirators or dust masks, especially when the air looks contaminated. Most of these larger visible particles would have been filtered by our highly efficient, built-in, air-cleaning system. Between the hairs in our nose, the mucous lining our airway, and the design of our bronchia and alveoli, most particles don't get far enough into our lungs to cause damage. We excrete some of this material when we blow our nose and the rest is swallowed and processed by the digestive system. When the air looks clean we often let our guard down and do not wear respiratory protection. It is often these invisible particles that travel far into our lungs and cause the most damage.

skin will absorb certain chemicals. Humans are especially susceptible to absorbing such chemicals as organic lead compounds, nitro compounds, organic phosphate pesticides, TNT, cyanides, aromatic amines, amides, and phenols.

With many substances, the rate of absorption and, in turn, the hazard levels increase in a warm environment. The extent to which a substance can be absorbed through the skin depends on the factors shown in Figure 11–2. Another factor is body site. Different parts of the body have different absorption capabilities. For example, the forearms have a lower absorption potential than do the scalp and forehead.

Figure 11–2 How substances can be absorbed through the skin.

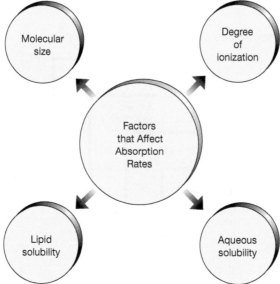

Ingestion

ingestion Entry through the mouth.

Ingestion, not a major concern in an industrial setting, is entry through the mouth.[2] An ingested substance is swallowed. It moves through the stomach into the intestines and from there into the bloodstream. Toxic agents sometimes enter the body by ingestion when they are accidentally consumed by workers eating lunch or a snack. Airborne contaminants can also rest on food or the hands and, as a result, be ingested during a meal or snack. The possibility of ingesting toxic agents makes it critical to confine eating and drinking to sanitary areas away from the work site and to make sure that workers practise good personal hygiene, such as washing their hands thoroughly before eating or drinking.

As it moves through the gastrointestinal tract, the toxic substance's strength may be diluted. In addition, depending on the amount and toxicity of the substance, the liver may be able to convert it to a nontoxic substance. The liver can, at least, decrease the level of toxicity and pass along the substance to the kidneys, where some of the substance is eliminated in the urine.

Injection

Injection involves the introduction of a substance into the body by way of a needle and syringe, compressed air, high-pressure hydraulic leaks, or any other capable medium. Consequently, this is not often a route of entry for a toxic substance in the workplace. Injection is sometimes used for introducing toxic substances in experiments involving animals. However, this approach can produce misleading research results because the needle bypasses some of the body's natural protective mechanisms.

injection   Entry into the body through punctured skin.

EFFECTS OF TOXIC SUBSTANCES

The effects of toxic substances vary widely, as do the substances themselves. However, all of the various effects and exposure times can be categorized as being either acute or chronic.

Acute effects and exposures involve a sudden dose of a highly concentrated substance. They are usually the result of an accident (a spill or damage to a pipe) that results in an immediate health problem ranging from irritation to death. Acute effects and exposures (1) are sudden, (2) are severe, (3) typically involve just one incident, and (4) cause immediate health problems. Acute effects and exposures are not the result of an accumulation over time.

acute effects and exposures   The effects of short-term exposure.

Chronic effects and exposures involve limited continual exposure over time. Consequently, the associated health problems develop slowly. The characteristics of chronic effects and exposures are (1) continual exposure over time, (2) limited concentrations of toxic substances, (3) progressive accumulation of toxic substances in the body and progressive worsening of associated health problems, and (4) little or no awareness of exposures on the part of affected workers.

chronic effects and exposures   The effects of exposure over time.

When a toxic substance enters the body, it eventually affects one or more body organs. Part of the liver's function is to collect such substances, convert them to nontoxic substances, and send them to the kidneys for elimination in the urine. However, when the dose is more than the liver can handle, toxins move on to other organs, producing a variety of different effects. The parts of the body that are affected by toxic substances are the blood, kidneys, heart, brain, central nervous system, skin, liver, lungs, and eyes. Figure 11–3 lists some of the more widely used toxic substances and the parts of the body that they endanger most.

Figure 11–3   Selected toxic substances and the parts of the body that they endanger most.

Blood	Kidneys	Heart	Brain
Benzene	Mercury	Aniline	Lead
Carbon monoxide	Chloroform		Mercury
Arsenic			Benzene
Aniline			Manganese
Toluene			Acetaldehyde

Eyes	Skin	Lungs	Liver
Cresol	Nickel	Asbestos	Chloroform
Acrolein	Phenol	Chromium	Carbon tetrachloride
Benzyl chloride	Trichloroethylene	Hydrogen sulphide	Toluene
Butyl alcohol		Mica	
		Nitrogen dioxide	

RELATIONSHIP OF DOSES AND RESPONSES

Health and safety professionals are interested in predictability when it comes to toxic substances. How much of a given substance is too much? What effect will a given dose of a given substance produce? These types of questions concern dose–response relationships. A **dose** of a toxic substance can be expressed in a number of different ways depending on the characteristics of the substance; for example, amount per unit of body weight, amount per body surface area, or amount per unit of volume of air breathed. Olishifski expresses the dose–response relationship mathematically as follows:[3]

$$(C) \times (T) = k$$

where

C = concentration

T = duration (time) of exposure

k = constant

Note that in this relationship, C times T is *approximately* equal to k. The relationship is not exact.

Three important concepts to understand relating to doses are *dose threshold*, *lethal dose*, and *lethal concentration*.

Dose Threshold

dose The amount of a substance, agent, or energy that enters the body; radiation dose is the amount of ionizing radiation absorbed per unit of mass any part of the body or the whole body.

The **dose threshold** is the minimum dose required to produce a measurable effect. Of course, the threshold is different for different substances. In animal tests, thresholds are established using such methods as (1) observing pathological changes in body tissues, (2) observing growth rates (are they normal or retarded?), (3) measuring the level of food intake (has there been a loss of appetite?), and (4) weighing organs to establish body weight to organ weight ratios.

dose threshold The minimum dose required to produce a measurable effect.

Lethal Dose

A **lethal dose** of a given substance is the dose that is highly likely to cause death. Such doses are established through experiments on animals. When lethal doses of a given substance are established, they are typically accompanied by information that is of value to medical professionals and industrial hygienists. Such information includes the type of animal used in establishing the lethal dose, how the dose was administered to the animal, and the duration of the administered dose. Lethal doses do not apply to inhaled substances. With these substances, the concept of lethal concentration is applied.

lethal dose The dose that is highly likely to cause death in the test subject by exposure through any means other than inhalation.

Lethal Concentration

A **lethal concentration** of an inhaled substance is the concentration that is highly likely to result in death. With inhaled substances, the duration of exposure is critical because the amount inhaled increases with every unprotected breath.

lethal concentration The concentration in air that causes death to the test subject when inhaled.

AIRBORNE CONTAMINANTS

It is important to understand the different types of airborne contaminants that may be present in the workplace.[4] Each type of contaminant has a specific definition that must be understood in order to develop effective health and safety measures to protect against it.

Figure 11–4 Common airborne contaminants.

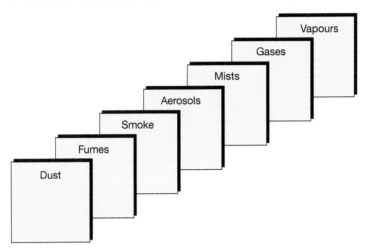

The most common types of airborne contaminants are dusts, fumes, smoke, aerosols, mists, gases, and vapours (Figure 11–4).

- *Dusts.* Dusts are various types of solid particles that are produced when a given type of organic or inorganic material is scraped, sawed, ground, drilled, handled, heated, crushed, or otherwise deformed. The degree of hazard represented by dust depends on the toxicity of the parent material and the size and level of concentration of the particles.
- *Fumes.* The most common causes of fumes in the workplace are such manufacturing processes as welding, heat treating, and metallizing, all of which involve the interaction of intense heat with a parent material. The heat volatilizes portions of the parent material, which then condense as they come in contact with cool air. The result of this reaction is the formation of tiny particles that can be inhaled.
- *Smoke.* Smoke is the result of the incomplete combustion of carbonaceous materials. Because combustion is incomplete, tiny soot or carbon particles remain and can be inhaled.
- *Aerosols.* Aerosols are liquid or solid particles that are so small they can remain suspended in air long enough to be transported over a distance. They can be inhaled.
- *Mists.* Mists are tiny liquid droplets suspended in air. Mists are formed in two ways: (1) when vapours return to a liquid state through condensation, and (2) when the application of sudden force or pressure turns a liquid into particles.
- *Gases.* Unlike other airborne contaminants that take the form of either tiny particles or droplets, gases are formless. Gases are actually formless fluids. Gases become particularly hazardous when they fill a confined, unventilated space. The most common sources of gases in an industrial setting are from welding and the exhaust from internal combustion engines.
- *Vapours.* Certain materials that are solid or liquid at room temperature and at normal levels of pressure, but turn to gas when heated or exposed to abnormal pressure. Evaporation is the most common process by which a liquid is transformed into a vapour.

In protecting workers from the hazards of airborne contaminants, it is important to know the permissible levels of exposure for a given contaminant and to continually monitor the level of contaminants using accepted measurement practices and technologies. The topic of exposure thresholds is covered later in this chapter.

EFFECTS OF AIRBORNE TOXIC MATERIALS

Airborne toxic substances are also classified according to the type of effect they have on the body. The primary classifications are shown in Figure 11–5 and explained in the following paragraphs. With all airborne contaminants, concentration and duration of exposure are critical concerns.

Figure 11–5 Airborne toxic substances.

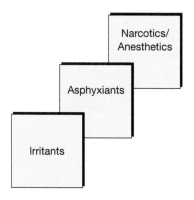

Irritants

irritants Substances that cause irritation to the skin, eyes, and the inner lining of the nose, mouth, throat, and upper respiratory tract.

Irritants are substances that cause irritation to the skin, eyes, and the inner lining of the nose, mouth, throat, and upper respiratory tract. However, they produce no irreversible damage.

Asphyxiants

asphyxiants Substances that can disrupt breathing so severely as to cause suffocation.

Asphyxiants are substances that can disrupt breathing so severely that suffocation results. Asphyxiants may be simple or chemical in nature. A simple asphyxiant is an inert gas that dilutes oxygen in the air to the point that the body cannot take in enough air to satisfy its needs for oxygen. Common simple asphyxiants include carbon dioxide, ethane, helium, hydrogen, methane, and nitrogen. Chemical asphyxiants, by chemical action, interfere with the passage of oxygen into the blood or the movement of oxygen from the lungs to body tissues. Either way, the end result is suffocation due to insufficient or no oxygenation. Common chemical asphyxiants include carbon monoxide, hydrogen cyanide, and hydrogen sulphide.

Narcotics and Anesthetics

narcotics Substances that produce numbness or stupor.

anesthetics Substances that can inhibit the normal operation of the central nervous system without causing serious or irreversible effects, when carefully controlled.

Narcotics and **anesthetics** are similar in that carefully controlled dosages can inhibit the normal operation of the central nervous system without causing serious or irreversible effects. This makes them particularly valuable in a medical setting. Dentists and physicians use narcotics and anesthetics to control pain before, during, and after surgery. However, if the concentration of the dose is too high, narcotics and anesthetics can cause unconsciousness and even death.

When this happens, death is the result of asphyxiation. Widely used narcotics and anesthetics include acetone, methyl-ethyl-ketone, acetylene hydrocarbons, ether, and chloroform.

EFFECTS OF CARCINOGENS

A **carcinogen** is any substance that can cause a malignant tumour or a neoplastic growth. A **neoplasm** is cancerous tissue or tissue that may become cancerous.

Medical researchers are not sure exactly how certain chemicals cause cancer. However, there are a number of toxic substances that are either known, or are strongly suspected, to be carcinogens. These include coal tar, pitch, creosote oil, anthracene oil, soot, lamp black, lignite, asphalt, bitumen waxes, paraffin oils, arsenic, chromium, nickel compounds, beryllium, cobalt, benzene, and various paints, dyes, tints, pesticides, and enamels.[5]

carcinogen Any substance that can cause a malignant tumour or a neoplastic growth.

neoplasm Cancerous tissue or tissue that might become cancerous.

ASBESTOS HAZARDS

Asbestos was once thought to be a miracle material because of its many useful characteristics, including fire resistance, heat resistance, mechanical strength, and flexibility. As a result, asbestos was widely used in commercial and industrial construction between 1900 and the mid-1970s (see Figure 11–6).[6]

Figure 11–6 Asbestos use 1900 to present.

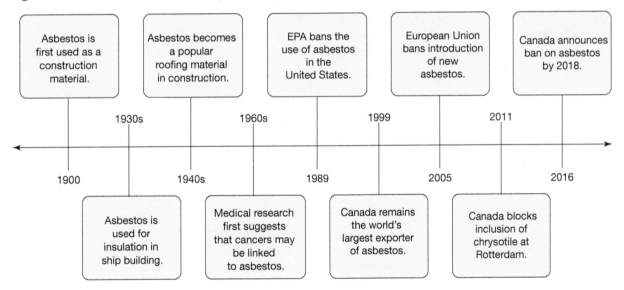

In the mid-1970s, medical research clearly tied asbestos to respiratory cancer, scarring of the lungs (now known as *asbestosis*), and cancer of the chest or abdominal lining (*mesothelioma*).[7] Although its use has been restricted in many countries since the 1970s and 1980s, the number of cases of asbestos-related respiratory diseases continued to rise into the 1990s, because of its lengthy **latency period**. The International Labour Organization reports that 100,000 deaths per year are related to occupational asbestos exposure.[8]

The following passage on **friable asbestos** shows why asbestos is still a concern even though its further use has been banned:

latency period Time after exposure to a hazardous product before symptoms appear.

friable asbestos Asbestos that is in a state of crumbling deterioration. When asbestos is in this state, it is most dangerous.

> When asbestos becomes friable (crumbly), it can release fibers into the air that are dangerous when inhaled. As asbestos-containing material (ACM) ages, it becomes less viable and more friable. Asbestos can be released into the air if it is disturbed during renovation or as a result of vandalism.[9]

Removing and Containing Asbestos

When an industrial facility is found to contain asbestos, health and safety professionals are faced with the question of whether to remove it or contain it. Before making this decision, the following factors should be considered:

- Is there evidence that the ACM is deteriorating? What is the potential for future deterioration?

- Is there evidence of physical damage to the ACM? What is the potential for future damage?

- Is there evidence of water damage to the ACM or spoilage? What is the potential for future damage or spoilage?[10]

>>> **SAFETY FACT** | Respirable Silica Exposure and Lung Disease

Silica is a very common mineral found in many materials common on construction sites, including soil, sand, concrete, masonry, rock, granite, and landscaping materials. Workers exposed to the respirable dust particles created by abrasive blasting, cutting, grinding, drilling, or otherwise disturbing these materials are at risk of developing the lung disease silicosis. Similar to asbestosis, when the microscopic particles are deposited in the lungs, scar tissue forms and in some cases cancer develops. The time from exposure to the onset of the disease or symptoms may be several decades.

There is no cure for silicosis. However, the health effects can be significantly reduced if detected early. Therefore it is important for workers to be assessed promptly after potential exposure. A chest X-ray and lung function tests will help establish a baseline, so that changes can be more readily detected.

Most provinces have regulations that specify how certain hazardous products such as asbestos are to be handled. For example, asbestos is one of 11 designated substances for which Ontario has specific regulations that govern how workers deal with the substance at work. Several approaches can be used for dealing with asbestos in the workplace. The most widely used are removal, enclosure, and encapsulation.

Removal   Asbestos removal is also known as *asbestos abatement.* The following procedures are recommended for removal of asbestos: (1) The area in question must be completely enclosed in walls of tough plastic, (2) the enclosed area must be ventilated by high-efficiency particulate absolute (HEPA)–filtered negative air machines (these machines work somewhat like a vacuum cleaner in eliminating asbestos particles from the enclosed area), (3) the ACM must be covered with a special liquid solution to cut down on the release of asbestos fibres, and (4) the ACM must be placed in leakproof containers for disposal.[11]

Enclosure   Enclosure of an area containing ACMs involves completely encapsulating the area in airtight walls.[12] The following procedures are recommended for enclosing asbestos: (1) Use HEPA-filtered negative air machines in conjunction with drills or any other tools that may penetrate or otherwise disturb ACMs, (2) construct the enclosing walls of impact-resistant and airtight materials, (3) post signs indicating the presence of ACMs within the enclosed area, and (4) note the enclosed area on the plans of the building.

Encapsulation   Encapsulation of asbestos involves spraying the ACMs with a special sealant that binds them together, thereby preventing the release of fibres.[13] The sealant should harden into a tough, impact-resistant skin. This approach is generally used only on acoustical plaster and similar materials.

Personal Protective Equipment for Asbestos Removal

It is important to use the proper types of personal protective clothing and respiratory devices. Clothing should be disposable and should cover all parts of the body.[14] According to Hughes, respirators used when handling asbestos should be "high-efficiency cartridge filter type (half-and-full-face types); any powered-air purifying respirator; any type C continuous-flow supplied-air, pressure-demand respirator, equipped with an auxiliary positive pressure self-contained breathing apparatus."[15]

INDOOR AIR QUALITY

Poor indoor air quality (IAQ) can cause a variety of health problems ranging from the temporary to the long-term. Health problems commonly associated with poor indoor air quality include allergic reactions, respiratory problems, eye irritation, sinusitis, bronchitis, and pneumonia. These collective symptoms are often referred to as **sick building syndrome**. Often, the cause of poor indoor air quality can be slipshod maintenance such as failure to keep fans, ductwork, and filters clean. Other contributors are the particles and gases that can be released by office equipment, carpets, paints, cleaning solvents, and office supplies.

sick building syndrome A set of ailments associated with a workplace. The symptoms can include watering eyes and runny nose, fatigue, dizziness, dry and/ or itchy skin, headaches, sore throat, nose bleeds, and nausea.

One of the keys to maintaining a high level of air quality is to have adequate air exchange. A challenge faced by building tenants and owners is keeping heating and cooling costs down while maintaining a healthy environment. When less fresh air, or makeup air, is entered into the system, the cost of heating or cooling goes down, but the concentration of toxic materials goes up while the oxygen level drops.

Important factors in a building's ability to eliminate contaminated air and bring in fresh air are:

- Ventilation
- Air infiltration rates
- Airflow rates in ducts
- Airflow patterns
- Fume exhaust

The most accurate methods available for measuring these factors fall under the broad heading of *tracer gas techniques*. A tracer gas is any gas or vapour not normally found in a building. The best have the following characteristics:

- Nontoxic
- Nonallergic at the levels used
- Chemically inert
- Odourless and tasteless
- Nonflammable and nonexplosive
- Easily transported
- Easily dispersed as an atmospheric gas
- Easily and economically measured with a high degree of reliability

The most widely used tracer gases are sulphur hexafluoride, halogenated refrigerants, and perfluorocarbons. To perform a tracer gas test, the following materials and equipment are needed:

- A suitable tracer gas
- A device for measuring tracer gas concentrations

- An air-sampling system
- A tracer gas injection system
- A data acquisition and control system

There are several different types of tracer gas tests, including tracer decay, constant concentration, buildup/decay, CO_2 measurement, and re-entrainment/recirculation. Regardless of the type of test used, the testing process involves the following steps:

1. Inject the tracer gas into the building.
2. Measure the concentration of the tracer gas in different parts of the building at different times over a certain period.

The data collected during a tracer gas test can give health and safety professionals the following types of information:

- Total air exchange rate for the building
- Air change rate due to the operation of the building's HVAC system
- Air change rate due to air infiltration and leakage
- Percentage of outside air supplied by the building's HVAC system
- Effectiveness of the ventilation system in removing contaminants
- Distribution of the ventilation air throughout the building

With this type of information available, health and safety personnel can determine whether there are pockets where contaminated air is trapped, whether the ventilation and air infiltration rates are sufficient, whether airflow rates through ducts are sufficient, whether airflow patterns are what they should be, and whether fume hoods are performing as they should. This type of information is needed to detect and prevent indoor air quality problems.

TOXIC MOULD AND INDOOR AIR QUALITY

Toxic mould has surfaced as an issue relating to IAQ. The issue is complicated by at least two factors. First, there are thousands of types of moulds, but only a few are toxic. Second, different people have different levels of sensitivity to mould. On the other hand, in those limited instances in which moulds are toxic, they can cause coughing, atypical asthma, nasal congestion, sinusitis, rhinitis, skin rashes, and fatigue. In severe cases, toxic moulds can be deadly.

The principal causal factor in most cases of toxic mould is inadequate ventilation. Consequently, an effective approach for preventing the accumulation of toxic mould in the workplace is to apply the following steps: (1) Check outdoor intakes and make sure they are not near trash storage areas, standing water, exhausts, or anything else that might contribute to the growth of mould; (2) make sure the drip pans are sloped sufficiently to prevent the accumulation of standing water; and (3) check ductwork regularly to ensure that the lining is dry and clean.

Toxic Mould Assessment and Remediation

Modern health and safety professionals must be prepared to deal with moisture and mould issues. It is important to investigate periodically to identify sources of moisture and mould. The following procedures may be used to guide investigations:

- **Look** for mould in likely locations such as around pipes, drains, windows, and dark, poorly ventilated areas.
- **Listen** to the feedback and comments of employees who might complain about allergies that could be affected by mould or about any aspect of IAQ.

- **Smell** the air in the work environment. You can tell if the air is damp, stale, or musty. If it is, there is a moisture problem, even if it is hidden under floors or behind walls.

- **Train** employees how to be "mould investigators" by showing them how to look, listen, and smell in their work environment.

- **Inventory** the principal areas of moisture and mould risk in your facility and monitor these high-risk areas continually.[16]

When mould is found, it is important to act. Mould remediation, in general terms, proceeds as follows: (1) Stop the moisture intrusion, (2) contain and isolate the moisture that is already present, (3) dry and filter the affected area, (4) remove anything in the affected area that cannot be dried, (5) kill existing bacteria with disinfectants and sanitizing agents, (6) clean and then reclean the area, and (7) take whatever steps are necessary to prevent any further moisture intrusion.

According to Alfred Draper III, an industrial hygienist who specializes in mould-related restoration and remediation, mould remediation projects can be divided into four classes, ranging from low impact to high. Class I remediation is just good housekeeping (for example, minimizing dust, using drop cloths, and cleaning up with HEPA-filtered vacuums). Class II requires the use of EPA-registered disinfectants, containing construction waste, and limiting access to work areas. Class III remediation projects require isolating the HVAC system and more robust barriers, and Class IV must have all of the previously mentioned precautions plus enhanced PPE and a decontamination facility.

THRESHOLD LIMIT VALUES

How much exposure to a toxic substance is too much? How much is acceptable? Guidelines that answer these questions for health and safety professionals are developed and issued annually by the American Conference of Governmental Industrial Hygienists (ACGIH). The guidelines are known as **threshold limit values (TLVs)**. The ACGIH describes threshold limit values as follows:

> Threshold limit values refer to airborne concentrations of substances and represent conditions under which it is believed that nearly all workers may be repeatedly exposed day after day without adverse effect. Because of wide variation in individual susceptibility, however, a small percentage of workers may experience discomfort from some substances at concentrations at or below the threshold limit; a smaller percentage may be affected more seriously by aggravation of a preexisting condition or by development of an occupational illness.
>
> Threshold limits are based on the best available information from industrial experience, from experimental human and animal studies, and, when possible, from a combination of the three. The basis on which the values are established may differ from substance to substance; protection against impairment of health may be a guiding factor for some, whereas reasonable freedom from irritation, narcosis, nuisance, or other forms of stress may form the basis for others.[17]

threshold limit values (TLVs) The levels of exposure at which all employees may be repeatedly exposed to specified concentrations of airborne substances without fear of adverse effects. Exposure beyond TLVs is considered hazardous.

ACGIH's Classifications of TLVs and BEIs

The ACGIH develops threshold limit values (TLVs) and **biological exposure indices (BEIs)** to help health and safety professionals control certain chemical, biological, and physical health hazards in the workplace.[18] TLVs and BEIs are not legal standards and are not intended to be; rather, they are guidelines. However, their impact is increasingly felt, and in a positive way. As government organizations and agencies continue to find that political considerations make it difficult to promulgate legally authorized standards in a timely manner, the ability of the ACGIH to produce TLV guidelines that are updated

biological exposure indices (BEIs) Procedures used to determine the amount of material absorbed into the human body.

annually makes its guidelines more and more valuable. Key concepts about TLVs and BEIs that should be understood by health and safety professionals are described below.

time-weighted average The level of exposure to a toxic substance to which a worker can be repeatedly exposed on a daily basis without suffering harmful effects.

short-term exposure limit The maximum concentration of a given substance to which employees may be safely exposed for up to 15 minutes without suffering irritation, chronic or irreversible tissue change, or narcosis to a degree sufficient to increase the potential for accidental injury, impair the likelihood of self-rescue, or reduce work efficiency.

ceiling The level of exposure that should not be exceeded at any time for any reason.

Threshold limit value–time-weighted average (TLV-TWA) The **time-weighted average** for a conventional 8-hour workday and a 40-hour workweek for a given substance to which it is believed that nearly all workers may be repeatedly exposed on a daily basis without suffering ill effects. For example, the TLV-TWA for liquefied petroleum gas is 1,000 parts per million (ppm).

Threshold limit value–short-term exposure limit (TLV-STEL) The concentration of a given substance to which it is believed that workers may be exposed continuously for short periods without suffering ill effects. A STEL is defined as a 15-minute TWA exposure that should not be exceeded at any time during the work-day period. Also, exposures above the TLV-TWA up to the STEL should not exceed 15 minutes and should not occur more than four times in a day (with at least 60 minutes between exposures). For example, the TLV-STEL for isopropyl ether is 310 ppm.

Threshold limit value–ceiling (TLV-C) The concentration of a given substance that should not be exceeded at any point during an exposure period.

Biological exposure indices The levels of determinants that are expected to be present in specimens taken from healthy workers who have been exposed to selected substances to the same extent as other workers with inhalation exposure to the substance at the TLV. For example, the BEI for acetone in the urine of a worker is 50 milligrams per litre (mg/L).

Physical agents Substances or factors that can introduce added stress on the human body so that the effects of a given substance at the TLV might be magnified. Physical factors include acoustics (noise), ergonomic conditions, ionizing radiation, lasers, nonionizing radiation, subfrequency and static electric fields, and thermal stress (cold and heat). For example, the TLV for average noise of 94 decibels (dB) is 1 hour per day.

Calculating a TWA

Time-weighted averages (TWAs) can be calculated for exposures to given substances.[19] Olishifski gives the following formula for calculating the TWA for an 8-hour day:

$$\frac{TWA - CaTa + CbTb + \ldots CnTn}{8}$$

where

Ta = time of the first exposure period during the 8-hour shift

Ca = concentration of the substance in question in period Ta

Tb = another time period during the same shift

Cb = concentration of the substance in question in period Tb

Tn = final time period in the 8-hour shift

Cn = concentration during period Tn

HAZARD RECOGNITION AND ASSESSMENT

The degree and nature of the hazard must be understood before effective hazard control procedures can be developed. This involves recognizing that a hazard exists and then making judgments about its magnitude with regard to chemical, physical, biological, and ergonomic stresses.

Questions that can be used for recognizing hazards in the workplace are as follows:

- What is produced?
- What raw materials are used in the process?
- What additional materials are used in the process?
- What equipment is used?
- What operational procedures are involved?
- What dust control procedures are involved?
- How are accidental spills cleaned up?
- How are waste by-products disposed?
- Is there adequate ventilation?
- Are processes equipped with exhaust devices?
- How does the facility layout contribute to employee exposure?
- Is properly working personal protective equipment available?
- Are safe operating procedures recorded, made available, monitored, and enforced?[20]

Olishifski recommends that all processes be subjected to the following hazard recognition procedures:

- Determine the exposure threshold for each hazardous substance identified when applying the questions just listed, including airborne contaminants.
- Determine the level of exposure to each hazardous substance.
- Determine which employees are exposed to each hazardous material, how frequently, and for how long.
- Calculate the TWAs to the exposure thresholds identified earlier.[21]

For hazard assessment, the following considerations are important: the nature of the material or substance involved, the intensity of the exposure, and the duration of the exposure. Key factors to consider are how much exposure is required to produce injury or illness; the likelihood that enough exposure to produce injury or illness will take place; the rate of generation of airborne contaminants; the total duration of exposure; and the prevention and control measures used.[22]

PREVENTION AND CONTROL

Most prevention and control strategies can be placed in one of the following four categories: (1) engineering controls, (2) ventilation, (3) personal protective equipment, and (4) administrative controls.[23] Examples of strategies in each category are given in the following paragraphs.

Engineering Controls

engineering controls Strategies such as the design of tools, equipment, workplace, or processes that eliminates the hazard at the source.

The category of **engineering controls** includes such strategies as replacing a toxic material with one that is less hazardous, redesigning a process to make it less stressful, or reducing exposure to hazardous materials or conditions. Other engineering controls might entail isolating a hazardous process to reduce the number of people exposed to it or introducing moisture to reduce dust.[24]

Ventilation

Exhaust ventilation involves trapping and removing contaminated air. This type of ventilation is typically used with such processes as abrasive blasting, grinding, polishing, buffing, and spray painting or finishing. It is also used in conjunction with open-surface tanks. Dilution ventilation involves simultaneously removing and adding air to dilute a contaminant to acceptable levels.[25]

Personal Protection Equipment

personal protective equipment (PPE) Any type of clothing or device that puts a barrier between the worker and the hazard (e.g., safety goggles, gloves, hard hats, and so on).

When the work environment cannot be made safe by any other method, **personal protective equipment (PPE)** is used as a last resort. PPE imposes a barrier between the worker and the hazard but does nothing to reduce or eliminate the hazard. Typical equipment includes safety goggles, face shields, gloves, boots, earmuffs, earplugs, full-body-coverage clothing, barrier creams, and respirators.[26]

Occasionally, in spite of an employee's best efforts in wearing PPE, his or her eyes or skin will be accidentally exposed to a contaminant. When this happens, it is critical to wash away or dilute the contaminant as quickly as possible. Specially designed eyewash and emergency wash stations such as those shown in Figures 11–7 and 11–8 should be readily available and accessible in any work setting where contaminants may be present.

Figure 11–7 Guardian Model 1815 eye-face station.

Image Courtesy of Guardian Equipment; Model G1815

Administrative Controls

Administrative controls involve limiting the exposure of employees to hazardous conditions using such strategies as rotating schedules, required breaks, work shifts, and other schedule-oriented strategies.[27]

Figure 11–8 Haws Model 8730 emergency polar shower booth.

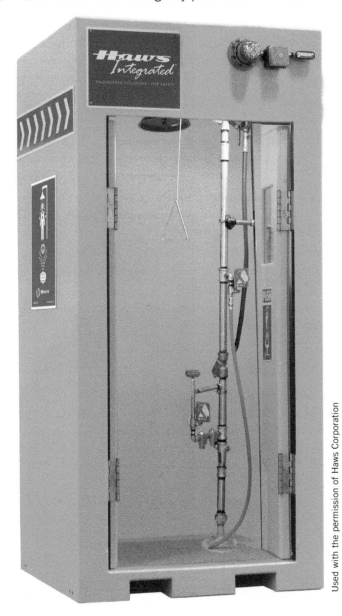

Used with the permission of Haws Corporation

Additional Strategies

The type of prevention and control strategies used will depend on the assessment of the specific hazards present in the workplace. The Society of Manufacturing Engineers recommends the following list of generic strategies that apply regardless of the setting:

- Practising **good housekeeping**, including workplace cleanliness, waste disposal, adequate washing and eating facilities, healthful drinking water, and control of insects and rodents.

  good housekeeping Proper cleaning and maintenance of a work area.

- Using special control methods for specific hazards, such as reduction of exposure time, film badges and similar monitoring devices, and continuous sampling with preset alarms.

- Setting up medical programs to detect intake of toxic materials.

- Providing training and education to supplement engineering controls.[28]

Self-Protection Strategies

One of the best ways to protect employees from workplace hazards is to teach them to protect themselves. The Workplace Hazardous Materials Information System (WHMIS), covered in the next chapter, along with the following rules of self-protection are designed to protect workers and provide them with the means to protect themselves:

1. **Know the hazards in your workplace.** Take the time to identify all hazardous materials and conditions in your workplace and know the safe exposure levels for each.

2. **Know the possible effects of hazards in your workplace.** Typical effects of workplace hazards include respiratory damage, skin disease and irritation, injury to the reproductive system, and damage to the blood, lungs, central nervous system, eyesight, and hearing.

3. **Use personal protective equipment properly.** Proper use of personal protective equipment means choosing the right equipment, getting a proper fit, correctly cleaning and storing equipment, and inspecting equipment regularly for wear and damage.

4. **Understand and obey safety rules.** Read warning labels before using any contained substance, handle materials properly, read and obey signs, and do only authorized work.

5. **Practise good personal hygiene.** Wash thoroughly after exposure to a hazardous substance, shower after work, wash before eating, and separate potentially contaminated work clothes from others before washing them.[29]

Guidelines for Respirators

The respirator is one of the most important types of personal protective equipment available to individuals who work in hazardous environments (see Figures 11–9 and 11–10). Because the performance of a respirator can mean the difference between life and death, Canadian Standards Association (CSA) publishes strict guidelines regulating the manufacture of respirators. The standard with which manufacturers must comply is CSA Z94.4-02, Selection, Use, and Care of Respirators.

Figure 11–9 Breathing protection devices.

kostrez/Shutterstock

Figure 11–10 Respirator.

Bruno Passigatti/123RF

There are two types of respirators: *air-filtering* and *air-supplying*. Air-filtering respirators filter toxic particulates out of the air. The particulate filters used in air-filtering respirators are divided into three classes, each class having three levels of efficiency as follows:

- Class N respirators may be used only in environments that contain no oil-based particulates. They may be used in atmospheres that contain solid or non-oil contaminants.

- Class R respirators may be used in atmospheres containing any contaminant. However, the filters in Class R respirators must be changed after each shift if oil-based contaminants are present.

- Class P respirators may be used in any atmosphere containing any particulate contaminant.

	Class N (Not Oil Resistant)	Class R (Oil Resistant)	Class P (Oil Proof)
Efficiency	95%	95%	95%
Efficiency	99%	99%	99%
Efficiency	99.97%	99.97%	99.97%

If there is any question about the viability of an air-filtering respirator in a given setting, employees should use air-supplying respirators. This type of respirator works in much the same way as an air tank for a scuba diver. Air from the atmosphere is completely blocked out, and fresh air is provided via a self-contained breathing apparatus.

GENERAL SAFETY PRECAUTIONS

Following are a number of general safety precautions that apply in any opened or confined spaces where explosive and combustible materials are present.

1. **Prohibit smoking.** Smoking should be prohibited in any areas of a plant where explosive and combustible materials are present. Eliminating potential sources of ignition is a standard safety precaution in settings where explosions and fire are possible. In the past, such areas were marked off as "restricted," and "No Smoking" signs were posted. It is becoming common practice to prohibit smoking on the premises altogether or to restrict smoking to designated areas that are well removed from hazard areas.

2. **Eliminate static electricity.** Static electricity occurs when dissimilar materials come into contact and then separate. If these materials are combustible or are near other materials that are combustible, an explosion can occur. Therefore, it is important to eliminate static electricity. The potential for the occurrence of static electricity can be reduced substantially by the processes of grounding and bonding. **Bonding** involves eliminating the difference in static charge potential between materials. *Grounding* involves eliminating the difference in static charge potential between a material and the ground. Figures 11–11, 11–12, and 11–13 illustrate these concepts.

bonding Method used to connect two pieces of equipment by a conductor. It involves eliminating the difference in static charge potential between materials.

Figure 11–11 How static electricity occurs.

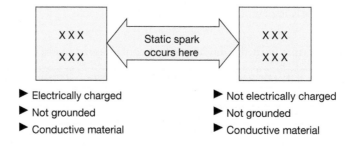

▶ Electrically charged   ▶ Not electrically charged
▶ Not grounded   ▶ Not grounded
▶ Conductive material   ▶ Conductive material

Figure 11–12 Bonding prevents static spark.

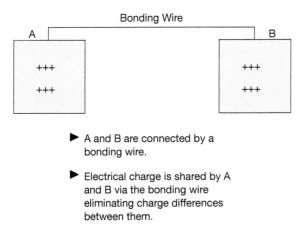

Bonding Wire

A   +++   +++

B   +++   +++

▶ A and B are connected by a bonding wire.

▶ Electrical charge is shared by A and B via the bonding wire eliminating charge differences between them.

Figure 11–13 Grounding prevents static spark.

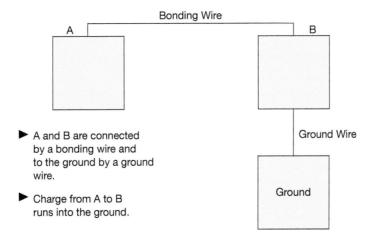

Bonding Wire

A

B

Ground Wire

Ground

▶ A and B are connected by a bonding wire and to the ground by a ground wire.

▶ Charge from A to B runs into the ground.

3. **Use spark-resistant tools.** Sparks from tools used in settings where explosive and combustible materials are present represent a threat that must be addressed. In such settings, spark-resistant tools should be used to the maximum extent possible. Wooden, leather-faced, and rubber-covered tools can help prevent sparks that might ignite volatile materials.[30]

SUMMARY

1. Industrial hygiene is a specialized field concerned with the effects of workplace stressors on human health, well-being, and comfort.

2. A toxic substance is one that has a negative effect on the health of a person or animal. The effect produced by a toxic substance depends on its properties, the amount of the dose, the level of exposure, and the individual's resistance.

3. The routes of entry for toxic agents are inhalation, absorption, and ingestion.

4. Exposures to toxic substances are either acute or chronic. Acute exposure involves sudden exposure to high concentrations of the substance in question. Chronic exposure involves limited but continual exposure to the substance in question.

5. The most common types of airborne contaminants are dusts, fumes, smoke, aerosols, mists, gases, and vapours.

6. Airborne contaminants are classified according to the type of effect that they have on the body. There are irritants, asphyxiants, and narcotics and anesthetics.

7. A carcinogen is any substance that can cause a malignant tumour or a neoplastic growth.

8. Asbestos, once thought to be a miracle material, is now known to be an extremely hazardous substance. It has been tied to respiratory cancer, scarring of the lungs, and cancer of the chest or abdominal lining. When identified in the workplace, asbestos should be handled by removal, enclosure, or encapsulation.

9. Mould in the workplace creates challenges for the hygienist, because there are thousands of types of mould and individual susceptibility varies among exposed workers.

10. The three most important concepts to understand concerning exposure thresholds are *time-weighted average (TWA)*, *short term exposure limit*, and *ceiling*.

11. The dose threshold is the minimum dose of a toxic substance required to produce a measurable effect. A lethal dose is one that is highly likely to cause death by any means other than inhalation. A lethal concentration is the concentration of an inhaled substance that is likely to cause death.

12. Hazard recognition procedures include determining the exposure threshold for each hazardous substance in the workplace, determining the level of exposure to each, determining which employees are exposed and for how long, and calculating the TWAs.

13. General prevention and control strategies include: (1) engineering controls (e.g., substitution, isolation, moisture to reduce dust, process changes), (2) ventilation (e.g., exhaust methods), (3) personal protective equipment (e.g., goggles, face shields, gloves, boots), and (4) administrative controls (e.g., rotating schedules, required breaks).

14. The Society of Manufacturing Engineers recommends the following list of generic strategies that apply regardless of the setting: (1) good housekeeping, (2) special control methods, (3) medical programs, and (4) training and education.

Key Terms and Concepts

Absorption
Acute effects and
    exposures
Anesthetics
Asphyxiants
Biological exposure
    indeces (BEI)
Biological agents
Bonding
Carcinogen
Ceiling
Chemical agents

Chronic effects and exposures
Dose
Dose threshold
Engineering controls
Friable asbestos
Good housekeeping
Industrial hygiene
Ingestion
Inhalation
Injection
Irritants
Latency period

Lethal concentration
Lethal dose
Narcotics
Neoplasm
Personal protective
    equipment (PPE)
Short-term exposure limit
Sick building syndrome
Threshold limit values
    (TLVs)
Time-weighted average
Toxic substances

Review Questions

1. Define the term *toxic substance*.

2. Briefly explain the typical categories of hazards in the workplace.

3. What are the most common routes of entry for toxic agents?

4. Describe the following types of airborne contaminants: dusts, fumes, smoke, mists, and gases.

5. What factors should be considered in deciding whether to remove or contain asbestos?

6. Explain the following ways of dealing with asbestos in the workplace: removal, enclosure, and encapsulation.

7. Briefly explain the following concepts relating to exposure thresholds: time-weighted average, short-term exposure limit, and ceiling.

8. Describe what is meant by *sick building syndrome*.

9. List the most important considerations when evaluating hazards in the workplace.

10. List five generic prevention and control strategies that can be used in any workplace.

11. Give an example of a prevention/control strategy in each of the following categories: engineering controls, ventilation, and personal protective equipment.

12. Explain five self-protection strategies that employees can use in the workplace.

13. List the factors that determine the effect that a toxic substance will have.

14. Explain the mathematical expression of the dose–response relationship.

15. Define the following terms: *dose threshold*, *lethal dose*, and *lethal concentration*.

16. Differentiate between acute and chronic effects and exposures.

17. List and describe the various classifications of airborne toxics.

18. What is a carcinogen?

19. What is a threshold limit value?

20. Define the following terms: *time-weighted average* and *ceiling*.

21. Explain the three classes of respirators.

Weblinks

American Conference of Governmental Industrial Hygienists (ACGIH)

www.acgih.org

ACGIH establishes TLVs and BEIs that are accepted throughout Canada and North America.

Canadian Centre for Occupational Health and Safety (CCOHS)

www.ccohs.ca

A federal government agency established to research and provide safety information resources to all Canadian workers.

The National Institute for Occupational Safety and Health (NIOSH)

https://www.cdc.gov/niosh

NIOSH, part of the US Centers for Disease Control and Prevention, is a research agency focused on the study of worker health and safety.

Endnotes

[1] J. B. Olishifski. "Overview of Industrial Hygiene," in *Fundamentals of Industrial Hygiene*, 3rd ed. (Chicago: National Safety Council, 1996), 17.

[2] Ibid., 14.

[3] Ibid., 148.

[4] Ibid., 18–19.

[5] Ibid., 369.

[6] Centers for Disease Control and Prevention. National Institute for Occupational Safety and Health (NIOSH). (No date). "NIOSH Safety and Health Topic: Asbestos." [Online]. Available: http://www.cdc.gov/niosh/topics/asbestos/. (Retrieved February 26, 2017).

[7] Ibid.

[8] J. Takala. International Labour Organization. (September 3, 2003). Asbestos Conference. [Online]. Available: http://www.ilo.org/wcmsp5/groups/public/—ed_protect/—protrav/—safework/documents/event/wcms_108063.pdf. (Retrieved March 3, 2017).

[9] Centers for Disease Control and Prevention. (April 4, 2000). "NIOSH Safety and Health Topic: Asbestos." National Institute for Occupational Safety and Health, 4–7. [Online]. Available: http://www.cdc.gov/niosh/asbestos.html.

[10] Ibid., 3–4.

[11] Ibid., 48.

[12] Ibid.

[13] Ibid.

[14] Ibid., 49.

[15] Ibid.

[16] A. Draper. "I Think It's Mold (Now What?)." *Occupational Health & Safety* 74, no. 5: 67–69.

[17] American Conference of Governmental Industrial Hygienists. *Threshold Limit Values* (Cincinnati, OH: American Conference of Governmental Industrial Hygienists, 2003), 3.

[18] Ibid., v–vi, 45, 44, 96, 112.

[19] Olishifski. "Overview of Industrial Hygiene," 21.

[20] Ibid.

[21] Ibid.

[22] Ibid., 22.

[23] Ibid., 25.

[24] Ibid.

[25] Ibid., 26.

[26] Ibid.

[27] Ibid., 27.

[28] Ibid., 24.

[29] Florida Department of Labor and Employment Security, Division of Safety, Toxic Substances Information Center. *What You Should Know About On-the-Job Health.*

[30] National Safety Council. "Industrial Hygiene and Chemical Agents." *Accident Prevention Manual for Industrial Operations* (Chicago: National Safety Council, 1999), 425.

Chapter 12

Workplace Hazardous Materials Information System (WHMIS), Globally Harmonized System of Classification and Labelling for Chemicals (GHS), and Transportation of Dangerous Goods (TDG)

MAJOR TOPICS

- Purpose of WHMIS
- WHMIS Legislation
- WHMIS Transition to the Globally Harmonized System (GHS)
- Roles, Responsibilities, and Duties under WHMIS 2015
- The Main Components of WHMIS 2015
- Transportation of Dangerous Goods (TDG)

PURPOSE OF WHMIS

One of the three basic rights Canadian workers enjoy is the *right to know* what hazards they may be exposed to on the job. Exposure to harmful chemicals is one such hazard—and one that is relevant to most workers. Although industrial environments most readily come to mind when we think about harmful chemicals in the workplace, products that can harm us in some manner are likely to be present in any workplace.

In 1988, the Workplace Hazardous Materials Information System (WHMIS) was introduced as Canada's hazard communication system for "**hazardous products.**" This national system, implemented through interlocking federal, provincial, and territorial legislation, serves as a major component in a worker's right to know, because it provides employers and workers with the information needed to handle and use these potentially harmful products safely.

WHMIS is changing to adopt new international standards for classifying hazardous chemicals and providing information on labels and safety data sheets. This system is being phased in between February 2015 and December 2018 to align with the Globally Harmonized System for Classifying and Labelling Chemicals (GHS). Countries around the world are adopting a consistent system to enable a single international system for chemical classification and labelling. The European Union, the United States, China, Japan, and other countries are implementing changes consistent with GHS,

hazardous products A product covered by the Hazardous Products Act that meets the criteria to be included in one or more of the WHMIS 2015 hazard classes.

and Canada is doing the same. Once updated, the system will continue to be called WHMIS in Canada—WHMIS 2015.

The WHMIS program is a Canada-wide system developed to provide Canadians with a consistent and effective means of dealing with hazardous materials in the workplace. The system was developed through the cooperation of industry, labour, and both federal and provincial and territorial governments and came into effect on October 31, 1988. The nature of this tripartite involvement is reflected in the design of the WHMIS logo seen in Figure 12–1.

Figure 12–1 WHMIS logo.

Workplace
Hazardous Materials
Information System

Système d'information sur
les matières dangereuses
utilisées au travail

WHMIS LEGISLATION

WHMIS was developed through cooperation between the federal and the provincial/territorial levels of government, and both jurisdictions enforce the legislation. The main area of concern for the federal WHMIS legislation is ensuring that suppliers and manufacturers of controlled products provide information to users through labelling and material safety data sheets (MSDSs). The provincial and territorial legislation is more concerned with employers obtaining adequate information on hazardous products and passing this on to the workers after the products have entered the workplace.[1]

The two key pieces of federal legislation that enable WHMIS 2015 are:

1. The Hazardous Products Act (HPA), which requires suppliers who sell or import a hazardous material for use in a workplace in Canada to provide labels and MSDSs to their customers.

2. The Hazardous Products Regulations (HPR), which has replaced the Controlled Products Regulation (CPR) and the Ingredient Disclosure List.

The provinces and territories have two pieces of legislation dealing with WHMIS. The Health and Safety Act for each jurisdiction outlines the general duties of employers and workers when dealing with hazardous materials; the more specific requirements are detailed in the regulations or code. The Health and Safety Act or its equivalent will have sections dealing in depth with toxic substances. For example, Part IV of the Ontario Occupational Health and Safety Act, titled Toxic Substances, refers to material identification and MSDSs. The acts and regulations listed in Figure 12–2 cover workers in provincial and territorial jurisdictions.

Figure 12–2 Provincial/territorial WHMIS legislation.

British Columbia	• Workers Compensation Act • Occupational Health and Safety Regulation, Part 5
Alberta	• Occupational Health and Safety Act • Occupational Health and Safety Code, Part 29, Workplace Hazardous Materials Information System (WHMIS), Sections 395 to 414
Saskatchewan	• Occupational Health and Safety Act • Occupational Health and Safety Regulations, 1996, Part XXII
Manitoba	• The Workplace Safety and Health Act • Manitoba Regulation 217/2006, Workplace Safety and Health Regulation, Part 35, Workplace Hazardous Materials Information Systems
Ontario	• Occupational Health and Safety Act • Workplace Hazardous Materials Information System Regulation
Quebec	• Act Respecting Occupational Health and Safety • Hazardous Products Information Regulation
New Brunswick	• Occupational Health and Safety Act • Workplace Hazardous Materials Information System Regulation
Nova Scotia	• Occupational Health and Safety Act • Workplace Hazardous Materials Information System (WHMIS) Regulations
PEI	• Occupational Health and Safety Act • Workplace Hazardous Materials Information System Regulations
Newfoundland and Labrador	• Occupational Health and Safety Act • Workplace Hazardous Materials Information System (WHMIS) Regulations
Yukon Territory	• Occupational Health and Safety Act • Workplace Hazardous Materials Information System Regulations
Northwest Territories and Nunavut	• Safety Act • Work Site Hazardous Materials Information System Regulations

Source: Canadian Centre for Occupational Health and Safety, WHMIS 1988 - General. From http://www.ccohs .ca/oshanswers/ legisl/intro_whmis.html.

WHMIS TRANSITION TO THE GLOBALLY HARMONIZED SYSTEM (GHS)

In order to give suppliers, workers, and employers an opportunity to adjust to the Globally Harmonized System of Classification and Labelling of Chemicals (GHS), the federal, provincial, and territorial governments are synchronizing their transition. The transition period goes from February 2015 to December 2018 (Figure 12–3). The purpose of the transition period is to allow time for:

• partners and stakeholders to make the necessary legislative, regulatory, and system adjustments;

• old labels and material safety data sheets (MSDSs) to be moved out of the supply chain and workplaces in a predictable manner;

• increased employer and worker awareness and understanding of changes to hazard classification and communication in WHMIS 2015; and

• consistency across Canada through coordination and alignment between federal, provincial, and territorial jurisdictions.[2]

Figure 12–3   WHMIS transition schedule.

Transition Phases				
Phases	**Timing**	**Suppliers**		**Employers***
		Manufacturers and Importers	**Distributors**	
*Consult appropriate FPT OHS regulator to confirm requirements and transition timing.				
Phase 1	From coming-into-force to May 31, 2017	Comply with CPR or HPR requirements	Comply with CPR or HPR requirements	Consult FPT OSH regulator
Phase 2	From June 1, 2017 to May 31, 2018	Comply with HPR requirements	Comply with CPR or HPR requirements	Comply with CPR or HPR requirements
Phase 3	From June 1, 2018 to November 30, 2018	Comply with HPR requirements	Comply with HPR requirements	Comply with CPR or HPR requirements
Completion	December 1, 2018	Comply with HPR requirements	Comply with HPR requirements	Comply with HPR requirements

ROLES, RESPONSIBILITIES, AND DUTIES UNDER WHMIS 2015

The role of the federal, provincial, and territorial governments is to develop, implement, and enforce legislation to protect workers' health and safety. Through this joint legislation the roles, responsibilities, and duties are placed upon suppliers/importers, employers, and workers.

Under WHMIS 2015, suppliers and importers of hazardous products will:

- ensure the appropriate classification of hazardous products,
- provide labels, and
- provide safety data sheets (SDSs, formerly MSDSs).

During the transition phase, suppliers must fully comply with either the WHMIS 1988 or WHMIS 2015 requirements for a specific controlled or hazardous product. The classification, label, and (M)SDSs must comply fully with the specific regulation chosen by the supplier, and not be a combination of the two.[3]

Employers must ensure that all hazardous products are properly labelled and make up-to-date SDSs readily available to workers. Employers also must provide worker education and training and ensure appropriate control measures to protect the health and safety of workers.

Under WHMIS 2015, employers must continue to:

- educate and train workers on the hazards and safe use of products,
- ensure that hazardous products are properly labelled,
- prepare workplace labels and SDSs as necessary,
- provide access to up-to-date SDSs for workers, and
- review the education and training provided to employees annually or whenever work conditions or hazard information changes.[4]

Workers still participate in WHMIS training programs, take necessary steps to protect themselves and their coworkers, and participate in identifying and controlling hazards.

THE MAIN COMPONENTS OF WHMIS 2015

Labels

Hazardous products used in the workplace must be labelled. In most cases, suppliers are responsible for labelling the hazardous products that they provide to customers. Employers are responsible for making sure that hazardous products that come into the workplace are labelled and for preparing and applying a workplace label when appropriate. There are two main types of WHMIS labels: supplier labels and workplace labels, and each is required to carry specific information.

supplier label   Identified by the WHMIS broken border, the supplier label is required as a condition of sale of hazardous products.

The **supplier label** must be written in English and French. It may be bilingual (as one label), or available as two separate labels (one each in English and French). See Figure 12–4.

Figure 12–4   Supplier label.

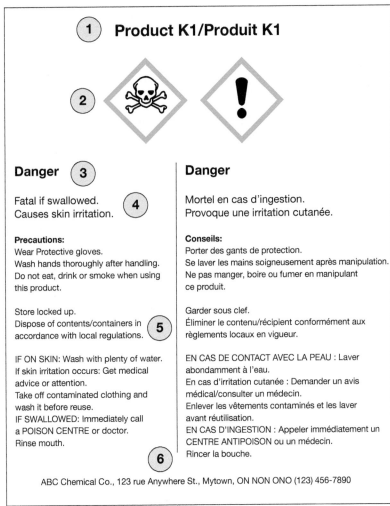

Source: Used with the permission of Canadian Centre for Occupational Health and Safety.

The supplier label must include the following information:

1. **Product Identifier.**   The product name exactly as it appears on the container and on the safety data sheet (SDS).

2. **Hazard Pictograms.**   Hazard pictograms, determined by the hazard classification of the product. In some cases, no pictogram is required.

3. **Signal Word (new for WHMIS 2015).** *Danger* or *Warning* is used to emphasize hazards and indicate the severity of the hazard.
4. **Hazard Statements.** Brief standardized statements of all hazards based on the hazard classification of the product.
5. **Precautionary Statements.** These statements describe recommended measures to minimize or prevent adverse effects from exposure to the product, including protective equipment and emergency actions. First aid is included in precautionary information.
6. **Supplier Identifier.** The company that made, packaged, sold, or imported the product, and is responsible for the label and SDS. Contact the supplier for additional product information.[5]

workplace label Required on hazardous products in the workplace, but may have less content than supplier labels.

Workplace label requirements fall under your provincial or territorial jurisdiction, or under the Canada Labour Code if you work in a federally regulated workplace. See your jurisdiction for specific criteria or changes to labelling requirements. A workplace label is required when:

- a hazardous product is produced (made) at the workplace and used in that workplace,
- a hazardous product is decanted (e.g., transferred or poured) into another container, or
- a supplier label becomes lost or illegible (unreadable).[6]

Under WHMIS 1988, workplace labels that required the following information, will be adequate in most jurisdictions. A sample workplace label is depicted in (Figure 12–5):

- Product name (matching the (M)SDS product name).
- Safe handling precautions, may include pictograms or other supplier label information.
- A reference to the (M)SDS (if available).

Figure 12–5 Workplace label.

METHANOL

FLAMMABLE—DO NOT USE NEAR AN OPEN FLAME OR PROCESSES THAT GENERATE SPARKS.

AVOID INHALING VAPOURS.

READ THE SAFETY DATA SHEET BEFORE USING THIS COMPOUND.

Safety Data Sheets (SDSs)

A safety data sheet (SDS) is a detailed technical document that is required from the supplier on the initial shipment of a controlled product. Worker access to SDSs is a requirement and employers must ensure that updated SDSs are obtained for all hazardous products used in the workplace. In Chapter 11, terminology related to toxicology was discussed. WHMIS training should provide the worker with an understanding of these terms and the ability to better decipher the information provided on the SDS.

Like the supplier labels, the SDS must be provided in both English and French. The appearance of the SDS may vary from manufacturer to manufacturer, but all SDSs must contain the information sections and in the order presented in Figure 12–6.

Hazard Classes/Categories

Under WHMIS 2015, hazardous products are divided into two hazard groups: physical hazards and health hazards. The hazard groups are further divided into hazard classes: 19

Figure 12–6 WHMIS 2015 Safety Data Sheet requirements.*

	SDS section	Information Requirements (partial list)
1	Identification	Product identifier, recommended use and restrictions on use, supplier contact information, emergency phone number.
2	Hazard identification	Classification (hazard class and category), label elements (including hazard pictogram, signal word, hazard statement, and precautionary statements), and other hazards (e.g., thermal hazards).
3	Composition/information on ingredients	For a hazardous product that is a substance: the chemical name, synonyms, CAS No. and the chemical name of impurities, stabilizing solvents and stabilizing additives where classified and that contribute to the classification of the product. For a hazardous product that is a mixture: for ingredients that present a health hazard: the chemical name, synonyms, CAS No. and concentration. Note: Confidential business information rules may apply.
4	First-aid measures	First-aid measures by route of exposure as well as most important symptoms/effects.
5	Firefighting measures	Suitable (and unsuitable) extinguishing media, specific hazards, special equipment, and precautions for firefighters.
6	Accidental release measures	Protective equipment, emergency procedures, methods, and materials for containment and clean up.
7	Handling and storage	Precautions for safe handling, conditions for storage, including any incompatibilities.
8	Exposure controls/personal protection	Exposure limits, engineering controls, personal protective equipment.
9	Physical and chemical properties	Appearance, odour, odour threshold, pH, melting/freezing point, boiling point and range, flash point, upper and lower flammable or explosive limits.
10	Stability and reactivity	Reactivity, chemical stability, possible hazardous reactions, conditions to avoid, incompatible materials, hazardous decomposition products.
11	Toxicological information	Description of various toxic effects by route of entry, including effects of acute or chronic exposure, carcinogenicity, reproductive effects, respiratory sensitization.
12	Ecological information	Aquatic and terrestrial toxicity (if available), persistence and degradability, bioaccumulative potential, mobility in soil.
13	Disposal considerations	Safe handling and methods of disposal, including contaminated packaging.
14	Transport information	UN number and proper shipping name, hazard classes, packing group.
15	Regulatory information	Safety, health, and environmental regulations specific to the product.
16	Other information	Other information, including date of the latest revision of the SDS.

*See website for further information in footnotes to this Safety Data Sheet.

Source: Used with the permission of Canadian Centre for Occupational Health and Safety.

physical hazard classes and 12 health hazard classes (see Figure 12–7). An explanation of each hazard class is provided in Figures 12–8 and 12–9.

Each hazard class contains one or more categories or "types." Numbers assigned to categories and letters to types of hazards indicate the relative hazard. For example, category 1 is the most hazardous within that class and may be further divided into subcategory 1A, which would be more severe than 1B. Category 2 may be further broken down, and so on. For more detailed information on the classification system, or any aspect of the information on the Hazardous Products Regulations, refer to Transport Canada's official Transportation of Dangerous Goods web page, provided in the weblinks at the end of this chapter.

Pictograms

The ten pictograms used in WHMIS 2015 are simple graphic images found on supplier labels and SDSs that readily indicate the type of hazard the product presents. The hash-mark border in WHMIS 1988 has now been replaced with a red, diamond-shaped border for

Figure 12–7 Physical and health hazard classes.

Physical Hazard Classes	Health Hazard Classes
• Combustible Dusts	• Acute Toxicity
• Corrosive to Metals	• Aspiration Hazard
• Flammable Aerosols	• Biohazardous Infectious Materials
• Flammable Gases	• Carcinogenicity
• Flammable Liquids	• Germ Cell Mutagenicity
• Flammable Solids	• Reproductive Toxicity
• Gases Under Pressure	• Respiratory or Skin Sensitization
• Organic Peroxides	• Serious Eye Damage/Eye Irritation
• Oxidizing Gases	• Skin Corrosion/Irritation
• Oxidizing Liquids	• Specific Target Organ Toxicity—Repeated Exposure
• Oxidizing Solids	• Specific Target Organ Toxicity—Single Exposure
• Pyrophoric Gases	• Health Hazards Not Otherwise Classified
• Pyrophoric Liquids	
• Pyrophoric Solids	
• Self-Heating Substances and Mixtures	
• Self-Reactive Substances and Mixtures	
• Simple Asphyxiants	
• Substances and Mixtures Which, in Contact with Water, emit Flammable Gases	
• Physical Hazards Not Otherwise Classified	

Source: Used with the permission of Canadian Centre for Occupational Health and Safety.

Figure 12–8 Physical hazards.

Hazard Class	General Description
Flammable gases Flammable aerosols Flammable liquids Flammable solids	These four classes cover products that have the ability to ignite (catch fire) easily and the main hazards are fire or explosion.
Oxidizing gases Oxidizing liquids Oxidizing solids	These three classes cover oxidizers, which may cause or intensify a fire or cause a fire or explosion.
Gases under pressure	This class includes compressed gases, liquefied gases, dissolved gases and refrigerated liquefied gases. Compressed gases, liquefied gases and dissolved gases are hazardous because of the high pressure inside the cylinder or container. The cylinder or container may explode if heated. Refrigerated liquefied gases are very cold and can cause severe cold (cryogenic) burns or injury.
Self-reactive substances and mixtures	These products may react on their own to cause a fire or explosion, or may cause a fire or explosion if heated.
Pyrophoric liquids Pyrophoric solids Pyrophoric gases	These products can catch fire very quickly (spontaneously) if exposed to air.
Self-heating substances and mixtures	These products may catch fire if exposed to air. These products differ from pyrophoric liquids or solids in that they will ignite only after a longer period of time or when in large amounts.
Substances and mixtures which, in contact with water, emit flammable gases	As the class name suggests, these products react with water to release flammable gases. In some cases, the flammable gases may ignite very quickly (spontaneously).

(continued)

Organic peroxides	These products may cause a fire or explosion if heated.
Corrosive to metals	These products may be corrosive (chemically damage or destroy) to metals.
Combustible dust	This class is used to warn of products that are finely divided solid particles. If dispersed in air, the particles may catch fire or explode if ignited.
Simple asphyxiants	These products are gases that may displace oxygen in air and cause rapid suffocation.
Physical hazards not otherwise classified	This class is meant to cover any physical hazards that are not covered in any other physical hazard class. These hazards must have the characteristic of occurring by chemical reaction and result in the serious injury or death of a person at the time the reaction occurs. If a product is classified in this class, the hazard statement on the label and SDS will describe the nature of the hazard.

Source: Used with the permission of Canadian Centre for Occupational Health and Safety.

Figure 12–9 Health hazards.

Hazard Class	General Description
Acute toxicity	These products are fatal, toxic or harmful if inhaled, following skin contact, or if swallowed. Acute toxicity refers to effects occurring following skin contact or ingestion exposure to a single dose, or multiple doses given within 24 hours, or an inhalation exposure of 4 hours. Acute toxicity could result from exposure to the product itself, or to a product that, upon contact with water, releases a gaseous substance that is able to cause acute toxicity.
Skin corrosion/irritation	This class covers products that cause severe skin burns (i.e., corrosion) and products that cause skin irritation.
Serious eye damage/eye irritation	This class covers products that cause serious eye damage (i.e., corrosion) and products that cause eye irritation.
Respiratory or skin sensitization	A respiratory sensitizer is a product that may cause allergy or asthma symptoms or breathing difficulties if inhaled. Skin sensitizer is a product that may cause an allergic skin reaction.
Germ cell mutagenicity	This hazard class includes products that may cause or are suspected of causing genetic defects (permanent changes (mutations) to body cells that can be passed on to future generations).
Carcinogenicity	This hazard class includes products that may cause or are suspected of causing cancer.
Reproductive toxicity	This hazard class includes products that may damage or are suspected of damaging fertility or the unborn child (baby). Note: There is an additional category which includes products that may cause harm to breast-fed children.
Specific target organ toxicity – single exposure	This hazard class covers products that cause or may cause damage to organs (e.g., liver, kidneys, or blood) following a single exposure. This class also includes a category for products that cause respiratory irritation or drowsiness or dizziness.
Specific target organ toxicity – repeated exposure	This hazard class covers products that cause or may cause damage to organs (e.g., liver, kidneys, or blood) following prolonged or repeated exposure.
Aspiration hazard	This hazard class is for products that may be fatal if they are swallowed and enter the airways.
Biohazardous infectious materials	These materials are microorganisms, nucleic acids or proteins that cause or are a probable cause of infection, with or without toxicity, in humans or animals.
Health hazards not otherwise classified	This class covers products that are not included in any other health hazard class. These hazards have the characteristic of occurring following acute or repeated exposure and have an adverse effect on the health of a person exposed to it—including an injury or resulting in the death of that person. If a product is classified in this class, the hazard statement will describe the nature of the hazard.

Source: Used with the permission of Canadian Centre for Occupational Health and Safety.

most pictograms; the Biohazardous Infectious Materials pictogram maintains its bold black circular border. As shown in Figure 12–10, each pictogram may represent several different classes and categories.

Figure 12–10 WHMIS pictograms.

Pictogram	Symbol	Class	Category and/or Type
	Flame (for fire hazards)	Flammable gases Flammable aerosols Flammable liquids Flammable solids Pyrophoric liquids Pyrophoric solids Pyrophoric gases Self-heating substances and mixtures Substances and mixtures which, in contact with water, emit flammable gases Self-reactive substances and mixtures Organic peroxides Category 1	Category 1 Category 1 and 2 Category 1, 2, and 3 Category 1 and 2 Category 1 Category 1 Category 1 Category 1 and 2 Category 1, 2, and 3 Types B*, C, D, E, and F Types B*, C, D, E, and F
	Flame over circle (for oxidizing hazards)	Oxidizing gases Oxidizing liquids Oxidizing solids	Category 1 Category 1, 2, and 3 Category 1, 2, and 3
	Gas cylinder (for gases under pressure)	Gases under pressure (compressed gas, liquefied gas, refrigerated liquefied gas, and dissolved gas)	
	Corrosion (for corrosive damage to metals, as well as skin and eyes)	Corrosive to metals Skin corrosion/irritation—Skin corrosion Serious eye damage/eye irritation—Serious eye damage	Category 1 Category 1, 1A, 1B, and 1C Category 1
	Exploding bomb (for explosion or reactivity hazards)	Self-reactive substances and mixtures Organic peroxides	Types A and B* Types A and B*
	Skull and crossbones (can cause death or toxicity with short exposure to small amounts)	Acute toxicity—Oral Acute toxicity—Dermal Acute toxicity—Inhalation	Category 1, 2, and 3 Category 1, 2, and 3 Category 1, 2, and 3
	Health hazard (may cause or suspected of causing serious health effects)	Respiratory or skin sensitization—Respiratory sensitizer Germ cell mutagenicity Carcinogenicity Reproductive toxicity Specific Target Organ Toxicity—Single exposure Specific Target Organ Toxicity—Repeated exposure Aspiration hazard	Category 1, 1A, and 1B Category 1, 1A, 1B, and 2 Category 1, 1A, 1B, and 2 Category 1, 1A, 1B, and 2 Category 1 and 2 Category 1 and 2 Category 1

	Exclamation mark (may cause less serious health effects or may damage the ozone layer**)	Acute toxicity—Oral, dermal, inhalation Skin corrosion/irritation—Skin irritation Serious eye damage/eye irritation—Eye irritation Respiratory or skin sensitization—Skin sensitizer Specific target organ toxicity—Single exposure	Category 4 Category 2 Category 2 and 2A Category 1, 1A, and 1B Category 3
	Environment ** (may cause damage to the aquatic environment		
	Biohazardous infectious materials (for organisms or toxins that can cause diseases in people or animals)	Biohazardous infectious materials	Category 1

*Both the Flame and Explosive pictogram are used for self-reactive substances and mixtures (Type B) and organic peroxides (Type B).

**The GHS system also defines an environmental hazard group. This group (and its classes) was not adopted by WHMIS 2015. However, you may see the environmental classes listed on labels and safety data sheets (SDSs). Including information about environmental hazards is allowed by WHMIS 2015.

Source: Used with the permission of Canadian Centre for Occupational Health and Safety.

Worker Education and Training

According to CCOHS, education refers to general or portable information such as how WHMIS works and the hazards of the products. For example, you will learn about the hazard classes (e.g., why a product is called a corrosive and what information you can find on labels and SDSs). Training refers to the site- and job-specific information for employees which will cover your workplace's procedures for storage, handling, use, disposal, emergencies, spills, and what to do in unusual situations. If a workplace uses hazardous products, there must be a WHMIS program in place and workers must be educated and trained so they understand the hazards, and know how to work safely with hazardous products.[7]

Education and training requirements fall under the WHMIS-related occupational health and safety regulations for the provinces, territories, and federally regulated workplaces. Consult your local jurisdiction for information on specific requirements.

Examples of topics that should be covered during education and training include:

- The information on both the supplier label and workplace label, and what that information means.

- The information on the safety data sheet (SDS) and what that information means.

- The procedures required for safe use, handling, and disposal of a hazardous product.

- Any other procedures required when the product is in a pipe, piping system, vessel, tank car, etc.

- The procedure to follow if the hazardous product may be present in the air and a worker may be exposed.

- All procedures that must be followed in an emergency that involves the hazardous product.[8]

All Canadian jurisdictions require that employers develop, implement, and maintain a worker WHMIS education and training program. This education and training is required for hazardous products that workers use as part of their jobs, or for products that workers may be exposed to at work. The employer has the general responsibility to provide all of the hazard information possible either from the supplier or based on information the employer is, or ought to be, aware of. Employers are also expected to consult with the health and safety committee (or representative) when developing, implementing, or reviewing the education and training programs. Education and training may be provided by the employer or by a qualified person or agency that the employer has chosen.

In addition, the employer must review their overall WHMIS education and training program, at least annually, or more often if there is a change in work conditions, hazard information, or similar. Refresher education and training is generally required:

- As needed to protect the worker's health and safety.
- If conditions of the workplace have changed.
- If new products are introduced.
- If the products have changed and now have different hazards.
- When new hazard information becomes available.
- If there is new information about safe use, handing, storage, or disposal.[9]

It is possible that some provinces or territories may add a requirement that employers must periodically evaluate workers' knowledge using written tests, practical demonstrations, or other means. Confirm these details with your local jurisdiction.

Workers must participate in the education and training sessions and follow the safe work procedures established by their employer. Workers should be able to answer these questions for every hazardous product they work with:

- What are the hazards of the product?
- How do I protect myself from those hazards?
- What do I do in case of an emergency?
- Where can I get further information?[10]

Exemptions for Suppliers and Importers

To factor in the needs of all parties and to accommodate unique situations, there are often a number of exceptions to be made when creating a set of rules. In WHMIS 2015, a few of these include:

- For hazardous products packaged in multi-containers, the outer container does not require a WHMIS label if:
  - the inner container label is visible and legible through the outer container, or
  - the outer container has a label that complies with the Transportation of Dangerous Goods (TDG) regulations.
- Small-capacity containers (100 ml or less) are not required to have precautionary or hazard statements on the label.
- Small-capacity containers (3 ml or less) where the label interferes with the normal use of the product are required to have a label that remains durable and legible only while in transport and storage.
- **Bulk shipment** and *unpackaged hazardous products* (such as bulk oil) are not required to have a label regardless of whether they are shipped or picked up at the supplier's location. All label information will be provided within sections 1 and 2 of the SDS, which will allow the purchaser to create a label.

bulk shipment A shipment of a hazardous product that is contained without intermediate packaging.

- For hazardous products that are complex mixtures or that contain an ingredient that is a complex mixture, a supplier may disclose the commonly known generic name of the complex mixture, along with its concentration, if the complex mixture is an ingredient of the hazardous product.

- Products that show a TDG regulation symbol on the label do not require a GHS pictogram for the same hazard.

- Hazardous products that are being transported through Canada, after being imported and before being exported, when the place of initial loading and the final destination are outside of Canada, are not required to have an SDS or label.

- A supplier is allowed to import a product that does not comply with the Hazardous Products Regulations (HPR) labelling requirement if they intend to bring the label into compliance prior to the product being resold in Canada or being used in a Canadian workplace.[11]

A variation on the labelling requirements would include the use of **placards** in place of labels. Placards may be used when a label is not feasible, such as when the product is not in a container or is not completely packaged, or while awaiting the label from the manufacturer. Placards must contain the same information as a workplace label: product identifier, safe handling information, and an SDS statement.

Another type of label found in some workplaces is a **laboratory label**. Two types of laboratory label are used: *supply house labels* and *sample labels*. Supply house labels are used on products for use in laboratories, and sample labels are used on samples sent to laboratories for analysis.

placards Alternative or temporary label used when workplace labels are not practical.

laboratory label Label required on controlled products that are intended solely to be used or tested in a lab. There are two types of laboratory labels: supply house labels and sample labels.

>>> **SAFETY FACT** | Consumer Products

Did you ever wonder why the can of multipurpose lubricant you purchased at the hardware store has different warning symbols on it than the same product you use at work? A different system of labelling is used for consumer products than is used for the workplace. The Consumer Chemicals and Containers Regulations, 2001 (CCCR, 2001) enforced by Health Canada has classified five hazard categories of products: toxic, corrosive, flammable, quick skin-bonding adhesives, and pressurized containers. The degree of the hazard is indicated by the border and the type of hazard by the inner symbol used as shown below in Figure 12–11.

Figure 12–11 Consumer Chemicals and Containers Regulations warning labels.

Symbol	The Danger	Product Examples
Explosive	This **container** can explode if it's heated or punctured. Flying pieces of metal or plastic can cause serious injuries, especially to the eyes.	• water repellant for shoes or boots in an aerosol container • spray paint in an aerosol container
Corrosive	This **product** will burn skin or eyes on contact, or throat and stomach if swallowed.	• toilet bowl cleaner • oven cleaner

(continued)

Figure 12–11 (*Continued*)

Flammable	This **product**, or its fumes, will catch fire easily if it's near heat, flames or sparks.	• contact adhesives • gasoline
Poison	Licking, eating, drinking, or sometimes smelling this **product** will cause illness or death.	• windshield washer fluid • furniture polish

Source: © All rights reserved. Consumer Chemicals and Containers Regulations. Health Canada, 2001. Adapted and reproduced with permission from the Minister of Health, 2016.

TRANSPORTATION OF DANGEROUS GOODS (TDG)

Each day dangerous goods are transported by land, air, and water to destinations around Canada. To minimize the potential harm to humans and the environment, the federal government has enacted legislation to regulate the transport of dangerous goods and the regulations thus created have been adopted by each provincial and territorial jurisdiction. The legislation is titled "Transportation of Dangerous Goods Act, 1992," or the **TDG Act, 1992**.

TDG Act, 1992 Federal legislation governing the transportation of dangerous goods.

safety marks Transportation of Dangerous Goods labelling convention used for the quick identification of dangerous goods.

Dangerous goods **safety marks** give a quick identification of dangerous goods in the event of an emergency situation such as a release of dangerous goods from a means of containment. Part 4 of the TDG Regulations requires dangerous goods safety marks to be displayed on a means of containment containing dangerous goods in transport to show the nature of the danger they pose. A dangerous goods safety mark can be a label, placard, orange panel, sign, mark, letter, word, number or abbreviation, or any combination of these things.

Dangerous goods safety marks are also an information tool for people involved in transportation, including truck drivers, train crews, loading-dock workers, reception personnel at a lab or a hospital, and aircraft loading personnel. Generally, labels are displayed on small means of containment (capacity less than or equal to 450 L) and placards are displayed on large means of containment (capacity greater than 450 L). For example, labels would be displayed on a box, while a placard would be displayed on a truck carrying the box.

The safety marks used in TDG must be:

- visible;
- legible;
- displayed against a background of contrasting colour;
- made of durable, weather-resistant material that will resist detachment or deterioration in the conditions to which they will be exposed; and
- displayed in the appropriate colour (safety marks must not be faded).[12]

Labels and placards are used to identify which of the nine classes of goods are being transported or packaged. During an emergency, labels and placards allow the responder to identify the transported product and assist in protecting people and mitigating environmental damage. The safety marks used for each class are illustrated in Figure 12–12. The nine classes are:

Class 1 – Explosives, including explosives within the meaning of the Explosives Act.

Class 2 – Gases: compressed, deeply refrigerated, liquefied, or dissolved under pressure.

Class 3 – Flammable and combustible liquids.

Class 4 – Flammable solids; substances liable to spontaneous combust; substances that, on contact with water, emit flammable gases (water-reactive substances).

Class 5 – Oxidizing substances, organic peroxides.

Class 6 – Toxic and infectious substances.

Class 7 – Radioactive materials and radioactive prescribed substances within the meaning of the Atomic Energy Control Act.

Class 8 – Corrosives.

Class 9 – Miscellaneous products, substances, or organisms considered by the Governor-in-Council to be dangerous to life, health, property, or the environment when handled, offered for transport, or transported and prescribed to be included in this case.[13]

While the act includes components relating to education for those packaging and transporting the dangerous goods, enforcement and identification of the transported goods are key elements. For those contravening the TDG Act, penalties can range from $50,000 for a first offence to $100,000 for subsequent offences and up to 2 years in prison for an indictable offence.

Figure 12–12 Safety Marks used for each class in the TDG system.

Safety Marks used for each Classes in the TDG Systems	
Safety Mark	**TDG Class**
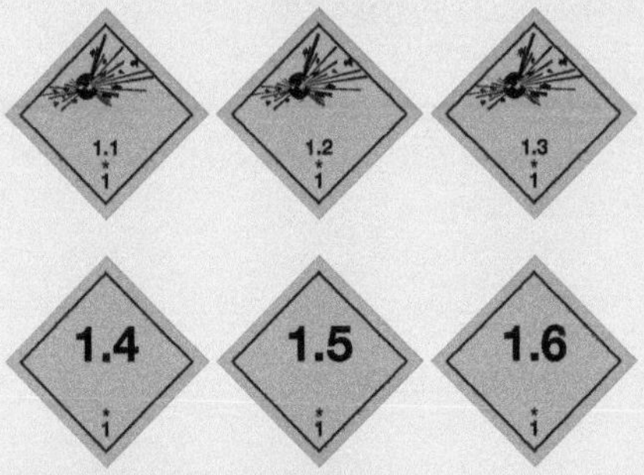	Class 1 Explosives Divisions 1–6 differentiated on the basis of hazard
	Class 2 Compressed Gases Division 1: Flammable Gases Division 2: Nonflammable, Non-toxic Division 3: Toxic Gases Division 4: Corrosive Gases Anhydrous Ammonia

(continued)

Figure 12–12 (Continued)

	Class 3 Flammable Liquids Divisions 1–3 differentiated on the basis of flashpoint and form of transport
	Class 4 Flammable Solids, Spontaneously Combustible, Dangerous When Wet Division 1: Flammable Solids Division 2: Substances Liable to Spontaneous Combustion Division 3: Substances That Emit Flammable Gases on Contact with Water
	Class 5 Oxidizing Substances and Organic Peroxides Division 1: Oxidizing Substances Division 2: Organic Peroxides
	Class 6 Poisonous and Infectious Substances Division 1: Poisonous Substances Division 2: Infectious Substances
	Class 7 Radioactive Materials
	Class 8 Corrosives
	Class 9 Miscellaneous Products or Substances Division 1: Miscellaneous Dangerous Goods Division 2: Environmentally Hazardous Substances Division 3: Dangerous Wastes

Source: © Her Majesty the Queen in Right of Canada, represented by the Minister of Transport (2017). This information has been reproduced with the permission of Transport Canada.

SUMMARY

1. Workplace Hazardous Materials Information System (WHMIS) supports the worker's right to know.

2. The WHMIS program is a Canada-wide system that was developed through the cooperation of industry, labour, and government.

3. The WHMIS program came into effect on October 31, 1988. WHMIS 2015 aligns with the Globally Harmonized System for Classifying and Labelling Chemicals (GHS).

4. Hazardous products covered by WHMIS can cause effects ranging from mild irritation to death.

5. Supplier labels are required on all controlled products shipped to the workplace.

6. Supplier labels require the following features: product identifier, hazard pictogram, signal word, hazard statements, precautionary statements, and supplier identifier.

7. Workplace labels need only the product name, safe handling instructions, and a reference to the SDS.

8. Safety data sheets (SDSs) provide technical data on the product and information for safe use.

9. Hazardous products will have at least one hazard class symbol associated with them and this must be visible on the supplier label. There are ten hazard pictograms used in WHMIS 2015.

10. There are 19 physical hazard classes and 12 health hazard classes.

11. The most prominent legislation covering the transportation of dangerous goods in Canada is the federal TDG Act, 1992.

12. The nine classes of goods under the TDG are explosives, gases, flammable and combustible liquids, flammable solids, oxidizing substances, toxic and infectious substances, radioactive materials, corrosives and miscellaneous products.

Key Terms and Concepts

Bulk shipment
Hazardous products
Laboratory label

Placards
Safety marks
Supplier label

TDG Act, 1992
Workplace label

Review Questions

1. How does the WHMIS 2015 program support Canadians' "right to know"?
2. Explain the role of the federal government versus the provinces and territories in enforcing WHMIS legislation.
3. List at least four changes that were made to WHMIS to align with the Globally Harmonized System for Classifying and Labelling Chemicals (GHS).
4. What items are required on a WHMIS 2015 supplier label?
5. What items are required on a WHMIS 2015 workplace label?
6. What information is contained on an SDS?
7. What are the WHMIS hazard class symbols and where are they used?
8. What is the purpose of TDG legislation?
9. What are the nine TDG hazard classes?

Weblinks

Health Canada

https://www.canada.ca/en/health-canada/services/environmental-workplace-health/occupational-health-safety/workplace-hazardous-materials-information-system.html

This is Health Canada's official WHMIS website. Answers to questions about the national program can be found here.

Canadian Centre for Occupational Health and Safety (CCOHS)

http://www.ccohs.ca/oshanswers/chemicals/whmis_ghs/program.html

On this site, CCOHS has summarized many of the key points about the WHMIS 2015 program.

Transport Canada

http://www.tc.gc.ca/eng/tdg/safety-menu.htm

This is Transport Canada's official Transportation of Dangerous Goods web page. Answers to questions about the TDG Act can be found here.

Endnotes

[1] Ontario Ministry of Labour. (February 2001). "Workplace Hazardous Materials Information System (WHMIS): A Guide to the Legislation." [Online]. Available: https://www.labour.gov.on.ca/english/hs/pubs/whmis/whmis_2.php (Retrieved March 11, 2017).

[2] Health Canada. (February 2015). "WHMIS Transition." [Online]. Available: http://www.hc-sc.gc.ca/ewh-semt/occup-travail/whmis-simdut/transition/index-eng.php. (Retrieved March 11, 2017).

[3] Canadian Centre for Occupational Health and Safety. (November 2016). "WHMIS 2015 Fact Sheets." [Online]. Available: http://www.ccohs.ca/products/publications/whmis_ghs/. (Retrieved March 11, 2017).

[4] Ibid.

[5] Canadian Centre for Occupational Health and Safety. (March 2017). "WHMIS 2015 Fact Sheets." [Online]. Available: http://www.ccohs.ca/oshanswers/chemicals/whmis_ghs/labels.html/. (Retrieved March 11, 2017).

[6] Ibid.

[7] Canadian Centre for Occupational Health and Safety. (March 2017). "WHMIS 2015 Fact Sheets." [Online]. Available: http://www.ccohs.ca/oshanswers/chemicals/whmis_ghs/education_training.html/. (Retrieved March 12, 2017).

[8] Ibid.

[9] Ibid.

[10] Ibid.

[11] Ibid.

[12] Health Canada. (February 2017). Part 4, *TDG Regulations, Dangerous Goods Safety Marks*. [Online]. Available: https://www.tc.gc.ca/eng/tdg/clear-part4-476.htm#sec41. (Retrieved March 26, 2017).

[13] Ibid.

Chapter 13
Biological Hazards

The modern health and safety professional must be concerned with various **bloodborne pathogens** including **hepatitis** B (HBV), hepatitis C (HCV), and the human immunodeficiency virus (HIV). In Canada, the **severe acute respiratory syndrome (SARS)** outbreak in 2003 played havoc with the country's health care system and even affected the economy, especially that of the Toronto area. Globally, health care agencies have also had to control the spread of diseases such as **avian influenza**, also known as "bird flu." The H1N1 "swine flu" pandemic in 2009 led to a sharp spike in hospital visits and admissions. In Canada, the 2009 H1N1 influenza pandemic caused 8,678 hospitalizations, 1,473 intensive care unit admissions, and 428 deaths. Responding to this pandemic cost Canada an estimated $2 billion.[1]

Through global trade and worldwide travel, these biological hazards are difficult to contain because they can **mutate** and spread rapidly. In recent years we have seen the spread of Ebola and Zika viruses and the devastation they caused. The World Health Organization (WHO) works with countries and coordinates research into the development of best practices and vaccines to deal with these diseases.

bloodborne pathogens Disease-producing agents found in the blood.

hepatitis An infection or inflammation of the liver.

severe acute respiratory syndrome (SARS) A respiratory infection similar to pneumonia.

avian influenza An infectious disease of birds caused by type A strains of the influenza virus.

mutate Undergo or cause to undergo genetic change. For pathogens, each mutation requires a new vaccine.

BIOLOGICAL AGENTS

biological agents Living things or substances produced by living things that may cause harm to humans.

Harmful **biological agents** are living microorganisms or toxins produced by living plants or animals that have the ability to cause disease or illness in humans. Health care workers and people who work with animals are at the greatest risk of exposure. As with chemical agents, previously discussed, exposure to biological agents may come from inhalation, ingestion, absorption, or through penetration of the skin. Different forms of biological agents may include:

bacteria Microscopic single-cell organisms found in food, water, and air.

- **Bacteria**—Microscopic single-cell organisms found in food, water, and air. Three forms of bacteria are coccus, bacillus, and spirillium. Anthrax and food-borne bacteria such as salmonella and staphylococcus are some of the most commonly known.

virus A microscopic organism that invades a host to reproduce.

- **Virus**—Microscopic organism that invades a host to reproduce. Hepatitis A and B, human immunodeficiency virus (HIV), and rabies are types of viruses of which we often hear.

parasite An animal or plant that lives in or on a host.

- **Parasites**—Organisms that live on or in a host and lay eggs to reproduce. Malaria, a disease to which 40 percent of the world's population is exposed, is caused by the plasmodium falciparum parasite. Tapeworms are another common parasite.

fungi Simple plants that feed on dead or living tissue of other organisms.

- **Fungi**—Simple plants that feed on dead or living tissue of other organisms. Mould, yeast, athlete's foot, and mushrooms are types of fungi.

AIDS IN THE WORKPLACE

AIDS Acquired immunodeficiency syndrome, the condition caused by the human immunodeficiency virus (HIV).

human immunodeficiency virus (HIV) The virus that causes acquired immunodeficiency syndrome (AIDS).

Acquired immunodeficiency syndrome (**AIDS**) is feared, misunderstood, and, therefore, remains one of the most difficult issues that health and safety professionals are likely to face today. Modern health and safety professionals need to know the facts about AIDS and be prepared to use these facts to make the workplace safer. The **human immunodeficiency virus (HIV)** is the virus that causes AIDS. HIV attacks the immune system, resulting in a chronic, progressive illness that leaves infected people vulnerable to opportunistic infections and cancers. Although the medical community has made significant progress in treating the symptoms and slowing the progression of the disease, AIDS is fatal and there is no cure.[2]

intravenous drug user One who is administered drugs by means of injecting them directly into their veins.

While the prevalence of AIDS infections in the health care and other industries is very low, many workers are at a high risk of exposure, especially from interaction with high-risk groups like **intravenous drug users** and those who have unprotected sex with multiple partners. The table in Figure 13–1 lists a number of high-risk occupations and the protective measures that workers in those occupations should take.

Figure 13–1 Preventive measures for occupations with potential exposure to the AIDS virus.

Preventive Measures for Reducing Occupational Exposure to the AIDS Virus	
Occupation	Preventive Measures
Surgeons, nurses, and nurses aides	Wash hands. Use gloves. Wear goggles, gowns, and masks if splashing of body fluids is expected. Use disposable needles, syringes, and devices for mouth-to-mouth resuscitation. Bag and label contaminated linen.

(continued)

Physicians and laboratory workers	Wash hands. Use coats and gloves. Wear goggles, gowns, and masks if splashing of body fluids is expected. Use disposable needles and syringes, mechanical pipetting devices, and biological safety cabinets. Disinfect work surfaces and equipment with sodium hypochlorite solution.
Ambulance workers	Wash hands. Use gloves. Use disposable needles, syringes, and devices for mouth-to-mouth resuscitation.
Dentists and other dental workers	Wash hands. Use gloves. Use disposable needles and syringes. Use goggles, gowns, and masks if splashing of blood is expected.
Embalmers	Wash hands. Use gloves, gowns, boot-covers, goggles, and masks. Use disposable surgical instruments. Sterilize reusable equipment. Disinfect work surfaces with sodium hypochlorite solution.
Police and firefighters	Wash hands. Use gloves. Use disposable devices for mouth-to-mouth resuscitation.
Mental health institution workers and correctional service workers	Wash hands. Use gloves. Keep cleaning equipment in restricted areas. Use disposable devices for mouth-to-mouth resuscitation.
Cleaners	Wash hands. Use gloves. Keep cleaning equipment in restricted areas.
Laundry workers	Wash hands. Use gloves.
Incinerator attendants	Wash hands. Use gloves.
Post-mortem attendants	Wash hands. Use gloves. Wear goggles, masks, and boot-covers if splashing of blood and body fluids is expected. Bag, label, and incinerate wastes.

Source: Canadian Centre for Occupational Health and Safety (CCOHS). October 29, 1997. "HIV/AIDS in the Workplace." Available: http://www.ccohs.ca/oshanswers/diseases/aids/aids.html.

The prevalence of AIDS, in 2014, among Canadians was demonstrated by the following facts:

- An estimated 75,500 Canadians were living with HIV at the end of 2014.

- The HIV prevalence rate was 212 per 100,000 people living in Canada.

- An estimated 16,020 people, just over 1 in 5 people, living with HIV in Canada were unaware that they had HIV. This represented 21 percent of the estimated number of people living with HIV.

- Canadians living with HIV included:
  - 39,630 gay men and other men who have sex with men. This represented 53 percent of all people living with HIV in Canada.

- 13,960 people who used injection drugs. (19 percent)
- 23,700 people whose HIV status was attributed to heterosexual sex. (31 percent)
- 610 people whose HIV status could not be attributed to sex or intravenous drug use. (1 percent)
- 6,850 Aboriginal people. (9 percent)
- 16,880 females. (22 percent)

- Populations with higher rates of infection included:
  - Three Aboriginal populations that had incidence rates 2.7 times higher than people of other ethnicities.
  - People from HIV-endemic countries (living in Canada) who had incidence rates 6.3 times higher than people of other ethnicities (living in Canada).
  - Men who had sex with men had incidence rates 131 times higher than other men.
  - People who injected drugs had incidence rates 59 times higher than people who did not inject drugs.
  - Males had incidence rates 3.4 times higher than females.[3]

Symptoms of AIDS

AIDS and various related conditions are caused when humans become infected with the human immunodeficiency virus (HIV). This virus attacks the human immune system, rendering the body incapable of repelling disease-causing microorganisms. Symptoms of the onset of AIDS are:

- Enlarged lymph nodes that persist.
- Persistent fevers.
- Involuntary weight loss.
- Fatigue.
- Diarrhea that does not respond to standard medications.
- Purplish spots or blotches on the skin or in the mouth.
- White, cheesy coating on the tongue.
- Night sweats.
- Forgetfulness.

How HIV Is Transmitted

HIV is transmitted in any of the following three ways: (1) unprotected sexual contact, (2) contact with blood or blood products, and (3) from mother to child during pregnancy or childbirth. Any act in which body fluids are exchanged can result in infection if either person is infected. The following groups of people are at the highest level of risk with regard to HIV: (1) those who have unprotected sexual contact with a person infected with HIV, (2) IV drug users who share needles, (3) people with a history of multiple blood transfusions or blood-product transfusions, such as hemophiliacs.

How HIV Is Not Transmitted

There is a great deal of misunderstanding about how HIV is transmitted. This can cause inordinate fear of HIV-positive workers among fellow employees. Health and safety professionals should know enough about HIV transmission to enable them to reduce employees' fears about being infected through casual contact with an HIV-positive person.

Occupational Health & Safety magazine provides the following clarifications concerning the ways in which AIDS is *not* transmitted:

> AIDS is a blood-borne, primarily sexually transmitted disease. It is not spread by casual social contact in schools, workplaces, public washrooms, or restaurants. It is not spread via handshakes, social kissing, coughs, sneezes, drinking fountains, swimming pools, toilet facilities, eating utensils, office equipment, or by being next to an infected person.
>
> No cases of AIDS have been reported from food being either handled or served by an infected person in an eating establishment.
>
> HIV is not spread by giving blood. New needles and transfusion equipment are used for every donor.
>
> HIV is not spread by mosquitoes or other insects.
>
> HIV is not spread by sexual contact between uninfected individuals—whether homosexual or heterosexual—if an exclusive sexual relation has been maintained.[4]

How AIDS Is Impacting the Workplace

The first step in dealing with AIDS at the company level is to develop a comprehensive AIDS policy. Health and safety professionals should be part of the team that drafts the initial policy and updates an existing policy. If a company has no AIDS policy, the health and safety professional should encourage the company to develop one. In all likelihood, most companies won't take much convincing.

According to Peter Minetos,

> Industry is doing its part to eliminate any unnecessary fear: Nearly half of companies surveyed offer their employees literature or other materials to keep them informed on the disease; more than half have an Employee Assistance Program (EAP) to deal with emotional problems concerning AIDS; two-thirds of those who have not yet addressed AIDS with employees plan to do so in the future.[5]

AIDS is having a widely felt impact in the workplace, particularly on employers. According to Minetos, employers are feeling the impact of AIDS in increased insurance premiums and health care costs, time-on-the-job losses, decreased productivity, AIDS-related lawsuits, increased stress, and related problems that result from misconceptions about AIDS.[6]

》》 DISCUSSION CASE   What Is Your Opinion?

David Westcott isn't sure what to do. As health and safety director for Peace Machining and Manufacturing, he is concerned about protecting employees from workplace hazards. On the other hand, he is also concerned about protecting the privacy of his employees. Hence the dilemma that he now faces: He has just learned that a lathe operator is HIV positive. Cuts and abrasions from metal chips are common among lathe operators and other machinists. In fact, the machining supervisor had to administer minor first aid to a machine operator less than an hour ago. What if the lathe operator is cut or scraped? What about the blood? Westcott wonders if he should warn the other employees about the operator's condition. What is your opinion?

The starting point for dealing with AIDS in the workplace is the development of a company policy that covers AIDS and other blood-borne pathogens. The policy should, at a minimum, cover the following areas: employee rights, testing, and education.

HEPATITIS B VIRUS (HBV) IN THE WORKPLACE

Although the spread of HIV receives more attention, there is a far greater risk from the spread of the hepatitis B virus (HBV). This blood-borne virus averages approximately six times the new cases per year compared with HIV. The hepatitis B virus is extremely strong compared with HIV. For example, it can live on surfaces for up to a week if it is exposed to air. Hepatitis B is also much more concentrated than HIV.

Hepatitis B is caused by a double-shelled virus. It can be transmitted in the following ways:

- Contact with blood
- Contact with body fluids including tears, saliva, and semen

The hepatitis B virus can live in body fluids for years. Carriers of the virus are at risk themselves, and they place others at risk. Persons infected with HBV may contract chronic hepatitis, cirrhosis of the liver, and primary hepatocellular carcinoma. An HBV-infected individual is over 300 times more likely to develop primary liver cancer than an uninfected individual from the same environment. Unfortunately, it is possible to be infected and not know it because the symptoms can vary widely from person to person.

The symptoms of hepatitis B are varied but include:

- Jaundice
- Joint pain
- Rash
- Internal bleeding

 SAFETY FACT Employees at Greatest Risk from Viral Hepatitis

Employees who are at the greatest risk of necrosis of liver cells from viral hepatitis are those who are elderly and those who have diabetes mellitus, cancer, or any other illness severe enough to require surgery or transfusions.

HBV Vaccination

Universal immunization against HBV is now part of the publicly funded vaccine programs offered in all provinces and territories. Immunization with hepatitis B vaccine is recommended for those people who are at increased risk of occupational infection, namely, those frequently exposed to blood, blood products, and body fluids that may contain the virus.[7] The vaccination must be offered within 10 days of a person's initial assignment to a job where exposure to blood or other potentially infectious materials can be "reasonably anticipated."

The hepatitis B vaccination is a noninfectious, yeast-based vaccine given in three injections in the arm. It is prepared from recombinant yeast cultures, rather than human blood or plasma. Thus, there is no risk of contamination from other blood-borne pathogens, nor is there any chance of developing HBV from the vaccine.

The second injection should be given 1 month after the first, and the third injection 6 months after the initial dose. More than 90 percent of those vaccinated develop immunity to the hepatitis B virus. To ensure immunity, it is important for individuals to receive all three injections. At this point it is unclear how long the immunity lasts, so booster shots may be required at some point in the future.

The vaccine causes no harm to those who are already immune or to those who may be HBV carriers. Although employees may opt to have their blood tested for antibodies to determine the need for the vaccine, employers may not make such screening a condition of receiving the vaccination, nor are employers required to provide prescreening.

Each employee should receive counselling from a health care professional when the vaccination is offered. This discussion will help an employee determine whether inoculation is necessary.

HEPATITIS C VIRUS (HCV) IN THE WORKPLACE

Hepatitis C virus (HCV) infection is a common chronic blood-borne infection. More than 5,000 individuals in Canada—mostly young people—get this virus each year.[8] Most of these people are chronically infected and may be unaware of their infection because they are not clinically ill. Infected people serve as a source of transmission to others and are at risk for chronic liver disease or other HCV-related chronic diseases during the first two or more decades following the initial infection. HCV is transmitted primarily through large or repeated direct percutaneous exposures to blood. Those most likely to get hepatitis C are:

- Drug users who share needles, spoons, straws, and other drug-related equipment that are contaminated with HCV.
- People who get tattoos or body parts pierced with dirty or unsterile needles and ink.
- People who received blood transfusions or blood products before 1992.
- People who share a razor or toothbrush with someone who has hepatitis C.[9]

Preventing and controlling HCV requires a comprehensive strategy comprised of primary and secondary activities.

Primary prevention activities:

- Screening and testing blood, plasma, organ, tissue, and semen donors.
- Virus inactivation of plasma-derived products.
- Risk-reduction counselling and services.
- Implementation and maintenance of infection control practices.

Secondary prevention activities:

- Identification, counselling, and testing of persons at risk.
- Medical management of infected persons.
- Education and training.
- Monitoring the effectiveness of prevention activities to develop improved prevention methods.

>>> **SAFETY FACT** Hepatitis C

Hepatitis C can be treated. It is important to find out if you have the virus and get treatment as soon as possible.

251,000 Canadians are infected with hepatitis C and, because there are no symptoms, 95,000 of them don't know it.

Most people newly infected with hepatitis C have no symptoms and are unaware of their infection, but they are still infectious.

Avoid the risk of hepatitis C: Don't share needles or intravenous drug equipment.

Hepatitis C is *not* spread by hugging, kissing, or shaking hands. It is *not* spread by means of food or water.

More than 5,000 Canadians—many of whom are young people—are infected with the hepatitis C virus each year.

There is no vaccine for hepatitis C.[10]

BREAKING THE CHAIN OF INFECTION

Outbreaks of diseases are not only a public health concern, but can have a major impact on workers and the organization. In spite of the public awareness campaigns, the empirical data supporting the importance of good hygiene practices, and the effectiveness of many vaccines, there are frequent outbreaks of different diseases, often due to low participation rates in vaccination campaigns. For example, measles (rubella), mumps (epidemic parotitis), and chicken pox (varicella) are diseases for which we can be very effectively immunized, yet these diseases continue to show up among school-age children and other populations.

The severe acute respiratory syndrome (SARS) outbreak in 2003 was a global concern that created chaos for many Canadian health care organizations and agencies. To control the pandemic caused by this respiratory infection similar to pneumonia, numerous infection and control procedures and standards were created. Many of these procedures apply to all types of infectious diseases.

Immunization

immunization The process whereby a person is made immune or resistant to an infectious disease, typically by the administration of a vaccine. Vaccines stimulate the body's own immune system to protect the person against subsequent infection or disease.

chain of infection A series of conditions that allow a disease to spread.

With today's crowded schools, malls, transportation, and recreational events, the opportunities for the spread of disease is tremendous. The transmission of some diseases can be devastating for certain populations, and clearly the benefits of these vaccines far outweigh the risks to the recipient and the people around them. **Immunization**, along with good hygiene practice, is needed to break the **chain of infection**.

Infection control principles employed by health care workers are aimed at breaking one or more links in this chain. The lost time and productivity of workers is one concern, but these workers passing the diseases on to their clients and colleagues can have a huge impact, especially in hospitals and senior care centres. Immunization breaks the chain of infection.

Handwashing

Handwashing is the most important hygiene measure in preventing the spread of infection. Hands must be washed before and after contact with a patient, after contact with body fluids, and after contact with items known to be contaminated with respiratory secretions. Plain soap may be used for routine handwashing.

Gloves

Gloves should be used as an additional measure, not as a substitute for handwashing. They should be used before contact with a patient, and they should be removed and hands washed prior to leaving a patient's room.

Gowns

Long-sleeved gowns should be worn by all health care workers if direct contact with the an infected patient is anticipated.

Mask, Eye Protection, Face Shield

Health Canada and the Centers for Disease Control and Prevention (CDC) in the US recommend N95-type respirators for use by health care workers during all patient contact.

N95 filters belong to a group of air-purifying particulate filters certified by the National Institute for Occupational Health and Safety (NIOSH), and these certifications are used in Canada.

Particulate respirators are the same as what used to be called dust, fume, and mist respirators or masks. N-type filters are for airborne solid and water-based particulates. The 95 in N95 means that the filter can capture or stop 95 percent of particulates 0.3 microns (micrometres) in diameter; but, to be effective, the respirators must be well-fitted to the face to prevent leakage around the edges.

Surgical masks, also known as procedural or medical masks, may offer some protection, but are designed to help prevent contamination of the work environment from large particles generated by the wearer/worker. Surgical masks may also be used to help reduce the risk of splashes or sprays of blood, body fluids, secretions, and excretions from reaching the wearer's mouth and nose. Surgical masks may also be worn by patients to help limit the spread of infections.[11]

PREVENTING AND RESPONDING TO NEEDLESTICK INJURIES

Needlestick injuries are not a major concern in most workplaces outside of the health care industry, but they are enough of a concern that health and safety professionals should know how to prevent them and how to respond when they occur. An excellent source of help for health and safety professionals concerning needlestick injuries is the National Institute for Occupational Health and Safety (NIOSH). NIOSH maintains a web page dedicated specifically to the prevention of needlestick injuries at http://www.cdc.gov/niosh/topics/bbp/safer.

needlestick injuries Injuries obtained through inadvertent puncture of the skin with hypodermic needles.

This web page recommends a five-step model for developing, establishing, and maintaining a needlestick-prevention program:

1. Form a sharps-injury prevention team.
2. Identify priorities.
3. Identify and screen safer medical devices.
4. Evaluate safer medical devices.
5. Institute and monitor the use of the safer medical devices selected.[12]

Safety Needles

Employees who work with needles for taking blood, giving injections, or inserting intravenous systems should be considered at high risk for becoming infected with HIV, hepatitis, or other blood-borne illnesses. Whether inserting an IV, taking blood, or giving a vaccination, medical personnel live with the reality of potential blood-borne pathogen exposure every minute of the day. Studies have consistently shown that 50 to 85 percent of health care workers who have contracted a blood-borne disease cannot identify when or how they were exposed to blood-borne pathogens.

In addition, whereas more than one million accidental needlesticks are reported each year, it is estimated that 66 percent of accidental needlesticks go unreported. With the use of injury prevention devices, the Centers for Disease Control and Prevention estimates that the number of accidental needlesticks could be reduced by 76 percent. However, not all devices that are called "safe" are safer. Injury prevention devices on syringes, IVs, catheters, blood-drawing equipment, vaccination instruments, lancets, and scalpels must require only one-handed operation to be considered safer. Some sheathing devices require two-handed operation and often result in an increase in needlestick injuries. Figure 13–2 contains examples of syringes with safety features.

Figure 13-2 Examples of syringes with safety features.

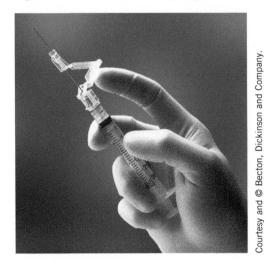

Courtesy and © Becton, Dickinson and Company.

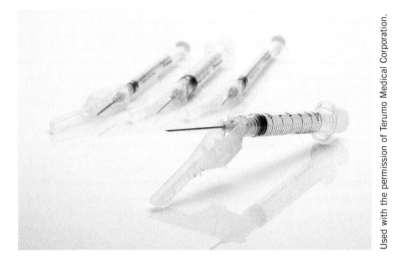

Used with the permission of Terumo Medical Corporation.

Responding to Needlestick Incidents

When, in spite of your best efforts at prevention, a needlestick injury does occur, the following steps are recommended:

1. Encourage bleeding where the skin is penetrated.

2. Wash the penetration area thoroughly with copious amounts of warm, soapy water (do not use a scrub brush).

3. If the eyes are somehow involved, wash them immediately with water.

4. If the mouth is somehow involved, rinse it immediately with water, but do not swallow.

5. Get the injured employee to the hospital as soon as possible.

6. Contact a clinical virologist.

7. Make sure that management personnel for the company in question are fully informed of the situation.[13]

METHICILLIN-RESISTANT STAPHYLOCOCCUS AUREUS (MRSA) IN THE WORKPLACE

methicillin-resistant Staphylococcus aureus (MRSA) A type of bacteria that is resistant to many antibiotics.

Methicillin-resistant Staphylococcus aureus (MRSA) is a potentially life-threatening infection caused by bacteria that mutate and become stronger and more resistant to antibiotics with each mutation. The problems associated with MRSA are now so widespread that it must be considered a workplace hazard. In fact, workers' compensation claims relating to MRSA are on the rise.[14] According to G. Burris, five events have led to the emergence of MRSA:

1. Bacteria are able to mutate.

2. Antibiotics have been overprescribed for decades (allowing bacteria to become resistant).

3. People stop taking their antibiotics as soon as symptoms subside rather than finishing the prescription as instructed.

4. Antibacterial soaps have proliferated and been overused (killing good bacteria and allowing harmful bacteria to become resistant).

5. There is a new tendency of people to skip showers after strenuous exercise or physical activity (dirty, moist, and salty skin is the perfect breeding environment for MRSA).[15]

Prevention Steps

1. **Ensure that employees wash their hands regularly and shower after strenuous physical activity.** MRSA and other bacteria live on the skin, making them vulnerable to handwashing and showers.

2. **Ensure that employees treat and cover wounds.** Breaks in the skin are the primary way that MRSA gains entry into the body. No matter how minor the cut, scratch, or abrasion may be, make sure it is cleaned, an over-the-counter wound-care treatment is applied, and the wound is covered.

3. **Do not allow employees to share personal items.** If your employees can shower and shave at work, do not allow them to share razors. MRSA can live in razors and on towels, benches, and clothing.

4. **Encourage employees to use a dryer rather than clothesline for drying towels and clothing.** The heat of a dryer can kill bacteria, but items hung out to dry are a potential breeding ground for MRSA.

5. **Ensure that employees wipe down and properly clean tools, work gear, and equipment.** Situations in which workers share tools, equipment, and gear are ripe for the spread of MRSA. Cleaning these items several times during the day and between shift changes can help prevent the infection. This also applies to gym equipment and benches if your employees work out.[16]

SUMMARY

1. Various forms of biological agents include bacteria, viruses, parasites, and fungi.

2. HIV is known to be transmitted in three ways: sexual contact, contact with blood or blood products, or from mother to child during pregnancy or childbirth. HIV is not spread through casual contact such as handshakes, eating utensils, sharing of toilet facilities, or coughing.

3. High-risk groups with regard to HIV are IV drug users, people with a history of multiple blood transfusions (including hemophiliacs), and sexually promiscuous people who do not take appropriate precautions during sex.

4. The following precautions will help to reduce the chances of contracting HIV: mutually monogamous relationship with an infection-free partner; avoidance of sex with a high-risk person without taking proper precautions; no use of intravenous drugs or, if you use, no sharing of needles; use of a protective device while practising live or simulated CPR; and use of safety needles.

5. AIDS is having an impact on the workplace in the form of higher insurance premiums, time-on-the-job losses, decreased productivity, cost of AIDS-related lawsuits, and increased stress.

6. A corporate AIDS policy should have at least three components: employee rights, testing, and education.

7. Hepatitis B (HBV) poses an even greater threat than HIV. It is caused by a double-shelled virus. HBV is transmitted through blood, tears, saliva, and semen. It can stay alive for years in body fluids.

8. Hepatitis C (HCV) infection is a common chronic blood-borne infection. Approximately 5,000 new cases are diagnosed in Canada every year. HCV is transmitted primarily through direct percutaneous exposure to blood.

9. The five-step model for preventing needlestick injuries is: (1) form a sharps-injury prevention team, (2) identify priorities, (3) identify and screen safer devices, (4) evaluate the safer devices, (5) institute and monitor the use of safer devices.

10. Methicillin-resistant Staphylococcus aureus (MRSA) is a potentially life-threatening infection caused by bacteria that mutate and become stronger and more resistant to antibiotics with each mutation.

Key Terms and Concepts

AIDS
Avian influenza
Bacteria
Biological agents
Bloodborne pathogens
Chain of infection
Fungi
Hepatitis

Human immunodeficiency
   virus (HIV)
Immunization
Intravenous drug user
Methicillin-resistant
   Staphylococcus aureus
   (MRSA)
Mutate

Needlestick injuries
Parasite
Severe acute respiratory
   syndrome (SARS)
Virus

Review Questions

1. What are four types of biological agents?
2. What do the acronyms *AIDS* and *HIV* mean?
3. List five symptoms associated with AIDS.
4. What are the three known ways that HIV is transmitted?
5. List the groups of people who are considered high risk with regard to AIDS.
6. List five ways that AIDS is *not* transmitted.
7. Describe the ways in which AIDS is having an impact in the workplace.
8. What are the minimum components of a corporate AIDS policy?
9. List four ways to guard against contracting HIV.
10. Explain why HBV poses more of a problem for safety personnel than HIV does.
11. Explain the primary prevention strategies for HCV.
12. What are the recommended steps in a needlestick prevention program?
13. What are five factors that contribute to the emergence of MSRA?

Weblinks

CCOHS

https://www.ccohs.ca/oshanswers/biol_hazards/

This Canadian Centre for Occupational Health and Safety web page has information on the biological hazards mentioned in the chapter, plus several others.

Health Canada / Public Health Agency of Canada

https://www.canada.ca/en/health-canada.html

Health Canada collaborates internationally and with its provincial and territorial counterparts to protect the health of Canadians against current and emerging health threats.

World Health Organization

http://www.who.int/en/

On this World Health Organization web page, the Department of Communicable Disease Surveillance and Response informs the reader about what the WHO is doing on a global scale to protect against outbreaks of diseases such as SARS and avian flu.

Endnotes

[1] National Collaboration Centre for Infectious Diseases. (2014). Canadian Healthcare Workers' Experiences during Pandemic H1N1 Influenza: Lessons from Canada's Response. [Online]. Available: https://nccid.ca/publications/canadian-healthcare-workers-experiences-during-pandemic-h1n1-influenza/. (Retrieved March 31, 2017).

[2] Health Canada. (May 2011). "HIV and AIDS." [Online]. Available: http://www.hc-sc.gc.ca/hc-ps/dc-ma/aids-sida-eng.php. (Retrieved April 1, 2017).

[3] Public Health Agency of Canada. (2017). "Summary: Estimates of HIV Incidence, Prevalence and Proportion Undiagnosed in Canada, 2014." [Online]. Available: http://www.catie.ca/sites/default/files/2014-HIV-Estimates-in-Canada-EN.pdf. (Retrieved April 1, 2017).

[4] "AIDS—The Basic Facts." *Occupational Health & Safety* 10, no. 3: 6.

[5] P. Minetos. "Corporate America vs. AIDS." *Safety & Health* 138, no. 6: 34.

[6] Ibid.

[7] Canada.ca. (March 2017). Page 7: Canadian Immunization Guide: Part 4 - Active Vaccines. [Online]. Available: https://www.canada.ca/en/public-health/services/publications/healthy-living/canadian-immunization-guide-part-4-active-vaccines/page-7-hepatitis-b-vaccine.html. (Retrieved December 21, 2017).

[8] Canada.ca. (September 09, 2009). "Hepatitis C" [Online]. Available: http://www.phac-aspc.gc.ca/hepc/hepatitis_c/drhepc. (Retrieved December 21, 2017).

[9] Ibid.

[10] Public Health Agency of Canada. (March 24, 2004). "Hepatitis C: About Hepatitis C." [Online]. Available: http://www.phac-aspc.gc.ca/hepc/hepatitis_c/aboutfacts.html. (Retrieved January 29, 2005).

[11] Canadian Centre for Occupational Health and Safety. (July 11, 2017). "OHS Answers: Respirators - Respirators Versus Surgical Masks." [Online]. Available: http://www.ccohs.ca/oshanswers/prevention/ppe/surgical_mask.html. (Retrieved December 21, 2017).

[12] "Web-Based Information Could Help Prevent Needlestick Injuries." *Occupational Health & Safety* 17, no. 11 (November 2002): 3.

[13] B. C. Yorker. "AIDS Testing." *AAOHN Journal* 36, no. 5: 231.

[14] G. Burris. "Preventing MSRA at Work." [Online]. Available: nsc.org/safetyhealth/pages/3.11workplacesolutionspreventingMRSA.aspx#.UToKfNbQq9E. (Retrieved July 8, 2013).

[15] Ibid.

[16] Ibid.

Chapter 14

Ergonomic Hazards: Work-Related Musculoskeletal Disorders (WMSDs)

MAJOR TOPICS

- Ergonomics Defined
- Human Factors and Ergonomic Hazards
- Factors Associated with Physical Stress
- Ergonomic Regulations and Standards in Canada
- Common Indicators of Problems
- Identifying Specific Ergonomic Problems
- Ergonomic Problem-Solving Strategies
- Economics of Ergonomics
- Work-Related Musculoskeletal Disorders (WMSDs)

The history of workplace development in the Western world is characterized by jobs and technologies designed to improve processes and productivity. All too often in the past, too little attention was given to the impact of the job process or technology on workers. As a result, work processes and machines have sometimes been unnecessarily dangerous. Another result has been that new technologies have sometimes failed to live up to expectations. This is because, even in the age of high technology, human involvement in work processes is still the key to the most significant and enduring productivity improvements. If a machine or system is uncomfortable, difficult, overly complicated, or dangerous to use, human workers will not be able to derive its full benefit.

The proliferation of uncomfortable and dangerous workplace conditions, whether created by job design or unfriendly technologies, is now widely recognized as harmful to productivity, quality, and worker health and safety. The advent of the science of ergonomics is making the workplace conform better to human characteristics and capabilities. This, in turn, is making the workplace a safer and healthier place.

ERGONOMICS DEFINED

Minimizing the amount of physical stress in the workplace requires continuous study of the ways in which people and technology interact. The insight gained from this study must then be used to improve the interaction. This is a description of the science of **ergonomics**. For the purpose of this book, ergonomics is defined as the science of conforming the workplace and all of its elements to the worker.

ergonomics The science of conforming the workplace and all of its elements to the worker.

Ergonomics is a multidisciplinary science that seeks to conform the workplace and all of its physiological aspects to the worker. Ergonomics involves the following:

- Using special design and evaluation techniques to make tasks, objects, and environments more compatible with human abilities and limitations.

- Seeking to improve productivity and quality by reducing workplace stressors, reducing the risk of injuries and illnesses, and increasing efficiency.

The word *ergonomics* is derived from the Greek language. *Ergon* is Greek for *work*; *nomos* means *laws*. Therefore, in a literal sense, ergonomics means *work laws*. In practice, it consists of the scientific principles (laws) applied in minimizing the physical stress associated with the workplace (work). Figure 14–1 summarizes some of the widely accepted benefits of ergonomics.

Figure 14–1 Benefits of ergonomics.

- Improved health and safety for workers
- Higher morale throughout the workplace
- Improved quality
- Improved productivity
- Improved competitiveness
- Decreased absenteeism and turnover
- Fewer workplace injuries/health problems

While there are benefits to be derived from ergonomics, there are also problems, both financial and health-related, that can result from giving too little attention to ergonomics. The matter is complicated further because health problems tend to multiply a company's financial problems. Consequently, modern health and safety professionals need to be well versed in ergonomics.

HUMAN FACTORS AND ERGONOMIC HAZARDS

When the topic of ergonomics is discussed, the term **human factors** will usually find its way into the conversation.[1] But what is meant by the term? Tillman and Tillman define it as follows:

human factors The science of human data applied to the environment, workplace, machine, tool, device, or system.

Consumers are demanding safe and effective products. However, not all people have control over products they use. Therefore, all products must be carefully designed. For example, if a child car seat fails because it does not fit the child or is difficult to install, everyone will lose: the child, the parent, the designer, and the manufacturer. . . . Human factors is a profession to help ensure that equipment and systems are safe and easy to operate by human beings. A human factors researcher gathers and analyzes data on human beings (how they work, their size, their capabilities and limitations). A human factors engineer works with designers as a team to incorporate data into designs to make sure people can operate and maintain the product or system. Human factors professionals then determine the skills needed to operate or maintain a finished product. Human factors is difficult to define because it is a compilation of many sciences dealing with both humans and machines. Some of the disciplines human factors experts are trained in include the following: psychology, anthropology, engineering, biology, medicine, education, and physiology.[2]

The terms *ergonomics* and *human factors* are often used interchangeably. While both describe the interaction between the operator and the job demands, a distinction may be made that ergonomics is primarily focused on how work and the work environment affects workers, while human factors is concerned with designs that reduce the potential for human error. In the context of health and safety, both have the same goal—to minimize harm to the worker.

Human Factors Defined

Tillman and Tillman further define human factors as a "science combining research and application of human data."[3] The concept can also be viewed as a science that bridges research about human beings and the application of that research to designing products and systems for human beings.

Human Factors in Action

Tillman and Tillman provide several examples of how the science of human factors fits into the systems design process. Perhaps the best way to get a feel for the concept of human factors is to consider several of these examples.

1. **Predesign analysis.** In this stage of the design process, human factors professionals conduct research to answer such questions as: What is the best way for humans to interact with computers? What factors contribute to fatigue and stress in an office environment? How can designers overcome these factors?
2. **Preliminary design.** In this stage, human factors professionals study machine and human capabilities to determine which tasks should be undertaken manually and which should be automated.
3. **Detail design and development.** In design and development, human factors professionals define the environment required for operator safety, enhanced operator performance, and the reduction or prevention of operator stress and fatigue.
4. **Test and evaluation.** In this stage of the process, human factors professionals test actual humans using the prototype equipment or system.[4]

Human Factors and Safety

Human factors can play an important role in both product safety and workplace safety (where many products are used). What follows is how the science of human factors can help reduce both product and workplace hazards.

1. **Hazard elimination by design.** Human error is frequently the root cause or a contributing cause of accidents on the job. Intelligent design can reduce human errors by providing controls that are simple to understand and operate and by allowing for human–machine interaction that is neither boring nor overly demanding physically.
2. **Provision and location of safety devices.** The design and location of safety devices such as emergency cutoff switches can reduce human error on the job, correspondingly reducing the chances of an accident.

3. **Provision of warning devices.** The colour, location, and wording of warning devices; the pitch and volume of warning signals; and the design of caution markings on gauges and video displays are all important factors in reducing the likelihood of human error that might lead to an accident. The science of human factors can help determine the appropriate way to apply all of these factors in a given setting.

4. **Establishment of procedures/provision of training.** When hazards cannot be realistically designed out of a system, administrative procedures for hazard reduction must be established and training relating to those procedures must be provided. Human factors professionals can help establish appropriate administrative procedures and help develop the necessary training.[5]

FACTORS ASSOCIATED WITH PHYSICAL STRESS

Eight variables that can influence the amount of physical stress experienced on the job are as follows:

1. Sitting versus standing.
2. Stationary versus moveable/mobile.
3. Large demand for strength/power versus small demand for strength/power.
4. Good horizontal work area versus bad horizontal work area.
5. Good vertical work area versus bad vertical work area.
6. Nonrepetitive motion versus repetitive motion.
7. Low surface versus high surface.
8. No negative environmental factors versus negative environmental factors.[6]

Sitting versus Standing

Generally speaking, sitting is less stressful than standing. Standing for extended periods, particularly in one place, can produce unsafe levels of stress on the back, legs, and feet. However, sitting can also be stressful unless the appropriate precautions are taken. These precautions include proper posture, a supportive backrest, and frequent standing/stretching/moving.

Stationary versus Mobile

Stationary jobs are those done primarily at one workstation. Of course, even these jobs involve movement at the primary workstation and occasional movement to other areas. Mobile jobs, on the other hand, require continual movement from one station to another. The potential for physical stress increases with stationary jobs when workers fail to take such precautions as periodically standing/stretching/moving. The potential for physical stress increases with mobile jobs when workers carry materials as they move from station to station.

Large versus Small Demand for Strength/Power

In classifying jobs by these two criteria, it is important to understand that repeatedly moving small amounts of weight over a period of time can have a cumulative effect equal to the amount of stress generated by moving a few heavy weights. Regardless of whether the stress results from lifting a few heavy objects or repeated lifting of lighter objects, jobs that demand larger amounts of strength/power are generally more stressful than those requiring less.

Good versus Bad Horizontal Work Area

horizontal work area The limits of the horizontal plane in which a worker is required to perform a task. A good horizontal work area is designed and positioned so that it does not require a worker to bend forward or to twist the body from side to side.

A good **horizontal work area** is one that is designed and positioned so that it does not require a worker to bend forward or to twist the body from side to side. Horizontal work areas that do require these movements are bad. Bad horizontal work surfaces increase the likelihood of physical stress.

Good versus Bad Vertical Work Area

vertical work area The limits of the vertical plane in which a worker is required to perform a task. A good vertical work area is designed and positioned so that workers are not required to lift their hands above their shoulders or bend down in order to perform any task.

A good **vertical work area** is designed and positioned so that workers are not required to lift their hands above their shoulders or bend down in order to perform any task. Vertical work areas that do require these movements are bad. Bad vertical work areas increase the likelihood of physical stress.

Nonrepetitive versus Repetitive Motion

repetitive motion Short-cycle motion that is repeated continually.

Repetitive motion jobs involve short-cycle motion that is repeated continually. Nonrepetitive jobs involve a variety of tasks that are not, or only infrequently, repeated. Repetition can lead to monotony and boredom. When this happens, the potential for physical stress increases.

>>> SAFETY FACT | Strains and Sprains

A sprain is a stretching or tearing of ligaments, the tough bands of fibrous tissue that connect two bones together in your joints. A strain is a stretching or tearing of muscle or tendons. A tendon is a fibrous cord of tissue that connects muscles to bones.

Injuries associated with poor ergonomics have a significant impact within the Canadian workplace. Strain and sprain injuries account for approximately half of all WCB claims. For example, in Alberta in 2015, sprains or strains continued to be the leading nature of injury accounting for 47.5 percent of lost time claims and 51.2 percent of disabling injury claims. This is more than the next three most common traumatic injuries and disorders: other traumatic injuries and disorders, fractures and dislocations, and superficial wounds.

Source: Based on Alberta Labour. (2016). "2015 Workplace Injury, Disease and Fatality StatisticsProvincial Summary." [Online]. Available: http://work.alberta.ca/documents/2015-ohs-data.pdf.

Low versus High Surface Contact

Surface stress can result from contact with hard surfaces such as tools, machines, and equipment. High surface contact jobs tend to be more physically stressful than low surface contact jobs.

Presence versus Absence of Environmental Factors

environmental factors Characteristics of the environment in which an employee works that can affect his or her state of mind or physical conditions, such as noise or distractions.

Generally, the more **environmental factors** with which a worker has to contend on the job, the more stressful the job. For example, personal protective equipment, although conducive to reducing environmental hazards, can increase the amount of physical stress associated with the job.

ERGONOMIC REGULATIONS AND STANDARDS IN CANADA

During the past decade, most jurisdictions have introduced legislation that directly or indirectly addresses workplace ergonomics. Guidelines, standards, and codes of practice are produced and published by various agencies in Canada. In their legislation, governments often reference various resources from organizations such as the Canadian Standards Association (CSA), the National Institute of Occupational Health and Safety (NIOSH), and others whose research is geared toward developing standards that protect workers from injury and illness.

Certain industries, such as health care, which have a disproportionately high number of musculoskeletal injuries (MSIs) due to client handling, have created excellent resources for their workers. Countless publications are produced to address office ergonomic concerns, which increase as our workforce becomes more sedentary. The Canadian Centre for Occupational Health and Safety (CCOHS) also has a broad range of resources available to help develop safe workplaces, such as the features of a "good" office chair, as seen in Figure 14–2.

Figure 14–2 Ergonomic chair.

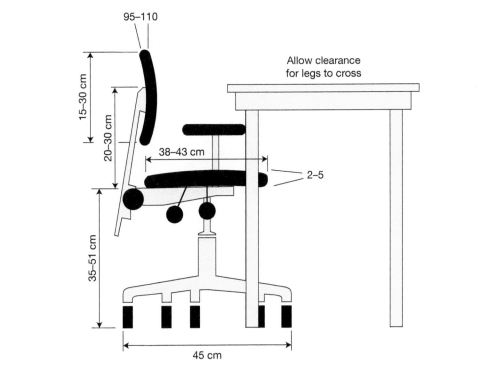

What do I need to know about selecting a good "ergonomic" chair?

The selection of a suitable chair is a critical step in preventing health problems in people who work in a sitting position. With the ergonomics approach, sitting is viewed as a specific, specialized activity, which is influenced by the way that a sitting person interacts with the working environment.

What are the features of a "good" chair?

Some features are mandatory for a good chair regardless of how you intend to use it:

- **Adjustability** – Check to see that seat height is adjustable.
- **Seat height range** – Check whether the seat height can be adjusted to the height recommended for the worker(s) who will use it. Other chairs may have to be selected for very short or tall workers.
- **Backrest** – Check to see that the backrest is adjustable both vertically and in the frontward and backward direction.
- **Seat depth** – Select the seats that suit the tallest and the shortest users.
- **Stability** – Check for the stability of the chair; a five-point base is recommended.

Source: Based on Canadian Centre for Occupational Health and Safety (CCOHS). (November 25, 1999). "OHS Answers, Ergonomics." Available: http://www.ccohs.ca/oshanswers/ergonomics/sitting/sitting_workchairs.html.

The Canadian Auto Workers, with the support of health care and safety associations, has been lobbying for ergonomic legislation that would provide enforceable standards that are consistent throughout the country. The most progressive and comprehensive ergonomic legislation in Canada is that in British Columbia. The health and safety regulations outline the specific requirements for a company's health and safety program to prevent MSIs. A chart showing the seven steps in the MSI prevention process from a booklet by the Workers' Compensation Board of BC, *Preventing Musculoskeletal Injuries, A Guide for Employers and Joint Committees*, is shown below in Figure 14–3.

Figure 14–3   The seven steps in the MSI prevention process.

Step 1
CONSULTATION
Consult with joint health and safety committee or worker health and safety representatives during each step in the MSI process below.

Step 2
EDUCATION
Educate workers about the risk factors, signs and symptoms of injury, and potential health effects.

Step 3
RISK IDENTIFICATION
Identify jobs with a risk of MSI.
Identify risk factors on these jobs.

Step 4
RISK ASSESSMENT
Assess identified risk factors to determine the degree of risk to the workers. Consult with affected workers and representative sample of other workers who perform the same tasks.

Step 5
RISK CONTROL
Implement control measures, where required, to eliminate or minimize the risk to workers.

Step 6
TRAINING
Train the worker in the use of control measures.

Step 7
EVALUATION
Evaluate control measures to determine their effectiveness to eliminate or minimize the risk of MSI. Where the risk has not been effectively controlled, re-examine the task.

Source: Used with the permission of WorkSafeBC (Workers' Compensation Board).

⟩⟩⟩ SAFETY FACT   Keys to a Successful Ergonomics Program

Regardless of the type of organization, the keys to having a successful ergonomics program are:

- Commitment on the part of top management.
- A written program.
- Employee involvement.
- Continuous monitoring of the program.
- Adjusting as necessary based on the results of monitoring.

COMMON INDICATORS OF PROBLEMS

Does my company have ergonomic problems? Are injuries and illnesses occurring because too little attention is paid to ergonomic factors? These are questions that modern health and safety professionals should ask themselves. But how does one answer such questions? According to NIOSH, the factors discussed in the following paragraphs can be examined to determine if ergonomic problems exist in a given company.[6]

Apparent Trends in Accidents and Injuries

By examining accident reports and documents such as workers' compensation accident forms, first-aid logs, insurance forms, and other available records of illnesses or injuries, health and safety professionals can identify trends if they exist. A pattern or a high incidence rate of a specific type of injury may indicate that an ergonomic problem exists.

>>> **SAFETY MYTH** | **Monday Morning Syndrome Debunked**

More workplace injury claims are filed on Monday than on any other day of the week. More than 23 percent of all workers' compensation claims are filed on Monday. This has led to a belief that employees are injuring themselves during non-work-related activities over the weekend and filing workers' compensation claims on Monday. The popular belief is that employees who don't carry personal medical insurance use this ploy to gain medical coverage under workers' compensation. However, a study conducted by Brian P. McCall and David Card under the auspices of the National Bureau of Economic Research raises questions about this belief. According to this study, the high incidence of workers' compensation claims filed on Monday can be attributed to factors such as the following:

- Lack of activity over the weekend, coupled with a sudden return to physical work on Monday.
- Effect of cold weather and age on muscles (Monday morning strains and sprains).

Source: Based on Brian P. McCall and David Card, "Is Workers' Compensation Covering Uninsured Medical Costs?" Working Paper No. 5058, National Bureau of Economic Research, Cambridge, MA, 1996, 18.

Work-Related Musculoskeletal Disorders (WMSDs)

Work-related musculoskeletal disorders (WMSDs) are usually used in reference to any group of painful disorders of muscles, tendons, and nerves. Factors associated with WMSDs include a high level of repetitive work, greater than normal levels of hand force, awkward posture, high levels of vibration, high levels of mechanical stress, extreme temperatures, and repeated hand-grasping or pinch-gripping. By observing the workplace and people at work, health and safety professionals can determine the amount of exposure that employees have to these factors and the potential for ergonomics-related problems. Other names used for WMSDs include:

work-related musculoskeletal disorders (WMSDs) A group of painful disorders of muscles, tendons, and nerves.

- repetitive strain injuries
- repetitive motion injuries
- cumulative trauma disorders
- occupational overuse syndrome
- regional musculoskeletal disorders
- soft tissue disorders

Absenteeism and High Turnover Rates

High absentee rates and high turnover rates can be indicators of ergonomic problems. People who are uncomfortable on the job to the point of physical stress are more likely to miss work or leave for less stressful conditions.

Employee Complaints

A high incidence of employee complaints about physical stress or poor workplace design can indicate the presence of ergonomic problems.

Employee-Generated Changes

Employees tend to adapt the workplace to their needs. The presence of many workplace adaptations, particularly those intended to decrease physical stress, can indicate the presence of ergonomic problems. Have employees added padding, used additional personal protective equipment, brought in extra lighting, or made other modifications? Such employee-generated changes may be evidence of ergonomic problems.

Poor Quality

Poor quality of work, although not exclusively caused by ergonomic problems, might be the result of such problems. Poor quality of work is an indicator that there may be ergonomic problems and suggests a need for closer inspection.

Manual Material Handling

The incidence of musculoskeletal injuries is typically higher in situations that involve a lot of manual material handling. Musculoskeletal injuries increase significantly when the job involves one or more of the following: lifting large objects, lifting bulky objects, lifting objects from the floor, and lifting frequently. When such conditions exist, the company exposes itself to ergonomic problems and therefore needs to place more emphasis on preventing musculoskeletal injuries.

IDENTIFYING SPECIFIC ERGONOMIC PROBLEMS

A task analysis of the job in question can identify specific ergonomic problems. Figure 14–4 lists the types of problems that can be identified by a thorough task analysis.[7]

Figure 14–4 Problems that can be pinpointed by a task analysis.

- Tasks that involve potentially hazardous movements
- Tasks that involve frequent manual lifting
- Tasks that involve excessive wasted motion or energy
- Tasks that are part of a poor operations flow
- Tasks that require unnatural or uncomfortable posture
- Tasks with high potential for psychological stress
- Tasks with a high fatigue factor
- Tasks that could or should be automated
- Tasks that involve or lead to quality control problems

General Observation

General observation of a worker or workers performing the task(s) in question can be an effective task analysis technique. The effectiveness is usually enhanced if the workers are not aware that they are being observed. When observing employees at work, be especially attentive to tasks requiring manual material handling and repetitive movements.

Questionnaires and Interviews

Questionnaires and interviews can be used for identifying ergonomic problems. Questionnaires are easier to distribute, tabulate, and analyze, but interviews generally provide more in-depth information.

Video Recording and Photography

Video recording technology has simplified the process of task analysis considerably. Video records the work being observed as it is done, it is silent so it is not intrusive, and such capabilities as freeze and playback enhance the observer's analysis capabilities significantly. Photography can also enhance the observer's analysis capabilities by recording each motion or step involved in performing a task. If photography is used, be aware that flashes can be disruptive. High-speed film will allow you to take photographs without using a flash.

Drawing or Sketching

Making a neat sketch of a workstation or a drawing showing workflow can help identify problems. Before using a drawing or sketch as part of a task analysis, make sure that it is accurate. Ask an employee who is familiar with the area or process that is sketched to check the drawing.

Measuring the Work Environment

Measurements can help identify specific ergonomic problems. How far must a worker carry the material manually? How high does a worker have to lift an object? How much does an object weigh? How often is a given motion repeated? Answers to these and similar questions can enhance the effectiveness of the analysis process.

Understanding the Ergonomics of Aging

When identifying specific ergonomic problems in the workplace, don't overlook the special challenges presented by aging workers. A good ergonomics program adapts the job to the person. Because nearly 30 percent of the workforce is 45 years of age or older, organizations must be prepared to adapt workstations to employees whose physical needs are different from those of their younger counterparts.

In adapting workstations and processes for employees who are 45 or older, keep the following rules in mind:

- Nerve conduction velocity, hand-grip strength, muscle mass, range of motion, and flexibility all begin to diminish at about age 45.
- Weight and mass tend to increase through the early 50s.
- Height begins to diminish beginning around age 30.
- Lower back pain is more common in people 45 years of age and older.
- Visual acuity at close range diminishes with age.[8]

These rules mean that health and safety professionals cannot take a one-size-fits-all approach to ergonomics. Adaptations for older workers must be individualized and should take aging factors into account.

ERGONOMIC PROBLEM-SOLVING STRATEGIES

The factors that influence stress were explained earlier in this chapter. These factors can be combined in different ways, and the ways in which they are combined determine the type and amount of stress experienced. For the purpose of recommending ergonomic problem-solving strategies, the following combinations can be used:

- Seated repetitive work with light parts
- Seated work with larger parts
- Seated control work
- Standing work
- Standing for heavy lifting and carrying
- Work with hands above chest height
- Work with hand tools
- Work with video display terminals (VDTs)[9]

Seated Repetitive Work with Light Parts

This type of work can produce more physical stress than one may suspect. Back, neck, shoulder, and lower leg pain are commonly associated with this fixed work position and repetitive motion. To solve these problems, it may be necessary to modify both the job and the workstation. Improvement strategies include the following:

- Include other work tasks to break the monotony of repetition.
- Use job rotation, with workers rotating through two or more different jobs.
- Adjust the height of the work surface and/or position.
- Use an adjustable chair equipped with hand, wrist, or arm supports as appropriate.
- Make sure that there is sufficient leg room (height, width, and depth).
- Use ergonomic devices to adjust the height and angle of work (see Figure 14–5).[10]

Figure 14–5 Adjust the angle of work to reduce stress.

Seated Work with Larger Parts

This type of work, which involves interacting with objects that may be too large to manipulate manually, is associated with assembly and welding jobs. Problems associated with this type of work are typically related to posture, illumination, reach, and lifting. Ergonomic strategies for improving work conditions include the following:

- Use technology to lift and position the work for easy access that does not require bending, twisting, and reaching.
- Use supplemental lighting at the work site.
- Use adjustable chairs and work surfaces as appropriate (see Figure 14–6).[11]

Figure 14–6 Use adjustable work surfaces to reduce stress.

Oleksandr Fediuk/123RF

Seated Control Work

This type of work involves sitting in one location and using wheels, levers, knobs, handles, and buttons to control a process, system, or piece of equipment. The physical stress associated with this type of work is typically the result of excessive vibration or bending and twisting to achieve better visibility. Ergonomic strategies for improving work conditions include the following:

- Use an adjustable swivel chair with inflatable back and seat support.
- Provide comfortable and convenient locations for control devices.
- Use control devices that meet the following standards: finger control systems that do not require more than five newtons (1.1 pounds) and hand levers that do not exceed 20 newtons (4.5 pounds).
- Position the control seat so that a clear line of sight exists between the work and the person controlling it.
- Provide a ladder if the workstation is more than 35 cm (14 inches) above ground.[12]

Standing Work

Jobs in this category involve standing without a great deal of repetitive motion, but they do involve handling medium to heavy materials. An example is a machine operator's job (lathe, mill, drill, punch, saw, and so on). Physical stress associated with this type of work includes leg, arm, and back strains. Occasionally, side strains occur when bending and twisting are necessary. Ergonomic strategies for improving work conditions include the following:

- Use adjustable machines and work surfaces to ensure the optimum height and position. When the machine height cannot be adjusted, portable platforms can serve the same purpose (Figure 14–7).

- When purchasing new machines, make sure there is a recess at the bottom for feet. This will allow the operator to stand close to the machine without having to bend over. Also, look for machines that have easily accessible controls that fall within a comfortable reach zone for operators.

- Provide ample free space around machines for moving material in and out, and to allow for ease of movement in servicing machines.[13]

Figure 14–7   Adjust machines or work surfaces to reduce stress.

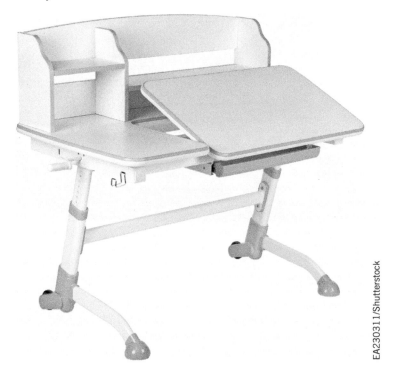

EA230311/Shutterstock

Standing for Heavy Lifting and Carrying

This type of work involves heavy lifting and moving material while standing. Lifting and moving may be relatively small parts of the job but are required somewhat regularly. The physical stress most commonly associated with this type of work is back and muscle strains resulting from improper lifting. Falls can also be a problem. Ergonomic strategies for improving work conditions include the following:

- Eliminate manual lifting to the extent possible using various lifting and hoisting technologies.

- Where manual lifting is necessary, train workers in proper lifting techniques.

- Provide sufficient room around all objects to allow lifting without twisting.

- Supply the appropriate personal protection equipment such as gloves and footwear that provide grip and traction, suitable for the environment (or conditions) in which they are used.

- Keep floors around materials to be lifted clean and dry to prevent slips.

- Do not allow manual carrying of heavy objects on stairs. Stairs increase the physical stress of carrying and, in turn, the potential for injury.[14]

Work with Hands above the Chest

This type of work can be done in either a standing or sitting position. It may or may not involve material handling. Physical stress associated with this type of work includes neck, upper body, and heart strain. Of these, the most potentially dangerous is heart strain. Prolonged work with the arms above shoulder level requires the heart to work harder to pump blood to the elevated areas. Ergonomic strategies for improving work conditions include the following:

- Eliminate manual lifting to the extent possible by raising the work floor using lifts and various other technologies.

- Use extension arms or poles when the work floor cannot be raised.

- When purchasing new machines, look for machines with controls that are easily accessible below the horizontal plane of a worker's shoulders.[15]

Work with Hand Tools

All of the types of work presented in this section may involve the use of hand tools to some extent. However, because hand tools introduce a variety of potential hazards that are inherent in their use, they are best examined as a separate work type. Physical stresses most commonly associated with the use of hand tools include **carpal tunnel syndrome (CTS)** and muscle strains of the lower arms, hands, and wrists. Ergonomic strategies for improving the work conditions focus primarily on improving hand positions during the use of tools, enhancing the worker's grip on tools, and minimizing the amount of twisting involved. Following are some of these strategies:

carpal tunnel syndrome (CTS)
An injury to the median nerve inside the wrist.

- Select tools that are designed to keep hands in the rest position (palm down, gently curved, thumb outstretched, and knuckle of the index finger higher than that of the little finger).

- Reduce stress on the hand by selecting tools that have thick, rather than thin, handles (a good range for the diameter is 2 cm to 3 cm [0.8 to 1.2 inches]).

- Select tools that have enhanced gripping surfaces on handles, such as knurling, filing, or other enhancements.

- To the extent possible, eliminate twisting by selecting tools designed so that the direction of movement or function is the same as the direction in which force is applied, or by using technology (e.g., a power screwdriver).

- For tools that do not involve twisting, select handles that have an oval-shaped cross-section.

- Select tools with handles made of hard, nonpermeable materials that will not absorb toxic liquids that could be harmful to the skin.[16]

The controversy over the use of back belts continues as both hard and anecdotal evidence supporting each side of the argument is added to the issue. While the evidence of their benefits may be compelling, NIOSH has come to the following conclusions:

- Back belts should *not* be considered as personal protective equipment.

- Back belts should *not* be recommended for use in occupational situations.

Their claim is that these belts can increase load on the cardiovascular system; reduce mobility, flexibility, and strength; and produce a false sense of security resulting in an increased risk of lifting heavier loads.

Work with Video Display Terminals (VDTs)

Primarily because of the all-pervasive integration of personal computers in the workplace, the video display terminal is now the most widely used piece of office equipment. This fact, coupled with the ergonomic hazards associated with VDTs, has created a whole new range of concerns for health and safety professionals. Using ergonomics to design a workstation can make VDTs easier, safer, more comfortable, and more efficient to use. Following are some strategies that can be used to reduce the hazards associated with VDTs:

- **Arrange the keyboard properly.** It should be located in front of the user, not to the side. Body posture and the angle formed by the arms are critical factors (see Figure 14–8).

- **Adjust the height of the desk.** Taller employees often have trouble working at *average* height desks. Raising the desk with wooden blocks can solve this problem.

- **Adjust the tilt of the keyboard.** The rear portion of the keyboard should be lower than the front.

- **Encourage employees to use a soft touch on the keyboard and mouse.** A hard touch increases the likelihood of injury.

- **Encourage employees to avoid wrist resting.** Resting the wrist on any type of edge can increase pressure on the wrist.

- **Place the mouse within easy reach.** Extending the arm to its full reach increases the likelihood of injury.

- **Remove dust from the mouse ball cavity.** Dust can collect, making it difficult to move the mouse. Blowing out accumulated dust once a week will keep the mouse easy to manipulate.

- **Locate the VDT at a proper height and distance.** The VDT's height should be such that the top line on the screen is slightly below eye level. The optimum distance between the VDT and user will vary from employee to employee, but it will usually be between 40 cm and 80 cm (16 and 32 inches).

- **Minimize glare.** Glare from a VDT can cause employees to adopt harmful postures. Changing the location of the VDT, using a screen hood, and closing or adjusting blinds and shades can minimize glare.

- **Reduce lighting levels.** Reducing the lighting level in the area immediately around the VDT can eliminate vision strain.

- **Dust the VDT screen.** VDT screens are magnets to dust. Built-up dust can make the screen difficult to read, contributing to eye strain.

- **Eliminate telephone cradling.** Cradling a telephone receiver between an uplifted shoulder and the neck while typing can cause a painful disorder called **cervical radiculopathy**

cervical radiculopathy
Compression of the cervical vertebrae in the neck.

(compression of the cervical vertebrae in the neck). Employees who need to talk on the telephone while typing should wear a headset.

- **Require typing breaks.** Continuous typing for extended periods should be avoided. **Repetitive strain injuries (RSIs)** are cumulative. Breaking up the repetitive motion in question (typing and clicking) can help prevent the accumulation of strain.[17]

repetitive strain injuries (RSIs)
A broad and generic term that encompasses a variety of injuries resulting from cumulative trauma to the soft tissues of the body.

Figure 14–8 Ergonomics of VDTs. The diagram highlights optimal postures and positions for the computer user.

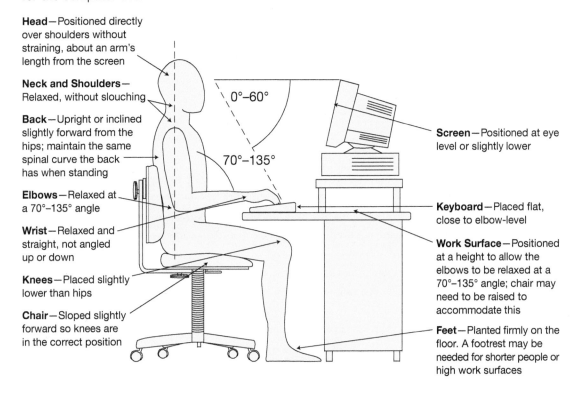

Head—Positioned directly over shoulders without straining, about an arm's length from the screen

Neck and Shoulders—Relaxed, without slouching

Back—Upright or inclined slightly forward from the hips; maintain the same spinal curve the back has when standing

Elbows—Relaxed at a 70°–135° angle

Wrist—Relaxed and straight, not angled up or down

Knees—Placed slightly lower than hips

Chair—Sloped slightly forward so knees are in the correct position

0°–60°

70°–135°

Screen—Positioned at eye level or slightly lower

Keyboard—Placed flat, close to elbow-level

Work Surface—Positioned at a height to allow the elbows to be relaxed at a 70°–135° angle; chair may need to be raised to accommodate this

Feet—Planted firmly on the floor. A footrest may be needed for shorter people or high work surfaces

>>> **DISCUSSION CASE** | **What Is Your Opinion?**

"We need to bring in an ergonomics consultant. I'm concerned that all of a sudden we are going to begin seeing WMSDs and back injuries resulting from some of our new processes and workstations. What do you think?"

Julia Penner, Safety Director for Manufacturing Technologies Corporation, thought over the question before answering. "We

don't need a consultant. The risk factors for WMSDs and back problems are well known in the business. Let me check a couple of reference books and get back to you."

Penner sees ergonomic issues as a normal part of her job. Her boss thinks an ergonomics expert is needed.

What is your opinion?

ECONOMICS OF ERGONOMICS

Perhaps the most under-researched subject relating to ergonomics is the cost effectiveness of health and safety. There are two main reasons for this: (1) Such research is often more complex and extensive than the health and safety measures that have been undertaken; and (2) many decision-makers think such studies are irrelevant because promoting health and safety is the right thing to do, regardless of costs. As with health and safety in general, there are no in-depth studies available that conclusively pin down the cost benefits of specific ergonomic measures.

According to T. Bedal,

> Does the application of ergonomic principles make good business sense? The good news is most industry experts believe ergonomics does make good business sense. But the bad news is that if you're looking for studies to prove ergonomics is worth the investment, you'll be hard-pressed to find them. Very few true cost–benefit analyses on applying ergonomic principles in an industrial setting have been done.[18]

There is disagreement among well-informed professionals on whether ergonomic improvements should be expected to meet the test of cost–benefit analysis. However, there is growing support for research that will produce reliable data. This point of view is beginning to characterize the outlook of health and safety professionals in government and in academe.[19] Consequently, it is important to understand the problems in attempting to undertake or participate in cost–benefit studies.

Inhibitors of Cost–Benefit Studies

A number of factors inhibit hard research into the economics of ergonomics. Bedal summarizes the most problematic of these:

- Record-keeping systems in industry are not sufficient to support such studies. As a result, a base of comparison from which to work has not been established.

- Industry does not track injuries and illnesses in ways that provide the controls necessary for true, hard research. There are no control groups against which to compare groups of injured workers.

- It is difficult and sometimes impossible to determine what improvements can be attributed directly to specific ergonomic strategies and what improvements should be attributed to other factors.

- Undertaking hard research studies requires a commitment of both time and money. A longitudinal study of the effects of a given ergonomic improvement may take 3 to 5 years to produce reliable data.

- Follow-up evaluations of injuries that summarize the direct and indirect costs do not exist to the extent necessary to contribute to hard research.[20]

▶▶▶ SAFETY FACT   The Economics of Ergonomics

The most common response to suggestions for ergonomic change in the workplace is, "It's too expensive." With the economic burden of musculoskeletal disorders (MSDs) in Canada estimated to be $22 billion annually, and a significant number of these disorders attributed to related workplace hazards, nothing could be further from the truth. In fact, both anecdotal reports and the published research show the exact opposite—most ergonomic interventions are "low in cost and high in value," with many yielding "significant and sustained cost savings" both immediately and in the long term. These savings can include reduced workers' compensation premiums. With these interventions often come benefits such as enhanced labour productivity and improved product quality.

Source: Workers' Health and Safety Centre. (February 2016). "The Economics of Ergonomics." [Online]. Available: https://www.whsc.on.ca/Search?searchtext=making+the+case&searchmode=anyword.

These inhibitors cannot be overcome unless industrial firms are willing to invest enormous sums of money and time. Although the data produced by such investments would be valuable, it is generally not perceived as adding to a company's bottom line. Therefore, industry is likely to continue to rely on academic and governmental agencies for research. In today's intensely competitive international marketplace, industry is likely to invest all available funds in efforts that are perceived as improving productivity and quality. Consequently, hard research into the economics of ergonomics may remain a low priority for some time to come.

WORK-RELATED MUSCULOSKELETAL DISORDERS (WMSDs)

The personal computer has become an all-pervasive and universal work tool. Jobs from the shop floor to the executive office now involve frequent, repetitive computer use. This means that people in the workplace are typing and clicking at an unprecedented pace. This frequent and, for some, constant computer use has led to an explosion of injuries heretofore seen mostly in the meatpacking industry. Collectively, these injuries are also known as **cumulative trauma disorders (CTDs)**. CTD, a term used synonymously with WMSD, is also an umbrella term that covers a number of injuries caused by forceful or awkward movements repeated frequently over time. Other aggravating factors that contribute to CTDs include poor posture, an improperly designed workstation, poor tool design, and job stress. CTDs are most common in the muscles, nerves, and tendons of the hands, arms, shoulders, and neck.

cumulative trauma disorders (CTDs) Injuries caused by forceful or awkward movements repeated frequently over time.

⟩⟩⟩ SAFETY FACT | Ergonomics in Office Automation

Increasing ergonomic problems resulting from office automation are leading to WMSDs. The types of WMSDs occurring most frequently are listed below.

Tendon-Related Disorders

- Tendinitis
- Tenosynovitis
- Stenosing tenosynovitis of the fingers (trigger finger)
- Stenosing tenosynovitis of the thumb (trigger thumb)
- DeQuervain's disease
- Ganglion cyst
- Lateral epicondylitis (tennis elbow)
- Bicipital tendinitis
- Rotator cuff tendinitis

Peripheral Nerve Entrapment

- Carpal tunnel syndrome
- Guyon's canal syndrome
- Radial tunnel syndrome
- Pronator teres syndrome

- Cubital tunnel syndrome

Vascular

- Hand-arm vibration syndrome (Raynaud's phenomenon)
- Ulnar artery thrombosis

Neurovascular

- Thoracic outlet syndrome

Muscular

- Focal dystonia
- Fibromyositis
- Tension neck syndrome
- Myositis

Joint/Joint Capsule

- Osteoarthritis
- Bursitis
- Synovitis

Source: Courtesy of Unimation, Inc.

Classifications of WMSDs

For years, WMSDs have been incorrectly referred to as *carpal tunnel syndrome*, which is actually just one type of WMSD. This is like referring to all trees as oaks. Figure 14–9 is a checklist of the most common WMSDs organized into four broad classifications.[21]

Muscle and Tendon Disorders   Tendons connect muscles to bones. They can accommodate very little in the way of stretching and are prone to injury if overused. Overworking a tendon can cause small tears in it. These tears can become inflamed and cause intense pain. This condition is known as **tendinitis**.

tendinitis Painful result of small tears in the tendon from overwork.

Figure 14–9 WMSD checklist—types of injury by classification.

Muscle and Tendon Disorders
- ✓ Tendinitis
- ✓ Muscle damage (myofacial)
- ✓ Tenosynovitis
- ✓ Stenosing tenosynovitis
  - • DeQuervain's disease
  - • Trigger finger (flexor tenosynovitis)
- ✓ Shoulder tendinitis
- ✓ Bicipital tendinitis
- ✓ Rotator cuff tendinitis
- ✓ Forearm tendinitis
  - • Flexor carpi radialis tendinitis
  - • Extensor tendinitis
  - • Flexor tendinitis
- ✓ Epicondylitis
- ✓ Ganglion cysts

Cervical Radiculopathy

Tunnel Syndromes
- ✓ Carpal tunnel syndrome
- ✓ Radial tunnel syndrome
- ✓ Sulcus ulnaris syndrome
- ✓ Cubital tunnel syndrome
- ✓ Guyon's canal syndrome

Nerve and Circulation Disorders
- ✓ Thoracic outlet syndrome
- ✓ Raynaud's disease

Myofacial muscle damage can also be caused by overexertion. It manifests itself in soreness that persists even when resting. Muscles may burn and be sensitive to the touch. When sore muscles become inflamed and swell, the symptoms are aggravated even further by nerve compression. Tendons that curve around bones are encased in protective coverings called *sheaths*. Sheaths contain a lubricating substance known as synovial fluid. When tendons rub against the sheath too frequently, friction is produced. The body responds by producing additional synovial fluid. Excess buildup of this fluid can cause swelling that, in turn, causes pressure on the surrounding nerves, causing a condition known as **tenosynovitis**.

tenosynovitis A condition resulting from an excess buildup of fluid that causes pressure on the surrounding nerve.

Chronic tenosynovitis is known as *stenosing tenosynovitis* of which there are two types: DeQuervain's disease and flexor tenosynovitis (trigger finger). DeQuervain's disease affects the tendon at the junction of the wrist and thumb. It causes pain when the thumb is moved or when the wrist is twisted. Flexor tenosynovitis involves the locking of a digit in a bent position, hence the term *trigger finger*. However, it can occur in any finger.

Shoulder tendinitis is of two types: bicipital and rotator cuff tendinitis. Bicipital tendinitis occurs at the shoulder joint where the biceps muscle attaches. The rotator cuff is a group of muscles and tendons in the shoulder that move the arm away from the body and turn it in and out. Pitchers in baseball and quarterbacks in football often experience rotator cuff tendinitis.

Forearm tendinitis is of three types: flexor carpi radialis tendinitis, extensor tendinitis, and flexor tendinitis. Flexor carpi radialis tendinitis causes pain in the wrist at the base of the thumb. Extensor tendinitis causes pain in the muscles in the top of the hand, making it difficult to straighten the hands. Flexor tendinitis causes pain in the fingers, making them difficult to bend.

Epicondylitis and *ganglion cysts* are two muscle and tendon disorders. Epicondylitis (lateral) affects the outside of the elbow, whereas epicondylitis (medial) affects the inside. The common term for this disorder is *tennis elbow*. Ganglion cysts grow on the tendon, tendon sheath, or synovial lining, typically on top of the hand, on the nail bed, above the wrist, or on the inside of the wrist.

Cervical Radiculopathy   This disorder is most commonly associated with holding a telephone receiver on an upraised shoulder while typing. This widely practised act can cause compression of the cervical discs in the neck, making it painful to turn the head. Putting the body in an unnatural posture while using the hands is always dangerous.

Tunnel Syndromes   Tunnels are conduits for nerves that are formed by ligaments and other soft tissues. Damage to the soft tissues can cause swelling that compresses the nerves that pass through the tunnel. These nerves are the median, radial, and ulnar nerves that pass through a tunnel in the forearm and wrist. Pain experienced with tunnel injuries can be constant and intense. In addition to pain, people with a tunnel injury might experience numbness, tingling, and a loss of gripping power. The most common **tunnel syndromes** are carpal tunnel syndrome, radial tunnel syndrome, sulcus ulnaris syndrome, cubital tunnel syndrome, and Guyon's canal syndrome.

tunnel syndromes   Injuries caused by compression of the nerves passing through a tunnel (a conduit formed by ligaments and other soft tissues).

Nerve and Circulation Disorders   When friction or inflammation causes swelling, both nerves and arteries can be compressed and restrict the flow of blood to muscles. This can cause a disorder known as *thoracic outlet syndrome*. The symptoms of this disorder are pain in the entire arm, numbness, coldness, and weakness in the arm, hand, and fingers.

If the blood vessels in the hands are constricted, *Raynaud's disease* can result. Symptoms include painful sensitivity, tingling, numbness, coldness, and paleness in the fingers. It can affect one or both hands. This disorder is also known as *hand-arm vibration syndrome* because it is associated with vibrating tools.

>>> **SAFETY FACT**   **WMSD: Work-Related or Non-Work-Related?**

WMSDs present a difficult challenge to health and safety professionals on two levels. First, identifying the source of an employee's injury can be difficult because of the interplay of non-work-related activities such as hobbies, playing musical instruments, medications, previous surgeries, hypertension, and other disorders. Second, treatment and rehabilitation can be hindered by outside activities. Consequently, prevention programs should be broad enough to take outside activities into account.

WMSD Risk Factors   Some of the risk factors for WMSDs of the upper extremities include:

- Repetitive and/or prolonged activities.
- Forceful exertions, usually with the hands (including pinch grips).
- Prolonged static postures.

- Awkward postures of the upper body, including reaching above the shoulders or behind the back, and twisting the wrists and other joints to perform tasks.
- Continued physical contact with work surfaces (soft tissue compression).
- Excessive vibration from power tools.
- Cold temperatures.
- Inappropriate or inadequate tool design.
- High wrist acceleration.
- Fatigue (inadequate recovery time).
- Failing to use gloves for protection.

Preventing WMSDs

The best way to prevent WMSDs is proper workstation design. In addition, it helps to make employees aware of the hazards that can cause it. These hazards include poor posture at the workstation, inappropriate positioning of the hands and arms, a heavy hand on a keyboard or mouse, and any other act that repeatedly puts the body in an unnatural posture while using the hands. Ergonomically sound workstations can help prevent WMSDs, especially when they can be modified to fit the individual employee. However, even the best ergonomic design cannot prevent a heavy hand on the keyboard or mouse. Consequently, ergonomics is only part of the answer. Following are some preventive strategies that can be applied in any organization.

1. **Teach employees the warning signs.** WMSDs occur cumulatively over time. They sneak up on people. Employees should be aware of the following warning signs: weakness in the hands or forearms, tingling, numbness, heaviness in the hands, clumsiness, stiffness, lack of control over the fingers, cold hands, and tenderness to the touch.

2. **Teach employees how to stretch.** Employees whose jobs involve repetitive motion such as typing may help prevent WMSDs by using stretching exercises. Limbering up the hands and forearms each day before starting work and again after long breaks such as the lunch hour may help eliminate the stress on muscles and tendons that can lead to WMSDs. The term *may* is used because there are still questions about the efficacy of stretching. There is no consensus in the ergonomics community on this preventive measure.

3. **Teach employees to start slowly.** Long-distance runners typically start slowly, letting their bodies adjust and their breathing find its rhythm. They pick up the pace steadily, until eventually settling in at a competitive pace. This approach is an excellent example of how employees in WMSD-prone jobs should work. Teach employees to limber up, then begin slowly and increase their pace gradually.

4. **Avoid the use of wrist splints.** Teach employees to position their hands properly without using wrist splints. Splints can cause the muscles that they support to atrophy, thereby actually increasing the likelihood of problems.

5. **Start an exercise group.** Exercises that strengthen the hands and forearms, coupled with exercises that gently stretch hand and forearm muscles, may contribute to muscle health. Exercises that strengthen the back can help improve posture, and good posture helps prevent WMSDs. As with stretching, there are uncertainties regarding the efficacy of exercise as a preventive measure.

6. **Select tools wisely.** WMSDs are most frequently associated with the repetitive use of VDTs and hand tools. Selecting and using hand tools properly can help prevent WMSDs. Figure 14–10 is a checklist for the proper selection and use of hand tools. Note that ergonomically designed hand tools will not overcome poor job design. Good job design and proper tool selection, together, are the best strategy.[22]

Figure 14–10   Checklist for safe selection and use of hand tools.

Use Anthropometric Data

Anthropometric data has to do with human body dimensions. Such data can be used to determine the proper handle length, grip span, tool weight, and trigger length when selecting tools.

Reduce Repetition

Repetition is a hazard that can and should be reduced using such strategies as the following:

- Limit overtime.
- Change the process.
- Provide mechanical assists.
- Require breaks.
- Encourage stretching and strengthening exercises.
- Automate where possible.
- Rotate employees regularly.
- Distribute work among more employees.

Reduce the Force Required

The more force required, the more potential for damage to soft tissue. Required force can be reduced using the following strategies:

- Use power tools wherever possible.
- Use the power grip instead of the pinch grip.
- Spread the force over the widest possible area.
- Eliminate slippery, hard, and sharp gripping surfaces.
- Use jigs and fixtures to eliminate the pinch grip.

Minimize Awkward Postures

Awkward postures contribute to CTDs. The following strategies can reduce posture hazards:

- Keep the wrist in a neutral position.
- Keep elbows close to the body (90°–110° where bent).
- Avoid work that requires overhead reaching.
- Minimize forearm rotation.

SUMMARY

1. Ergonomics is a multidisciplinary science that seeks to conform the workplace and all of its physiological aspects to the worker.

2. The word *ergonomics* is derived from the Greek language. *Ergon* means *work* and *nomos* means *laws*.

3. Human factors is a science that acts as a bridge between research about human beings and the application of that research to designing products and systems for human beings.

4. Common factors that can influence the amount of physical stress associated with a given job include sitting, mobility, demand for strength/power, work area, type of motion, amount of surface contact, and environmental factors.

5. Guidelines, standards, and codes of practice produced and published by various agencies in Canada are used to support ergonomic legislation in most jurisdictions.

6. Common indicators of the existence of ergonomic problems include noticeable trends in accidents and injuries, a high incidence of work-related musculoskeletal disorders (WMSDs), absenteeism and high turnover rates, employee complaints, employee-generated changes, poor quality, and a high incidence of manual material handling.

7. Procedures for identifying specific ergonomic problems include general observation, questionnaires and interviews, video recording and photography, drawing or sketching, measuring, and understanding aging.

8. In devising ergonomic problem-solving strategies, work might be divided into the following categories: seated repetitive work with light parts, seated work with larger parts, seated control work, standing work, standing work for heavy lifting and carrying, work with hands above chest height, work with hand tools, and work with video display terminals (VDTs).

9. There are two main reasons for this: (1) Such research is often more complex and extensive than the health and safety measures that have been undertaken; and (2) many decision-makers think such studies are irrelevant because promoting health and safety is the right thing to do, regardless of costs.

10. Work-related musculoskeletal disorders (WMSDs) is an umbrella term used to reference any group of painful disorders of muscles, tendons, and nerves.

Key Terms and Concepts

Carpal tunnel syndrome
  (CTS)
Cervical radiculopathy
Cumulative trauma
  disorders (CTDs)
Environmental factors

Ergonomics
Horizontal work area
Human factors
Repetitive motion
Repetitive strain injuries
  (RSIs)

Tendinitis
Tenosynovitis
Tunnel syndromes
Vertical work area
Work-related musculoskeletal
  disorders (WMSDs)

Review Questions

1. Define the term *ergonomics*. Explain its origins.

2. Explain how the following opposing factors can influence the amount of physical stress associated with a job: sitting versus standing, large versus small demand for strength/power, nonrepetitive versus repetitive motion.

3. Explain the concept of human factors and how it relates to ergonomics.

4. Define the term work-related musculoskeletal disorders (WMSDs). Describe the most common types.

5. List at least five risk factors associated with WMSDs.

6. List and briefly explain three common indicators of the existence of ergonomic problems.

7. Describe three approaches that can be used to pinpoint specific ergonomic problems.

8. Describe an ergonomic problem-solving strategy for each of the following types of work: seated repetitive work with light parts, work with hands above chest height, and work with hand tools.

9. Explain why so little hard research has been done concerning the economics of ergonomics.

Weblinks

Canadian Centre for Occupational Health and Safety (CCOHS)

www.ccohs.ca/oshanswers/ergonomics/

Canada's national occupational health and safety resource has available information on numerous ergonomic issues facing Canadian workers.

Worksafe BC

https://www.worksafebc.com/en/health-safety/hazards-exposures/ergonomics

On this site, one can see information by Canada's most comprehensive and progressive ergonomics legislation and programs.

Endnotes

[1] P. Tillman and B. Tillman. *Human Factors Essentials* (New York: McGraw-Hill, 1991), 3–22.

[2] Ibid., 3–4.

[3] Ibid., 9.

[4] Ibid., 12–13.

[5] Ibid., 21–22.

[6] Swedish Work Environment Fund. *Making the Job Easier: An Ergonomics Idea Book* (Chicago: National Safety Council, 1998), 1–5.

[7] National Institute for Occupational Health and Safety (NIOSH). "Elements of Ergonomics Programs." [Online]. Available: http://www.cdc.gov/niosh.

[8] S. Minter. "Ergonomic Challenge: The Aging Workforce." *Occupational Hazards* 64, no. 9 (September 2002): 6.

[9] NIOSH. "Elements of Ergonomics Programs," 13–14.

[10] Ibid., 14.

[11] Ibid., 15.

[12] NIOSH, 16.

[13] Ibid., 17.

[14] Ibid., 18.

[15] Ibid., 19.

[16] Ibid., 20.

[17] Roberta Carson. "Ergonomic Innovations: Free to a Good Company," *Occupational Hazards* (January 1996): 61–64.

[18] T. Bedal. "The Economics of Ergonomics: What Are the Paybacks?" *Safety & Health*, 142, no. 4: 34.

[19] Ibid., 38.

[20] Ibid., 39.

[21] Emil Pascarelli and Deborah Quilter. *Repetitive Strain Injury* (New York: Wiley, 1994), 49–62.

[22] Roberta Carson. "Ergonomically Designed Tools." *Occupational Hazards* (September 1995): 50.

Chapter 15
Mechanical Hazards and Machine Safeguarding

MAJOR TOPICS

- Common Mechanical Injuries
- Requirements for Safeguards
- Point-of-Operation Guards
- Point-of-Operation Devices
- Machine Guarding Self-Assessment
- Feeding and Ejection Systems
- Robot Safeguards
- Control of Hazardous Energy (Lockout/Tagout Systems)
- General Precautions
- Basic Program Content
- Taking Corrective Action

Failure to provide proper machine guards and enforce their use can be costly for companies. Mechanical hazards that are not properly guarded are implicated in thousands of workplace injuries every year, with imposed fines that range from hundreds to hundreds of thousands of dollars. *OHS Canada* magazine reports on numerous industrial accidents each week, and liberally scattered throughout are stories of limbs and lives lost due to mechanical failures and a disregard for machine guarding.

mechanical hazards Hazards associated with power-driven machines, whether automated or manually operated.

Mechanical hazards are those associated with power-driven machines, whether automated or manually operated. Concerns about mechanical hazards date back to the Industrial Revolution and the earliest days of mechanization.

The introduction of machines driven by steam, hydraulic, or electric power brought new hazards into the workplace. In spite of advances in safeguarding technologies and techniques, mechanical hazards are still a major concern today. In addition, automated machines have introduced new concerns.

COMMON MECHANICAL INJURIES

In an industrial setting, people interact with machines that are designed to drill, cut, shear, punch, chip, staple, stitch, abrade, shape, stamp, and slit such materials as metals, composites, plastics, and elastomers. If appropriate safeguards are not in place or if workers fail to follow safety precautions, these machines can apply the same procedures to humans. When this happens, the types of **mechanical injuries** that result are typically the result of cutting and tearing, shearing, crushing, breaking, straining and spraining, or puncturing (see Figure 15–1).

mechanical injuries Injuries that have occurred due to misuse of a power-driven machine.

Figure 15–1 Some common mechanical hazards.

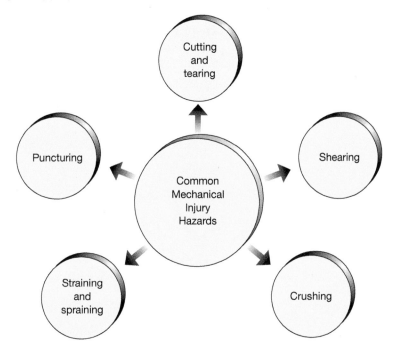

Cutting and Tearing

A cut occurs when a body part comes in contact with a sharp edge. The human body's outer layer consists of the following, starting from the outside: *epidermis*, the tough outer covering of the skin; *dermis*, the greatest part of the skin's thickness; *capillaries*, the tiny blood vessels that branch off the small arteries and veins in the dermis; *veins*, the blood vessels that collect blood from the capillaries and return it to the heart; and *arteries*, the larger vessels that carry blood from the heart to the capillaries in the skin. The seriousness of **cutting** or **tearing** the skin depends on how much damage is done to the skin, veins, arteries, muscles, and even bones.

cutting Occurs when a body part comes in contact with a sharp edge.

tearing Occurs when shear, friction, and/or blunt force causes the separation of skin layers.

Shearing

To understand what **shearing** is, think of a paper cutter. It shears the paper. Power-driven shears for severing paper, metal, plastic, elastomers, and composite materials are widely used in manufacturing. In times past, such machines often amputated fingers and hands. These tragedies typically occurred when operators reached under the shearing blade to make an adjustment or placed materials there and activated the blade before fully removing their hand. Safeguards against shearing accidents are explained later in this chapter.

shearing Results from forces being applied to a body by two contacting parts moving parallel to the plane of contact.

Crushing

crushing Occurs when a part of the body is caught between two hard surfaces that progressively move together, thereby crushing anything between them.

Injuries from **crushing** can be particularly debilitating, painful, and difficult to heal. They occur when a part of the body is caught between two hard surfaces that progressively move together, thereby crushing anything between them. Crushing hazards can be divided into two categories: *squeeze-point* types and *run-in point* types.

Squeeze-point hazards exist where two hard surfaces, at least one of which must be in motion, push close enough together to crush any object that may be between them. The process can be slow, as in a manually operated vise, or fast, as with a metal-stamping machine.

Nip point (pinch point) Point of convergence of two parts, with at least one moving.

Nip point hazards, also known as **pinch-point** hazards, exist where two objects, at least one of which is rotating, come progressively closer together. Any gap between them need not become completely closed. It need only be smaller than the object or body part lodged in it. Meshing gears and belt pulleys are examples of nip-point hazards (see Figures 15–2, 15–3, and 15–4).

Figure 15–2 This nip point can pull hands, feet, or articles of clothing.

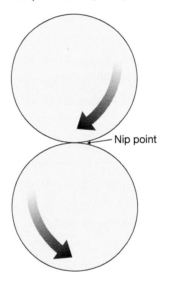

Figure 15–3 Fingers might get caught between the bench top and the revolving wheel.

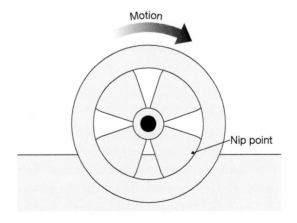

Figure 15–4 Nip points can catch fingers, hands, hair, clothing, etc. with dangerous results.

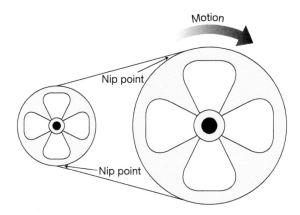

Body parts can also be crushed in other ways, for example, a heavy object falling on a foot or a hammer hitting a finger. However, these are impact hazards, which are covered in Chapter 16.

Breaking

Machines used to deform engineering materials in a variety of ways can also cause broken bones. A break in a bone is known as a *fracture*. Fractures are classified as simple, compound, complete, and incomplete.

A simple fracture is a break in a bone that does not pierce the skin. A compound fracture is a break that has broken through the surrounding tissue and skin. A complete fracture divides the affected bone into two or more separate pieces. An incomplete fracture leaves the affected bone in one piece but cracked.

Fractures are also classified as transverse, oblique, and comminuted. A transverse fracture is a break straight across the bone. An oblique fracture is diagonal. A comminuted fracture exists when the bone is broken into a number of small pieces at the point of fracture.

Straining and Spraining

There are numerous situations in an industrial setting when straining of muscles or spraining of ligaments is possible. A strain results when muscles are overstretched or torn. A sprain is the result of torn ligaments in a joint. Strains and sprains can cause swelling and intense pain.

Puncturing

Punching machines that have sharp tools can puncture a body part if safety precautions are not observed or if appropriate safeguards are not in place. **Puncturing** results when an object penetrates straight into the body and pulls straight out, creating a wound in the shape of the penetrating object. The greatest hazard with puncture wounds is the potential for damage to internal organs.

puncturing Results when an object penetrates straight into the body and pulls straight out, creating a wound in the shape of the penetrating object.

REQUIREMENTS FOR SAFEGUARDS

The various machine motions present in modern industry involve mechanisms that rotate, reciprocate, or do both. This equipment includes tools, bits, chucks, blades, spokes, screws, gears, shafts, belts, and a variety of different types of stock. Safeguards can be devised to protect workers from harmful contact with such mechanisms while at the same time allowing work to progress at a productive rate. The National Safety Council has established the following requirements for safeguards.

1. **Prevent contact.** Safeguards should prevent human contact with any potentially harmful machine part. The prevention extends to machine operators and any other person who might come in contact with the hazard.

2. **Be secure and durable.** Safeguards should be attached so that they are secure. This means that workers cannot render them ineffective by tampering with or disabling them. This is critical because removing safeguards in an attempt to speed production is a common practice. Safeguards must also be durable enough to withstand the rigours of the workplace. Worn-out safeguards won't protect workers properly.

3. **Protect against falling objects.** Objects falling onto moving machine mechanisms increase the risk of accidents, property damage, and injury. Objects that fall on a moving part can be quickly hurled out, creating a dangerous projectile. Therefore, safeguards must do more than just prevent human contact. They must also shield the moving parts of machines from falling objects.

4. **Create no new hazard.** Safeguards should overcome the hazards in question without creating new ones. For example, a safeguard with a sharp edge, unfinished surface, or protruding bolts introduces new hazards while protecting against the old.

5. **Create no interference.** Safeguards can interfere with the progress of work if they are not properly designed. Such safeguards are likely to be disregarded or disabled by workers feeling the pressure of production deadlines.

6. **Allow safe maintenance.** Safeguards should be designed to allow the more frequently performed maintenance tasks (e.g., lubrication) to be accomplished without the removal of guards. For example, locating the oil reservoir outside the guard with a line running to the lubrication point will allow for daily maintenance without removing the guard.[1]

The design and construction of safeguards are highly specialized activities requiring a strong working knowledge of machines, production techniques, and safety. It is critical that all of the factors explained in this section be considered and accommodated during the design process.

POINT-OF-OPERATION GUARDS

Guards are most effective when used at the point of operation, which is where hazards to humans exist. Point-of-operation hazards are those caused by the shearing, cutting, or bending motions of a machine. Pinch-point hazards result from guiding material into a machine or transferring motion (e.g., from gears, pressure rollers, or chains and sprockets). Single-purpose safeguards, because they guard against only one hazard, typically are permanently fixed and nonadjustable. Multiple-purpose safeguards, which guard against more than one hazard, typically are adjustable.[2]

Point-of-operation guards are of three types, each with its own advantages and limitations: fixed, interlocked, and adjustable (Figure 15–5).

point-of-operation guards Machine guards that provide protection right at the point where the user operates the machine.

Figure 15–5 Point-of-operation guards.

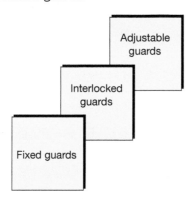

- **Fixed guards** provide a permanent barrier between workers and the point of operation. They offer the following advantages: They are suitable for many specific applications, can be constructed in-plant, require little maintenance, and are suitable for high-production, repetitive operations. Limitations include the following: They sometimes limit visibility, are often limited to specific operations, and sometimes inhibit normal cleaning and maintenance.

fixed guards Guards that provide a permanent barrier between workers and the point of operation.

- **Interlocked guards** shut down the machine when the guard is not securely in place or is disengaged. The main advantage of this type of guard is that it allows safe access to the machine for removing jams or conducting routine maintenance without the need for taking off the guard. There are also limitations. Interlocked guards require careful adjustment and maintenance and, in some cases, can be easily disengaged.

interlocked guards Guards that shut down the machine when the guard is not securely in place or is disengaged.

- **Adjustable guards** provide a barrier against a variety of different hazards associated with different production operations. They have the advantage of flexibility. However, they do not provide as dependable a barrier as other guards do, and they require frequent maintenance and careful adjustment.

adjustable guards Devices that provide a barrier against a variety of different hazards associated with different production operations.

Figures 15–6 through 15–11 show various guards used in modern manufacturing settings.

Figure 15–6 Series 12 PRO-TECH-TOR GATE GUARD used on an open-back power press.

Courtesy of Protech Systems.

Figure 15–7 Series 17 CHECKMATE RIVET GUARD used on a foot-operated riveting machine.

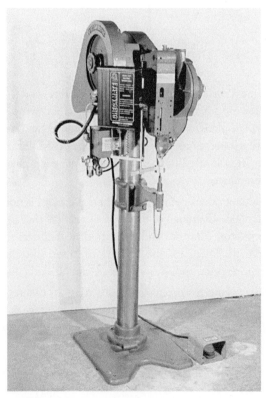

Courtesy of Protech Systems.

Figure 15–8 When the doors are opened, the milling tool stops automatically.

David L Goetsch.

Figure 15–9 In order for this shearing machine to cut, both the foot pedal and the hand button must be engaged.

David L Goetsch.

Figure 15–10 This door protects the operator in the event of an exploding or shattering grinding wheel.

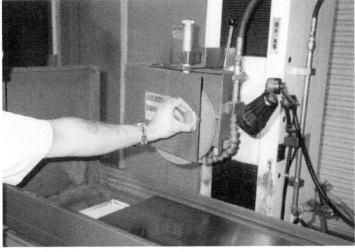

David L Goetsch.

Figure 15–11 The safety door on this drilling machine must be closed or the drill will not operate.

David L Goetsch.

POINT-OF-OPERATION DEVICES

A number of different point-of-operation devices can be used to protect workers. The most widely used are explained in the following paragraphs.

photoelectric devices Optional devices that shut down the machine any time the light field is broken.

- **Photoelectric devices** are optical devices that shut down the machine whenever the light field is broken. These devices allow operators relatively free movement. They do have limitations, including the following: They do not protect against mechanical failure, they require frequent calibration, and they can be used only with machines that can be stopped.

radio-frequency devices Capacitance devices that brake the machine if the capacitance field is interrupted by a worker's body or another object.

- **Radio-frequency devices** are capacitance devices that brake the machine if the capacitance field is interrupted by a worker's body or another object. These devices have the same limitations as photoelectric devices.

electromechanical devices Contact bars that allow only a specified amount of movement between the worker and the hazard.

- **Electromechanical devices** are contact bars that allow only a specified amount of movement between the worker and the hazard. If the worker moves the contact bar beyond the specified point, the machine will not cycle. These devices have the limitation of requiring frequent maintenance and careful adjustment.

pullback devices Devices that pull the operator's hands out of the danger zone when the machine starts to cycle.

- **Pullback devices** pull the operator's hands out of the danger zone when the machine starts to cycle. These devices eliminate the need for auxiliary barriers. However, they also have limitations. They limit operator movement, must be adjusted for each individual operator, and require close supervision to ensure proper use.

restraint devices Devices that hold back the operator from the danger zone.

- **Restraint devices** hold the operator back from the danger zone. They work well, with little risk of mechanical failure. However, they do limit the operator's movement, must be adjusted for each individual operator, and require close supervision to ensure proper use.

safety trip devices Devices that include trip wires, trip rods, and body bars that stop the machine when tripped.

- **Safety trip devices** include trip wires, trip rods, and body bars. All of these devices stop the machine when tripped. They have the advantage of simplicity. However, they are limited in that all controls must be activated manually. They protect only the operator and may require the machine to be fitted with special fixtures for holding work.

- **Two-hand controls** require the operator to use both hands concurrently to activate the machine (e.g., a paper cutter or metal-shearing machine). This ensures that hands cannot stray into the danger zone. Although these controls do an excellent job of protecting the operator, they do not protect onlookers or passers-by. In addition, some two-hand controls can be tampered with and made operable using only one hand.

- **Gates** provide a barrier between the danger zone and workers. Although they are effective at protecting operators from machine hazards, they can obscure the work, making it difficult for the operator to see.[3]

two-hand controls Controls that require the operator to use both hands concurrently to activate the machine.

gates Guards that provide a barrier between the danger zone and workers.

Figure 15–12 is a point-of-operation device that shuts down the machine when an operator's hand breaks a light beam. How quickly will the machine shut down? The stopping distance equation is as follows:

$$SD = \text{Stoptime [seconds} \times \text{hand speed constant 63"/second]}$$

Figure 15–12 Series 25 EAGLE EYE INFRA-RED LIGHT BARRIER. A point-of-operation guarding system on a roller press machine.

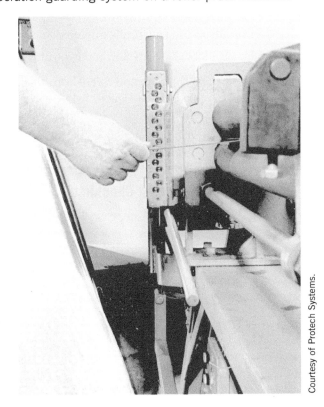

Courtesy of Protech Systems.

MACHINE GUARDING SELF-ASSESSMENT

One of the most effective ways to ensure that machines are properly guarded is to conduct periodic self-assessments. These self-assessments can be conducted by safety personnel, supervisors, or employees. Developing self-assessment criteria and encouraging supervisors and employees to use them daily is an excellent strategy for health and safety professionals. The following questions can be used for conducting machine guarding self-assessments:

1. Are all machines that might expose people to rotating parts, nip points, flying chips, sparks, flying particles, or other similar hazards properly guarded?

2. Are all mechanical power transmission belts and the nip points they create properly guarded?

3. Are all exposed power shafts located less than seven feet above the working level properly guarded?

4. Are all hand tools and other hand-operated equipment inspected regularly for hazardous conditions?

5. Is compressed air used to clean tools, machines, equipment, and parts reduced to less than 200 kilopascals or 30 pounds per square inch (psi)?

6. Are power saws and similar types of equipment properly guarded?

7. Are the tool rests for grinding wheels set to within 3 millimetres or less of the grinding wheel?

8. Are hand tools regularly inspected on a systematic basis for burred ends, cracked handles, and other potentially hazardous conditions?

9. Are all compressed gas cylinders inspected regularly and systematically for obvious signs of defects, deep rusting, or leakage?

10. Do all employees who handle and store gas cylinders and valves know how to do so without causing damage?

11. Are all air receivers periodically and systematically inspected, including safety valves?

12. Are all safety valves tested regularly, systematically, and frequently?[4]

The Canadian Auto Workers (CAW) Health and Safety Department provides a thorough machine guarding checklist as reproduced in Figure 15–13.

Figure 15–13 Machine guarding checklist.

Machine Guarding Checklist

GUARDING REQUIREMENTS

1. Do the guards prevent workers' hands, arms, and other body parts from making contact with dangerous moving parts?
   Yes ❑   No ❑

2. Are the guards firmly secured and not easily removable?
   Yes ❑   No ❑

3. Do the guards ensure that no objects will fall into the moving parts or explode out?
   Yes ❑   No ❑

4. Do the guards permit safe, comfortable, and relatively easy operation of the machine?
   Yes ❑   No ❑

5. Can the machine be oiled or greased without removing the guard?
   Yes ❑   No ❑

6. Does the machine automatically shut down when the guard is removed?
   Yes ❑   No ❑

7. Can the existing guards be improved?
   Yes ❑   No ❑

MECHANICAL HAZARDS

The point-of-operation:

1. Is there a point-of-operation guard provided for the machine?
   Yes ❑   No ❑

2. Does it keep the operator's hands, fingers, body out of the danger area?
   Yes ❑   No ❑

3. Is there evidence that the guards have been tampered with or removed?
   Yes ❑   No ❑

4. Could you suggest a more practical, effective guard?
   Yes ❑   No ❑

5. Could changes be made on the machine to eliminate the point-of-operation hazard entirely?
   Yes ❑   No ❑

Power transmission apparatus:

1. Are there any unguarded gears, sprockets, pulleys, or flywheels on the apparatus?
   Yes ❑   No ❑

(continued)

2. Are there any exposed belts or chain drives?

Yes ❑   No ❑

3. Are there any exposed set screws, key ways, collars, etc.?

Yes ❑   No ❑

4. Are starting and stopping controls within easy reach of the operator?

Yes ❑   No ❑

5. If there is more than one operator, are separate controls provided?

Yes ❑   No ❑

Other moving parts:

1. Are guards provided for all hazardous moving parts of the machine, including auxiliary parts?

Yes ❑   No ❑

EDUCATION AND TRAINING

1. Do operators and skilled trades workers have the necessary education and training in how to use the guards?

Yes ❑   No ❑

2. Does the education include examples of workers in your workplace or elsewhere who might have lost their life or their limbs from lack of machine guarding?

Yes ❑   No ❑

3. Have production workers and skilled trades workers been trained in where the guards are located, how they provide protection, and what hazards they protect against?

Yes ❑   No ❑

4. Have production workers and skilled trades workers been trained in how and under what circumstances guards can be removed?

Yes ❑   No ❑

5. Have workers been trained in the procedure to follow if they notice guards that are damaged, missing, or inadequate?

Yes ❑   No ❑

6. Do skilled trades workers have the necessary education and training in how to build the safety aspects of guards?

Yes ❑   No ❑

PROTECTIVE EQUIPMENT AND PROPER CLOTHING

1. Is protective equipment required?

Yes ❑   No ❑

2. If protective equipment is required, is it appropriate for the job, in good condition, kept clean and sanitary, and stored carefully when not in use?

Yes ❑   No ❑

3. Is the operator dressed safely for the job (no loose-fitting clothing or jewelry)?

Yes ❑   No ❑

MACHINE MAINTENANCE AND REPAIR

• Have skilled trades workers received up-to-date instruction on the machines they service?

Yes ❑   No ❑

• Do skilled trades workers lock out the machine from all of its energy sources before beginning repairs?

Yes ❑   No ❑

• Is the maintenance equipment itself properly guarded?

Yes ❑   No ❑

Source: Used with the Permission of CAW Health and Safety Department.

FEEDING AND EJECTION SYSTEMS

Feeding and ejection systems can be effective safeguards if properly designed and used. The types of feeding and ejection systems available for use with modern industrial machines are summarized as follows:

- **Automatic feed** systems feed stock to the machine from rolls. Automatic feeds eliminate the need for operators to enter the danger zone. Such systems are limited in the types and variations of stock that they can feed. They also typically require an auxiliary barrier guard and frequent maintenance.

- **Semiautomatic feed** systems use a variety of approaches for feeding stock to the machine. Prominent among these are chutes, moveable dies, dial feeds, plungers, and sliding bolsters. They have the same advantages and limitations as automatic feed systems.

automatic feed A system that feeds stock to the machine from rolls.

semiautomatic feed A system that uses a variety of approaches for feeding stock to the machine.

automatic ejection   A system
that ejects work pneumatically or
mechanically.

- **Automatic ejection** systems eject the work pneumatically or mechanically. The advantage of either approach is that operators don't have to reach into the danger zone to retrieve workpieces. However, these systems are restricted to use with relatively small stock. Potential hazards include blown chips or debris and noise. Pneumatic ejectors can be quite loud.[5]

semiautomatic ejection   A system
that ejects the work using
mechanisms that are activated
by the operator.

- **Semiautomatic ejection** systems eject the work using mechanisms that are activated by the operator. Consequently, the operator does not have to reach into the danger zone to retrieve workpieces. These systems do require auxiliary barriers and can be used with a limited variety of stock.

ROBOT SAFEGUARDS

Robots have become commonplace in modern industry. The health and safety concerns relating to robots are covered in Chapter 25. Only the guarding aspects of robot safety are covered in this section. The main hazards associated with robots are (1) entrapment of a worker between a robot and a solid surface, (2) impact with a moving robot arm, and (3) impact with objects ejected or dropped by the robot.

work envelope   The total three-
dimensional area established by
a robot's full range of motion,
within which the moving parts of
a robot actually move.

The best guard against these hazards is to erect a physical barrier around the entire perimeter of a robot's **work envelope** (the three-dimensional area established by the robot's full range of motion). This physical barrier should be able to withstand the force of the heaviest object that a robot could eject.

Various types of shutdown guards can also be used. A guard containing a sensing device that automatically shuts down the robot if any person or object enters its work envelope can be effective. Another approach is to put sensitized doors or gates in the perimeter barrier that automatically shut down the robot as soon as they are opened.

These types of safeguards are especially important because robots can be deceptive. A robot that is not moving at the moment may simply be at a stage between cycles. Without warning, it might make sudden and rapid movements that could endanger any person inside the work envelope.

CONTROL OF HAZARDOUS ENERGY (LOCKOUT/TAGOUT SYSTEMS)

The specific requirements for lockout/tagout systems may be found in the industrial regulations for most jurisdictions in Canada. However, when prosecuting employers for failing to meet the health and safety requirements, the legal team will frequently refer to sections of the legislation dealing with "due diligence." Progressive companies will often adopt the standards of the CSA, ANSI (the American National Standards Institute), or other international agencies as a minimum requirement for lockout/tagout procedures. The lockout/tagout standards identify the proper procedures for shutting down machines and equipment, and locking or tagging them out so that accidental or inadvertent activation does not occur.

Lockout/Tagout Language

lockout/tagout system   A system
for incapacitating a machine until
it can be made safe to operate.
Lockout means physically locking
up the machine so that it cannot
be used without removing the
lock. *Tagout* means applying a
tag that warns employees not to
operate the machine in question.

The following terms and phrases are frequently used in the language of a **lockout/tagout system**. All health and safety professionals should know and understand these terms:

Affected employee. Employees who perform their jobs in areas in which the procedure in question is implemented and in which serving or maintenance operations are performed. Affected employees do not implement energy control procedures unless they are authorized.

Authorized employee. Employees who perform service or maintenance on a machine and use lockout/tagout procedures for their own protection.

Capable of being locked out. A device is considered to be capable of being locked out if it meets one of the following requirements: (1) It has a hasp to which a lock can be attached; (2) it has another appropriate integral part through which a lock can be attached; (3) it has a built-in locking mechanism; or (4) it can be locked without permanently dismantling, rebuilding, or replacing the energy-isolating device.

Energized. Machines, equipment, and tools are energized if they are connected to an energy source or when they still contain stored or residual energy even after being disconnected.

Energy-isolating device. Any mechanical device that physically prevents the release or transmission of energy (e.g., circuit breakers, disconnect switches, blocks, etc.).

Energy source. Any source of power that can activate a machine or piece of equipment (e.g., electrical, mechanical, hydraulic, pneumatic, chemical, thermal, etc.).

Lockout. Placing a lockout device (see Figure 15–14) such as a padlock on an energy-isolating device to prevent the accidental or inadvertent energizing of a machine during maintenance or servicing.

Figure 15–14 Lockout system.

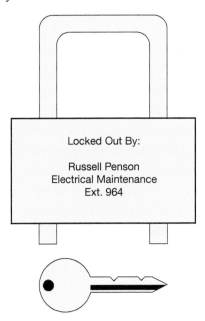

Lockout device. Any device that uses a positive means to keep an energy-isolation device in the *safe* position to prevent the accidental or inadvertent energizing of a machine or piece of equipment.

Tagout. Placing a tag (see Figure 15–15) on an energy-isolation device to warn people so that they do not accidentally or inadvertently energize a machine or piece of equipment.

Tagout device. Any prominent warning device such as a tag that can be affixed to an energy-isolation device to prevent the accidental or inadvertent energizing of a machine or piece of equipment.

Figure 15-15 Tagout system.

Evaluating Lockout/Tagout Programs

Lockout/tagout violations are frequently cited during onsite inspections. The following questions can be used to evaluate an organization's lockout/tagout program:

- Is all machinery or equipment capable of movement required to be de-energized or disengaged and blocked or locked out during cleaning, servicing, adjusting, or setting up operations?

- Where the power disconnect for equipment does not disconnect the electrical control circuit, are the appropriate electrical enclosures identified?

- If the power disconnect for equipment does not disconnect the electrical control circuit, is a means provided to ensure that the control circuit can be disconnected and locked out?

- Is it required to lock out main power disconnects instead of locking out control circuits?

- Are all equipment control valve handles equipped with a means for locking out?

- Does the lockout procedure require that stored energy—whether it is mechanical, hydraulic, or air—be released or blocked before the equipment is locked out for repairs?

- Are appropriate employees provided with individually keyed personal safety locks?

- Are these employees required to keep personal control of their keys while they have safety locks in use?

- Is only the employee exposed to the hazard required to install or remove the safety lock?

- Are employees required to check the safety lockout by attempting a startup after making sure no one is exposed?

- After the safety is checked, does the employee again place the switch in the *off* position?

- Are employees instructed always to push the control circuit stop button before re-energizing the main power switch?

- Are all employees who are working on locked-out equipment identified by their locks or accompanying tags?

- Are enough accident prevention signs, tags, and safety padlocks provided for any reasonably foreseeable repair emergency?

- When machine operations, configuration, or size require the operator to leave his or her control station to install tools or perform other operations, is he or she required to lock or tag out separately any parts of the machine that could move if accidentally activated?

- If the equipment or lines cannot be shut down, locked out, and tagged, is a safe job procedure established and rigidly followed?

- Have employees been trained not to start machinery or equipment if it is locked out or tagged out?

- Are all workers notified when the machinery or equipment they usually use is shut down and locked out for maintenance or servicing purposes?

- After maintenance is completed, is the machinery checked to ensure that nonessential items have been removed and the machine is operationally intact?

- Before the machinery is activated, are employees removed from possible danger?

- When the machinery is fully operational, are employees notified?[6]

>>> SAFETY FACT | Machines That Are Not Properly Locked Out Can Kill

Failure to properly lock out machines can be fatal. It was in the case of 18-year-old David Ellis, who was killed when he was pulled into an industrial dough mixer on the second day of his short-term job in a bakery. Like too many young temporary employees, David had been given no safety training and was unaware of the potential hazards in his job. David's father, Rob, has become a well-known ambassador in making workplaces safer, particularly for young workers.

GENERAL PRECAUTIONS

The types of safeguards explained in this chapter are critical. In addition to these specific safeguards, there are also a number of general precautions that apply across the board in settings where machines are used. Some of the more important general precautions are as follows:

- All operators should be trained in the safe operation and maintenance of their machines.

- All machine operators should be trained in the emergency procedures to take when accidents occur.

- All employees should know how to activate emergency shutdown controls. This means knowing where the controls are and how to operate them.

- Inspection, maintenance, adjustment, repair, and calibration of safeguards should be carried out regularly.

- Supervisors should ensure that safeguards are properly in place when machines are in use. Employees who disable or remove safeguards should be disciplined appropriately.

- Operator teams (two or more operators) of the same system should be trained in coordination techniques and proper use of devices that prevent premature activation by a team member.

- Operators should be trained and supervised to ensure that they dress properly for the job. Long hair, loose clothing, neckties, rings, watches, necklaces, chains, and earrings can become caught in equipment and pull the employee into the hazard zone.

- Shortcuts that violate safety principles and practices should be avoided. The pressures of deadlines should never be the cause of unsafe work practices.

- Other employees who work around machines but do not operate them should be made aware of the emergency procedures to take when an accident occurs.

Steve Ryan, Director of Manufacturing, is not happy with his colleague Lisa Ross who is Director of Health and Safety at Robbins Engineering Corporation. Ross has ordered two machines in the manufacturing department tagged out until point-of-operation guards are replaced. The machining supervisor, in an attempt to increase output, had his machinists remove the guards. As a result, there have been several minor injuries and a couple of more serious near misses. The issue is short-term productivity versus the health and safety of employees. What is your opinion on this issue?

BASIC PROGRAM CONTENT

Machine safeguarding should be organized, systematic, and comprehensive. A company's safeguarding program should have at least the following elements:

- A safeguarding policy that is part of a broader companywide health and safety policy.
- Machine hazard analysis.
- Lockout/tagout materials and procedures.
- Employee training.
- Comprehensive documentation.
- Periodic safeguarding audits (at least annually).

TAKING CORRECTIVE ACTION

What should be done when a mechanical hazard is observed? The only acceptable answer to this question is: Take *immediate corrective action*. The specific action indicated will depend on what the problem is. Figure 15–16 shows selected examples of problems and corresponding corrective actions.

Figure 15–16   Selected examples of problems and corresponding actions.

Problem	Action
Machine is operating without the safety guard.	Stop machine immediately and activate the safety guard.
Maintenance worker is cleaning a machine that is operating.	Stop machine immediately and lock or tag it out.
Visitor to the shop is wearing a necktie as he observes a lathe in operation.	Immediately pull the visitor back and have him remove the tie.
An operator is observed disabling a guard.	Stop the operator, secure the guard, and take disciplinary action.
A robot is operating without a protective barrier.	Stop the robot and erect a barrier immediately.
A machine guard has a sharp, ragged edge.	Stop the machine and eliminate the sharp edge and ragged burrs by rounding it off.

These are only a few of the many different types of problems that require corresponding corrective action. Regardless of the type of problem, the key to responding is immediacy. As shown in the examples given earlier in this chapter, waiting to take corrective action can be fatal.

SUMMARY

1. The most common mechanical injuries are cutting and tearing, shearing, crushing, breaking, straining and spraining, and puncturing.

2. Strains are the result of overstretched or torn muscles. Sprains are the result of torn ligaments.

3. All safeguards should prevent contact, be secure and durable, protect against falling objects, create no new hazard, create no interference, and allow safe maintenance.

4. Point-of-operation devices come in a variety of different types, including photoelectric, radio-frequency, electromechanical, pullback, restraint, safety trip, two-hand controls, and gates.

5. Feeding and ejection systems can be effective safeguards if properly designed and used. These systems come in two types: automatic and semiautomatic.

6. *Lockout* means physically locking the machine. *Tagout* means applying a tag that warns employees not to operate the machine.

7. The main mechanical hazards associated with robots are as follows: (1) entrapment of a worker between a robot and a solid surface, (2) impact with a moving robot arm, and (3) impact with objects ejected or dropped by the robot. The best safeguard for a robot is a barrier around the perimeter of its work envelope. Sensitized doors or gates in the barrier can also decrease the hazard potential.

8. When hazards or hazardous behaviours are observed, corrective action should be taken immediately. Waiting to act can be fatal.

Key Terms and Concepts

Adjustable guards	Lockout/tagout system	Restraint devices
Automatic ejection	Mechanical hazards	Safety trip devices
Automatic feed	Mechanical injuries	Semiautomatic ejection
Crushing	Nip point (pinch point)	Semiautomatic feed
Cutting	Photoelectric devices	Shearing
Electromechanical devices	Point-of-operation guards	Tearing
Fixed guards	Pullback devices	Two-hand controls
Gates	Puncturing	Work envelope
Interlocked guards	Radio-frequency devices	

Review Questions

1. List and briefly explain the common types of mechanical injury hazards.
2. Explain the concept of safeguarding.
3. What are the requirements all safeguards should meet?
4. Describe the three types of point-of-operation guards.
5. Describe four types of point-of-operation devices.
6. What are the relative advantages and disadvantages of feeding and ejection systems?
7. Describe the primary hazards associated with robots.
8. Explain how to guard against the hazards associated with robots.

9. What is a lockout system?
10. What is a tagout system?
11. Explain how to evaluate lockout/tagout programs.

Weblinks

Canadian Auto Workers

www.caw.ca/en/services-departments-health-safety-environment-blowing-in-the-wind-machine-guarding-prevents-deaths-pdf.htm

This booklet, "Blowin' in the Wind: Machine Guarding Prevents Death," provides a sobering look at the effects of poor machine guarding, along with lots of useful tips and tools for improving or implementing a machine guarding program in the workplace.

Canada's Occupational Health & Safety Magazine

www.ohscanada.com

Canada's Occupational Health & Safety magazine. Available in print or digital format.

MySafeWork

www.MySafeWork.com

At the age of 18, David Ellis was killed in a workplace accident. He was given limited training and no supervision. It was his second day on the job. After his death, David's father, Rob Ellis, started MySafeWork, a not-for-profit organization and registered charity.

Endnotes

[1] National Safety Council. *Guards: Safeguarding Concepts Illustrated*, 6th ed. (Chicago: National Safety Council, 1997), 2–3.

[2] Ibid., 36.

[3] Ibid., 38–39.

[4] [Online]. Available: http://online.misu.nodak.edu/19577/BADM309 checklist.htm.

[5] Ibid., 44.

[6] L. Johnson. "The 'Red Flags' of LOTC." *Occupational Health & Safety* 68, no. 3: 55.

Chapter 16

Falling, Impact, Acceleration, Lifting, and Standing Hazards with Appropriate Personal Protective Equipment (PPE)

MAJOR TOPICS

- Causes of Falls
- Kinds of Falls
- Walking and Slipping
- Ladder Safety
- Impact and Acceleration Hazards
- Lifting Hazards
- Standing Hazards
- Hand Protection
- Personal Protective Equipment
- Forklift Safety (Powered Industrial Trucks)

Some of the most common accidents in the workplace happen as the result of slipping, falling, and improper lifting. **Impact accidents** from falling objects are also common causes of injuries. This chapter provides the information needed by modern health and safety professionals to prevent such accidents. It also provides specific information about head, hand, back, eye, face, and foot protection.

impact accidents Involve a worker being struck by or against an object.

CAUSES OF FALLS

Falls represent about 15 percent of lost time injuries in Canada. About 60,000 workers are injured each year due to fall accidents.[1] Clearly, falls are a major concern of health and safety professionals. The primary causes of falls are:

- A foreign object on the walking surface.
- A design flaw in the walking surface.

- Slippery surfaces.
- An individual's impaired physical condition.[2]

foreign object Any object that is out of place or in a position to trip someone or cause a slip.

design flaw A defect in equipment or in the work space that can lead to an accident or injury.

A **foreign object** is any object that is out of place or in a position to trip someone or cause a slip. There are innumerable **design flaws** that may cause a fall. A poorly designed floor covering, a ladder that does not seat properly, or a catwalk that gives way are all examples of design flaws that may cause falls. Slippery surfaces are particularly prevalent in industrial plants where numerous different lubricants and cleaning solvents are used.

Automobile accidents are often caused when a driver's attention is temporarily drawn away from the road by a visual distraction. This is also true in the workplace. Anything that distracts workers visually can cause a fall. When a person's physical condition is impaired for any reason, the potential for falls also increases. This is a particularly common problem among aging workers. Understanding these causes is the first step in developing fall prevention techniques.

KINDS OF FALLS

Workers who are at risk of falling 3 metres are required to wear fall protection equipment, such as safety belts and lanyards or full body harnesses, such as that seen in Figure 16–1. Fall arrest equipment should meet the latest edition of the CSA Z259.1 standards for safety belts and lanyards and CSA standard Z259.10 for full body harnesses. While 3 metres is generally the rule, numerous situations in various jurisdictions call for fall protection at lower elevations. For example, in Ontario, workers must be protected from falling from heights of more than 1.2 metres if the work area is used as a path for a wheelbarrow or similar equipment.

Figure 16–1 Personal fall arrest harness.

John Tomaselli/123RF

On the other hand, more common falls are "surface falls." Such falls can be divided into the following four categories:

- **Trip and fall** accidents occur when workers encounter an unseen foreign object in their path. When the employee's foot strikes the object, he or she trips and falls.
- **Stump and fall** accidents occur when a worker's foot suddenly meets a sticky surface or a defect in the walking surface. Expecting to continue at the established pace, the worker falls when his or her foot is unable to respond properly.
- **Step and fall** accidents occur when a person's foot encounters an unexpected step down (e.g., a hole in the floor or a floorboard that gives way). This can also happen when an employee thinks he or she has reached the bottom of the stairs when, in reality, there is one more step.
- **Slip and fall** accidents occur when the worker's centre of gravity is suddenly thrown out of balance (e.g., an oily spot causes a foot to shoot out from under the worker). This is the most common type of fall.[3]

trip and fall An accident that occurs when a worker encounters an unseen foreign object in his or her path.

stump and fall An accident that occurs when a worker's foot suddenly meets a sticky surface or a defect in the walking surface.

step and fall An accident that occurs when a person's foot encounters an unexpected step down.

slip and fall Accidents that occur when the worker's centre of gravity is suddenly thrown out of balance.

WALKING AND SLIPPING

Judging by the number of injuries that occur each year as a result of slipping, it is clear that walking can be hazardous to a worker's health. This is, in fact, the case when walking on an unstable platform. A stable platform for walking is any surface with a high degree of traction that is free of obstructions. It follows that an unstable platform is one lacking traction, one on which there are obstructions, or both.

Measuring Surface Traction

In order to understand *surface traction*, one must have a basis for comparison. An effective way for comparing the relative traction of a given surface is to use the **coefficient of friction**, which is a numerical comparison of the resistance of one surface (shoe or boot) against another surface (floor).

Figure 16–2 is a continuum showing coefficient of friction ratings from very slippery to good traction. Surfaces with a coefficient of friction of 0.2 or less are very slippery and very hazardous. At the other end of the continuum, surfaces with a coefficient of friction of 0.4 or higher have good traction.

coefficient of friction A numerical correlation of the resistance of one surface against another surface.

Figure 16–2 Coefficients of friction and relative traction ratings.

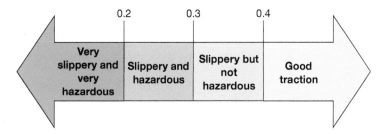

To gain a feel for what different coefficients actually mean, consider the following: (1) ice has a coefficient of friction of 0.1, (2) concrete has a coefficient of 0.43, (3) linoleum has a coefficient of 0.33, and (4) waxed white oak has a coefficient of 0.24. Compare these coefficients with Figure 16–2 to determine the degree of hazard and how the surfaces compare.

Factors That Decrease Traction

Good housekeeping can be a major factor in reducing slip and fall hazards. Water, oil, soap, coolant, and cleaning solvents left on a floor can decrease traction and turn an otherwise safe surface into a danger zone. For example, the friction coefficient of concrete (0.43) is reduced by almost 15 percent if the concrete is wet. Rubber-soled shoes can decrease slipping hazards somewhat, but changing the type of shoe is not enough to ensure safety. Additional precautions are needed.

Strategies for Preventing Slips

Modern health and safety professionals are concerned with preventing slips and falls, and slip prevention should be a part of a company's overall health and safety program. Here are some strategies that can be used to help prevent slipping:

1. **Choose the right material from the outset.** Where the walking surface is to be newly constructed or an existing surface is to be replaced, health and safety professionals should encourage the selection of surface materials that have the highest possible coefficient of friction. Getting it right from the start is the best way to prevent slipping accidents.

2. **Retrofit an existing surface.** If it is too disruptive or too expensive to replace a slippery surface completely, **retrofit** it with friction enhancement devices or materials. Such devices or materials include runners, skid strips, carpet, grooves, abrasive coatings, grilles, and textured coverings.

retrofit Renovating rather than replacing.

3. **Practise good housekeeping.** Regardless of the type of surface, keep it clean and dry. Spilled water, grease, oil, solvents, and other liquids should be removed immediately. When the surface is intentionally made wet, as when cleaning or mopping, rope off the area and erect warning signs.

4. **Require nonskid footwear.** Employees who work in areas where slipping is likely to be a problem should be required to wear shoes with special nonskid soles. This is no different from requiring steel-toed boots to protect against falling objects. **Nonskid footwear** should be a normal part of a worker's personal protective equipment.

nonskid footwear Shoes that have special nonskid soles.

5. **Inspect surfaces frequently.** Employees who are working to meet production deadlines may be so distracted that they don't notice a wet surface, or they may notice it but feel too rushed to do anything about it. Consequently, health and safety professionals should conduct frequent inspections and act immediately when a hazard is identified.[4]

In addition to these generic strategies, safety experts were asked by *Occupational Hazards* magazine to give their top five strategies for preventing slips and falls. Their responses are summarized as follows.

Malcolm Robbins of Robbins & Associates recommends the following strategies:

1. Do not rely on cleanup and maintenance. Safety mats, slip-resistant safety shoes, and nonslip flooring are more reliable.

2. Ramps and sloped floor surfaces require higher friction values than level walking surfaces do.

3. Warning signs have limited value. Where used, however, they should warn of the dangerous condition, indicate what could happen, and show how to avoid the problem.

4. Focus on areas with open walking space, such as large plants, warehouses, and supermarkets.

5. Use lighting and paint effectively to draw attention to steps, speed bumps, and other obstacles.[5]

Robert J. Brungraber, president of Slip-Test, Inc., highlights the following concerns and strategies:

1. Balance slip resistance against other needs. Floors in hospital operating rooms and kitchens, for example, must be smooth enough to be easy to clean and disinfect.

2. Accidents occur on wet floors. Clean and dry them as soon as possible.

3. Surprises lead to accidents. A wet floor on a rainy day is not as surprising (or as dangerous) as a wet floor from a spill on a sunny day.

4. Don't overlook workplace areas such as bathrooms and lunchrooms.

5. Slip, trip, and fall hazards put non-employees such as visitors and customers at risk. There is no exclusive remedy protection against non-employee suits.[6]

Foot Protection

The various regulations for most Canadian jurisdictions state that where a worker is exposed to foot injury hazards, appropriate foot protection shall be worn. Depending on the type of work being conducted, several types of foot injuries may be present. The major kinds of injuries to the feet and toes are from the following:

- Falls or impact from sharp or heavy objects (this type accounts for 60 percent of all injuries).
- Compression when rolled over by or pressed between heavy objects.
- Punctures through the sole of the foot.
- Conductivity of electricity or heat.
- Electrocution from contact with an energized, conducting material.
- Slips on unstable walking surfaces.
- Hot liquid or metal splashed into shoes or boots.
- Temperature extremes.[7]

The key to protecting workers' feet and toes is to match the protective measure with the hazard. This involves the following steps: (1) Identify the various types of hazards present in the workplace, (2) identify the types of footwear available to counter the hazards, and (3) require that proper footwear be worn. Shoes selected should meet all applicable CSA standards and have the corresponding CSA markings. For the proper selection of safety footwear, the table in Figure 16–3 shows the standard markings used to identify various safety features and their application.

Modern safety boots that provide comprehensive foot and toe protection are available. The best safety boots provide all the following types of protection:

- *Steel toe* for impact protection.
- *Rubber* or *vinyl* for chemical protection.
- *Puncture-resistant soles* for protection against sharp objects.
- *Slip-resistant soles* for protection against slippery surfaces.
- *Electricity-resistant material* for protection from electric shock.

Many employers and construction associations simply require that the worker wear Grade 1 CSA-certified footwear. The "grade" refers to the ability of the toe to withstand impact. Grade 1 withstands an impact of 125 joules (the equivalent of a 12.75 kilogram object dropped from a height of 1 metre).

Figure 16–3 Selection of safety footwear.

Protective Footwear Markings

Outside labels	Location	Criteria	Intended application
(green triangle with ®)	The label shall appear at ankle height or on the tongue of the right shoe.	Green triangle indicates sole puncture protection with a Grade 1 protective toe to withstand impacts up to 125 joules.	For any industrial environment, especially that of construction, where sharp objects (such as nails) are present; heavy work environments.
(white triangle with ®)	The label shall appear at ankle height or on the tongue of the right shoe.	Yellow triangle indicates sole puncture protection with a Grade 2 protective toe to withstand impacts up to 90 joules.	For light industrial work environments requiring puncture protection as well as toe protection.
(Ω ®)	The label shall appear at ankle height or on the tongue of the right shoe.	White rectangle with orange Greek letter omega indicates soles that provide resistance to electric shock.	For any industrial environment where accidental contact with live electrical conductors can occur. **Warning:** *Electrical shock resistance deteriorates with wear and in a wet environment.*
(SD ®)	The label shall appear at ankle height or on the tongue of the right shoe.	Yellow rectangle with green "SD" and grounding symbol indicates soles are static-dissipative.	For any industrial environment where a static discharge can create a hazard for workers or equipment.
(C ®)	The label shall appear at ankle height or on the tongue of the right shoe.	Red rectangle with black "C" and grounding symbol indicates soles are electrically conductive.	For any industrial environment where low-power electrical charges may create a hazard for workers or equipment.
(fir tree ®)	The label shall appear at ankle height or on the tongue of the right shoe.	White label with green fir tree symbol indicates chainsaw protective footwear.	For forestry workers and others exposed to hand-held chainsaws or other cutting tools.
(® in blue rectangle)	The label shall appear on the outside of the right shoe.	Blue rectangle indicates a Grade 1 protective toe with no protective sole.	For industrial work environments not requiring puncture protection.
(® in grey rectangle)	The label shall appear on the outside of the right shoe.	Grey rectangle indicates a Grade 2 protective toe with no protective sole.	For institutional and non-industrial work environments not requiring puncture protection.

Note: *The ® symbol indicates the preferred positioning for the registered identifying logo or mark of the certifying agency.*

Source: Used with the permission of Canadian Centre for Occupational Health and Safety.

LADDER SAFETY

Jobs that involve the use of ladders (see Figure 16–4) introduce their own set of safety problems, one of which is an increased potential for falls. Many accidents involving ladders result from improper use. Following a simple set of rules for the proper use of ladders can reduce the risk of falls and other ladder-related accidents. The Construction Safety Association of Ontario (CSAO) recommends that the following be considered before ladder use:

- Check ladder for defects.
- Clear scrap and material away from the base and the top of the ladder, since getting on and off the ladder is relatively hazardous.
- Secure the base against accidental movement. It is also a good idea to secure the top of the ladder as well.
- Set the ladder on a firm, level surface. On soft, uncompacted rough soil, use a mudsill.
- Single-width, job-built ladders are meant for only one worker at a time. A double-width ladder can be used by two workers, provided they are on opposite sides.
- Make sure the rails on the ladder reach at least 90 cm above the landing. This allows for a secure grip while stepping on or off.

Figure 16–4 Portable ladder/stair.

Sanchai khudpin/123RF.

four-to-one-ratio The distance from the wall to the base of the ladder should be 1/4 (up to 1/3) the distance from the ground to the top of the ladder.

- Set straight or extension ladders 30 cm out for every 90 to 120 cm up. The base should be out 1/4 to 1/3 the height (**four-to-one-ratio**).
- Before setting up a ladder, always check for overhead powerlines.
- Do not position ladders against flexible or moveable surfaces.
- Always face the ladder while climbing or working on it.
- Maintain three-point contact when climbing up or down.
- Keep your centre of gravity inside the side rails. Your belt buckle should never be outside the side rails.
- When climbing up or down, never carry tools or materials in your hand. Use a hoist rope instead.
- Keep boots free of mud, grease, or any material that could cause a loss of footing.

lanyard A flexible line for connecting the body belt or body harness to a deceleration device, lifeline, or anchorage.

- When working 3 metres or more above the ground or floor, wear a safety belt or harness with the **lanyard** tied off to the structure.
- Never straddle the space between the ladder and another object.
- Use fall arrest equipment such as ladder-climbing devices or lifelines when working from long ladders or vertical fixed ladders.
- Never use ladders horizontally as scaffold planks, runways, or for any other service for which they were not designed.
- Stand no higher than the third or fourth rung from the top. Maintain knee contact for balance.
- Do not splice short ladders together to make a long ladder.
- Do not use ladders for bracing.
- Do not set up ladders in doorways, passageways, or locations where they can be knocked over.
- Do not rest a ladder on its rungs. Ladders must rest on their side rails.
- Get help when erecting long, heavy, or awkward ladders to prevent overexertion.
- Before erecting, using, or working from ladders, always check for electrical hazards.
- Never use aluminum ladders near live electrical equipment or wires.[8]

Inspecting Ladders

Taking a few moments to look over a ladder carefully before using it can prevent a fall. It is a good starting point to look for visible manufacturer and CSA markings on all purchased ladders. For job-built ladders, specific details are given in the relevant regulations for each jurisdiction. The Construction Safety Association of Ontario recommends the following when inspecting a ladder:

- Inspect ladders for structural rigidity.
- Inspect nonskid feet for wear, embedded material, and proper pivot action on swivel feet.
- Replace frayed or worn ropes on extension ladders with type and size equal to original rope.
- Check aluminum ladders for dents and bends in the side rails, steps, and rungs.
- Check wooden ladders for cracks, splits, or rot.
- Check all ladders for grease, oil, caulking, embedded stone and metal, or other material that could make them unsafe.[9]

IMPACT AND ACCELERATION HAZARDS

An employee working on a catwalk drops a wrench. The falling wrench accelerates over the 5-metre drop and strikes an employee below. Had the victim not been wearing a hard hat he might have sustained serious injuries from the impact. A robot loses its grip on a part, slinging it across the plant and striking an employee. The impact from the part breaks one of the employee's ribs. These are examples of accidents involving **acceleration** and impact. Any type of fall also involves acceleration and impact because, having fallen, a person's rate of fall accelerates (increases) until striking a surface (impact). Motor vehicle accidents are also examples of acceleration and impact.

acceleration Increase in the speed of a falling object before impact.

Because falls were covered in the previous section, this section will focus on hazards relating to the acceleration and impact of objects. Approximately 25 percent of the workplace accidents that occur each year as a result of acceleration and impact involve objects that become projectiles.

Protection from Falling or Accelerating Objects

Objects that fall, are slung from a machine, or otherwise become projectiles pose a serious hazard to the heads, faces, feet, and eyes of workers. Consequently, protecting workers from projectiles requires the use of appropriate personal protective equipment and strict adherence to safety rules by all employees.

Head Protection

People who sustain head injuries on the job account for less than 5 percent of all lost time accidents in Canada each year. However, due to the potential severity of these accidents, the safety practitioner should be aware of the risk of such injuries and the means to protect the worker. Falling objects are involved in many of these accidents. These injuries occur in spite of the fact that many of the victims wear hard hats. Such statistics have been the driving force behind the development of tougher, more durable hard hats.

Originally introduced in 1919, the hard hats first used for head protection in an industrial setting were inspired by the helmets worn by soldiers in World War I. Such early versions were made of varnished resin-impregnated canvas. As material technology evolved, hard hats were made of vulcanized fibre, then aluminum, and then fibreglass. Today's hard hats are typically made from the thermoplastic material polyethylene, using the injection-molding process. Basic hard hat design has not changed radically since before World War II. Hard hats are designed to provide limited protection from impact, primarily to the top of the head. The amount of impact transmitted to the head, neck, and spine is reduced as the suspension straps stretch; therefore, do not put anything between the suspension and the shell.[10]

The Canadian Standards Association (CSA), American National Standards Institute (ANSI), and International Standards Organization (ISO) all have standards that define the minimum performance for hard hats along with other safety devices. While testing methods often vary among these organizations, the standards usually result in products of similar integrity.

The standard for hard hats used by jurisdictions from Newfoundland and Labrador to Yukon is the CSA Z94.1-92. This standard calls for testing hard hats for impact attenuation and penetration resistance as well as electrical insulation. Hard hats are also designed to limit penetration of sharp objects that may hit the top of the hard-hat shell and to provide some lateral penetration protection.[11]

Hard hats should be inspected regularly for cracks and deep scratches and replaced when any defects are found. Ensure that the replacement hat bears the CSA label. Do not paint hard hats, because paint can reduce impact resistance and hide other defects.

Hard hats can help reduce the risk associated with falling or projected objects, but only if they are worn. In addition to making the use of hard hats mandatory when appropriate and supervising to ensure compliance, Feuerstein recommends the use of incentives.[12] According to Feuerstein,

> It would seem that the sweetest offer a head-injury prevention program makes is a work environment free of injuries from falling objects. But sometimes this ultimate reward is too abstract to excite employees. They need to be led into safety for its own sake by concrete incentives, such as intra-department competition, monetary rewards for good suggestions, points toward prizes, and peer recognition for the most improved behavior.[13]

Eye and Face Protection

Eye and face protection are critical in the modern workplace. Eye injuries are a common and costly phenomenon. The Canadian National Institute for the Blind (CNIB) reports that thousands of workers sustain on-the-job eye injuries that result in permanent damage or blindness. The financial cost in lost production time, medical expenses, and workers' compensation is borne by all of society eventually, but the human cost borne by the injured workers and their families can be devastating. So why is this continuing to happen?

First, too many people are not wearing eye protection. And second, they are not wearing the right kind of eye protection.

Eye and face protection typically consist of safety glasses, safety goggles, or face shields. A face shield is a secondary protection device and should be worn with safety glasses or goggles. The face shield will protect against direct splashes or projectiles, but the eyes are protected from airborne or deflected particles if safety glasses or goggles are worn. The standard generally adopted for face and eye protective devices in Canadian jurisdictions is the CSA Z94.3–Eye and Face Protectors standard. It requires that industrial eye and face protective devices protect against certain eye and face hazards to a specific level, but the standard does not include factors such as style, appearance, comfort, or service life.

⧸⧸⧸ SAFETY FACT — Contact Lenses in a Chemical Environment

For years, it was commonly thought among health and safety professionals that workers should not wear contact lenses in a chemical environment. In fact, until 2003 the National Institute for Occupational Safety and Health (NIOSH) recommended that workers in chemical environments not wear contact lenses. However, over time much has been learned about this issue. Contact lenses may, in fact, be worn in chemical environments, and NIOSH has published an "intelligence bulletin" (number 59) explaining how to safely wear contact lenses in chemical environments.

Source: B. Weissman. "Contact Lenses in a Chemical Environment." *Occupational Health & Safety* 74, no. 10: 56-58.

Frequently seen in Canada along with the CSA logo is the ANSI Z87 marking for face and eye protective devices. The ANSI standard Z87.1 requires that eye and face protective devices pass two impact tests: a high-mass, low-speed test and a low-mass, high-speed test. Figure 16–5 summarizes the purpose of the tests and their individual requirements concerning impact and penetration. The standard and testing methods that were established in 1968 have been revised numerous times and are updated every 2 to 5 years. Most of these revisions have been to meet technical requirements and clarify testing parameters; however, the basic testing criteria shown in Figure 16–5 remains virtually unchanged. Figures 16–6 and 16–7 are examples of the types of devices available for eye and face protection.

Figure 16–5   ANSI Standard Z87.1.

High-Mass Impact Test—Purpose

This test is intended to ensure the level of mechanical integrity of a protective device and a level of protection from relatively heavy, pointed objects travelling at low speeds. Frames shall be capable of resisting impact from a 500-gram (17.6-ounce) missile with a 30-degree conical heat-treated tip and a 1-mm (.039-inch) radius dropped from a height of 130 cm (51.2 inches). No parts or fragments shall be ejected from the protector that could contact an eye.

High-Velocity Impact Test—Purpose

This test is intended to ensure a level of protection from high-velocity, low-mass projectiles. Frames shall be capable of resisting impact from 6.35-mm (¼-inch) steel balls weighing 1.06 grams (.04 ounce) at 45.72 metres/second (150 feet per second [fps] from 0 degrees to 90 degrees for frames; 76.2 metres/second (250 fps) for goggles; 91.44 metres/second (300 fps) for face shields.

Impact Test—Drop Ball

A 25.4-mm (1-inch) steel ball, weighing 68 grams (2.4 ounces), free fall from 127 cm (50 inches).

Lens Thickness

Thickness is 3.0 mm (.118 inch) except lenses that withstand high velocity impact, then 2.0-mm (.079-inch) thickness is acceptable.

Impact Test—Penetration

Lens shall be capable of resisting penetration from a Singer needle on a holder weighing 44.2 g (1.56 ounces) dropped freely from 127 cm (50 inches).

Figure 16–6   Safety glasses that wrap around for lateral protection.

RomboStudio/Shutterstock.

Figure 16–7   Welding hood with facemask.

Nikitin Victor/Shutterstock.

The high-mass impact test determines the level of protection provided by face and eye protective devices from relatively heavy, pointed objects that are moving at low speeds. The high-velocity impact test determines the level of protection provided from low-mass objects moving at high velocity.

Assessing the Workplace for Eye Hazards   The type of eye protection needed in a given setting depends on the type of work done in that setting and the corresponding hazards. Before establishing a vision protection program, it is necessary to assess the workplace. OSHA recommends using the following questions in making a workplace assessment:

- Do employees perform tasks that may produce airborne dust or flying particles?
- Do employees work near others who perform tasks that may produce airborne dust or flying particles?
- Do employees handle hazardous liquid chemicals or blood?
- Do employees work near others who handle hazardous liquid chemicals or blood?
- Do employees work in situations that may expose their eyes to chemical or physical irritants?
- Do employees work in situations that may expose their eyes to intense light or lasers?[14]

First Aid for Eye Injuries   Even with proper eye protection, there is still the risk that an employee may sustain an injury. Even the best vision protection program is not perfect. When this happens, the following guidelines for first aid apply:

- Be gentle with the employee. Don't add to the injury with rough treatment.
- Do not attempt to remove objects embedded in the eyeball.
- Rinse the eyes with copious amounts of water for 15 to 30 minutes to remove the chemicals. Call for professional help. Cover both eyes after the rinsing has been completed.
- Never press on an injured eye or put any pressure on it (as when covering the eyes).
- Do not allow the employee to rub his or her eyes.[15]

LIFTING HAZARDS

Back injuries that result from improper lifting are among the most common in an industrial setting. **Manual materials handling (MMH)** is the most common cause of occupational fatigue and lower back pain. About three of every four Canadians whose job includes MMH suffer pain due to back injury at some time. Such back injuries account for about one third of all lost work and 40 percent of all compensation costs. More important than financial cost is human suffering. Each year about 8,000 Canadian workers are permanently disabled by back injuries. Many others are unable to return to their former jobs. Their lives are profoundly disrupted.[16]

Back injuries in the workplace are typically caused by improper lifting, reaching, sitting, and bending. **Lifting hazards** such as poor posture, ergonomic factors, and personal lifestyles also contribute to back problems. Consequently, a company's overall health and safety program should have a back safety/lifting component.

Workers should be aware of the maximum load that can be safely lifted. The universally accepted standard for manual lifting weight limits is the *revised NIOSH equation for the design and evaluation of manual lifting tasks*. The NIOSH lifting equation takes into account weight plus several other variables in lifting tasks that contribute to the risk of injury. For example, if the situation requires frequent lifts or lifting loads far away from the body, there is an increased risk of injury. Under these conditions, the weight limit would be reduced from a baseline weight or *load constant* (LC) to a *recommended weight limit* (RWL). A load constant (LC) of 23 kg was established by NIOSH as a load that, under ideal conditions, is safe for 75 percent of females and 90 percent of males.[17] For more information on the NIOSH lifting equation, see the weblinks at the end of this chapter.

manual materials handling (MMH) Moving goods or equipment without the aid of machinery.

lifting hazards Any factors that, if not properly dealt with, may lead to an injury from lifting.

Back Safety/Lifting Program

Prevention is critical in back safety. Consequently, health and safety professionals need to know how to establish back safety programs that overcome the hazards of lifting and other activities. Dr. Alex Kaliokin recommends the following six-step program:

1. **Display poster illustrations.** Posters that illustrate proper lifting, reaching, sitting, and bending techniques should be displayed strategically throughout the workplace. This is as important in offices as in the plant. Clerical and office personnel actually sustain a higher proportion of back injuries than employees in general. Sitting too long without standing, stretching, and walking can put as much pressure on the back as lifting.

2. **Pre-employment screening.** Pre-employment screening can identify people who already have back problems when they apply. This is important because more than 40 percent of back injuries occur in the first year of employment, and the majority of these injuries are related to pre-existing back problems.

3. **Regular safety inspections.** Periodic inspections of the workplace can identify potential problem areas so that corrective action can be taken immediately. Occasionally bringing a workers' compensation consultant in to assist with an inspection can help identify hazards that company personnel may miss.

4. **Education and training.** Education and training designed to help employees understand how to lift, bend, reach, stand, walk, and sit safely can be the most effective preventive measure undertaken. Companies that provide back safety training report a significant decrease in back injuries.

5. **Use external services.** A variety of external health care agencies can help companies extend their programs. Identify local health care providing agencies and organizations, what services they can provide, and a contact person in each. Maintaining a positive relationship with these external service contact people can increase the services available to employers.

6. **Map out the prevention program.** The first five steps should be written down and incorporated in the company's overall health and safety program. The written plan should be reviewed periodically and updated as needed.[18]

In spite of a company's best efforts, back injuries will still occur. Consequently, health and safety professionals should be familiar with the treatment and therapy that injured employees are likely to receive. Treatment for reconditioning addresses five goals: restoring function, reducing pain, minimizing deficits in strength, reducing lost time, and returning the body to pre-injury fitness levels.[19]

A concept that is gaining acceptance in bridging the gap between treatment or therapy and a safe return to work is known as *work hardening*.[20] Work hardening and its objectives are explained as follows: In specially designed "work centres," various workstations, exercise equipment, and aggressive protocols are used for work reconditioning. The objectives are:

- A return to maximum physical abilities as soon as possible.
- Improvement of general body fitness.
- Reducing the likelihood of re-injury.
- Work simulation that duplicates real work conditions.[21]

The work centres referred to above replicate in as much detail as possible the injured employee's actual work environment. In addition to undergoing carefully controlled and monitored therapy in the work centre, the employee is encouraged to use exercise equipment. Employees who undergo work centre therapy should have already completed a program of acute physical therapy and pain management, and they should be medically stable.[22]

Health and safety managers can help facilitate the fastest possible safe resumption of duties by injured employees by identifying local health care providers that use the work hardening approach. Such services and local providers of them should be made known to upper management so that the company can take advantage of them.

Proper Lifting Techniques

One of the most effective ways to prevent back injuries is to teach employees proper lifting techniques. Following are lifting techniques that should be taught as part of an organization's safety program.

1. Plan Ahead

- Determine if you can lift the load. Is it too heavy or too awkward?
- Decide if you need assistance.
- Check your route to see whether it has obstructions or slippery surfaces.

2. Lift with Your Legs, Not Your Back

- Bend at your knees, keeping your back straight.
- Position your feet close to the object.
- Centre your body over the load.
- Lift straight up smoothly; don't jerk.
- Keep your torso straight; don't twist while lifting or after the load is lifted.
- Set the load down slowly and smoothly with a straight back and bent knees; don't let go until the object is on the floor.

3. Push, Don't Pull

- Pushing puts less strain on your back; don't pull objects.
- Use rollers under the object whenever possible.

STANDING HAZARDS

Consider this statement by Roberta Carson, a certified professional ergonomist: "Prolonged standing or walking is common in industry and can be very painful. Lower back pain, sore feet, varicose veins, swelling in the legs, general muscular fatigue, and other health problems have been associated with prolonged standing or walking."[23] Carson recommends the following precautions for minimizing standing hazards:[24]

Anti-Fatigue Mats

Anti-fatigue mats provide cushioning between the feet and hardworking surfaces such as concrete floors (see Figure 16–8). This cushioning effect can reduce muscle fatigue and lower back pain. However, too much cushioning can be just as bad as too little. Consequently, it is important to test mats on a trial basis before buying a large quantity. Mats that become slippery when wet should be avoided. In areas where chemicals are used, be sure to select mats that will hold up to chemicals.

Figure 16–8 Padded mat.

Used with the permission of Wearwell, Inc.

Shoe Inserts

When anti-fatigue mats are not feasible because employees must move from area to area and, correspondingly, from surface to surface, shoe inserts may be the answer. Such inserts are worn inside the shoe and provide the same type of cushioning the mats provide. Shoe inserts can help reduce lower back, foot, and leg pain. It is important to ensure proper fit. If inserts make an employee's shoes too tight, they will do more harm than good. In such cases, employees may need to wear a slightly larger shoe size.

Foot Rails

Foot rails added to workstations can help relieve the hazards of prolonged standing. Foot rails allow employees to elevate one foot at a time by about 10 cm. The elevated foot rounds out the lower back, thereby relieving some of the pressure on the spinal column. Placement of a rail is important. It should not be placed in a position that inhibits movement or becomes a tripping hazard.

Workplace Design

A well-designed workstation can help relieve the hazards of prolonged standing. The key is to design workstations so that employees can move about while they work and can adjust the height of the workstation to match their physical needs.

Sit/Stand Chairs

Sit/stand chairs are higher-than-normal chairs that allow employees who typically stand while working to take quick mini-breaks and return to work without the hazards associated with getting out of lower chairs. They have the advantage of giving the employee's feet, legs, and back an occasional rest without introducing the hazards associated with lower chairs.

Proper Footwear

Proper footwear is critical for employees who stand for prolonged periods. Well fitting, comfortable shoes that grip the work surface and allow free movement of the toes are best.

HAND PROTECTION

In Canada, the hand is the body part most frequently injured. Canadians suffer about 500,000 hand injuries every year. Hand injuries are both serious and costly for employers and for employees. The range of hazards include needlestick injuries, cuts, pinching, chemical exposure, vibration, and temperature extremes.

Where the risk of hand injuries is present in the workplace, an assessment of the control measures, including glove selection, should be completed to ensure that they are best suited for the individual situation. Selecting just the right gloves for the job is not a simple task. A poorly fitted pair of gloves, for example, cannot offer the degree of protection that a responsible employer or employee wants. Yet, because manufacturers have not developed a consistent set of metrics for sizing gloves, the only way to determine whether a pair fits properly is for the employee to try them on.

And fit is just one of the problems faced when selecting gloves. Other critical features include the protection capability, comfort, and tactile sensitivity of the gloves. Often, greater comfort and tactile sensitivity can mean less protection. Correspondingly, greater protection can mean less comfort and tactile sensitivity.

Common Glove Materials

Depending on the individual hazards available in a given situation, the right gloves for the application may be made of a variety of different materials (see Figures 16–9 and 16–10). The most widely used materials in manufacturing gloves are as follows:

- **Leather.** Offers comfort, excellent abrasion resistance, and minimum cut resistance.
- **Cotton.** Offers comfort, minimal abrasion resistance, and minimum cut resistance.
- **Aramids.** Offer comfort, good abrasion resistance, excellent cut resistance, and excellent heat resistance.
- **Polyethylene.** Offers comfort, excellent abrasion resistance, and minimal cut resistance. Gloves made of this material should not be subjected to high temperatures.
- **Stainless steel cord (wrapped in synthetic fibre).** Offers comfort, good abrasion resistance, and optimal cut resistance.
- **Chain link or metal mesh.** Offers very little comfort, but maximum abrasion and cut resistance.
- **Butyl rubber.** Offers little comfort, but has excellent resistance to heat, ozone, tearing, and certain chemicals including alcohols, aldehydes, ketones, esters, nitriles, gases, amides, acids, and nitro compounds.
- **Viton rubber.** Offers little comfort, but performs well with chemicals that butyl rubber cannot protect against, including aliphatics, halogenated compounds, and aromatics. Like butyl gloves, viton gloves also perform well in handling alcohols, gases, and acids.[25]

Figure 16–9 Cut-resistant work glove.

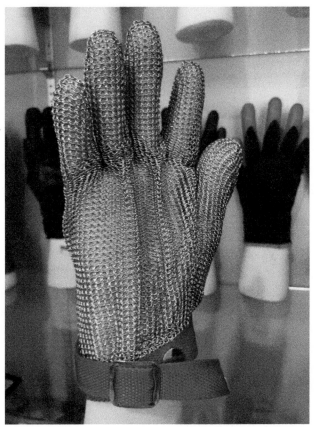

Mark_vyz/Shutterstock

Figure 16–10 Natural rubber gloves.

Marcin Balcerzak/Shutterstock.

PERSONAL PROTECTIVE EQUIPMENT

Personal protective equipment (PPE) is a critical component in the safety program of most organizations. PPE, however, should be considered a last line of defence against injuries and employed only after all practical engineering and administrative controls have been used. Head, hand, back, eye, face, foot, skin, and breathing protection all involve the use of PPE. Unfortunately, it can be difficult to convince employees to wear PPE properly or, sometimes, to wear it at all. Employees often balk at the perceived "inconvenience" of PPE. They don't like the way it looks or how it feels. They find it cumbersome to work in or time-consuming to put on and take off. Sometimes, they just forget.

Making employees comfortable with PPE is a serious and sometimes difficult challenge for health and safety professionals. The following strategies can be used to meet this challenge:

- **Make maximum use of engineering and administrative controls.** PPE should be the last line of defence in protecting employees from hazardous conditions. Before adopting PPE, organizations should first use every engineering and administrative control available to minimize potential hazards. If employees see that the organization is doing its part by applying these controls, they will be less reluctant to do their part in properly using PPE.

- **Ensure the optimum choice of PPE by using risk assessment.** Employees know when there is a mismatch between the hazards they face and the PPE they are provided. PPE should be selected on the basis of a comprehensive risk assessment. This approach helps employers make the optimum choice when selecting PPE. Employees who know that the PPE provides adequate protection from hazards will be more likely to use it.

- **Involve employees in all aspects of the PPE program.** Always involve employees when making decisions that affect them. This is good policy for two reasons: (1) Employees may be able to provide input that will improve the quality of the decisions being made because they understand the work tasks being discussed, and (2) employees who are involved in the decision-making are more likely to buy into and support the resulting decision.

- **Provide comprehensive education and training programs.** Employees need to understand why PPE is important and how to properly use it. Employers should never assume that employees understand the "why" or "how" of PPE. Training programs should begin with the *why* aspects, cover them thoroughly, and give employees ample opportunities to ask questions and voice concerns. Once employees understand why PPE is important, they should be given comprehensive training on how to use it properly. No employee should be expected to use PPE without first understanding why and how they should use it.

- **Reinforce the proper use of PPE and challenge its improper use.** Employers should never fall into the trap of taking PPE use for granted. Proper behaviour relating to PPE should be reinforced by supervisors and managers. Correspondingly, improper use should be challenged. Employers should use PPE properly themselves and reward employees who follow suit. Rewards need not be formal. Publicly complimenting an employee can be reward enough. Correspondingly, when an employee is seen failing to use the required PPE or using it improperly, that employee should be corrected. However, whereas compliments are given publicly, correction should be done in private.

- **Be sensitive to fit, comfort, and style issues.** Ill-fitting PPE poses a double problem: (1) It may not provide the necessary protection because of the improper fit; and (2) if it does not fit well, employees may be reluctant to wear it because it is uncomfortable. Style can also be a problem in that employees are often self-conscious about their appearances. All of these factors should be considered when choosing PPE.

- **Work to make PPE a normal part of the uniform.** By applying these strategies, employers can make PPE a normal part of the uniform. When this happens, using PPE will become standard operating procedure, and its proper use will cease to be an issue.[26]

FORKLIFT SAFETY (POWERED INDUSTRIAL TRUCKS)

Powered industrial truck or forklift safety is included here because forklift-related injuries often result from impact or acceleration hazards. Some jurisdictions in Canada have no specific requirements for forklift operators to be trained, but all operators should be competent to operate the machine and meet training and certification requirements prescribed by the employer. Lift trucks used in many workplaces are powerful and heavy machines that are potentially very hazardous when under the control of an untrained operator.

Employees who drive forklifts should understand that they are different from cars and trucks in several ways. The primary differences are as follows:

- Forklifts are typically steered by the rear wheels.
- An empty forklift can be more difficult to steer than one with a load.
- Forklifts are frequently driven in reverse.
- Forklifts have three-point suspension so that the centre of gravity can move from the rear of the vehicle closer to the front when it is loaded.

Because of these differences, it is important to ensure that only properly trained employees drive forklifts and that these employees follow some basic rules of accident prevention. The rules fall into four categories: (1) general, (2) lifting, (3) travelling, and (4) placing.

1. General Rules apply to all phases of forklift operation:

- Keep arms, hands, and legs inside the vehicle at all times.
- Face in the direction of travel at all times.
- If the load blocks your view, drive backward.
- Allow plenty of room for braking—at least three vehicle lengths.
- Make sure there is sufficient overhead clearance before moving a load.

2. Rules for Lifting a Load

- Make sure the load is within the capacity of the forklift.
- Make sure forks are positioned properly.
- Make sure the load is properly balanced.
- Make sure the load is secure.
- Raise the load to the proper height.
- Run the forks all the way into the pallet and tilt the mast back to stabilize the load before moving.
- Back out and stop completely before lowering the load.

3. Rules for Travelling with a Load

- Always give pedestrians the right-of-way.
- Never allow passengers on the forklift.
- Keep the forks low while moving.
- Keep the load tilted back slightly while moving.
- Drive slowly; a forklift is not a car.
- Slow down at all intersections; stop and sound the horn at blind intersections.
- Drive up and back down ramps and inclines.
- Never lift or lower the load when travelling.
- Keep to the right just as you do when driving a car.
- Watch for oil, grease, and wet spots that could inhibit traction.
- Cross railroad tracks at a skewed angle, never at a right angle.
- Watch for edges on loading docks and other changes in elevation.

4. Rules for Placing a Load

- Stop the forklift completely before raising or lowering the load.
- Move slowly and cautiously with the load raised.
- Never walk or stand under a raised load or allow anyone else to do so.
- Be certain the forks have cleared the pallet before turning and before changing height.
- Stack the load square and straight.
- Check behind and on both sides before backing up.

SUMMARY

1. The primary causes of falls are a foreign object on the walking surface, a design flaw in the walking surface, a slippery surface, and a person's impaired physical condition.

2. Most falls fit into one of four categories: trip and fall, stump and fall, step and fall, and slip and fall.

3. The coefficient of friction between surfaces is an effective method for measuring the traction of a walking surface. A coefficient of friction of 0.2 or less means the surface is very slippery and very hazardous. A coefficient of 0.4 or higher means there is good traction. Coefficients of friction decrease when a surface is wet.

4. Strategies for preventing slips include the following: choose the right material from the outset, retrofit an existing surface, practise good housekeeping, require nonskid footwear, and inspect surfaces frequently.

5. Dos and don'ts of ladder safety include checking for slipperiness, allowing only one person on the ladder at a time, securing the base and top on a level surface, applying the four-to-one ratio, facing the ladder when climbing, avoiding leaning, and always holding on with one hand.

6. Protection from impact injuries from falling or projected objects includes personal protective equipment to protect the head (hard hats), eyes and face (goggles or face shields), and feet (footwear).

7. Back safety/lifting programs should have the following components: poster illustrations, pre-employment screening, regular safety inspections, education and training, external services, and a written map of the program.

8. Standing hazards can be minimized by using the following: anti-fatigue mats, shoe inserts, foot rails, improved workplace design, sit/stand chairs, and protective footwear.

9. The most widely used materials in manufacturing gloves for hand protection are leather, cotton, aramids, polyethylene, stainless steel cord, chain link or metal mesh, butyl rubber, and viton rubber.

10. Personal protective equipment should be the last line of defence protecting employees from hazards. Before using PPE, every feasible engineering and administrative control should be employed.

11. Lift trucks used in many workplaces are powerful and heavy machines that are potentially very hazardous when under the control of an untrained operator.

Key Terms and Concepts

Acceleration	Lanyard	Slip and fall
Coefficient of friction	Lifting hazards	Step and fall
Design flaw	Manual materials	Stump and fall
Foreign object	handling (MMH)	Trip and fall
Four-to-one ratio	Nonskid footwear	
Impact accidents	Retrofit	

Review Questions

1. List the primary causes of falls.
2. Explain briefly the most common kinds of falls.
3. Explain how surface traction is measured.
4. List and briefly explain five strategies for preventing slips.
5. With reference to your local legislation, under what conditions are the requirements for fall protection enhanced?
6. What is a lanyard?

7. Are safety glasses or goggles required when wearing a face shield? Explain.

8. What is the current standard used in your jurisdiction for vision protection devices?

9. What should an employee look for when inspecting a ladder?

10. List six major kinds of injuries to the foot and toes that occur in the workplace each year.

11. List four ways to minimize standing hazards.

12. Explain the strategies for proper lifting that should be taught as part of the safety program.

13. What are the critical factors to consider when selecting gloves?

14. What potential problems are created with PPE?

Weblinks

Canadian Centre for Occupational Health and Safety

www.ccohs.ca/oshanswers/ergonomics/niosh/calculating_rwl.html

An easy-to-use weight calculator based on the revised NIOSH lifting equation.

American National Standards Institute (ANSI)

www.ansi.org

ANSI guidelines and standards are adopted by numerous industries and jurisdictions throughout North America.

Ontario Workplace Safety & Prevention Services

http://wsps.ca/Home.aspx

The Ontario Workplace Safety & Prevention Services website has a comprehensive collection of information and resources on a broad range of safety topics.

Endnotes

1 Canadian Centre for Occupational Health and Safety. (November 27, 1997). "OHS Answers." [Online]. Available: http://www.ccohs.ca/oshanswers/safety_haz/falls.html. (Retrieved March 4, 2005).

2 G. LaBar. "Standing Tall against Slips and Falls." *Occupational Hazards* (April 1998): 40–42.

3 Ibid.

4 Ibid., 42.

5 Ibid.

6 Ibid.

7 C. Brickman. "Heart & Sole." *Occupational Health & Safety* 68, no. 4: 35.

8 Construction Safety Association of Ontario. *Health and Safety Manual*, rev. ed. (CSAO, 1999), 69.

9 Ibid., 72.

10 Canadian Centre for Occupational Health and Safety. (November 27, 1997). "OHS Answers." [Online]. Available: https://www.ccohs.ca/oshanswers/prevention/ppe/headwear.html. (Retrieved July 31, 2017).

[11] Ibid.

[12] P. Feuerstein. "Head Protection Looks Up." *Safety & Health* 144, no. 3: 39.

[13] Ibid.

[14] J. Hensel. "Setting Up a Vision Program." *Occupational Health & Safety* 68, no. 10: 36.

[15] Ibid.

[16] Canadian Centre for Occupational Health and Safety. (November 27, 1997). "OHS Answers." [Online]. Available: http://www.ccohs.ca/oshanswers/ergonomics/mmh/hlth_haz.html. (Retrieved August 4, 2004).

[17] Canadian Centre for Occupational Health and Safety. (November 27, 1997). "OHS Answers." [Online]. Available: http://www.ccohs.ca/oshanswers/ergonomics/niosh/assessing.html.(Retrieved March 4, 2005).

[18] A. Kaliokin. "Six Steps Can Help Prevent Back Injuries and Reduce Compensation Costs." *Safety & Health* 138, no. 4: 50.

[19] B. Urborg. "How to Comply with OSHA's Ergonomic Standard." [Online]. Available: http://www.nsc.org/news/nr11601.htm. (Retrieved May 2003).

[20] Ibid.

[21] Ibid.

[22] Ibid.

[23] R. Carson. "Stand by Your Job." *Occupational Health & Safety* (April 1994): 38.

[24] Ibid., 40–42.

[25] T. Busshart. "A Cut Above." *Occupational Safety & Health* 67, no. 1: 36.

[26] T. Andrews. "Getting Employees Comfortable with PPE." *Occupational Hazards* 62, no. 1: 35–38.

Chapter 17
Hazards of Temperature Extremes and Chemical Burns

MAJOR TOPICS

- Thermal Comfort
- Heat Stress and Strain
- Cold Stress
- Burns and Their Effects
- Chemical Burns

Part of providing a safe and healthy workplace is appropriately controlling the temperature, humidity, and air distribution in work areas. A work environment in which the temperature is not properly controlled can be uncomfortable. Extremes of either heat or cold can also be more than uncomfortable—they can be dangerous. Heat stress, cold stress, and burns are major concerns of modern health and safety professionals. This chapter provides the information that professionals need to know to overcome the hazards associated with extreme temperatures.

Note that when converting incremental changes from Celsius to Fahrenheit, the usual conversion factor or conversion tables are not able to be used. A change of 1 degree Celsius is equivalent to a change of 1.8 degrees Fahrenheit or $\Delta\ 1°C = \Delta\ 1.8°F$.

THERMAL COMFORT

Thermal comfort in the workplace is a function of a number of different factors.[1] Temperature, humidity, air distribution, personal preference, and acclimatization are all determinants of comfort in the workplace. However, determining optimum conditions is not a simple process.

To fully understand the hazards posed by temperature extremes, health and safety professionals must be familiar with several basic concepts related to thermal energy. The most important of these are summarized here:

- **Conduction** is the transfer of heat between two bodies that are touching, or from one location to another within a body. For example, if an employee touches a workpiece that has just been welded and is still hot, heat will be conducted from the workpiece to the hand. Of course, the result of this heat transfer is a burn.

- **Convection** is the transfer of heat from one location to another by way of a moving medium (a gas or a liquid). Convection ovens use this principle to transfer heat from an electrode by way of gases in the air to whatever is being baked.

- **Metabolic heat** is produced within a body as a result of activity that burns energy. All humans produce metabolic heat. This is why a room that is comfortable when occupied by just a few people may become uncomfortable when it is crowded. Unless the thermostat is lowered to compensate, the metabolic heat of a crowd will cause the temperature of a room to rise to an uncomfortable level.

- **Environmental heat** is produced by external sources. Gas or electric heating systems produce environmental heat, as do sources of electricity and a number of industrial processes.

- **Radiant heat** is the result of electromagnetic nonionizing energy that is transmitted through space without the movement of matter within that space.

The human body is constantly producing heat, equivalent to about 75 watts when sleeping and up to 700 watts while performing heavy work. The net heat exchange rate should maintain a core temperature of 37°C (98.6°F). Including the factors mentioned above, a formula is given below to show that as work intensity (internal heat production) increases, so must the net heat exchange from the body.

$$H = S + E + R + C$$

where

H = rate of internal heat production

S = rate of heat storage in the body

E = rate of loss by evaporation

R = rate of radiant energy exchange with surroundings

C = rate of loss by convection

conduction The transfer of direct thermal energy between two bodies that are touching or from one location to another within a body.

convection The transfer of heat from one location to another by way of a moving medium.

metabolic heat Produced within a body as a result of activity that burns energy.

environmental heat Heat that is produced by sources outside the body.

radiant heat The result of electromagnetic nonionizing energy that is transmitted through space without the movement of matter within that space.

HEAT STRESS AND STRAIN

The key question that must be answered by health and safety professionals concerning employees whose work may subject them to heat stress is:

> What are the conditions to which most adequately hydrated, unmedicated, healthy employees may be exposed without experiencing heat strain or any other adverse effects?

ACGIH (formerly known as the American Conference of Governmental Industrial Hygienists) publishes a comprehensive manual to help health and safety professionals answer this question for the specific situations and conditions that they face. This manual, titled *TLVs and BEIs: Threshold Limit Values for Chemical Substances and Physical Agents and Biological Exposure Indices*, provides reliable guidance and should be in every health and safety professional's library. Most jurisdictions in Canada base their regulations, standards, or guidelines on these temperature exposure indices. In addition to using the information contained in this manual, all health and safety professionals should have a comprehensive heat stress management program in place and apply sound professional judgment where temperature extremes are an issue.[2]

Heat Stress Defined

Heat stress is the net heat load to which a worker may be exposed from the combined contributions of metabolic cost of work, environmental factors (i.e., air temperature, humidity, air movement, and radiant heat exchange), and clothing requirements. A mild or moderate heat stress may cause discomfort and may adversely affect performance and safety, but it is not harmful to health. As the heat stress approaches human tolerance limits, the risk of heat-related disorders increases.[3]

Heat Strain Defined

Heat strain is the overall physiological response resulting from heat stress. The physiological adjustments are dedicated to dissipating excess heat from the body. **Acclimatization** is a gradual physiological adaptation that improves an individual's ability to tolerate heat (or cold) stress.

Recognizing Heat Strain

Health and safety professionals, supervisors, and coworkers should know how to recognize heat strain. The following factors are signs of excessive heat strain. Exposure to heat stress should be stopped immediately for any employee experiencing any of these symptoms:

- A sustained rapid heart rate (180 beats per minute minus the employee's age in years is a normal rapid heart rate). For example, if a 40-year-old employee has a sustained heart rate of 150 beats per minute, this is a problem because the heart rate exceeds 140 (180 minus 40) beats per minute.
- Core body temperature is greater than 38.5°C (101.3°F).
- Recovery rate 1 minute after a peak work effort is greater than 110 beats per minute.
- Sudden and severe fatigue, nausea, dizziness, or light-headedness.

These symptoms can be assessed on the spot at any given moment in time. In addition to these, other symptoms can be monitored only over a period of time. Employees are at greater risk of excessive heat strain if they experience any of the following:

- Profuse sweating that continues for hours.
- Weight loss of more than 1.5 percent of body weight during one work shift.
- Urinary sodium excretion of less than 50 moles in a 24-hour period.

≫≫ SAFETY FACT | **Symptoms of Heat Exhaustion**

Employees need to be able to observe and recognize the symptoms of heat exhaustion in themselves and their coworkers. The following are observable symptoms of heat exhaustion:

- Fatigue
- Nausea and/or vomiting
- Headache

- Light-headedness
- Clammy, moist skin
- Pale or flushed complexion
- Fainting when trying to stand
- Rapid pulse

Clothing

Heat is most easily removed from the body when there is free movement of cool dry air over the skin's surface. This promotes the evaporation of sweat from the skin, which is the body's principal cooling mechanism. Clothing impedes this process, some types more than others. Encapsulating suits and clothing that is impermeable or highly resistant to the flow of air and water vapour increase the potential for heat strain.

When assessing heat stress hazards in the workplace, health and safety professionals should consider the added effect of clothing. For example, the **wet bulb globe temperature (WBGT)** of working conditions should be increased by 3.5°C (6.3°F) for employees wearing cloth overalls. This factor increases to 5°C (9.0°F) with double cloth overalls.

The basic instrumentation used to determine WBGT consists of three thermometers that are exposed to different conditions that affect the amount of heat exchange from the body. A wet sock covers the first thermometer and simulates the effect of sweat evaporating from the body. A second temperature reading takes into account the radiant heat load on the body, by placing the thermometer inside a black globe. Thirdly, the ambient temperature is measured and included in the WBGT calculation. However, this reading has the least effect on the final value.

Because the WBGT is influenced by air temperature, radiant heat, and humidity, it can be helpful in establishing a threshold for making judgments about working conditions. WBGT values can be calculated using the following formula:

wet bulb globe temperature (WBGT) A measure of the heat stress in direct sunlight, which takes into account temperature, humidity, wind speed, and solar heat load.

1. Exposed to Direct Sunlight

$$WBGT = 0.7T_{nwb} \text{ to } 0.2T_g + 0.1T_{db}$$

T_{nwb} = Natural wet bulb temperature

T_g = Globe temperature

T_{db} = Dry bulb (air) temperature

2. Not Exposed to Direct Sunlight

$$WBGT = 0.7T_{nwb} + 0.3T_g$$

These formulas for WBGT give health and safety professionals a starting point for making judgments. The WBGT must be adjusted for clothing, work demands, and the employee's acclimatization state. The key is to ensure that employees never experience a core body temperature of 38°C (100°F) or higher. Figures 17–1 and 17–2 provide screening criteria for heat stress exposure. Once the WBGT has been calculated and adjusted for clothing, these figures may be used for factoring in work demands and acclimatization. To use Figures 17–1 and 17–2, apply them to the following example:

> Several acclimatized employees have a job to do that has a work demand of 75 percent work and 25 percent rest. The WBGT in the work area has been computed as 26°C. The work is considered "heavy." Because the employees will wear long-sleeved shirts and long trousers made of woven material, however, an additional 3.5°C must be added: 26°C + 3.5°C = 29.5°C. Using the proper column and row of Figure 17–1, we see that the allowable WBGT under those conditions is 27.5°C. Because the calculated and adjusted WBGT is 29.5°C, there is a problem. In order to work in these conditions, the employees should adjust the work demand to 25 percent work and 75 percent rest. We can see from Figure 17–1 that under the adjusted conditions the allowable WBGT is 30°C, so 29.5°C falls safely within that level.

Heat Stress Management

Health and safety professionals should continually emphasize the importance of paying attention to recognizable symptoms of heat stress. In addition, they should ensure that a

Figure 17–1 Criteria for determining the allowable work periods for acclimatized employees.

Screening Criteria (°C) Acclimatized Employees				
Work Demands	Light Work	Moderate Work	Heavy Work	Very Heavy Work
100% Work	29.5	27.5	26.0	—
75% Work 25% Rest	30.5	28.5	27.5	—
50% Work 50% Rest	31.5	29.5	28.5	27.5
25% Work 75% Rest	32.5	31.0	30.0	29.5

Source: American Conference of Government Industrial Hygienists (ACGIH).

Figure 17–2 Criteria for determining the allowable work periods for employees who are not acclimatized.

Screening Criteria (°C) Not Acclimatized Employees				
Work Demands	Light Work	Moderate Work	Heavy Work	Very Heavy Work
100% Work	27.5	25.0	22.5	—
75% Work 25% Rest	29.0	26.5	24.5	—
50% Work 50% Rest	30.0	28.0	26.5	25.0
25% Work 75% Rest	31.0	29.0	28.0	26.5

Source: American Conference of Government Industrial Hygienists (ACGIH).

comprehensive heat stress management program is in place. Such a program should consist of both general and specific controls.

General Controls The ACGIH recommends the following general controls:

- Provide accurate verbal and written instructions, training programs, and other information about heat stress and strain.

- Encourage drinking small volumes (approximately 250 ml) of cool water about every 20 minutes.

- Permit self-limitation of exposure.

- Encourage coworker observation to detect signs and symptoms of heat strain in others.

- Counsel and monitor those employees who take medications that may compromise normal cardiovascular, blood pressure, body temperature regulation, renal, or sweat gland functions, as well as those who abuse or who are recovering from the abuse of alcohol and other intoxicants.

- Encourage healthy lifestyles, ideal body weight, and electrolyte balance.
- Adjust expectations of those returning to work after absence from heat stress situations and encourage consumption of salty foods (with approval of the employee's physician if on a salt-restricted diet).
- Consider medical screening to identify those susceptible to systemic heat injury.[4]

Specific Controls   The ACGIH recommends the following specific controls:

- Establish engineering controls that reduce the metabolic rate, provide general air movement, reduce process heat and water-vapour release, and shield radiant heat sources, among others.
- Consider administrative controls that set acceptable exposure times, allow sufficient recovery, and limit physiological strain.
- Consider personal protection that has been demonstrated to be effective for the specific work practices and conditions at the location.[5]

Acclimatization   Acclimatization is the process of gradually enabling the body to better cope with temperature extremes. The process of acclimatization can take from 1 to 3 weeks depending on the general physical condition of the worker. Younger and physically fit people become acclimatized quicker. The worker will benefit from enhanced cardiovascular fitness, which keeps heart rate and core temperature lower during high temperature activities. Other benefits to the acclimatized worker include increased sweating efficiency and a decrease in electrolyte (salt) loss.

The benefits of acclimatization are lost more quickly than they are gained. In as few as 2 or 3 days a loss can occur. Workers returning from a break of as little as a couple of days should reduce their workload until their acclimatization has improved. Many Canadian workers who work outdoors are well versed in the annual ritual of acclimatization. In central areas of the country the temperatures faced by many workers can range from –30°C (–22°F) in the winter to 30°C (86°F) in summer. In many parts of our vast country, getting "used to" hot outdoor working conditions is not a problem. In most parts of Yukon, the Northwest Territories, and Nunavut, the mean daily temperature rarely exceeds 0°C (32°F) for 8 months of the year and the summertime high is normally less than 20°C (68°F).

⟫⟫⟫ SAFETY FACT | Humidex and Wind Chill Warnings

When Canadians hear a weather forecast, along with the temperature we often get humidex and wind chill numbers. The humidex indicates how hot we would feel in the summer. As the humidity of the air increases, the perceived temperature also rises because evaporation of our sweat is less efficient.

Environment Canada provides the following humidex guidelines:

Humidex level below 29°C (84°F) – comfortable.

Humidex level 30°C to 39°C (86°F to 102°F) – some discomfort.

Humidex level 40°C to 45°C (104°F to 113°F) – uncomfortable, avoid exertion.

Humidex level over 45°C (113°F) – dangerous, probable heat stroke.

In the winter, of course, we are more concerned with how cold it feels outside. Wind chill is the cooling sensation created by the temperature and the wind together. Moving air causes evaporation from our skin and a resulting increase in loss of body heat. So the wind chill provides a better indication of the risk of hypothermia and frostbite to those outside who are not dressed properly or sheltered from the wind than does the air temperature alone. In 2003 Environment Canada began using an improved index based on new wind chill research on precisely how long it takes for exposed skin to freeze. For example, with a wind chill index of –40, which is not uncommon for many parts of Canada, it would take from 5 to 10 minutes for exposed skin to become frostbitten.

COLD STRESS

hypothermia The condition that results when the body's core temperature drops to dangerously low levels, below 35°C (95°F).

cold stress Physical or mental stress that results from working in cold conditions.

Excessive exposure to cold can lead to **hypothermia**, which can be fatal. The goal of health and safety professionals in protecting employees from **cold stress** is to prevent the deep body temperature from falling below 36°C (98.6°F) and to prevent cold injuries to body extremities, especially the hands, feet, and head. A fatal exposure to cold typically results from failure to remove the employee from a cold air environment or immersion in cold water.[6]

Excessive exposure to cold stress, even when not fatal, can result in impaired judgment, reduced alertness, and poor decision-making. All of these factors increase the likelihood of accidents and injuries. Figure 17–3 shows the effects of allowing the core body temperature to fall to selected levels.

Figure 17–3 The body's response to reducing its core temperature.

Effects of Reducing the Core Body Temperature

Core Temperature

°C	°F	Body's Response
37.6	99.6	Normal rectal temperature
36.0	96.8	Metabolic rate increases
35.0	95.0	Pronounced shivering
33.0	91.4	Severe hypothermia
30.0	86.0	Progressive loss of consciousness begins
24.0	75.2	Pulmonary edema
20.0	68.0	Cardiac standstill

Whether employees are simply exposed to cold air or are immersed in cold water, wind can magnify the level of cold stress. Figure 17–4 shows the effect of wind on selected temperatures. To read this chart, locate the actual temperature in the row across the top (4°C, –7°C, –18°C, –29°C, –40°C), then find the applicable wind speed in the column at the left, and the chart will give you the equivalent temperature. For example, if employees are working in an environment that is –18°C (–4°F) and has a wind speed of 24 kilometres per hour (km/h), the equivalent temperature is –36°C (–33°F)

Figure 17–4 Effect of wind on the actual temperature.

Wind Speed (in km/h)	Cooling Effect of Wind Actual Temperature (°C) and Equivalent Temperatures (°C)				
	4	–7	–18	–29	–40
8	3	–9	–21	–32	–44
24	–6	–20	–36	–50	–65
40	–9	–26	–42	–59	–76
64	–2	–29	–47	–65	–82

Source: US Army Research Institute of Environmental Medicine.

Preventing Cold Stress

When the equivalent air temperature reaches –32°C (–25.6°F), continuous exposure of skin should not be allowed. At equivalent air temperatures of 2°C (35.6°F), employees who are immersed in water or whose clothing gets wet should be treated for hypothermia immediately. Figure 17–5 shows selected TLVs for employees who work in environments with temperatures below freezing.

Figure 17–5 Partial table for determining TLVs in selected circumstances.

<table>
<tr><td colspan="9" align="center">TLVs for a Four-Hour Shift</td></tr>
<tr><td colspan="2">Air Temperature</td><td colspan="2">No Wind</td><td colspan="2">8 km/h (5 mph) Wind</td><td colspan="2">16 km/h (10 mph) Wind</td></tr>
<tr><td>C°</td><td>F°</td><td>Max. Work Time</td><td>No. of Breaks</td><td>Max. Work Time</td><td>No. of Breaks</td><td>Max. Work Time</td><td>No. of Breaks</td></tr>
<tr><td>–32 to –34</td><td>–25 to –29</td><td>75 min.</td><td>2</td><td>55 min.</td><td>3</td><td>40 min.</td><td>4</td></tr>
<tr><td>–35 to –37</td><td>–30 to –34</td><td>55 min.</td><td>3</td><td>40 min.</td><td>4</td><td>30 min.</td><td>5</td></tr>
<tr><td>–38 to –39</td><td>–35 to –39</td><td>40 min.</td><td>4</td><td>30 min.</td><td>5</td><td colspan="2" align="center">Non–emergency Work Prohibited</td></tr>
<tr><td colspan="9">Note: This applies to workers properly dressed in dry clothing.</td></tr>
</table>

Source: ACGIH (American Conference of Government Industrial Hygienists).

To use Figure 17–5, locate the applicable temperature in the left-hand column, then, reading across the top, locate the applicable wind speed. For example, employees working a 4-hour shift in an environment with an air temperature of –32°C (–25.6°F) and an 8-km/h wind should be exposed for no longer than 55 minutes at a time and should warm up at least three times during the shift.

When work is to be performed in an environment with an air temperature of 4°C (39.2°F) or less, total body protective clothing is advisable. What follows are several strategies that can be used to decrease the hazards of cold stress:

- When working in a setting in which wind is a factor, reduce the effect of the wind by (1) erecting a windscreen, or (2) wearing wind-breaking clothing.

- When working in a setting in which clothing may get wet, apply one or more of the following strategies: (1) With light work, wear an outer layer of impermeable clothing; (2) with heavier work, wear an outer layer that is water repellent, but not impermeable (change outerwear as it becomes wet); (3) select outer garments that are ventilated to prevent internal wetting from sweat; (4) if clothing gets wet before going into the cold environment, change first; (5) change socks daily or more often to keep them dry; and (6) use vapour barrier boots to help keep the feet dry.

- If adequate protective clothing that is appropriate for the conditions in question is not available, the work should be modified or suspended until conditions change or the clothing is available.

When work is to be performed in an environment with an air temperature of –12°C (10.4°F), the following additional strategies should be applied:

- Employees should be under continuous observation using either direct supervision or the buddy system.

- The work rate should be paced to avoid sweating. When heavy work is necessary, employees should take frequent warming breaks in heated shelters. If clothing becomes wet—internally or externally—it should be changed during a break.

- Do not allow new employees to work full time in these conditions until they have several days to become accustomed to the conditions and the necessary protective clothing.

- When determining the required work level for employees (light, heavy, or very heavy), consider the weight and bulkiness of protective clothing.

- Organize work in cold environments to minimize long periods of sitting or standing still. Never use unprotected metal chairs or seats.

- Before allowing employees to work in a cold environment, make sure they have been trained in health and safety procedures for working in cold environments. Figure 17–6 is a checklist of topics that should be covered as a minimum during employee training.

- When work in a refrigerated room is required, the air velocity should be minimized and maintained at 1 metre per second (200 fpm) or less.

- When work outdoors in snow is required, employees should be provided with special safety goggles that protect the eyes from ultraviolet light, glare, and blowing ice crystals.

- Employees who suffer from diseases or take medications that inhibit normal body functions or that reduce normal body tolerances should be prohibited from working in environments where temperatures are at –1°C (30.2°F) or less.

- Employees who are routinely exposed to the following conditions should be medically certified as being suitable for work in such conditions: (1) air temperatures of less than –24°C (–11.2°F) with wind speeds less than 8 km/h (5 mph), and (2) air temperatures of less than –18°C (–0.4°F) with wind speeds greater than 8 km/h (5 mph).

Figure 17–6 Checklist for training employees who will work in a cold environment.

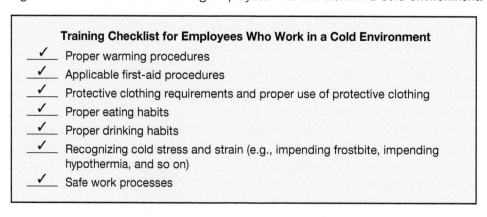

Training Checklist for Employees Who Work in a Cold Environment
- ✓ Proper warming procedures
- ✓ Applicable first-aid procedures
- ✓ Protective clothing requirements and proper use of protective clothing
- ✓ Proper eating habits
- ✓ Proper drinking habits
- ✓ Recognizing cold stress and strain (e.g., impending frostbite, impending hypothermia, and so on)
- ✓ Safe work processes

THERMAL BURNS AND THEIR EFFECTS

One of the most common hazards associated with heat in the workplace is the burn. Burns can be especially dangerous because they disrupt the normal functioning of the skin, which is the body's largest organ and the most important in terms of protecting other organs. It is necessary first to understand the composition of, and purpose served by, the skin to understand the hazards that burns can represent.

Human Skin

Human skin is the tough, continuous outer covering of the body. It consists of the following two main layers: (1) the outer layer, which is known as the **epidermis**; and (2) the inner layer, which is known as the **dermis**, **cutis**, or **corium**. The dermis is connected to the underlying subcutaneous tissue.

The skin serves several important purposes, including protection of body tissue, sensation, secretion, excretion, and respiration (see Figure 17–7). Protection from **fluid loss**, water penetration, ultraviolet radiation, and infestation by microorganisms is a major function of the skin. The sensory functions of touching, sensing cold, feeling pain, and sensing heat involve the skin.

epidermis The outer layer of human skin.

dermis (also called *cutis* or *corium*) The inner layer of human skin.

fluid loss Depletion of necessary body fluids, primarily through perspiration.

Figure 17–7 Functions of the human skin.

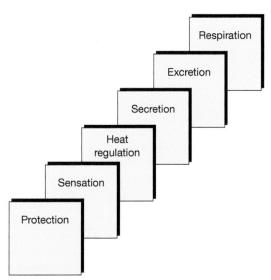

The skin helps regulate body heat through the sweating process. It excretes sweat that takes with it **electrolytes** and certain toxins. This helps keep the body's fluid level in balance. By giving off minute amounts of carbon dioxide and absorbing small amounts of oxygen, the skin also aids slightly in respiration.

electrolytes Minerals that are needed for the body to maintain the proper metabolism and for cells to produce energy.

What makes burns particularly dangerous is that they can disrupt any or all of these functions depending on their severity. The deeper the penetration, the more severe the burn.

Severity of Burns

The severity of a burn depends on several factors. The most important of these is the depth to which the burn penetrates. Other determining factors include the location of the burn, the age of the victim, and the amount of burned area.

The most widely used method of classifying burns is by degree (i.e., first-, second-, or third-degree burns). Modern health and safety professionals should be familiar with these classifications and what they mean.

First-degree burns are minor and result only in a mild inflammation of the skin, known as *erythema*. Sunburn is a common form of first-degree burn. It is easily recognizable as a redness of the skin that makes the skin sensitive and moderately painful to the touch.

Second-degree burns are easily recognizable from the blisters that form on the skin. If a second-degree burn is superficial, the skin will heal with little or no scarring. A deeper

first-degree burns Burns that result in a mild inflammation of the skin known as erythema.

second-degree burns Burns that result in blisters forming on the skin.

second-degree burn will form a thin layer of coagulated, dead cells that feels leathery to the touch. A temperature of approximately 99°C (210°F) can cause a second-degree burn in as little as 15 seconds of contact.

Third-degree burns are very dangerous and can be fatal depending on the amount of body surface area affected. A third-degree burn penetrates through both the epidermis and the dermis. A deep third-degree burn will penetrate body tissue. Third-degree burns can be caused by both moist and dry hazards. Moist hazards include steam and hot liquids; these cause burns that appear white. Dry hazards include fire and hot objects or surfaces; these cause burns that appear black and charred.

In addition to the depth of penetration of a burn, the amount of surface area covered is also a critical concern. This amount is expressed as a percentage of **body surface area (BSA)**. Figure 17–8 shows how the percentage of BSA can be estimated. Burns covering over 75 percent of BSA are usually fatal.

Figure 17–8 Estimating percentage of body surface area (BSA) burned.

Right arm	9% of BSA
Left arm	9% of BSA
Head/neck	9% of BSA
Right leg	18% of BSA
Left leg	18% of BSA
Back	18% of BSA
Chest/stomach	18% of BSA
Perineum	1% of BSA

Using the first-, second-, and third-degree burn classifications in conjunction with BSA percentages, burns can be classified further as minor, moderate, or critical. According to Mertz, these classifications can be summarized as follows.[7]

Minor Burns

All first-degree burns are **minor burns**. Second-degree burns covering less than 15 percent of the body are considered minor. Second-degree burns can be considered minor provided they cover only 2 percent or less of BSA.

Moderate Burns

Second-degree burns that penetrate the epidermis and cover 15 percent or more of BSA are considered moderate. Second-degree burns that penetrate the dermis and cover from 15 to 30 percent of BSA are considered **moderate burns**. Third-degree burns can be considered moderate provided they cover less than 10 percent of BSA and are not on the hands, face, or feet.

Critical Burns

Second-degree burns covering more than 30 percent of BSA or third-degree burns covering over 10 percent of BSA are considered **critical burns**. Even small-area third-degree burns to the hands, face, or feet are considered critical because of the greater potential for **infection** of these areas by their nature. In addition, burns that are complicated by other injuries (fractures, soft tissue damage, and so on) are considered critical.

third-degree burns Burns that penetrate through both the epidermis and the dermis. They may be fatal.

body surface area (BSA) When assessing the severity of burns, the amount of body surface area that is covered with burns is an important factor.

minor burns All first-degree burns are considered minor as well as second-degree burns covering less than 15 percent of the body.

moderate burns Second-degree burns covering less than 30 percent of the body and third-degree burns covering less than 10 percent of the body.

critical burns Second-degree burns covering more than 30 percent of the body and third-degree burns covering over 10 percent of the body.

infection The body's response to contamination by a disease-producing microorganism.

CHEMICAL BURNS

Chemicals are widely used in modern industry even by companies that do not produce them as part of their product base. Many of the chemicals produced, handled, stored, transported or otherwise used in industry can cause burns similar to those caused by heat (i.e., first-, second-, and third-degree burns). The hazards of chemical burns are very similar to those of thermal burns.

Chemical burns, like thermal burns, destroy body tissue; the extent of destruction depends on the severity of the burn. However, chemical burns continue to destroy body tissue until the chemicals are washed away completely.

chemical burns Burn damage to the skin caused by chemicals such as acids and alkalies.

The severity of the burn produced by a given chemical depends on the following factors:

- Corrosive capability of the chemical.

- Concentration of the chemical.

- Temperature of the chemical or the solution in which it is dissolved.

- Duration of contact with the chemical.[8]

Effects of Chemical Burns

Different chemicals have different effects on the human body. The harmful effects of selected, widely used chemicals are summarized in Figure 17–9.[9] These are only a few of the many chemicals commonly used in industry today. All serve an important purpose; however, all carry the potential for serious injury.

Figure 17–9 Harmful effects of selected, widely used chemicals.

Chemical	Potential Harmful Effect
Acetic acid	Tissue damage
Liquid bromide	Corrosive effect on the respiratory system and tissue damage
Formaldehyde	Tissue hardening
Lime	Dermatitis and eye burns
Methylbromide	Blisters
Nitric/sulphuric acid mixture	Severe burns and tissue damage
Oxalic acid	Ulceration and tissue damage
White phosphorus	Ignites in air causing thermal burns
Silver nitrate	Corrosive/caustic effect on the skin
Sodium (metal)	Ignites with moisture causing thermal burns
Trichloracetic acid	Tissue damage

The primary hazardous effects of chemical burns are infection, loss of body fluids, and shock.[10]

Infection The risk of infection is high with chemical burns—as is it with heat-induced burns—because the body's primary defence against infection-causing microorganisms (the skin) is penetrated. This is why it is so important to keep burns clean. Infection in a burn wound can cause *septicemia* (blood poisoning).

Fluid Loss Body fluid loss in second- and third-degree burns can be serious. With second-degree burns, the blisters that form on the skin often fill with fluid that seeps out of damaged tissue under the blister. With third-degree burns, fluids are lost internally and this can cause the same complications as a hemorrhage. If these fluids are not replaced properly, the burns can be fatal.

Shock **Shock** is a depression of the nervous system. It can be caused by both physical and psychological trauma. In cases of serious burns, it may be caused by the intense pain that can occur when skin is burned away, leaving sensitive nerve endings exposed. Shock from burns can come in the following two forms: (1) primary shock, which is the first stage and results from physical pain or psychological trauma; and (2) secondary shock, which comes later and is caused by a loss of fluids and plasma proteins resulting from the burns.

First Aid for Chemical Burns

There is a definite course of action that should be taken when chemical burns occur, and the need for immediate action cannot be overemphasized. Flooding the affected area with water, especially in the case of caustic chemicals, will reduce the severity of the damage. In the case of chemical burns to the eyes, the continuous flooding should continue for at least 15 minutes. The eyelids should be held open to ensure that chemicals are not trapped under them.

Clothing is another consideration when an employee comes in contact with a caustic chemical. If chemicals have saturated the employee's clothes, they must be removed quickly. The best approach is to remove the clothes while flooding the body or the affected area. If necessary for quick removal, clothing should be ripped or cut off.

The critical need to apply water immediately in cases of chemical burns means that water must be readily available. Health and safety professionals should ensure that special eyewash and shower facilities are available wherever employees handle chemicals.

SUMMARY

1. Important thermal-related terms include conduction, convection, metabolic heat, environmental heat, and radiant heat.

2. Heat stress is the net load to which a worker may be exposed from the combined contributions of metabolic cost of work, environmental factors, and clothing requirements.

3. The goal in protecting employees from cold stress is to prevent the deep body temperature from falling below 36°C (98.6°F).

4. Heat stress can be prevented by applying the following strategies: medical screening and supervision, orientation and training, proper work practices, and engineering and administrative controls.

5. Wind or air movement causes the body to sense coldness beyond what the thermometer registers. This phenomenon is known as the wind-chill factor. This should be considered when planning work schedules.

6. The most common form of cold stress is hypothermia.

7. The most widely used method of classifying burns is by degree: first-, second-, and third-degree burns. The amount of surface area covered by burns is expressed as a percentage of body surface area (BSA). Burns are also classified as minor, moderate, and critical.

8. The severity of chemical burns depends on the corrosive capability of the chemical, the concentration and temperature of the chemical, and the duration of contact.

9. The primary hazards associated with chemical burns beyond the damage to the body tissues are infection, fluid loss, and shock. The most important first aid for chemical burns is immediate and continual flushing with water.

Key Terms and Concepts

Acclimatization
Body surface area (BSA)
Chemical burns
Cold stress
Conduction
Convection
Corium
Critical burns
Cutis
Dermis

Electrolytes
Environmental heat
Epidermis
First-degree burns
Fluid loss
Heat stress
Heat strain
Hypothermia
Infection
Metabolic heat

Minor burns
Moderate burns
Radiant heat
Second-degree burns
Shock
Third-degree burns
Wet bulb globe
    temperature (WBGT)

Review Questions

1. Define the following thermal comfort–related terms: *conduction*, *convection*, and *metabolic heat*.

2. What is heat stress?

3. What is heat strain?

4. What are the symptoms of heat exhaustion?

5. How can heat strain be recognized?

6. How does clothing affect the cooling process?

7. What factors influence the WBGT?

8. Describe the various general controls in heat stress management.

9. How can cold stress be prevented?

10. How does wind movement affect the way the body perceives temperature?

11. Describe the symptoms of cold stress and hypothermia.

12. Describe the various components of a cold stress prevention program.

13. Describe the various purposes served by the skin.

14. Describe and differentiate among first-, second-, and third-degree burns.

15. Describe and differentiate among minor, moderate, and critical burns.

16. List the factors that determine the severity of a chemical burn.

17. Explain the hazards of chemical burns besides tissue damage.

18. What should you do if an employee accidentally splashes a caustic chemical on himself or herself?

Weblinks

Canadian Centre for Occupational Health and Safety

www.ccohs.ca/oshanswers/phys_agents

CCOHS offers information for workers who are exposed to potentially harmful hot or cold environments, both indoors and out.

The Weather Office

http://weather.gc.ca/canada_e.html

The weather web page from Environment and Natural Resources on the Government of Canada website contains weather facts, trivia, and lots of great tips on working or playing in Canada's extreme temperatures.

Environment and Climate Change Canada (ECCC)

www.ec.gc.ca/default.asp?lang=en&n=FD9B0E51-1

The website contains information on climate change and the effect it has on our planet, weather, health, air quality, and links to related facts and figures.

Endnotes

[1] American Conference of Governmental Industrial Hygienists (ACGIH). 2003 *TLVs and BEIs* (Cincinnati: 2003), 172–181.

[2] Ibid., 180–188.

[3] Ibid., 181.

[4] Ibid., 187.

[5] Ibid.

[6] Ibid., 171–179.

[7] Patricia M. Mertz. "Burn Study." Unpublished paper. University of Miami School of Medicine, Department of Dermatology and Cutaneous Surgery, Miami, FL, October 2000, 2.

[8] National Safety Council. "Chemical Burns." Data Sheet 1–523 Rev. 87 (Chicago: National Safety Council): 1.

[9] Ibid., 3–4.

[10] Ibid., 2.

Chapter 18
Pressure and Confined Space Hazards

PRESSURE HAZARDS DEFINED

Pressure is defined in physics as the force exerted against an opposing fluid or solid distributed over a surface. This may be expressed in force or weight per unit of area, such as kilograms/centimetres squared (or psi [pounds per square inch]). Units of pressure are also commonly expressed as pascals or kilopascals (the air in your car tires is under about 200 kilopascals of pressure [30 psi], and the atmosphere is at approximately 101.3 kPa [14.7 psi]); a pascal is equal to one Newton per square metre (N/m). A **hazard** is a condition with the potential of causing injury to personnel, damage to equipment or structures, loss of material, or lessening of the ability to perform a prescribed function. Thus, a **pressure hazard** is a hazard caused by a dangerous condition involving pressure. Critical injury and damage can occur with relatively little pressure.

pressure The force exerted against an opposing fluid or solid distributed over a surface.

hazard A condition with the potential of causing injury to personnel, damage to equipment or structures, loss of material, or lessening of the ability to perform a prescribed function.

pressure hazard A hazard caused by a dangerous condition involving pressure.

We perceive pressure in relation to the earth's atmosphere. Approximately 21 percent of the atmosphere is oxygen, with most of the other 79 percent being nitrogen. In addition to oxygen and nitrogen, the atmosphere contains trace amounts of several inert gases: argon, neon, krypton, xenon, and helium.

At sea level, the pressure of the earth's atmosphere averages 101.3 kilopascals (101,325 N/m), or 1.013 millibars, or 760 mm Hg (29.92 inches), or 14.7 psi, depending on the measuring scale used.[1] The international system of measurement uses newtons per square metre (N/m)—that is, pascals. However, in human physiology studies, the typical unit is millimetres of mercury (mm Hg).

Atmospheric pressure is usually measured using a **barometer**. As the altitude above sea level increases, atmospheric pressure decreases in a nonlinear fashion. For example, at 5,486.4 metres (18,000 feet) above sea level, the barometric pressure is equal to 390 mm Hg. Half of this pressure, around 195 mm Hg, can be found at 7,010.4 metres (23,000 feet) above sea level.

Boyle's law states that the product of a given pressure and volume is constant with a constant temperature:

$$P_1V_1 = P_2V_2, \text{ when } T \text{ is constant}$$

Air moves in and out of the lungs because of a pressure gradient or difference in pressure. When atmospheric pressure is greater than pressure within the lungs, air flows down this pressure gradient from the outside into the lungs. This is called **inspiration**, inhalation, or breathing in, and occurs with greater lung volume than at rest (i.e., the lungs are expanded). When pressure in the lungs is greater than atmospheric pressure, air moves down a pressure gradient outward from the lungs to the outside. **Expiration** occurs when air leaves the lungs and the lung volume is less than the relaxed volume, increasing pressure within the lungs.

Gas exchange occurs between air in the lung alveoli and gas in solution in blood. The pressure gradients causing this gas exchange are called *partial pressures*. **Dalton's law of partial pressures** states that in a mixture of theoretically ideal gases the pressure exerted by the mixture is the sum of the pressures exerted by each component gas of the mixture:

$$P_A = P_O + P_N + P_{else}$$

Air entering the lungs immediately becomes saturated with water vapour. Water vapour, although it is a gas, does not conform to Dalton's law. The partial pressure of water vapour in a mixture of gases is not dependent on its fractional concentration in that mixture. Water vapour partial pressure, instead, is dependent on its temperature. From this exception to Dalton's law comes the fact that at the normal body temperature of 37°C (98.6°F), water vapour maintains a partial pressure of 47 mm Hg as long as that temperature is maintained. With this brief explanation of how pressure is involved in human breathing, we now focus on the various sources of pressure hazards.

SOURCES OF PRESSURE HAZARDS

There are many sources of pressure hazards—some natural, most created by humans. Because the human body comprises approximately 85 percent liquid, which is virtually incompressible, increasing pressure does not create problems by itself. Problems result from air being trapped or expanded within body cavities.

When sinus passages are blocked so that air cannot pass easily from the sinuses to the nose, expansion of the air in the sinuses can lead to problems. The same complications can occur with air trapped in the middle ear's eustachian tube. As Boyle's law states, gas volume increases as pressure decreases. Expansion of the air in blocked sinus passages or the middle ear occurs with a rapid increase in altitude or a rapid ascent under water. This can cause pain and, if not eventually relieved, disease. Under extreme circumstances of rapid ascent from underwater diving or high-altitude decompression, lungs can rupture.

Nitrogen absorption into the body tissues can become excessive during underwater diving and breathing of nitrogen-enriched air. Nitrogen permeation of tissues occurs in proportion to the partial pressure of nitrogen taken in. If the nitrogen is permeating tissues faster than the person can breathe it out, bubbles of gas may form in the tissues.

Decompression sickness can result from the decompression that accompanies a rapid rise from sea level to at least 5,500 metres (18,044 feet) or a rapid ascent from around 40 to 20 metres (131 to 66 feet) under water. Several factors influence the onset of decompression sickness:

- A *history* of previous decompression sickness increases the probability of another attack.

- *Age* is a component. Being over thirty increases the chances of an attack.

- *Physical fitness* plays a role. People in better condition have a reduced chance of the sickness. Previously broken bones and joint injuries are often the sites of pain.

- *Exercise* during the exposure to decompression increases the likelihood and brings on an earlier onset of symptoms.

- *Low temperature* increases the probability of the sickness.

- *Speed of decompression* also influences the sickness. A rapid rate of decompression increases the possibility and severity of symptoms.

- *Length of exposure* of the person to the pressure is proportionately related to the intensity of symptoms. The longer the exposure, the greater the chances of decompression sickness.

A reduction in partial pressure can result from reduced available oxygen and cause a problem in breathing known as **hypoxia**. Too much oxygen or oxygen breathed under pressure that is too high is called **hyperoxia**. Another partial pressure hazard, *nitrogen narcosis*, results from a higher-than-normal level of nitrogen pressure.

When breathed under pressure, nitrogen causes a reduction of cerebral and neural activity. Breathing nitrogen at great depths under water can cause a feeling of euphoria and loss of reality called *nitrogen narcosis*. At depths greater than 30 metres (98 feet), nitrogen narcosis can occur even when breathing normal air. The effects may become pathogenic at depths greater than 60 metres (198 feet), with motor skills threatened at depths greater than 90 metres (295 feet). Cognitive processes deteriorate quickly after reaching a depth of 100 metres (328 feet).

decompression sickness Sickness that can result from the decompression that accompanies a rapid rise from sea level to at least 5,500 metres (18,044 feet) or a rapid ascent from around 40 to 20 metres (131 to 66 feet) under water.

hypoxia Too little oxygen getting to body tissues.

hyperoxia Too much oxygen or oxygen breathed under too high a pressure.

BOILERS AND PRESSURE HAZARDS

A boiler is a closed vessel in which water is heated to form steam, hot water, or high-temperature water under pressure.[2] Potential safety hazards associated with boilers and other pressurized vessels include the following:

- Design, construction, or installation errors.

- Poor or insufficient training of operators.

- Human error.

- Mechanical breakdown or failure.

- Failure or blockage of control or safety devices.

- Insufficient or improper inspections.

- Improper application of equipment.

- Insufficient preventive maintenance.[3]

Through years of experience, a great deal has been learned about how to prevent accidents associated with boilers. Union Gas Association recommends the daily, weekly, monthly, semiannual, and annual boiler inspection schedule found in Figure 18–1. Always ensure that the equipment manufacturer's specifications and maintenance schedules are followed.

Figure 18–1 Recommended gas/oil-fired boiler inspection schedule.

Recommended Gas/Oil-Fired Boiler Inspection Schedules

It is very important that preventive maintenance be performed on an established schedule. Following are recommendations on schedules as well as suggestions to assist in maximizing the uptime of your boiler and associated equipment.

Daily*	Weekly	Monthly	Semiannually	Annually
Check water level	Check for tight closing of fuel valves	Inspect burner	Clean low water cutoff(s)	Clean fireside surfaces
Blowdown boiler	Check fuel and air linkage	Analyze combustion	Check oil preheater	Clean breeching
Blowdown water column	Check indicating lights and alarms	Check cams	Inspect refractory	Clean waterside surfaces
Check combustion visually	Check operating and limit controls	Inspect for flue gas leaks	Clean oil pump strainer and filter	Check oil storage tanks
Treat water according to the established program	Check safety and interlock controls	Inspect for hot spots	Clean air cleaner and air/oil separator	Check fluid levels on hydraulic valves
Record boiler operating pressure/temperature	Check low water cutoff(s) operation	Review boiler blowdown procedures	Check pump coupling alignment	Check gauge glass
Record feedwater pressure/temperature	Check for leaks, noise, vibration, unusual conditions	Check combustion air supply	Reset combustion	Remove and recondition safety valves
Record flue gas temperature	Check operation of all motors	Check all filter elements	Inspect mercury switches	Check oil pumps
Record oil pressure and temperature	Check general burner operation	Check fuel systems		Check boiler feed pumps
Record gas pressure	Check lubricating oil levels	Check belt drives		Check condensate receivers
Record atomizing pressure	Check flame scanner assembly	Check lubrication requirements		Check chemical feed systems
Check general boiler/ burner operation	Check packing glands			Tighten all electrical terminals

* Daily items may be performed more than once daily.

Source: Union Gas. (2000–2004). "Recommended Gas/Oil Fired Boiler Inspection Schedule." http://www.uniongas.com/business/otherci/techsol/heating/boiler/inspection.asp.

HIGH-TEMPERATURE WATER HAZARDS

High-temperature water (HTW) is exactly what its name implies—water that has been heated to a very high temperature, but not high enough to produce steam.[4] In some cases, HTW can be used as an economical substitute for steam (e.g., in industrial heating systems). It has the added advantage of releasing less energy (pressure) than steam does.

In spite of this, there are hazards associated with HTW. Human contact with HTW can result in extremely serious burns and even death. The two most prominent sources of hazards associated with HTW are operator error and improper design. Proper training and careful supervision are the best guards against operator error.

The design of HTW systems is a highly specialized process that should be undertaken only by experienced engineers. Mechanical forces such as **water hammer**, thermal expansion, thermal shock, or faulty materials cause system failures more often than do thermodynamic forces. Therefore, it is important to allow for such causes when designing an HTW system.

The best designs are simple and operator-friendly. Designing too many automatic controls into an HTW system can create more problems than it solves by turning operators into mere attendants who are unable to respond properly to emergencies.

water hammer A series of loud noises caused by pressurized liquid flow suddenly stopping.

HAZARDS OF UNFIRED PRESSURE VESSELS

Not all pressure vessels are fired. Unfired pressure vessels include compressed air tanks, steam-jacketed kettles, digesters, and vulcanizers, as well as others that can create heat internally by various means rather than by external fire.[5] The various means of creating internal heat include (1) chemical action within the vessel, and (2) application of some heating medium (electricity, steam, hot oil, and so on) to the contents of the vessel. The potential hazards associated with unfired pressure vessels include hazardous interaction between the material of the vessel and the materials that will be processed in it; inability of the filled vessel to carry the weight of its contents and the corresponding internal pressure; inability of the vessel to withstand the pressure introduced into it plus pressure caused by chemical reactions that occur during processing; and inability of the vessel to withstand any vacuum that may be created accidentally or intentionally.

The most effective preventive measure for overcoming these potential hazards is proper design. Specifications for the design and construction of unfired pressure vessels include requirements in the following areas: working pressure range, working temperature range, type of materials to be processed, stress relief, welding or joining measures, and radiography. Designs that meet the specifications set forth for unfired pressure vessels in such codes as the ASME (American Society of Mechanical Engineers) Boiler and Pressure Vessel Code (Section VIII) will overcome most predictable hazards. ASME codes are internationally recognized and are available through the CSA. The CSA Boiler, Pressure Vessel, and Pressure Piping Code can be found in CSA publication number is B51-14. Beyond proper design, the same types of precautions taken when operating fired pressure vessels can be used when operating unfired vessels. These include continual inspection, proper housekeeping, periodic testing, visual observation (for detecting cracks), and the use of appropriate safety devices.

HAZARDS OF HIGH-PRESSURE SYSTEMS

The hazards most commonly associated with high-pressure systems are leaks, pulsation, vibration, release of high-pressure gases, and whiplash from a broken high-pressure pipe, tubing, or hose.[6] Strategies for reducing these hazards include limiting vibration through the use of vibration dampening (anchored pipe supports), decreasing the potential for leaks by limiting the number of joints in the system, using pressure gauges, placing shields or barricades around the system, using remote control and monitoring, and restricting access.

CRACKING HAZARDS IN PRESSURE VESSELS

One of the most serious hazards in pressure vessels is the potential for cracking.[7] Cracking can lead to either a complete rupture or to leaks. The consequences of a complete rupture include (1) blast effects due to the sudden expansion of the contents of the vessel, and (2) possible injuries and damage from fragmentation. The consequences of a leak include (1) suffocation or poisoning of employees depending on the contents of the vessel, (2) explosion and fire, and (3) chemical and thermal burns from contact with the contents of the vessel.

Pressure vessels are used in many different applications to contain various types of substances ranging from water to extremely toxic chemicals. Leakage or rupture may occur in welded seams, bolted joints, or at nozzles. Figure 18–2 is a diagram of a typical pressure vessel showing the potential points of leakage and rupture. The types of vessels that are most susceptible to leakage and rupture, primarily because of the processes they are part of or their contents, are described below.

Figure 18–2 Diagram of a typical pressure vessel showing potential points for leakage or rupture.

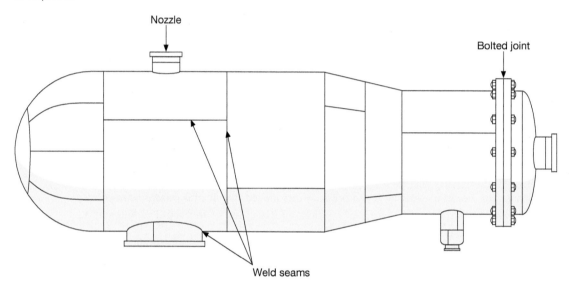

Deaerator Vessels

Deaeration is the process of removing noncondensible gases, primarily oxygen, from the water used in steam generation. Deaerator vessels are used in such applications as power generation, pulp and paper processing, chemical processing, and petroleum refining. The most common failures associated with deaerator vessels are (1) cracks caused by water hammer at welded joints that were not post weld heat treated, and (2) cracks caused by corrosion fatigue.

Amine Vessels

The *amine process* removes hydrogen sulphide from petroleum gases such as propane and butane. It can also be used for removing carbon dioxide in some processes. Amine vessels are used in petroleum refineries, gas treatment facilities, and chemical plants. The most common failures associated with amine vessels are cracks in stressed or unrelieved welds.

Wet Hydrogen Sulphide Vessels

Any fluid that contains water and hydrogen sulphide is considered wet hydrogen sulphide. Many of the vessels used to contain wet hydrogen sulphide are made of steel. Hydrogen is generated when steel is exposed to such a mixture. Dissolved hydrogen can cause cracking, blistering, and embrittlement, particularly in high-strength steels. Consequently, low-strength steels are recommended for wet hydrogen sulphide vessels.

Ammonia Vessels

Vessels for the containment of ammonia are widely used in commercial refrigeration systems and chemical processes. Such ammonia vessels are typically constructed as spheres of carbon steel. The water and oxygen content in ammonia can cause carbon steel to crack, particularly near welds.

Pulp Digester Vessels

The process used to digest pulp in the manufacture of paper involves the use of a weak water solution of sodium hydroxide and sodium sulphide in a temperature range of 110°C to 140°C (or 230°F to 284°F). The most common failure in pulp digester vessels is cracking along welded seams due primarily to caustic stress corrosion.

NONDESTRUCTIVE TESTING OF PRESSURE VESSELS

To prevent leakage or rupture, it is necessary to examine pressure vessels periodically. There are five widely used nondestructive methods for testing: (1) visual examination, (2) liquid penetration test, (3) magnetic particle test, (4) X-ray radiography, and (5) ultrasonic test. Visual, liquid penetration, and magnetic particle tests can detect only those defects that are either on the surface or near it. Radiographic and ultrasonic tests can detect problems within the material. Consequently, the visual, liquid penetration, and magnetic particle tests are referred to as *surface tests*. Radiography and ultrasonic are called *volumetric tests*.

Visual Examination

A visual examination consists of taking a thorough look at the vessel to detect signs of corrosion, erosion, or hydrogen blistering. In order to conduct a dependable visual examination of a pressure vessel, it is necessary to have a clean surface and good lighting.

Liquid Penetration Test

This test involves placing a specially formulated liquid penetrant over an area and letting it seep in. When the penetrant is removed from the surface, some of it remains entrapped in the area of discontinuity. A developing agent is then applied, which draws out the entrapped penetrant and magnifies the discontinuity. The process can be enhanced by adding fluorescent chemicals to the penetrant to aid in the detection of problems.

Magnetic Particle Test

This test is based on the fact that discontinuities in or near the surface of a pressure vessel disturb magnetic flux lines that are induced in a ferromagnetic material. Disturbances are detected by applying fine particles of ferromagnetic material to the surface of the vessel. The necessary magnetic field is produced most frequently using the "prod" technique in which electric current is run through an area by applying opposing "prods" (contact probes). A drawback of this test is that corners and surface irregularities in the vessel material can produce the same disturbances as defects. Consequently, special care is needed when using this test in a region with corners or welded joints. Because this test works only with ferromagnetic material, its use is limited to vessels made of carbon and low-alloy steels.

X-Ray Radiography Test

This test amounts to making an X-ray negative of a given portion of the vessel. The process works in the same way as those used by physicians and dentists. Irregularities such as holes, voids, or discontinuities produce a greater exposure (darker area) on the X-ray negative.

Ultrasonic Test

ultrasonic testing Use of acoustic waves for detecting foreign objects.

This test is similar to radar and other uses of electromagnetic and acoustic waves for detecting foreign objects. Short signals are induced into the material. Waves that are reflected back from discontinuities are detected by one or more transducers. **Ultrasonic testing** requires an electronic system for generating a signal, a transducer system for converting the electrical signal into mechanical vibrations and vice versa, and an electronic system for amplifying, processing, and displaying the return signal.

PRESSURE DANGERS TO HUMANS

The term *anoxia* refers to the rare case of a total lack of oxygen. Hypoxia, a condition that occurs when the available oxygen is reduced, can occur while ascending to a high altitude or when oxygen in air has been replaced with another gas, which may happen in some industrial situations. Employees who work in an environment that is under pressure must undergo decompression procedures before returning to a normal atmosphere.[8] Such procedures are planned based on the amount of pressure to which the employee is subjected and for how long.

altitude sickness A form of hypoxia associated with high altitudes.

Altitude sickness is a form of hypoxia associated with high altitudes. Ascent to an altitude of 3,000 metres (9,843 feet) above sea level can result in a feeling of malaise, shortness of breath, and fatigue. A person ascending 4,300 to 4,600 metres (14,108 to 15,092 feet) may experience euphoria, along with a reduction in powers of reason, judgment, and memory. Altitude sickness includes a loss of **useful consciousness** at 6,100 to 7,600 metres (20,013 to 24,934 feet). After approximately 5 minutes at this altitude, a person may lose consciousness. The loss of consciousness comes approximately 1 minute or less at 9,000 metres (29,528 feet). Over 11,500 metres (37,730 feet), most people lose consciousness within 30 seconds and may fall into a coma and possibly die.

useful consciousness A state of consciousness in which a person is clearheaded and alert enough to make responsible decisions.

Hyperoxia, or an increased concentration of oxygen in air, is not a common situation. Hyperbaric chambers or improperly calibrated scuba equipment can create conditions that may lead to convulsions if pure oxygen is breathed for greater than 3 hours. Breathing air at a depth of around 100 metres (328 feet) can be toxic and is equivalent to breathing pure oxygen at a depth of 20 metres (66 feet).

At high pressures of oxygen, around 2,000 to 5,000 mm Hg, dangerous cerebral problems such as dizziness, twitching, vision deterioration, and nausea may occur. Continued exposure to these high pressures will result in confusion, convulsion, and eventual death.

trapped gas effects With a decrease in pressure, gases in the body increase in volume. These occurrences often cause pain or discomfort and may result in injuries if the pressure change is rapid.

Changes in total pressure can induce **trapped gas effects**. With a decrease in pressure, trapped gases will increase in volume (according to Boyle's law). Trapped gases in the body include air pockets in the ears, sinuses, and chest. Divers refer to the trapped gas phenomenon as the *squeeze*. Jet travel causes the most commonly occurring instance of trapped gas effects. Takeoff and landing may cause relatively sudden shifts in pressure, which may lead to discomfort and pain. With very rapid ascent or descent, injury can develop.

Lung rupture can be caused by a swift return to the surface from diving or decompression during high-altitude flight. This event is rare and happens only if the person is holding his or her breath during the decompression.

evolved gas effects Happens when gas is being absorbed faster than it is being exhaled. These bubbles of gas, which are often nitrogen, may form in the blood and other tissues.

Evolved gas effects are associated with the absorption of nitrogen into body tissues. When breathed, nitrogen can be absorbed into all body tissues in concentrations proportional to the partial pressure of nitrogen in air. When a person is ascending in altitude, on the ground, in flight, or under water, nitrogen must be exhaled at a rate equal to or exceeding the absorption rate to avoid evolved gas effects.

If the nitrogen in body tissues such as blood is being absorbed faster than it is being exhaled, bubbles of gas may form in the blood and other tissues. Gas bubbles in the tissues may cause decompression sickness, which can be painful and occasionally fatal. Early symptoms of this disorder occur in body bends or joints such as elbows, knees, and shoulders. The common name for decompression sickness is the **bends**.

When the formation of gas bubbles is due to rapid ambient pressure reduction, it is called **dysbarism**.[9] The major causes of dysbarism are (1) the release of gas from the blood, and (2) the attempted expansion of trapped gas in body tissues. The sickness may occur with the decompression associated with rapidly moving from sea level (considered zero) to approximately 6,100 metres (20,013 feet) above sea level. Dysbarism is most often associated with underwater diving or working in pressurized containers (such as airplanes). Obese and older people seem to be more susceptible to dysbarism and decompression sickness.

Dysbarism manifests itself in a variety of symptoms. The **creeps** are caused by bubble formation in the skin, which causes an itchy, crawling, rashy feeling in the skin. Coughing and choking, resulting from bubbles in the respiratory system, are called the **chokes**. Bubbles occurring in the brain, although rare, may cause tingling and numbing, severe headaches, spasticity of muscles, and in some cases, blindness and paralysis. Dysbarism of the brain is, however, rare. Rapid pressure change may also cause pain in the teeth and sinuses.[10]

Aseptic necrosis of bone is a delayed effect of decompression sickness. Blood in the capillaries supplying the bone marrow may become blocked with gas bubbles, which can cause a collection of platelets and blood cells to build up in a bone cavity. The marrow generation of blood cells can be damaged as a result, as well as the maintenance of healthy bone cells. Some bone areas may become calcified, with severe complications when the bone is involved in a joint. Employees who work in an environment that is under pressure must undergo decompression procedures before returning to a normal atmosphere.

bends Common name for decompression sickness.

dysbarism The formation of gas bubbles due to rapid ambient pressure reduction.

creeps Itchy, crawling, rashy feeling in the skin caused by bubble formation in the skin.

chokes Coughing and choking, resulting from bubbles in the respiratory system.

aseptic necrosis A delayed effect of decompression sickness involving damage to marrow generation and healthy bone cells.

MEASUREMENT OF PRESSURE HAZARDS

Confirming the point of pressurized gas leakage can be difficult. After a gas has leaked out to a level of equilibrium with its surrounding air, the symptoms of the leak may disappear. There are several methods of detecting pressure hazards:

- *Sounds* can be used to signal a pressurized gas leak. Gas discharge may be indicated by a whistling noise, particularly with highly pressurized gases escaping through small openings. Workers should not use their fingers to probe for gas leaks as highly pressurized gases may cut through tissue, including bone.

- *Cloth streamers* may be tied to the gas vessel to help indicate leaks.

- *Soap solutions* may be smeared over the vessel surface so that bubbles are formed when gas escapes. A stream of bubbles indicates gas release.

- *Scents* may be added to gases that do not naturally have an odour. For instance, the odour sometimes smelled in homes that cook or heat with natural gas is not the gas itself but a scent added to it.

- *Leak detectors* that measure pressure, current flow, or radioactivity may be useful for some types of gases.

- *Corrosion* may be the long-term effect of escaping gases. Metal cracking, surface roughening, and general weakening of materials may result from corrosion.

There are many potential causes of gas leaks. The most common of these are as follows:

- *Contamination* by dirt can prevent the proper closing of gas valves, threads, gaskets, and other closures used to control gas flow.

- *Overpressurization* can overstress a gas vessel, permitting gas release. The container closure can distort and separate from gaskets, leading to cracking.

- *Excessive temperatures* applied to dissimilar metals that are joined can cause unequal thermal expansion, loosening the metal-to-metal joint and allowing gas to escape. Materials can crack because of excessive cold, which can also result in gas escape. Thermometers are often used to indicate the possibility of gas release.

- *Operator errors* can lead to hazardous gas release from improper closure of valves, inappropriate opening of valves, or overfilling of vessels. Proper training and supervision can reduce operator errors.

Destructive as well as nondestructive methods may be used to detect pressure leaks and incorrect pressure levels. **Nondestructive testing** methods do not harm the material being tested. Nondestructive methods may include mixing dye penetrants and magnetic or radioactive particles with the gas and then measuring the flow of the gas. Ultrasonic and X-ray waves are another form of nondestructive testing and are often used to characterize materials and detect cracks or other leakage points.

Destructive testing methods destroy the material being checked. Proof pressures generate stresses to the gas container, typically 1.5 to 1.667 times the maximum expected operating pressure for that container. Strain measurements may also be collected to indicate permanent weakening changes to the container material that remains after the pressure is released. **Proof pressure tests** often call for the pressure to be applied for a specified time and released. Stress and strain tests are then applied to the material. Proof pressure tests may or may not result in the destruction of the container being tested.

REDUCTION OF PRESSURE HAZARDS

The reduction of pressure hazards can often be achieved by improving the standard of maintenance and by inspection of equipment that measures or uses high-pressure gases. Proper storage of pressurized containers can reduce many pressure hazards. Pressurized vessels should be stored in locations away from cold or heat sources, including the sun. Cryogenic compounds (those that have been cooled to unusually low temperatures) may boil and burst the container when not kept at the proper temperatures. The whipping action of pressurized flexible hoses can also be dangerous. Hoses should be firmly clamped at the ends when pressurized.

Gas compression can occur in sealed containers exposed to heat. For this reason, aerosol cans must never be thrown into or exposed to a fire. Aerosol cans may explode violently when exposed to heat, although most commercially available aerosols are contained in low–melting point metals that melt before pressure can build up.

Pressure should be released before working on equipment. Gauges can be checked to ensure that pressure has been released before any work on the pressurized system is begun. When steam equipment is shut down, liquid can condense within the system. This liquid (as well as any dirt in the system, which would make the problem worse) can become a propellant, which can strike bends in the system, causing loud noises and possibly doing damage.

Water hammer is a shock effect caused by pressurized liquid flow suddenly stopping. This shock effect can produce loud noises. In addition, the momentum of the liquid is conducted back upstream in a shock wave that can damage pipe fittings and valves. Using air chambers in the system and avoiding the use of quick-closing valves reduces this hazard.

Negative pressures or **vacuums** are pressures below atmospheric level. Negative pressures and vacuums can cause closed containers to collapse. Storage tanks and tanker trucks, for example, need to have makeup air enter as the contents are emptied, or a negative pressure will result inside the tank. (The gas tank in the cars we drive would collapse as we used its contents if the gas cap didn't have a "vacuum valve" incorporated into it.) A change in temperature can also create a negative pressure situation: For instance, as a tank cools in the evening after sitting all day in the sun, the pressure can drop to the point where collapse would be a real possibility if air were not allowed to enter. Vessel wall thickness must be designed to sustain the load imposed by the differential in pressure caused by negative pressure. Most vessels can easily handle the pressure from within for which they were designed, because the material from which they are constructed cannot easily stretch, but the same container would collapse under the force of surprisingly little suction (vacuum or low pressure). A simple, everyday illustration of this physical fact is trying to blow up a two-litre plastic bottle by breathing into it. No matter how hard you blow, you will not be able to do it. However, if you try to suck the air out of it, it collapses quite readily!

>>> DISCUSSION CASE | What Is Your Opinion?

Richard Parker, safety director for a small manufacturer of pressurized metal containers, was visiting a friend when he saw something that really bothered him. While the friend was cleaning up his yard, he threw all of his trash into a fire contained in a metal drum. Parker noticed two aerosol cans being thrown in the fire and quickly warned his friend of the danger of explosion. The friend laughed and shrugged off his warning, saying, "There is no danger. The can will melt before it explodes." Who is right in this situation? What is your opinion?

Figure 18–3 describes several methods to reduce the hazards associated with pressurized containers.

Figure 18–3 Reduction of pressure hazards.

- Install valves so that failure of a valve does not result in a hazard.
- Do not store pressurized containers near heat or sources of ignition.
- Train and test personnel dealing with pressurized vessels. Only tested personnel should be permitted to install, operate, maintain, calibrate, or repair pressurized systems. Personnel working on pressure systems should wear safety face shields or goggles.
- Examine valves periodically to ensure that they are capable of withstanding working pressures.
- Operate pressure systems only under the conditions for which they were designed.
- Relieve all pressure from the system before performing any work.
- Label pressure system components to indicate inspection status as well as acceptable pressures and flow direction.
- Connect pressure relief devices to pressure lines.
- Do not use pressure systems and hoses at pressure exceeding the manufacturer's recommendations.
- Keep pressure systems clean.
- Keep pressurized hoses as short as possible.
- Avoid banging, dropping, or striking pressurized containers.
- Secure pressurized cylinders by a chain to prevent toppling.
- Store acetylene containers upright.
- Examine labels before using pressurized systems to ensure correct matching of gases and uses.

CONFINED SPACE HAZARDS

confined space An area with limited means of egress that is large enough for a person to fit into, but is not designed for occupancy.

A **confined space** is any area with limited means of entry and exit that is large enough for a person to fit into but is not designed for occupancy. Examples of confined spaces include vaults, vats, silos, ship compartments, train compartments, sewers, and tunnels. What makes confined spaces hazardous, beyond those factors that define the concept, is their potential to trap toxic and explosive vapours and gases.

Certain substances have upper and lower flammable limits (sometimes referred to as "explosive limits," a less accurate label because some will flame without exploding). The lower flammable limit (LFL) is the lowest concentration of a gas or a vapour that can generate a flame when in the presence of a sufficient ignition source. The upper flammable limit (UFL) is the highest concentration that can propagate a flame. The range between these two extremes is the flammable/explosive range (Figure 18–4).

Figure 18–4 Flammable/explosive range for vapours and gases.

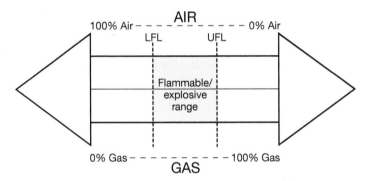

In confined spaces, explosion hazards exist when the concentration of flammable gases is between the LFL and the UFL. It is common practice to consider a 10 percent explosimeter reading, or 10 percent of the LFL, as a safe working environment.[11]

Health and safety professionals should be cautious, however, in assuming that 10 percent of an LFL for a given substance constitutes an acceptable atmosphere. According to John Rekus, "Although 10 percent of the LFL may be acceptable for confined space entry *from a fire and explosion perspective*, this level may pose a concentration of gases or vapours that greatly exceeds the TLV. In addition combustible gas meters generally lack sufficient selectivity and sensitivity to detect air contaminants at levels that pose a potential health hazard. In fact, the meter may indicate a zero reading even when concentrations exceed the TLV. In these cases, more sensitive instruments will be needed to evaluate the atmosphere."[12]

Using a concentration of 10 percent of the LFL can be dangerous for two reasons: (1) The gas sensor used may be inaccurate, and (2) the TLV for some substances is exceeded at the LFL. For example, the TLV for acetone is 500 ppm, but the 10 percent LFL for acetone is 2,500 ppm—five times the TLV.

Health and safety professionals are well advised to take the following precautions when dealing with confined spaces that may have a toxic environment. First, use the most sensitive detection instruments available. Detector tubes, portable gas chromatographs, and infrared analyzers are all more accurate than combustible gas sensors. Second, compare the 10 percent LFL for any substance in question with its TLV, and let the TLV take precedence.

To ensure that a confined space is safe, the following questions should be asked and answered in the affirmative before allowing entry. A negative response to even one of these questions means that entry into the confined space in question is not yet safe.

- Are access and exit equipment, such as ladders and steps, in good working condition?

- Has the confined space been properly purged of toxic vapours and other toxic substances?

- Are all lines that transport potentially hazardous substances into or through the confined space turned off and properly capped?
- Are all moving equipment and moving parts of equipment in the confined space shut down and locked out?
- Has proper ventilation (natural or mechanical) been provided?
- Has the atmosphere inside the confined space been checked by appropriately sensitive detection devices?
- Have provisions been made to continually monitor the atmosphere inside the confined space during work?

In addition to the toxic and explosive hazards associated with confined spaces, there are often physical hazards. For example, tunnels frequently contain pipes that can trip an employee or that can leak, leaving liquid on the floor that can cause a fall. Empty liquid or gas storage vessels may contain mechanical equipment or pipes that must be carefully manoeuvred around, often in the dark.

WORKING IN CONFINED SPACES

Before entering a confined space, a worker should take the following measures:

1. **Shut down equipment/power.** Any equipment, steam, gas, power, or water in the confined space should be shut off and locked or tagged to prevent its accidental activation. Turning off valves for fuel, water, or product supply may not be adequate; blanking any lines will prevent these from entering the space if the valve is inadvertently opened.

2. **Test the atmosphere.** Test for the presence of airborne contaminants and to determine the oxygen level in the confined space. Fresh, normal air contains 20.8 percent oxygen. Ontario regulations for industrial establishments, R.R.O. 1990, Reg. 851, are typical of most Canadian jurisdictions in specifying the minimum and maximum safe levels of oxygen as 18 percent and 23 percent, respectively. Atmospheric tests indicate the hazard present and help determine the protective measures required. Figures 18–5 and 18–6 are examples of devices used for checking the atmosphere.

3. **Ventilate the space.** Spaces containing airborne contaminants should be purged to remove them. Such areas should also be ventilated to keep contaminants from building up again while an employee is working in the space.

4. **Have rescue personnel stand by.** Never allow an employee to enter a confined space without having rescue personnel standing by in the immediate vicinity. These personnel should be fully trained and properly equipped. It is not uncommon for an untrained, improperly equipped employee to be injured or killed trying to rescue a colleague who gets into trouble in a confined space.

5. **Maintain communication.** An employee outside the confined space should stay in constant communication with the employee inside. Communication can be visual, verbal, or electronic (radio, telephone), depending on the distance between the employee inside and the entry point.

6. **Use a lifeline.** A lifeline attached to a full-body harness and a block and tackle will ensure that the employee who is inside can be pulled out should he or she lose consciousness. The apparatus should be rigged so that one employee working alone can pull an unconscious employee out of the confined space.

Ventilation of Confined Spaces

Before allowing employees to enter a confined space, it is important to make the space as safe as possible.[13] One of the most effective strategies for doing so is ventilation. Because

Figure 18–5 Portable gas detection.

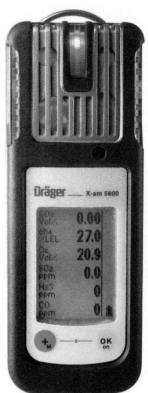

Figure 18–6 Stationary gas detection.

confined spaces vary in size, shape, function, and hazard potential, there must be a number of different methods for ventilating them.

Before ventilating a confined space, it should be *purged*. Purging is the process of initially clearing the space of contaminants. Once the area has been purged, ventilation can begin. Ventilation is the process of continually moving fresh air through a space. Ventilation, when properly done, will accomplish the following:

- Dilute and replace airborne contaminants that may still be present in the confined space.
- Ensure an adequate supply of oxygen (between 18 and 23 percent).
- Exhaust contaminants produced by work performed in the confined space (e.g., welding, painting, and so on).

Ventilation and Local Exhaust

Providing ventilation in a confined space can maintain a comfortable temperature, it can remove odours, and it can dilute contaminants. However, never depend solely on general ventilation to remove toxic contaminants from the air. To eliminate the hazards posed by toxic contaminants such as solvent vapours and welding fumes, it is necessary to exhaust the confined space aggressively. The combination of initial purging, local exhaust, and ventilation is the ideal approach. If contaminant concentrations remain too high even with this approach, employees should wear an appropriate respirator.

Rescue Preparation

The time to think about getting injured employees out of a confined space is well before they enter the space in the first place.[14] Every year, employees are killed trying to save an injured colleague inside a confined space. In an attempt to save injured colleagues, well-meaning employees, who are neither properly trained nor adequately equipped, often fall victim to the toxic atmosphere themselves and die. This is a tragic circumstance made even more so because it is unnecessary and avoidable.

With the right amount of planning and training, employees can be quickly and effectively rescued from confined spaces. Planning should answer the following questions:

- What types of injuries or incidents may occur in a given space?
- What types of hazards may be present in the space?
- What precautions should be taken by rescue personnel entering the space (e.g., lifelines, hoist, respirator, and so on)?
- How much manoeuvring room is there in the confined space?
- What if the victim needs first aid before he or she can be moved?

All of these questions should be answered in the organization's emergency action plan. In addition, all members of the rescue team should have received the training necessary to respond quickly, safely, and effectively. An effective response is one that is appropriate to the magnitude of the incident and is carried out safely.

⟫⟫ DISCUSSION CASE   What Is Your Opinion?

"You'll be fine as long as you wear your respirator," said the supervisor to the employee as he entered the empty vessel. "There might be some residual toxic gas left over, but there won't be much. If you don't breathe it, the gas can't hurt you. Get in, do the inspection, and get out. It shouldn't take 5 minutes."

Is this supervisor giving the employee accurate advice? What is your opinion?

SUMMARY

1. Pressure is defined in physics as the force exerted against an opposing fluid or solid.

2. Pressure is perceived in relation to the earth's atmosphere.

3. Barometers are used to measure atmospheric pressure.

4. Boyle's law states that the product of a given pressure and volume is constant with constant temperature:

$$P_1V_1 = P_2V_2, \text{ when } T \text{ is constant}$$

5. Inspiration is breathing air into the lungs; this can occur only when the pressure inside the lungs is lower than the atmospheric pressure (i.e., when the lungs are expanded).

6. Expiration occurs when air leaves the lungs; this can occur only when the pressure inside the lungs is higher than the atmospheric pressure (i.e., when the lung space is contracted).

7. Dalton's law of partial pressures states that in a mixture of ideal gases, the pressure exerted by the mixture is the sum of the pressures exerted by each component gas of the mixture:

$$P_A = P_O + P_N + P_{else}$$

8. Water vapour, although a gas, does not conform to Dalton's law.

9. Increasing pressure on the body does not by itself create problems.

10. Decompression sickness can occur from the decompression involved with a rapid rise from sea level to 5,500 metres (18,044 feet) or a rapid ascent from around 40 to 20 metres (131 to 66 feet) under water.

11. In extreme instances of rapid ascent from underwater diving or high-altitude decompression, lung rupture can occur.

12. Factors involved with decompression sickness include previous exposure history, age, physical fitness, exercise, low temperature, speed of decompression, and length of exposure.

13. The bends are an example of decompression sickness.

14. Aseptic necrosis of bone can be a delayed effect of decompression sickness.

15. Hypoxia is a reduction of available oxygen to body tissues.

16. Breathing nitrogen at great depths under water can cause a feeling of euphoria and loss of reality called *nitrogen narcosis*.

17. Evolved gas effects are associated with the absorption of nitrogen into body tissues.

18. Altitude sickness is a form of hypoxia.

19. Altitude sickness may involve a loss of useful consciousness.

20. Hyperoxia is an increased concentration of oxygen in air and is not common.

21. Trapped gas effects can result from changes in total pressure.

22. Dysbarism is the rapid formation of gas bubbles in the tissue due to rapid ambient pressure reduction.

23. The creeps are caused by bubble formation in the skin.

24. Formation of bubbles in the respiratory system is called the *chokes*.

25. Pressure vessels are of many types including deaerator, amine, wet hydrogen sulphide, ammonia, and pulp digester vessels.

26. Nondestructive testing of pressure vessels can be accomplished by visual examination, liquid penetration test, magnetic particle test, X-ray radiography test, and ultrasonic testing.

27. Several methods can be used to detect pressure hazards: sounds, cloth streamers, soap solutions, scents, leak detectors, and visual checks for corrosion.

28. Detection of pressure hazards includes destructive and nondestructive testing.

29. Proof pressures can be used to test container strength of containers designed to hold a pressurized gas.

30. Pressurized vessels should be stored away from cold or heat sources, including the sun.

31. Aerosol cans should not be discarded in fires or disposed of by any method using heat.

32. Water hammer is a series of loud noises caused by pressurized liquid flow suddenly stopping.

33. Negative pressures or vacuums are pressures below atmospheric level.

34. A confined space may be described as an area with limited means of entry and exit that is large enough for a person to fit into but is not designed for occupancy.

Key Terms and Concepts

Altitude sickness
Aseptic necrosis
Barometer
Bends
Boyle's law
Chokes
Confined space
Creeps
Dalton's law of
    partial pressures

Decompression sickness
Destructive testing
Dysbarism
Evolved gas effects
Expiration
Hazard
Hyperoxia
Hypoxia
Inspiration
Negative pressures

Nondestructive testing
Pressure
Pressure hazard
Proof pressure tests
Trapped gas effects
Ultrasonic testing
Useful consciousness
Vacuums
Water hammer

Review Questions

1. Against which references is pressure measured? How are these references measured?
2. Define *inspiration* and *expiration*.
3. Explain Dalton's law of partial pressures.
4. Does water vapour conform to Dalton's law?
5. Briefly discuss decompression sickness.
6. What do length of exposure, the bends, the chokes, and aseptic necrosis of bone have in common?
7. Define *hypoxia* and *hyperoxia*.
8. Explain nitrogen narcosis.
9. Discuss altitude sickness.
10. What is the relationship between trapped gas effects and dysbarism?
11. What is the difference between destructive and nondestructive testing?
12. Briefly explain proof pressures.
13. What causes vacuums?

14. Explain three ways to conduct nondestructive testing of pressure vessels.

15. What six measures should be taken before working in confined spaces?

Weblinks

American Society of Mechanical Engineers (ASME)

www.asme.org

ASME's standards for pressure vessels are accepted by most North American jurisdictions. These standards and codes and other news and articles can be found on their website.

Government of Canada, Justice Laws Website

http://laws.justice.gc.ca/eng/regulations/SOR-88-600/

Diving operations are used extensively with the offshore oil industry. This site is a link to the draft Canada Oil and Gas Diving Regulations.

Technical Standards & Technical Authority (TSSA)

www.tssa.org

On this website TSSA, which regulates all pressure-retaining components manufactured or used in Ontario, provides information on training and standards for pressure vessels and other products.

Endnotes

[1] Occupational Safety and Health Administration. "Pressure Vessel Guidelines." OSHA Technical Manual (Washington, DC: Occupational Safety and Health Administration, 2000), sec. IV, ch. 3, 30.

[2] Ibid., 31.

[3] Ibid.

[4] Ibid.

[5] Ibid.

[6] Ibid., 38.

[7] Ibid., 39.

[8] OSHA Regulations Title 29. Code of Federal Regulations, Part 1926 (Subpart S, Appendix A), Decompression Tables. [Online]. Available: osha.gov. (Retrieved July 13, 2013).

[9] Occupational Safety and Health Administration. "Pressure Vessel Guidelines." OSHA Technical Manual (Washington, DC: Occupational Safety and Health Administration, 2000), sec. IV, ch. 3, 39.

[10] Ibid.

[11] Eric LeBreton. Transport Canada. (December 11, 2002). "Confined Space." [Online]. Available: http://www.tc.gc.ca/canutec/en/articles/documents/confined.htm. (Retrieved, January 15, 2005).

[12] John F. Rekus. "Confined Spaces: Is 10 Percent LFL Safe?" Occupational Hazards 62, no. 5 (May 2000): 72.

[13] John F. Rekus. "Confined Space Ventilation." Occupational Hazards (March 1996): 35–38.

[14] John F. Rekus. "Confined Space Rescue Planning." Occupational Hazards (March 1996): 45–48.

Chapter 19
Electrical Hazards

Contemplate the following scenario: An electrical worker was rewiring a junction box that powered a piece of machinery. He mistakenly thought he'd shut off the juice to the junction box. The circuits in the box were not properly labelled or marked. When he touched a 277-volt conductor inside the box with a pair of uninsulated pliers, he was electrocuted.[1] This scenario demonstrates the importance of electrical safety. Electrocution accounts for about 20 percent of all fatalities in the construction industry.[2]

ELECTRICAL HAZARDS DEFINED

Electricity is the flow of negatively charged particles called *electrons* through an electrically conductive material. Electrons orbit the nucleus of an atom, which is located approximately in the atom's centre. The negative charge of the electrons is neutralized by particles called **neutrons**, which act as temporary energy repositories for the interactions between positively charged particles, called **protons**, and **electrons**.

Figure 19–1 shows the basic structure of an atom, with the positively charged nucleus in the centre. The electrons are shown as energy bands of negatively charged particles in orbit. Each ring of electrons contains a particular quantity of negative charges. The basic characteristics of a material are determined by the number of electron rings and the number

electricity The flow of negatively charged particles called *electrons* through an electrically conductive material.

neutrons Particles that neutralize the negative charge of electrons. They act as temporary energy repositories between positively charged particles called *protons* and *electrons*.

protons Positively charged particles.

electrons Negatively charged particles.

Figure 19–1 Basic structure of an atom.

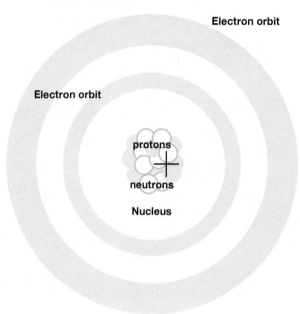

of electrons in the outer rings of its atoms. A *positive charge* is present when an atom (or group of atoms) in a material has too many electrons in its outer shell. In all other cases, the atom or material carries a *negative charge*.

Electrons that are freed from an atom and are directed by external forces to travel in a specific direction produce *electrical current*, also called *electricity*. **Conductors** are substances that have many free electrons at room temperature and can conduct electricity. **Insulators** do not have a large number of free electrons at room temperature and do not conduct electricity. Substances that are neither conductors nor insulators can be called **semiconductors**. Pure conductors offer little **resistance** to the flow of electrons. Insulators, on the other hand, have very high resistance to electricity. Semiconductors have a medium-range resistance to electricity. The higher the resistance, the lower the flow of electrons. Resistance is measured in **ohms**.

The path of this flow of electrons is from a negative source to a positive point, because opposite charges attract one another. The *potential difference* between two points in a circuit is measured by **voltage**. The higher the voltage, the more likely it is that electricity will flow between the negative and positive points.

When a surplus or deficiency of electrons on the surface of a material exists, **static electricity** is produced. This type of electricity is called *static* because there is no positive material nearby to attract the electrons and cause them to move. Friction is not required to produce static electricity, although it can increase the charge of existing static electricity. When two surfaces of opposite static electricity charges are brought into close range, a discharge, or spark, will occur. The spark from static electricity is often the first clue that such static exists. A common example is the sparks that come from rustling woollen blankets in dry heated indoor air.

Electrical current, as we have said, is produced by the flow of electrons. The unit of measurement for current is **amperes** (or amps). One amp is a current flow of 6.28×10^{18} electrons per second. Current is usually designated by I. **Ohm's law** describes the relationship among volts, ohms, and amps. One ohm is the resistance of a conductor that has a current of one amp under the potential of one volt. Ohm's law is stated as:

$$V = IR$$

conductors Substances that have many free electrons at room temperature and can conduct electricity.

insulators Substances that have few free electrons and that resist the flow of electrical current.

semiconductors Substances that are neither conductors nor insulators.

resistance A tendency to block flow of electric current.

ohms Measure of resistance.

voltage Measures the potential difference between two points in a circuit.

static electricity A surplus or deficiency of electrons on the surface of a material.

amperes The unit of measurement for electrical current.

Ohm's law Description of the relationship among volts, ohms, and amps. One ohm is the resistance of a conductor that has a current of one amp under the potential of one volt.

where

V = potential difference in volts

I = current flow in amps

R = resistance to current flow in ohms

Power is measured in wattage (or **watts**) and can be determined from Ohm's law:

$$W = VI \text{ or } W = I^2R$$

watts   Measure of electrical power.

where

W = power in watts

Most industrial and domestic use of electricity is supplied by **alternating current** (or AC current). In Canada, standard AC circuits cycle 60 times per second. (The same system is used in the United States and Mexico, but Europe uses a completely different system.) The number of cycles per second is known as frequency and is measured in hertz (Hz). Because voltage cycles in AC current, an effective current for AC circuits is computed that is slightly less than the peak current during a cycle.

alternating current   Electrical current in which the direction of flow alternates from one direction to the other.

A **direct current** (or DC current) has been found to generate as much heat as an AC current that has a peak current 41.4 percent higher than the DC. The ratio of effective current to peak current can be determined by

direct current   An electrical current flowing in one direction only.

(Effective current)/(Peak current) = (100%)/(100% + 41.4%) = 0.707 or 70.7%

Effective voltages are computed using the same ratios as effective current. A domestic 110-volt circuit has an effective voltage of 110 volts, with peaks of voltage over 150 volts.

The path of electrical current must make a complete loop for the current to flow. This loop includes the source of electrical power, a conductor to act as the path, a device to use the current (called a **load**), and a path to the ground. The earth maintains a relatively stable electrical charge and is a good conductor. The earth is considered to have **zero potential** because of its massive size. Any electrical conductor pushed into the earth is said to have zero potential. The earth is used as a giant common conductor back to the source of power.

load   A device that uses currents.

zero potential   State of a neutral electrical charge.

Electrical hazards occur when a person makes contact with a conductor carrying a current and they simultaneously contact the ground or another object that includes a conductive path to the ground. This person completes the circuit loop by providing a load for the circuit and thereby enables the current to pass through his or her body. Electrical current passing through the human body causes a shock. The quantity and path of this current determines the level of damage to the body. People can be protected from this danger by insulating the conductors, insulating the people, or isolating the danger from the people.

electrical hazards   Potentially dangerous situations related to electricity (e.g., a bare wire).

Typical 110-volt circuit wiring has a hot wire carrying current, a neutral wire, and a ground wire. The neutral wire may be called a *grounded conductor*, with the ground wire being called a *grounding conductor*. Neutral wires usually have white insulation, hot wires have red or black insulation, and ground wires have green insulation or are bare. Figure 19–2 shows a typical three-wire circuit.

The hot wire carries an effective voltage of 110 volts with respect to the ground. The neutral wire carries nearly zero voltage with respect to the ground. If the hot wire makes contact with an unintended conductor, such as a metal equipment case, the current can bypass the load and go directly to the ground. With the load skipped, the ground wire is a low-resistance path to the earth and carries the highest current possible for that circuit.

When the load is bypassed, as we have just described, it is called a **short circuit**. Short circuits can be another source of electrical hazard if a human is the conductor to the ground, thereby bypassing the load.

short circuit   A circuit in which the load has been removed or bypassed.

Figure 19–2 Typical three-wire circuit.

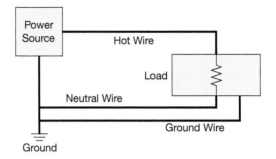

SOURCES OF ELECTRICAL HAZARDS

Short circuits are one of many potential electrical hazards that can cause electrical shock. Another hazard is water, which considerably decreases the resistance of materials, including humans. The resistance of wet skin can be as low as 450 ohms, whereas dry skin has an average resistance of 600,000 ohms. According to Ohm's law, the higher the resistance, the lower the current flow. When the current flow is reduced, the probability of electrical shock is also reduced.

The major causes of electrical shock are:

- Contact with a bare wire carrying current. The bare wire may have deteriorated insulation or be normally bare.

- Working with electrical equipment that lacks the **UL label** for safety inspection.

- Electrical equipment that has not been properly grounded. Failure of the equipment can lead to short circuits.

- Working with electrical equipment on damp floors or other sources of wetness.

- Static electricity discharge.

- Using metal ladders to work on electrical equipment. These ladders can provide a direct line from the power source to the ground, again causing a shock.

- Working on electrical equipment without ensuring that the power has been shut off.

- Lightning strikes.

Figure 19–3 depicts some of these electrical shock hazards.

Electrostatic Hazards

Electrostatic hazards are minor shocks caused by static electricity. These shocks can result from a single discharge or from multiple discharges of static. Instances of electrostatic discharge include the following:

- A nonconductive material briskly rubbed over a stationary surface can create an electrostatic charge. One common example of this is scuffing shoes across a wool or nylon carpet. Multilayered clothing can also cause static sparks (as the layers of fabric rub against each other).[3]

- Large sheets of plastic, when moved, can discharge sparks.

- Farm grain silos and mine shafts can accumulate a static charge; the resulting sparks can cause organic (e.g., grain) and metallic dusts to ignite causing fires or explosions.

- Conveyor belts. Depending on their constituent material, conveyor belts can rub the materials being transported and cause static sparks.

UL label Underwriters Laboratories is a world-leading organization in product safety testing and certification.

electrostatic hazards Shocks from static electricity discharge.

Figure 19–3 Electrical shock hazards.

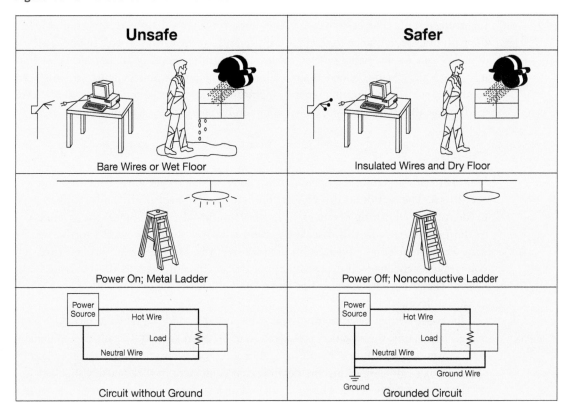

- Vehicle tires rolling across a road surface.
- Friction between a flowing liquid and a solid surface.[4]

The rate of discharge of electrical charges increases with lower humidity. Buildup of electrostatic charge is generally greater on cold, dry winter days. Adding humidity to the air is not commonly used to combat static discharge, however, because overly moist air can result in an uncomfortable working environment and can adversely affect equipment.[5]

Arcs and Sparks Hazards

When conductors are in close proximity or accidentally touch, an electrical arc can jump the air between the conductors to complete a circuit. This arc can ignite combustible gases or dusts, causing a fire or an explosion. When the electric arc is a discharge of static electricity, it is called a *spark*. In a highly combustible atmosphere, sparks can also cause fires or explosions. A spark or arc may involve relatively little or a great deal of power and is usually discharged into a small space.

Combustible and Explosive Materials

High currents moving through contaminated liquids may cause the contaminants to expand rapidly and explode. This situation is particularly dangerous with contaminated oil-filled circuit breakers or transformers. A poor match between current or polarity and capacitors can also cause an explosion. In each of these cases, the conductor is not capable of carrying a current of such high magnitude. Overheating from high currents can also lead to short circuits, which in turn may generate fires or explosions.

Lightning Hazards

Lightning is static charges from clouds, involving very high voltage and current, that follow the path of least resistance to the earth. If this path to the earth involves humans, serious disability can result, including electrocution. Lightning can also damage airplanes from intracloud and cloud-to-cloud flashes. Electrical equipment and building structures are commonly subject to lightning hazards. Lightning tends to strike the tallest object on the earth below the clouds, making trees a common natural path for lightning.

Improper Wiring

Improper wiring permits equipment to operate normally but can result in hazardous conditions. The section of this chapter on detection of electrical hazards discusses tests to identify unsafe wiring practices. One common mistake is to "jump" the ground wire to the neutral wire. In this case, the ground wire is actually connected to the neutral wire. Equipment usually operates in a customary way, but the hazard occurs when low voltages are generated on exposed parts of the equipment, such as the housing. If the neutral circuit becomes corroded or loose, the voltage on the ground wire increases to a dangerous level.

Improper wiring (or miswiring) can cause other hazards. When the ground is connected improperly, the situation is referred to as an **open ground**. Usually the equipment with this miswiring will operate normally. But if a short occurs in the equipment circuitry without proper grounding, anyone touching that equipment may be severely shocked.

Reversed polarity occurs when the hot and neutral wires have been reversed. A worker who is not aware that the black lead (hot) and white lead (neutral) have been reversed could be injured or could cause further confusion by connecting the improperly wired circuit to another apparatus. If a short between the on/off switch and the load occurs as a result, the equipment might run indefinitely, regardless of the switch position. In a reversed polarity light bulb socket, the screw threads become conductors.[6]

Temporary wiring installations sometimes remain in place for years until an accident occurs. Flexible wiring should rarely be substituted for fixed wiring in permanent buildings. When using flexible cord, a loose knot should be tied in it when the plug is installed or replaced. The knot can prevent a pull on the cord from being transmitted to electrical connections such as the plug.

Insulation Failure

The degradation of insulation can cause a bare wire, resulting in a shock to anyone coming in contact with that wire. Most insulation failure is caused by environments toxic to insulation. These environments include the following:

- Direct sunlight or other sources of ultraviolet light, which can induce gradual breakdown of plastic insulation material.

- Sparks or arcs from discharging static electricity, which can result in burned-through holes in insulation.

- Repeated exposure to elevated temperatures, which can produce slow but progressive degradation of insulation material.

- Contact with abrasive surfaces, which can result in erosion of the material strength of the insulation.

- Substance incompatibility with the atmosphere around the insulation and the insulation material, which can induce chemical reactions. Such reactions may include oxidation or dehydration of the insulation and eventual breakdown.

- Animals such as rodents or insects chewing or eating the insulation material, leading to exposure of the circuit. Insects can also pack an enclosed area with their bodies so tightly that a short circuit occurs. This is a common occurrence with electrical systems near water, such as pump housings and television satellite dishes.

- Moisture and humidity being absorbed by the insulation material, which may result in the moisture on the insulation carrying a current.

Equipment Failure

There are several ways in which equipment failure can cause electrical shocks. Electrical equipment designers attempt to create devices that are explosion-proof, dust-ignition-proof, and spark-proof. Following are some of the more common types of equipment failure:

- Wet insulation can become a conductor and cause an electrical shock.

- Portable tool defects can result in the device's housing carrying an electric current. Workers do not expect housings to be charged and may be shocked when they touch a charged tool housing.

- Broken power lines carry great amperage and voltage, and contact with them can cause severe disability or death.

- When equipment is not properly grounded or insulated, an unshielded worker can receive a substantial electrical shock.

Hazardous Locations for Electrical Equipment

Section 18 of the Canadian Electrical Code (CE Code) classifies hazardous locations for electrical equipment. There are three basic classes: Class I for flammable vapours and gases, Class II for combustible dusts, and Class III for ignitable fibres. There are also two divisions of hazard categories. Division I has more stringent requirements for electrical installation than does Division II. Figure 19–4 gives examples for each location category.[7]

Figure 19–4 Hazardous electrical equipment location categories.

Class	Group	Division I	Division II
I. Flammable vapours and gases	A. Acetylene B. Hydrogen C. Ether D. Hydrocarbon fuels and solvents	Normally explosive; flammable paint spray areas	Not normally in explosive concentration; adjacent to paint spray area
II. Combustible dusts	E. Metal dusts F. Carbon dusts G. Flour, starch, grain, plastic, or chemical dusts	Conductive or ignitable dusts may be present; grain mills or processors	Not normally in ignitable concentration; grain storage areas
III. Ignitable fibres	Textiles, woodworking	Handled or used in manufacturing; cotton gins	Stored or handled in storage, not in manufacturing; excelsior storage

ELECTRICAL HAZARDS TO HUMANS

freeze The inability to voluntarily release one's grip from a conductor of electricity.

let-go current The highest current level at which a person in contact with a conductor of electricity can release the grasp of the conductor.

The greatest danger to humans suffering electrical shock results from current flow. The voltage determines whether a particular person's natural resistance to current flow will be overcome. Skin resistance can vary between 450 ohms and 600,000 ohms, depending on skin moisture.[8] Some levels of current **freeze** a person to the conductor; in that case the person cannot voluntarily release his or her grasp. **Let-go current** is the highest current level at which a person in contact with the conductor can release the grasp of the conductor. Figure 19–5 shows the relationship between amperage dosage and danger with a typical domestic 60-cycle AC current.

Figure 19–5   Effects of electrical current on the human body (60-cycle AC current).

Dose in Current in Milliamps	Effect on Human Body
Less than 1	No sensation, no perceptible effect.
1	Shock perceptible, reflex action to jump away. No direct danger from shock but sudden motion may cause accident.
More than 3	Painful shock.
6	Let-go current for women.*
9	Let-go current for men.*
10–15	Local muscle contractions. Freezing to the conductor for 2.5% of the population.
30–50	Local muscle contractions. Freezing to the conductor for 50% of the population.
50–100	Prolonged contact may cause collapse and unconsciousness. Death may occur after 3 minutes of contact due to paralysis of the respiratory muscles.
100–200	Contact of more than a quarter of a second may cause ventricular fibrillation of the heart and death. AC currents continuing for more than one heart cycle may cause fibrillation.
Over 200	Clamps and stops the heart as long as the current flows. Heart beating and circulation may resume when current ceases. High current can produce respiratory paralysis, which can be reversed with immediate resuscitation. Severe burns to the skin and internal organs. May result in irreparable body damage.

*Difference between men and women is based on the relative body mass of the "average"-sized man and woman (60-cycle AC current).

The severity of injury with electrical shock depends not only on the dosage of current, as shown in Figure 19–5, but also on the path taken through the body by the current. The path is influenced by the resistance of various parts of the body at the time of contact with the conductor. The skin is the major form of resistance to current flow. Current paths through the heart, brain, or trunk are generally much more injurious than paths through extremities.

PREVENTION OF ARC FLASH INJURIES

Arc flash injuries occur in the workplace every day in this country. Many of these injuries lead to severe burns and even death, which is doubly tragic because these accidents can be prevented. An **arc flash** is an electrical short circuit that travels through the air rather than flowing through conductors, bus bars, and other types of equipment. The uncontrolled energy released by an arc flash can produce high levels of heat and pressure. It can also cause equipment to explode, sending dangerous shrapnel flying through the air.[9]

Arc flashes are sometimes produced by electrical equipment malfunctions, but a more common cause is accidental human contact with an electrical circuit or conductor. For example, a person working near a piece of energized electrical equipment might accidentally drop a tool that then makes contact with an electrical circuit or conductor. The result is an arc flash that can injure or even kill the worker, not to mention damaging the equipment.

Arc flashes become even more hazardous when workers are wearing flammable clothing instead of appropriate PPE. Arc flashes can produce sufficient heat to easily ignite clothing, cause severe burns, and even damage hearing (hearing damage is caused by the high level of pressure that can be released by an arc flash). The best and most obvious way to prevent arc flash injuries is to de-energize the electrical equipment in question and lock or tag it out before beginning maintenance or service work on it.

DETECTION OF ELECTRICAL HAZARDS

Several types of test equipment can be used to verify electrical equipment safety. A **circuit tester** is an inexpensive piece of test equipment with two wire leads capped by probes and connected to a small bulb. Most circuit testers test at least a 110- to 220-volt range. This simple tester can ensure that power has been turned off before electrical maintenance begins. The tester can also be used to determine whether housings and other equipment parts are carrying a current. When one of the leads makes contact with a hot wire and the other lead connects to a grounded conductor, the bulb lights.

A **receptacle wiring tester** is a device with two standard plug probes for insertion into an ordinary 110-volt outlet and a probe for the ground. Indicator lights show an improperly wired receptacle (outlet). This tester will not indicate a properly wired outlet, but it will reveal an incorrectly wired one. However, there are several types of miswiring that are not disclosed by using this tester, including the ground-wire-to-neutral-wire mistake. Figure 19–6 also lists the meaning of lit indicator lights on the receptacle wiring tester.

A **continuity tester** can be used to determine whether a conductor is properly grounded or has a break in the circuit. Continuity is checked on circuits that are disconnected from a

circuit tester   An inexpensive piece of test equipment with two wire leads capped by probes and connected to a small bulb.

receptacle wiring tester   A device with two standard plug probes for insertion into an ordinary 110-volt outlet and a probe for the ground. It is used to detect an improperly wired receptacle (outlet).

continuity tester   Tool used to determine whether a conductor is properly grounded or has a break in the circuit.

Figure 19–6 Receptacle wiring tester indicator lights.

Used with the permission of General Electric, Inc.

power source. Continuity testers often have an alligator clip on one end of a wire and a bulb and probe on the other end of the same wire. One terminal of the tester can be connected to the equipment housing; the other terminal is connected to a known ground. If the bulb does not light, the equipment is shown to be improperly grounded. With a circuit, the bulb lights when a current is capable of passing through the complete circuit. The unlit bulb of a continuity tester indicates a break in the circuit.

REDUCTION OF ELECTRICAL HAZARDS

Grounding of electrical equipment is the primary method of reducing electrical hazards. The purpose of grounding is to safeguard people from electrical shocks, reduce the probability of a fire, and protect equipment from damage. Grounding ensures a path to the earth for the flow of excess current. Grounding also eliminates the possibility of a person being shocked by contact with a charged capacitor. The actual mechanism of grounding was discussed at the beginning of this chapter.

⧉⧉⧉ SAFETY FACT — **Arc Flash Seriously Injures Electrician**

Ontario's Electrical Safety Authority (ESA) reported that an electrician was seriously injured and was treated in hospital for second- and third-degree burns. On Monday, January 23, an arc flash event occurred while an electrician was installing a cable into an energized panel. The ESA has identified a disturbing trend in which electricians are being killed or seriously injured on the job. The ESA reports:

- Between 2006 and 2015, 40 workers died and another 127 workers were critically injured from electrical contact.

- Repair and maintenance work continues to be the most common type of activity associated with electrical-related fatalities and injuries on the job.

- On average, there is one electrical worker fatality per year in Ontario, and more than 5,500 visits to the emergency room caused by critical electrical-related occupational injuries.

Source: Electrical Safety Authority of Ontario, Media Advisory, January 30, 2017. *Arc Flash Seriously Injures Electrician.* [Online]. Available: https://www.esasafe.com/assets/files/esasafe/Newsroom/MEDIA-ADVISORY-Arc-Flash-notice-Jan26-FINAL.pdf. (Retrieved April 22, 2017). Used with the permission of Electrical Safety Authority.

---

electrical system grounding When one conductor of the circuit is connected to the earth.

Electrical system grounding is achieved when one conductor of the circuit is connected to the earth. Power surges and voltage changes are attenuated and usually eliminated with proper system grounding. Bonding is used to connect two pieces of equipment by a conductor. Bonding can reduce potential differences in electrical charge between the pieces of equipment and thus reduce the possibility of sparking. Bonding and grounding together are used for entire electrical systems.

Separate equipment grounding involves connecting all metal frames of the equipment in a permanent and continuous manner. If an insulation failure occurs, the current should return to the system ground at the power supply for the circuit. The equipment ground wiring will be the path for the circuit current, enabling circuit breakers and fuses to operate properly. The exposed metal parts of the equipment shown in Figure 19–7 must be grounded or provided with double insulations.[10]

ground fault circuit interrupter (GFCI) Detects the flow of current to the ground and opens the circuit, thereby interrupting the flow of current.

A **ground fault circuit interrupter (GFCI)**, also called a *ground fault interrupter* (GFI), can detect the flow of current to the ground and open the circuit, thereby interrupting the flow of current. When the current flow in the hot wire is greater than the current in the neutral wire (because instead of returning via the neutral wire the current has taken another route to the ground), a **ground fault** has occurred. The GFCI provides a safety measure for a person who becomes part of the ground fault circuit (that is, the current is passing through them to the ground) by opening the circuit and thereby stopping the flow

ground fault When the current flow in the hot wire is greater than the current in the neutral wire.

Figure 19-7 Equipment requiring grounding or double insulation.

Portable electric tools such as drills and saws.
Communication receivers and transmitters.
Electrical equipment in damp locations.
Television antenna towers.
Electrical equipment in flammable liquid storage areas.
Electrical equipment operated with over 150 volts.

of electricity. The GFCI cannot interrupt current passing between two circuits or between the hot and neutral wires of a three-wire circuit. To ensure safety, equipment must be grounded as well as protected by a GFCI.

There are several options for reducing the hazards associated with static electricity. The primary hazard of static electricity is the transfer of charges to surfaces with lower potential. When the spark of static electricity jumps from one surface to another, it can deliver a shock; the spark can also ignite anything flammable (gas, dust, etc.) that is in the area. Bonding and grounding are two means of controlling static discharge. **Humidification** is another mechanism for reducing electrical static, as was discussed in the section on sources of electrical hazards. Increased moisture in the air increases the conductivity of the air and also of any object around that absorbs the moisture, reducing the likelihood of a static charge building up. Raising the humidity above 65 percent substantially reduces charge accumulation.[11]

Antistatic materials have also been used effectively to reduce electrical static hazards. Such materials either increase the surface conductivity of the charged material or absorb moisture, which reduces resistance and the tendency to accumulate charges.

Ionizers and electrostatic neutralizers ionize the air surrounding a charged surface to provide a conductive path for the flow of charges. Radioactive neutralizers include a radioactive element that emits positive particles to neutralize collected negative electrical charges. Workers need to be safely isolated from the radioactive particle emitter.

Fuses consist of a metal strip or wire that melts if a current above a specific value is conducted through the metal. Melting the metal causes the circuit to open at the fuse, thereby stopping the flow of current. Some fuses are designed to include a time lag before melting to allow higher currents during startup of the system or as an occasional event.

Magnetic circuit breakers use a solenoid (a type of coil) to surround a metal strip that connects to a tripping device. When the allowable current is exceeded, the magnetic force of the solenoid retracts the metal strip, opening the circuit. Thermal circuit breakers rely on excess current to produce heat and bending in a sensitive metal strip. Once bent, the metal strip opens the circuit. Circuit breakers differ from fuses in that they are usually easier to reset after tripping and often provide a lower time lag or none at all before being activated.

Double insulation is another means of increasing electrical equipment safety. Most double-insulated tools have plastic nonconductive housings in addition to standard insulation around conductive materials.

There are numerous methods of reducing the risk of electrocution by lightning. The stored energy will ultimately discharged as it is dissipated into the earth (or to ground), therefore it is important to stay away from conducting materials that provide a path to ground, or avoid becoming that path. Lightning hazard control includes using lightning rods and avoiding tall objects and flammable materials, not touching conductive materials, not using the telephone, not touching the walls of metal buildings, and not standing near open doors and windows during electrical storms.[12]

humidification Adding moisture to the air to reduce electrical static.

ionizers Devices that ionize the air surrounding a charged surface to provide a conductive path for the flow of charges.

fuses Consist of a metal strip or wire that will melt if a current above a specific value is conducted through the metal.

double insulation A means of increasing electrical equipment safety.

interlocks Mechanisms that automatically break the circuit when an unsafe situation is detected.

Another means of protecting workers is isolating the hazard from the workers or vice versa. **Interlocks** automatically break the circuit when an unsafe situation is detected. For instance, elevator doors typically have interlocks to ensure that the elevator does not move when the doors are open. Interlocks can be used around high-voltage areas to keep personnel from entering the area. Warning devices to alert personnel about detected hazards can also be used and include lights, coloured indicators, on/off blinkers, audible signals, or labels.

It is better to design safety into the equipment and system than to rely on human behaviour such as reading and following labels. Figure 19–8 summarizes the many methods of reducing electrical hazards.

Figure 19–8 Summary of safety precautions for electrical hazards.

- Ensure that power has been disconnected from the system before working with it. Test the system for de-energization. Capacitors can store current after power has been shut off.
- Allow only fully authorized and trained people to work on electrical systems.
- Do not wear conductive material such as metal jewelry when working with electricity.
- Screw bulbs securely into their sockets. Ensure that bulbs are matched to the circuit by the correct voltage rating.
- Periodically inspect insulation.
- If working on a hot circuit, use the buddy system and wear protective clothing.
- Do not use a fuse with a greater capacity than was prescribed for the circuit.
- Verify circuit voltages before performing work.
- Do not use water to put out an electrical fire.
- Check the entire length of electrical cord before using it.
- Use only explosion-proof devices and nonsparking switches in flammable liquid storage areas.
- Enclose uninsulated conductors in protective areas.
- Discharge capacitors before working on the equipment.
- Use fuses and circuit breakers for protection against excessive current.
- Provide lightning protection on all structures.
- Train people working with electrical equipment on a routine basis in first aid and cardiopulmonary resuscitation (CPR).

PERMANENT ELECTRICAL SAFETY DEVICES

An emerging technology in electrical safety is the permanent electrical safety device (PESD). PESDs have excellent potential to help workers safely isolate electrical energy, especially when used as part of an organization's lockout/tagout procedures. "With PESDs incorporated into safety procedures, installed correctly into electrical enclosures, and validated before and after each use, workers can transition the once-risky endeavor of verifying voltage into a less precarious undertaking that never exposes them to voltage. . . . Every electrical incident has one required ingredient: voltage. Electrical safety is radically improved by eliminating exposure to voltage while still validating zero energy from outside the panel."[13]

CANADIAN ELECTRICAL STANDARDS

In Canada, the rules and regulations regarding installation, wiring, and maintenance of electrical equipment are governed by the Canadian Electrical Code (CE Code). To accommodate differences in climate, geography, and industry, the provinces and territories make amendments to the Canadian code to deal with unique situations in their own jurisdictions. For example, the provinces in Atlantic Canada may include regulations in the code to deal with corrosion from the salt air, whereas in Yukon, the Code covers the requirements for split receptacles at driveway locations because of the need to "plug in" vehicles during the winter.[14]

On the municipal level, electrical standards are often incorporated into that town, city, or region's building code requirements. These regulations are enforced by local inspectors whose approval is required at various stages of the construction or renovation project. A competent electrician will know under which jurisdiction each project falls and will seek out and comply with the standards for that area.

SUMMARY

1. Electricity is the flow of negatively charged particles through an electrically conductive material.

2. Atoms have a centrally located nucleus that consists of protons and neutrons. Electrons orbit the nucleus.

3. Conductors are substances that have many free electrons at room temperature and can conduct electricity.

4. Insulators do not have a large number of free electrons at room temperature and do not conduct electricity.

5. When a surplus or deficiency of electrons on the surface of a material exists, static electricity is produced.

6. Resistance is measured in ohms.

7. Current flow is measured in amperes (amps).

8. Ohm's law is $V = IR$, where V = volts, I = amps, and R = ohms.

9. Power is measured in wattage (watts).

10. Watts (W) are calculated by $W = VI$ or $W = IR$.

11. Frequency is measured in hertz (Hz).

12. A load is a device that uses electrical current.

13. Common 110-volt circuits include a hot wire, a neutral wire, and a ground wire.

14. A short circuit is one in which the load has been removed or is bypassed.

15. Sources of electrical hazards include contact with a bare wire, missing UL labels for safety inspection, improper grounding of equipment, dampness, static electricity discharge, metal ladders, power sources remaining on during electrical maintenance, and lightning strikes.

16. Electrostatic hazards are minor shocks caused by static electricity.

17. A spark or arc involves little power and is discharged into a small space.

18. If the conductor is not capable of carrying a particular amperage of current, the material surrounding the conductor can become overheated and explode or burst into flame.

19. Lightning is a collection of static charges from clouds following the path of least resistance to the earth.

20. Lightning tends to strike the tallest object on the earth.

21. Jumping the ground wire to the neutral wire is unsafe wiring.

22. Open grounds are those with improperly connected ground wires.

23. Reversing the hot and neutral wires results in reversed polarity and an unsafe situation.

24. Most insulation failure is caused by an environment toxic to insulation.

25. Electrical equipment designers attempt to create devices that are explosion-proof, dust-ignition-proof, and spark-proof.

26. The Canadian Electrical Code (CE Code) classifies hazardous locations for electrical equipment.

27. The level of danger to humans from electrical shock is determined by the amount of current flow and the path through the body that the current takes.

28. Above a particular amperage of current, people freeze to conductors and are unable to let go of the conductor.

29. Circuit testers can ensure that power has been turned off.

30. A receptacle wiring tester indicates improperly wired outlets.

31. A continuity tester can be used to check whether a conductor is properly grounded or has a break in the circuit.

32. Grounding ensures a path to the earth for the flow of excess current.

33. Bonding and grounding increase the safety for entire electrical systems.

34. A GFCI can detect current flow to the ground and open the circuit.

35. A ground fault occurs when the current in the hot wire is greater than the current in the neutral wire.

36. Antistatic materials and ionizers reduce electrical static buildup.

37. Fuses and circuit breakers open a circuit with excess amperage.

38. Double insulation increases electrical safety.

39. Lightning hazard control includes using lightning rods and avoiding tall objects and flammable materials, not touching conductive materials, not using the telephone, not touching the walls of metal buildings, and not standing near open doors and windows during electrical storms.

40. Interlocks automatically breaks the circuit when an unsafe condition is detected.

Key Terms and Concepts

Alternating current	Direct current	Electrons
Amperes	Double insulation	Electrostatic hazards
Circuit tester	Electrical hazards	Freeze
Conductors	Electrical system grounding	Fuses
Continuity tester	Electricity	Ground fault

Ground fault circuit
    interrupter (GFCI)
Humidification
Insulators
Interlocks
Ionizers
Let-go current
Lightning

Load
Neutrons
Ohms
Ohm's law
Open ground
Protons
Receptacle wiring
    tester

Resistance
Semiconductors
Short circuit
Static electricity
UL label
Voltage
Watts
Zero potential

Review Questions

1. Describe the structure of an atom.

2. Define zero potential. Explain the relationship between zero potential and grounding.

3. Discuss the proper wiring of a three-wire circuit.

4. Explain what each of the following terms measure: *volt*, *amp*, *ohm*, *hertz*, and *watt*.

5. Define *open ground*.

6. Explain *freeze* and *let-go current*.

7. How do continuity testers, circuit testers, and receptacle wiring testers operate?

8. Discuss how bonding and grounding work together to increase electrical safety.

9. How do ionizers and antistatic materials work? Why does humidification work?

10. Who administers electrical safety in federal, provincial, and municipal jurisdictions?

Weblinks

Canadian Standards Association

www.csa.ca

The CSA website gives lists of standards that can be viewed and ordered. The CSA learning centre also posts training opportunities.

Electrical Safety Authority

www.esasafe.com

A comprehensive electrical safety resource for work and home.

International Brotherhood of Electrical Workers

www.ibew.org

On this site the viewer can find news, stories, and links to the latest developments in the Canada/US electrical industry.

Endnotes

[1] "Worker Shocked to Death: Equipment Not Labeled." Facility Manager's Alert 8, no. 181 (January 16, 2003): 3.

[2] Construction Safety Association of Ontario. (Spring 2000). "Electrocution." [Online]. Available: http://www.csao.org/uploadfiles/magazine/vol11no1/shock.htm. (Retrieved November 10, 2004).

[3] National Fire Protection Association. "Electrical Safety in the Workplace" (Quincy, MA: National Fire Protection Association, 2000), 57.

[4] Ibid., 59.

[5] H. R. Kavianian and C. A. Wentz, Jr. *Industrial Safety* (New York: Van Nostrand Reinhold, 1990), 231.

[6] C. Ray Asfahl. *Industrial Safety and Health Management* (Upper Saddle River, NJ: Prentice Hall, 1990), 347.

[7] National Fire Protection Association. *Electrical Safety*, 103.

[8] Kavianian and Wentz. *Industrial Safety*, 214.

[9] W. Wallace. "NFPA 70E: Performing the Electrical Flash Hazard Analysis." *Occupational Health & Safety* 74, no. 8: 38–44.

[10] Kavianian and Wentz. *Industrial Safety*, 218.

[11] National Fire Protection Association. "Electrical Safety," 109.

[12] Kavianian and Wentz. *Industrial Safety*, 232.

[13] P. Allen. "Using Permanent Safety Devices." *Occupational Health & Safety*, 81, no. 1: 36.

[14] William Graham. (February 2003). The Canadian Electrical Code, Part I. CLB Media Inc. [Online]. Available: http://www.ebmag.com/EBFEB03/feb03_contracting.html. (Retrieved November 10, 2004).

Chapter 20
Fire Hazards and Life Safety

FIRE HAZARDS DEFINED

Fire hazards are conditions that favour fire development or growth. Three elements are required to start and sustain fire: (1) oxygen, (2) fuel, and (3) heat. Because oxygen is naturally present in most earth environments, fire hazards usually involve the mishandling of fuel or heat.

Fire, or **combustion**, is a chemical reaction between oxygen and a combustible fuel. Combustion is the process by which fire converts fuel and oxygen into energy, usually in the form of heat. By-products of combustion include light and smoke. For the reaction to start, a source of ignition, such as a spark or open flame, or a sufficiently high temperature is needed. Given a sufficiently high temperature, almost every substance will burn. The **ignition temperature** or **combustion point** is the temperature at which a given fuel can burst into flame.

fire hazards Conditions that favour the ignition and spread of fire

fire or combustion A chemical reaction between oxygen and a combustible fuel.

ignition temperature (or combustion point) The temperature at which a given fuel can burst into flame.

Fire is a chain reaction. For combustion to continue there must be a constant source of fuel, oxygen, and heat. These three components have traditionally been represented by a *fire triangle* as seen in Figure 20–1. However, to sustain combustion, a fourth component is necessary: a chemical chain reaction. To include each of these elements, a four-plane triangular figure is used in the pictorial representation. The three outer triangles of the *fire tetrahedron* represent the fuel, oxygen, and heat, and the centre triangle represents the chemical chain reaction with which they interact, also seen in Figure 20–1. **Exothermic** chemical reactions create heat. Combustion and fire are exothermic reactions and can often generate large quantities of heat. **Endothermic** reactions consume more heat than they generate. An ongoing fire usually provides its own sources of heat. It is important to remember that cooling is one of the principal ways to control a fire or put it out.

exothermic Chemical reactions that create heat.

endothermic Chemical reactions that consume more heat than they generate.

Figure 20–1   Fire triangle and fire tetrahedron.

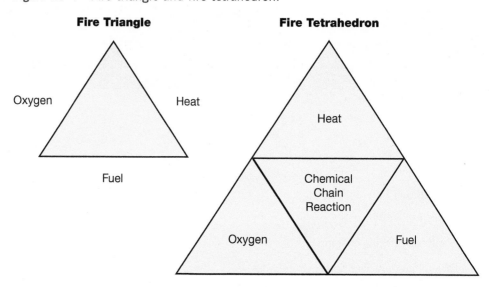

All chemical reactions involve forming and breaking chemical bonds between atoms. In the process of combustion, materials are broken down into basic elements. Loose atoms form bonds with each other to create molecules of substances that were not originally present.

Carbon is found in almost every flammable substance. When a substance burns, the carbon is released and then combines with the oxygen that *must* be present to form either carbon dioxide or carbon monoxide.

Carbon dioxide is produced when there is more oxygen than the fire needs. It is not toxic, but it can be produced in such volumes that it seriously reduces the concentration of oxygen in the air surrounding the fire site. Carbon monoxide—a colourless, odourless, deadly gas—is the result of incomplete combustion of a fuel. It is produced when there is insufficient oxygen to efficiently burn the fuel present. In general, most fires have insufficient oxygen and therefore produce large quantities of carbon monoxide. It is important in any intentional industrial fire that the fuel be consumed as completely as possible. This will reduce ash and minimize smoke and gases, including carbon monoxide.

Synthetic polymers, found in plastics and vinyls, often form deadly fumes when they are consumed by fire, or when they melt or disintegrate from being near fire or high heat. It should be presumed that burning, melting, or disintegrating plastic at a fire site is releasing toxic fumes.

Liquids and solids, such as oil and wood, do not burn directly but must first be converted into a flammable vapour by heat. Hold a match to a sheet of paper, and the paper will burst into flames. Look closely at the paper, and you will see that the paper is not burning. The flames reside in a vapour area just above the surface of the sheet.

Vapours will burn only at a specific range of mixtures of oxygen and fuel, determined by the composition of the fuel. At the optimum mixture, a fire burns, generates heat and some light, and produces no other by-products. In an unintentional fire, the mixture is constantly changing as more or less oxygen is brought into the flames and more or less heat is generated, producing more or less vapours and flammable gases.

Remove the fire's access to fuel or remove the oxygen, and the fire dies. Although a spark, flame, or heat may start a fire, the heat that a fire produces is necessary to sustain it. Therefore, a fire may be extinguished not only by removing the fuel source or starving it of oxygen but by cooling it below the combustion point. Even in an oxygen-rich, combustible environment, such as a hospital oxygen tent, fire can be avoided by controlling heat and eliminating sparks and open flames.

An **explosion** is a very rapid, contained fire. When the gases produced exceed the pressure capacity of the vessel, a rupture or explosion must result. The simplest example is a firecracker. The fuse, which usually contains its own source of oxygen, burns into the centre of a firecracker. The surrounding powder ignites, and the heat produced vaporizes the balance of the explosive material and ignites it. The tightly wrapped paper of the firecracker cannot contain the expanding gases. The firecracker explodes, in much less time than was required to read about it.

Heat always flows from a higher temperature to a lower temperature, never from a lower temperature to a higher temperature without an outside force being applied. Fires generate heat, which in turn is necessary to sustain the fire. Excess heat is then transferred to surrounding objects, which may ignite, explode, or decompose. Heat transfer is accomplished by three means, usually simultaneously: (1) conduction, (2) radiation, and (3) convection.

Conduction is direct thermal energy transfer between two bodies that are touching or from one location to another within a body. On a molecular level, materials near a source of heat absorb the heat, raising their kinetic energy. **Kinetic energy** is the energy resulting from a moving object. Energy in the form of heat is transferred from one molecule to the next. Materials conduct heat at varying rates. Metals are very good conductors of heat. Concrete and plastics are poor conductors, hence good insulators. Nevertheless, a heat buildup on one side of a wall—even if it is made of a material like concrete that is a poor conductor—will eventually transfer to the other side of the wall by conduction.

Radiation is the electromagnetic wave transfer of heat to a solid and includes alpha rays, beta rays, gamma rays, X-rays, neutrons, high-speed electrons, and high-speed protons. Waves travel in all directions from the fire and may be reflected off surfaces, as well as absorbed by them. Absorbed heat may raise the temperature beyond a material's combustion point, and then a fire erupts. Heat may also be conducted through a vessel to its contents, which will expand and may explode. An example is the spread of fire through an oil tank field. A fire in one tank can spread to nearby tanks through radiated heat, raising the temperature and pressure of the other tank contents.

Convection is the transfer of heat from one location to another by way of a moving medium (a gas or a liquid). The gases may be the direct products of fire, the results of chemical reaction, or additional gases brought to the fire by the movement of air and heated at the fire surfaces by conduction. Convection determines the general direction of the spread of a fire. Convection causes fires to rise as heat rises and to move in the direction of the prevailing air currents.

All three forms of heat transfer are present at a campfire. A metal poker left in a fire gets red hot at the flame end. Heat is conducted up the handle, which gets progressively hotter until the opposite end of the poker is too hot to touch. People around the fire are warmed principally by radiation, but only on the side of their body that is facing the fire. People farther away from the fire will be warmer on the side of their body facing the fire than the backs of people closer to the fire. Marshmallows toasted above the flames are heated by convection (see Figure 20–2).

explosion A very rapid, contained fire.

conduction The transfer of direct thermal energy between two bodies that are touching or from one location to another within a body.

kinetic energy The energy resulting from a moving object.

radiation The electromagnetic wave transfer of heat to a solid and includes alpha rays, beta rays, gamma rays, X-rays, neutrons, high-speed electrons, and high-speed protons.

convection The transfer of heat from one location to another by way of a moving medium.

Figure 20–2 Campfire.

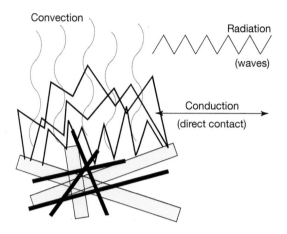

Spontaneous combustion is rare, but it can happen. Organic compounds decompose through natural chemical processes. As they degrade, they release methane gas (natural gas), an excellent fuel. The degradation process—a chemical reaction—produces heat. In a forest, the concentrations of decomposing matter are relatively minimal, and both the gas and the heat vent naturally.

A classic example of spontaneous combustion is a pile of oil-soaked rags. A container of oil seldom ignites spontaneously. A collection of clean fabrics seldom bursts into flames. Rags soaking completely within oil are usually safe. One oil-soaked rag is unlikely to cause a problem. However, in a pile of oil-soaked rags—especially in a closed container—the chemistry is quite different.

The fibres of the rags expose a large surface area of oil to oxidation. The porous nature of rags allows additional oxygen to be absorbed, replacing the oxygen already consumed. When the temperature rises sufficiently, the surface of the oil on the rags vaporizes, and this leads to combustion.

Hypergolic reactions occur when mixing fuels. Oxidizers produce a rapid heat buildup, causing immediate combustion at room temperature with no apparent source of ignition. Although the term *hypergolic* originated with rocket propellants, the phenomenon has been around for a long time. *Pyrophor hypergolic* fuels are those that self-ignite in the presence of oxygen found at normal atmospheric concentrations. One example is white phosphorus, which is kept underwater. If it starts to dry out, the phosphorus erupts in flames.

SOURCES OF FIRE HAZARDS

Almost everything in an industrial environment can burn. Metal furniture, machines, plaster, and concrete block walls are usually painted. Most paints and lacquers will easily catch fire. Oxygen is almost always present. Therefore, the principal method of fire suppression is passive—the absence of sufficient heat. Within our environment, various conditions elevate the risk of fire and so are termed *fire hazards*.

For identification, fires are classified according to their properties, which relate to the nature of the fuel. The properties of the fuel directly correspond to the best means of combating a fire (see Figure 20–3).

Without a source of fuel, there is no fire hazard. However, almost everything in our environment can be a fuel. Fuels occur as solids, liquids, vapours, and gases.

Solid fuels include wood, building decorations and furnishings such as fabric curtains and wall coverings, and synthetics used in furniture. What would an office be without paper? What would most factories be without cardboard and packing materials such as

Figure 20–3 Classes of fire.

Class A fires	Solid materials such as wood, plastics, textiles, and their products: paper, housing, clothing.
Class B fires	Flammable liquids and gases.
Class C fires	Electrical (referring to live electricity situations, not including fires in other materials started by electricity).
Class D fires	Combustible, easily oxidized metals such as aluminum, magnesium, titanium, and zirconium.
Special categories	Extremely active oxidizers or mixtures, flammables containing oxygen, nitric acid, hydrogen peroxide, and solid missile propellants.

Source: Based on National Fire Association. *Fire Protection Handbook*, 18th ed. (Quincy, MA: National Fire Protection Association, 1997).

Styrofoam moulds and panels, shredded or crumpled papers, bubble wrap, and shrink wrap? All of these materials easily burn.

Few solid fuels are, or can be made, fireproof. Even fire walls do not stop fires, although they are defined by their ability to slow the spread of fire. Wood and textiles can be treated with fire- or flame-retardant chemicals to reduce their flammability.

Solid fuels are involved in most industrial fires, but mishandling flammable liquids and flammable gases is a major cause of industrial fires. Two frequently confused terms applied to flammable liquids are *flash point* and *fire point*. The **flash point** is the lowest temperature for a given fuel at which vapours are produced in sufficient concentrations to flash in the presence of a source of ignition. The **fire point** is the minimum temperature at which the vapours continue to burn, given a source of ignition. The **auto-ignition temperature** is the lowest point at which the vapours of a liquid or solid self-ignite *without* a source of ignition.

Flammable liquids have a flash point below 37.8°C (100°F). **Combustible** liquids have a flash point at or higher than 37.8°C. Both flammable and combustible liquids are further divided into the three classifications shown in Figure 20–4.

flash point The lowest temperature for a given fuel at which vapours are produced in sufficient concentrations to flash in the presence of a source of ignition.

fire point The minimum temperature at which the vapours or gas continue to burn, given a source of ignition.

auto-ignition temperature The lowest temperature at which a vapour-producing substance or a flammable gas will ignite without the presence of a spark or a flame.

flammable Any substance with a flash point below 37.8°C (100°F).

combustible Any substance with a flash point of 37.8°C (100°F) or higher.

Figure 20–4 Classes of flammable and combustible liquids.

Flammable Liquids

Class I–A	Flash point below 22.8°C (73°F), boiling point below 37.8°C (100°F).
Class I–B	Flash point below 22.8°C (73°F), boiling point at or above 37.8°C (100°F).
Class I–C	Flash point at or above 22.8°C (73°F), but below 37.8°C (100°F).

Combustible Liquids

Class II	Flash point at or above 37.8°C (100°F), but below 60°C (140°F).
Class III–A	Flash point at or above 60°C (140°F), but below 93.3°C (200°F).
Class III–B	Flash point at or above 93.3°C (200°F).

As the temperature of any flammable liquid increases, the amount of vapour generated on the surface also increases. Safe handling, therefore, requires both a knowledge of the properties of the liquid and an awareness of ambient temperatures in the work or storage place. The **explosive range**, or *flammable range*, defines the concentrations of a vapour or gas in air that can ignite from a source. The auto-ignition temperature is the lowest temperature at which liquids spontaneously ignite.

explosive range The concentrations of a vapour or gas in air that can ignite from a source.

Most flammable liquids are lighter than water. If the flammable liquid is lighter than water, water cannot be used to put the fire out.[1] The application of water floats the fuel and spreads a gasoline fire. Crude oil fires burn even while floating on fresh water or seawater.

Unlike solids (which have a definite shape and location) and unlike liquids (which have a definite volume and are heavier than air), gases have no shape. Gases expand to fill the volume of the container in which they are enclosed, and they are frequently lighter than air. Released into air, gas concentrations are difficult to monitor due to the changing factors of air current direction and temperature. Gases may stratify in layers of differing concentrations but often collect near the top of the container in which they are enclosed. Concentrations found to be safe when sampled at a workbench level may be close to, or exceed, flammability limits if sampled just above head height.

The products of combustion are gases, flame (light), heat, and smoke. Smoke is a combination of gases, air, and suspended particles, which are the products of incomplete combustion. Many of the gases present in smoke and at a fire site are toxic to humans. Other, usually nontoxic, gases may replace the oxygen normally present in air. Most fatalities associated with fire are from breathing toxic gases and smoke, and from being suffocated because of lack of oxygen. Gases that may be produced by a fire include acrolein, ammonia, carbon monoxide, carbon dioxide, hydrogen bromide, hydrogen cyanide, hydrogen chloride, hydrogen sulphide, sulphur dioxide, and nitrogen dioxide. Released gases are capable of travelling across a room and randomly finding a spark, flame, or adequate heat source, then flashing back to the source of the gas.

The National Fire Protection Association (NFPA) has devised the NFPA 704 system for quick identification of hazards presented when substances burn (see Figure 20–5). The NFPA's red, blue, yellow, and white diamonds are used on product labels, shipping cartons, and buildings. Ratings within each category are 0 to 4, where zero represents no hazard and four the most severe hazard level. The colours refer to a specific category of hazard:

Red = flammability

Blue = health

Yellow = instability

White = special information

Although we do not think of electricity as burning, natural and generated electricity play a large role in causing fires. Lightning strikes cause many fires every year. In the presence of a flammable gas or liquid mixture, one spark can produce a fire. Electrical lines and equipment can cause fires either by a short circuit that provides an ignition spark, by arcs, or by resistances generating a heat buildup. Electrical switches and relays commonly arc as contact is made or broken.

Another source of ignition is heat in the form of hot surfaces. It is easy to see the flame hazard present when cooking oil is poured on a very hot grill. The wooden broom handle leaning up against the side of a hot oven may not be as obvious a hazard. Irons used in textile manufacturing and dry-cleaning plants also pose a heat hazard.

Space heaters frequently have hot sides, tops, backs, and bottoms in addition to the heat-generating face. Hot plates, coffeepots, and coffee makers often create heated surfaces. Many types of electric lighting generate heat, which is transferred to the lamp housing.

Engines produce heat, especially in their exhaust systems. Compressors produce heat through friction, which is transferred to their housings. Boilers produce hot surfaces, as do steam lines and equipment using steam as power. Radiators, pipes, flues, and chimneys all have hot surfaces. Metal stock that has been cut by a blade heats up as does the blade. Surfaces exposed to direct sunlight become hot surfaces and transmit their heat by conduction to their other side. Heated surfaces are a potential source of fire.

Figure 20–5 Identification of fire hazards.

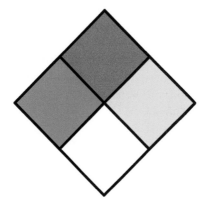

Flammability has a red background and is the top quarter of the diamond.

0   No hazard. Materials are stable during a fire and do not react with water.
1   Slight hazard. Flash point well above normal ambient temperature.
2   Moderate hazard. Flash point is slightly above normal ambient temperature.
3   Extreme fire hazard. Gases or liquids that can ignite at normal temperature.
4   Extremely flammable gases or liquids with very low flash points.

Health has a blue background and is the left quarter of the diamond.

0   No threat to health.
1   Slight health hazards. Respirator is recommended.
2   Moderate health hazard. Respirator and eye protection required.
3   Extremely dangerous to health. Protective clothing and equipment is required.
4   Imminent danger to health. Breathing or skin absorption may cause death. A fully encapsulating suit is required.

Reactive has a yellow background and is the right quarter of the diamond.

0   No hazard. Material is stable in a fire and does not react with water.
1   Slight hazard. Materials can become unstable at higher temperatures or react with water to produce a slight amount of heat.
2   Moderate or greater hazard. Materials may undergo violent chemical reaction, but will not explode. Materials react violently with water directly or form explosive mixtures with water.
3   Extreme hazard. Materials may explode given an ignition source or have violent reactions with water.
4   Constant extreme hazard. Materials may polymerize, decompose, explode, or undergo other hazardous reactions on their own. Area should be evacuated in event of a fire.

Special information has a white background and is the bottom quarter of the diamond.

This area is used to note any special hazards presented by the material.

FIRE DANGERS TO HUMANS

Direct contact with flame is obviously dangerous to humans. Flesh burns, as do muscles and internal organs. The fact that, by some estimations, we are 80 percent water does not mitigate the fact that virtually all of the other 20 percent burns. Nevertheless, burns are not the major cause of death in a fire.

National Fire Protection Association statistics show that most people die in fires from suffocating or breathing smoke and toxic fumes. Carbon dioxide can lead to suffocation because it can be produced in large volumes, depleting oxygen from the air. Many fire extinguishers use carbon dioxide because of its ability to starve the fire of oxygen while simultaneously cooling the fire. The number one killer in fires is carbon monoxide, which is produced in virtually all fires involving organic compounds. Carbon monoxide is produced in large volumes and can quickly reach lethal dosage concentrations.

Figure 20–6 shows the major chemical products of combustion. Other gases may be produced under some conditions. Not all of these gases are present at any particular fire site. Many of these compounds will further react with other substances often present at a fire. For example, sulphur dioxide will combine with water to produce sulphuric acid. Oxides of nitrogen may combine with water to produce nitric acid. Sulphuric acid and nitric acid can cause serious acid burns.

Figure 20–6   Major chemical products of combustion.

Product	Fuels	Pathology
Acrolein	Cellulose, fatty substances, woods, and paints	Highly toxic irritant to eyes and respiratory system.
Ammonia (NH_3)	Wool, silk, nylon, melamine, refrigerants, hydrogen-nitrogen compounds	Somewhat toxic irritant to eyes and respiratory system.
Carbon dioxide (CO_2)	All carbon and organic compounds	Not toxic, but depletes available oxygen.
Carbon monoxide (CO)	All carbon and organic compounds	Can be deadly.
Hydrogen chloride (HCN)	Wool, silk, nylon, paper, polyurethane, rubber, leather, plastic, wood	Quickly lethal asphyxiant.
Hydrogen sulphide (H_2S)	Sulphur-containing compounds, rubber, crude oil	Highly toxic gas. Strong odour of rotten eggs, but quickly destroys sense of smell.
Nitrogen dioxide (NO_2)	Cellulose nitrate, celluloid, textiles, other nitrogen oxides	Lung irritant, causing death or damage.
Sulphur dioxide (SO_2)	Sulphur and sulphur-containing compounds	Toxic irritant.

DETECTION OF FIRE HAZARDS

Many automatic fire detection systems are used in industry today. These systems can warn of the presence of smoke, radiation, elevated temperature, or increased light intensity. *Thermal expansion detectors* use a heat-sensitive metal link that melts at a predetermined temperature to make contact and ultimately sound an alarm. Heat-sensitive insulation, which melts at a predetermined temperature, can be used to initiate a short circuit and thereby activating the alarm.

Photoelectric fire sensors detect changes in infrared energy that is radiated by smoke, often by the smoke particles obscuring the photoelectric beam. A relay is open under acceptable conditions and closed to complete the alarm circuit when smoke interferes.

Ionization or *radiation sensors* use the tendency of a radioactive substance to ionize when exposed to smoke. The substance becomes electrically conductive with smoke exposure and permits the alarm circuit to be completed.

Ultraviolet or *infrared detectors* sound an alarm when the radiation or rapid changes in radiation intensities from flames is detected.

REDUCING FIRE HAZARDS

The best way to reduce fires is to prevent them. A major cause of industrial fires is hot, poorly insulated machinery and processes. One means of reducing a fire hazard is the isolation of the three triangle elements: fuel, oxygen, and heat. In the case of fluids, closing a valve may stop the fuel element.

Fires may also be prevented by the proper storage of flammable liquids. Liquids should be stored as follows:

- In flame-resistant buildings that are isolated from places where people work. Proper drainage and venting should be provided for such buildings.
- In tanks below ground level.
- On the first floor of multi-storey buildings.

Substituting less flammable materials is another effective technique for fire reduction. A catalyst or fire inhibitor can be employed to create an endothermic energy state that eventually smothers the fire. Several ignition sources can be eliminated or isolated from fuels by way of the following actions:

- Prohibit smoking near any possible fuels.
- Store fuels away from areas where electrical sparks from equipment, wiring, or lightning may occur.
- Keep fuels separate from areas where there are open flames. These may include welding torches, heating elements, or furnaces.
- Isolate fuels from tools or equipment that may produce mechanical or static sparks.

Other strategies for reducing the risk of fires are as follows:

- Clean up spills of flammable liquids as soon as they occur. Properly dispose of the materials used in the cleanup.
- Keep work areas free from extra supplies of flammable materials (e.g., paper, rags, boxes, and so on). Have only what is needed on hand, with the remaining inventory properly stored.
- Run electrical cords along walls rather than across aisles or in other heavy traffic areas. Cords that are walked on can become frayed and dangerous.
- Turn off the power and completely de-energize equipment before conducting maintenance procedures.
- Don't use spark- or friction-prone tools near combustible materials.
- Routinely test fire extinguishers.

FIRE EXTINGUISHING SYSTEMS

In larger or isolated industrial facilities, an employee fire brigade may be created. **Standpipe and hose systems** provide the hose and pressurized water for firefighting. Hoses for these systems usually vary from 25 mm (1 inch) to 63 mm (2.5 inches) in diameter.[2]

standpipe and hose systems Systems that provide the hose and pressurized water for firefighting.

Automatic sprinkler systems are an example of a fixed extinguishing system, so called because the sprinklers are fixed in position. There are two types of sprinkler systems: wet and dry. Wet systems are most common; they are water-filled and discharge water as soon as a sprinkler head is opened. A dry system is used where the chance of freezing exists; in a dry system the pipes contain air or nitrogen gas, and when a sprinkler opens, the air escapes and water enters the system. Both systems are triggered when a predetermined heat threshold is breached.

Portable fire extinguishers are classified by the types of fire they can most effectively reduce. Figure 20–7 describes the four major fire extinguisher classifications. Blocking or shielding the spread of fire can include covering the fire with an inert foam, inert powder, nonflammable gas, or water with a thickening agent added. The fire may suffocate under such a covering. Flooding a liquid fuel with nonflammable liquid can dilute the fuel to the point where it will not burn. Figures 20–8, 20–9, and 20–10 are photographs of effective fire prevention equipment.

Figure 20–7   Fire extinguisher characteristics.

Fire Class	Extinguisher Contents	Mechanism	Disadvantages
A	Foam, water, dry chemical	Chain-breaking cooling, smothering, and diluting	Freezing if not kept heated.
B	Dry chemical, bromotrifluoromethane and other halogenated compounds, foam, CO_2	Chain-breaking smothering, cooling, and shielding	Halogenated compounds are toxic.
C	Bromotrifluoromethane, CO_2, dry chemical	Chain-breaking smothering, cooling, and shielding	Halogenated compounds are toxic; fires may ignite after CO_2 dissipates.
D	Specialized powders such as graphite, sand, limestone, soda ash, sodium chloride	Cooling, smothering	Expensive; cover of powder may be broken with resultant reignition.

Figure 20–8   Fireproof storage cabinet.

Courtesy of Justrite®.

Disaster Preparations

Training employees may be the most successful life-saving preparation for a fire disaster. Company fire brigade members should be trained and tested at least quarterly. Disaster preparation initially requires management commitment and planning, and response and

Figure 20–9 Fire-protective drums on a poly spill pallet.

Courtesy of Justrite®.

Figure 20–10 Fire-protective drums stored in an outside storage cabinet.

Courtesy of Justrite®.

recovery practice by the fire brigade on a regular basis. Regular but less frequent fire drills for all personnel are also necessary.

Disaster preparations also include the integration of company planning with community plans. Community disaster relief agencies such as the police, fire department, Red Cross, and hospitals should be consulted and informed of company disaster preparation plans.

Preventing Office Fires

The shop floor is not the only part of the plant where fire hazards exist. Offices are also susceptible to fires. The following strategies are helpful in preventing office fires:

- Periodically check electrical circuits and connections. Replace frayed or worn cords immediately.
- Make sure that extension cords and other accessories are UL- or CSA-approved and used only as recommended.
- Make sure there is plenty of air space around copying machines and other office machines that can overheat.
- Locate heat-producing appliances away from the wall or anything else that can ignite.
- Frequently inspect personal appliances such as hot plates, coffeepots, and cup warmers. Assign responsibility for turning off such appliances every day to a specific person.
- Keep aisles, stairwells, and exits clear of paper, boxes, and other combustible materials.[3]

DEVELOPMENT OF FIRE SAFETY STANDARDS

The purpose of modern fire safety standards is the protection of life and the prevention of property damage. However, the impetus for developing standards has always been and continues to be the occurrence of major disasters. Typically, standards are developed after a major tragedy occurs in which property is damaged on a large scale and lives are lost. Public shock turns into an outcry for action. A flurry of political activity follows, and agencies and organizations that develop standards are called on to develop new standards.

The trend in fire safety standards is toward performance-based standards and away from the traditional specification-based approach. An example of each type of standard will help to illustrate the difference. A specification-based standard may require that brick, concrete, or steel material be used in a given type of building. A performance-based standard may specify that materials used have a 1-, 2-, or 4-hour fire resistance rating.[4] Advances in the testing of engineering materials will help overcome most of the barriers to full development and implementation of performance-based standards.

A. E. Cote summarizes his views on the future of fire safety standards as follows:

> Codes and standards will survive in the 21st century. They may, however, be considerably different from the codes and standards we now have. They certainly will be based more on standardized fire tests, models, data, and related science and engineering than on consensus judgment. How much more will depend on the extent to which there is widespread acceptance of the anticipated breakthroughs in fire science and in related modeling and calculation methods.[5]

FIRE REGULATIONS IN CANADA

Jurisdiction over fire protection in Canada remains with the provinces and territories. While a national fire code exists (National Fire Code of Canada, or NFC), most provinces have developed their own fire codes, which are usually modelled after the NFC. The NFC was developed to provide national consistency among various provincial, territorial, and municipal jurisdictions, but modifications are frequently made to account for geographical, social, and economic variations. One must also consider that the NFC is only one component of the total life safety system incorporated into the design and construction of buildings. The NFC works in conjunction with other codes such as electrical, building, and plumbing codes. Below is a list of the relationships between the National Fire Code and the codes in each jurisdiction:

- *Yukon, Northwest Territories, Nunavut, Saskatchewan, and Manitoba.* Territory/province–wide adoption of the National Fire Code with some modifications and additions.

- *Nova Scotia and Quebec.* No province-wide fire code. Some municipalities adopt the National Fire Code.

- *Alberta and British Columbia.* Province-wide fire code substantially the same as the national code, but with variations that are primarily additions.

- *Ontario.* Province-wide fire code based on the national code but with significant variations in content and scope. The Ontario Fire Code differs more from the National Fire Code than the codes of other provinces/territories do.

- *New Brunswick.* Province-wide adoption of the National Fire Code with some modifications and additions.

- *Prince Edward Island.* Province-wide fire code not based on the National Fire Code. Major municipalities adopt aspects of the National Building Code pertaining to fire and life safety that are cross-referenced in the National Fire Code.

- *Newfoundland and Labrador.* Province-wide adoption of the National Fire Code and aspects of the National Building Code pertaining to fire and life safety that are cross-referenced in the National Fire Code.[6]

Figure 20–11 summarizes fire prevention and suppression strategies.

Figure 20–11 Fire prevention and suppression summary.

- Use the least flammable materials whenever possible.
- Analyze the company to determine types of potential fires and provide appropriate sprinklers and/or extinguishers.
- Develop a database of the flammability of materials available in the company.
- Store containers or flammable materials away from sources of heat or sparks and away from humans.
- Do not permit smoking near flammable materials.
- Include a venting mechanism in storage containers and locate them near a drain.
- Minimize fuel storage container size to reduce the size of the fire that may involve those fuels.
- Isolate fuels from sources of heat.
- Include a smoke detection system and portable fire extinguishers in the facility. Extinguishers should be easily available to every workstation.
- Make sure sources of heat have controlling mechanisms and are near fire detection equipment.
- Check fire extinguishing equipment regularly.
- Perform periodic inspections for new fire hazards and reappraisal of existing fire hazards.
- Train plant personnel in basic fire prevention, which should include periodic fire drills.
- Make sure fire brigade personnel are well trained, tested, and regularly practise fire control.
- Stress cleanliness and an organized method of disposal of flammable materials.

LIFE SAFETY

Life safety involves protecting the vehicles, vessels, and lives of people in buildings and structures from fire. The primary reference source for life safety is the *NFPA 101: Life Safety Code*, published by the National Fire Protection Association. The code applies to new and existing buildings. It addresses the construction, protection, and occupancy features necessary to minimize the hazards of fire, smoke, fumes, and panic. A major part of the code is devoted to the minimum requirements for design of egress necessary to ensure that occupants can quickly evacuate a building or structure.

Basic Requirements for Life Safety

The information in this section is a summary of the broad fundamental requirements of the *NFPA 101: Life Safety Code* of the National Fire Protection Association. More specific requirements relating to means of egress and features of fire protection are explained in the following sections. In this section, the term *structure* refers to a business structure or building.

means of egress A route for exiting a building or other structure.

- Every structure, new and existing, that is to be occupied by people must have a **means of egress** and other fire protection safeguards that, together, meet the following criteria: (1) ensure that occupants can promptly evacuate or be adequately protected without evacuating, and (2) provide sufficient backup safeguards to ensure that human life is not endangered if one system fails.

- Every structure must be constructed or renovated, maintained, and operated in such a way that occupants are (1) protected from fire, smoke, or fumes; (2) protected from fire-related panic; (3) protected long enough to allow a reasonable amount of time for evacuation; and (4) protected long enough to defend themselves without evacuating.

- In providing structures with means of egress and other fire protection safeguards, the following factors must be considered: (1) character of the occupancy, (2) capabilities of occupants, (3) number of occupants, (4) available fire protection, (5) height of the structure, (6) type of construction, and (7) any other applicable concerns.

- No lock or other device may be allowed to obstruct egress in any part of a structure at any time that it is occupied. The only exceptions to this requirement are mental health detention and correctional facilities. In these, the following criteria are required: (1) responsible personnel must be available to act in the case of fire or a similar emergency, and (2) procedures must be in place to ensure that occupants are evacuated in the event of an emergency.

- All exits in structures must satisfy the following criteria: (1) be clearly visible or marked in such a way that an unimpaired individual can readily discern the route of escape, (2) all routes to a place of safety must be arranged or clearly marked, (3) any doorway and passageway that may be mistaken as a route to safety must be arranged or clearly marked in such a way as to prevent confusion in an emergency, and (4) all appropriate steps must be taken to ensure that occupants do not mistakenly enter a dead-end passageway.

- Egress routes and facilities must be included in the lighting design wherever artificial illumination is required in a structure.

- Fire alarm systems must be provided in any facility that is large enough or so arranged that a fire itself may not adequately warn occupants of the danger. Fire alarms should alert occupants to initiate appropriate emergency procedures.

- In any structure or portion of a structure in which a single means of egress may be blocked or overcrowded in an emergency situation, at least two means of egress must be provided. The two means of egress must be arranged in such a way as to minimize the possibility of both becoming impassable in the same emergency situation.

- All stairs, ramps, and other means of moving from floor to floor must be enclosed (or otherwise protected) to afford occupants protection when used as a means of egress in an emergency situation. These means of vertical movement should also serve to inhibit the spread of fire, fumes, and smoke from floor to floor.

- Compliance with the requirements summarized herein does not eliminate or reduce the need to take other precautions to protect occupants from fire hazards, nor does it permit the acceptance of any condition that could be hazardous under normal occupancy conditions.[7]

Means of Egress

This section explains some of the more important issues in the *NFPA 101: Life Safety Code* relating to means of egress. Students and practitioners who need more detailed information are encouraged to refer to the *NFPA 101: Life Safety Code*.

1. **Doors.** Doors that serve as exits must be designed, constructed, and maintained in such a way that the means of egress is direct and obvious. Windows that could be mistaken for doors in an emergency situation must be made inaccessible to occupants.

2. **Capacity of means of egress.** The means of egress must have a capacity sufficient to accommodate the occupant load of the structure calculated in accordance with the requirements of the *NFPA 101: Life Safety Code*.

3. **Number of means of egress.** Any component of a structure must have a minimum of two means of egress (with exceptions as set forth in the code). The minimum number of means of egress from any storey or any part of a storey is three for occupancy loads of 500 to 1,000 and four for occupancy loads of more than 1,000.

4. **Arrangement of means of egress.** All exits must be easily accessible at all times in terms of both location and arrangement.

5. **Measurement of travel distance to exits.** The travel distance to at least one exit must be measured on the walking surface along a natural path of travel beginning at the most remote occupied space and ending at the centre of the exit. Distances must comply with the code.

6. **Discharge from exits.** All exits from a structure must terminate at a public way or at yards, courts, or open spaces that lead to the exterior of the structure.

7. **Illumination of means of egress.** All means of egress shall be illuminated continuously during times when the structure is occupied. Artificial lighting must be used as required to maintain the necessary level of illumination. Illumination must be arranged in such a way that no area is left in darkness by a single lighting failure.

8. **Emergency lighting.** Emergency lighting for all means of egress must be provided in accordance with the code. In cases where maintaining the required illumination depends on changing from one source of power to another, there shall be no appreciable interruption of lighting.

9. **Marking of means of egress.** Exits must be marked by readily visible, approved signs in all cases where the means of egress is not obviously apparent to occupants. No point in the exit access corridor shall be more than 30.5 metres (100 feet) from the nearest sign.

10. **Special provisions for high hazard areas.** If an area contains contents that are classified as highly hazardous, occupants must be able to exit by travelling no more than 22.9 metres (75 feet). At least two means of egress must be provided, and there shall be no dead-end corridors.[8]

A 3-hour fire wall will provide protection for 3 hours, right? Not necessarily. In fact, any relationship between a fire rating and the reality of fire resistance may be little more than coincidental. The problem is that the factors used to determine fire ratings are outdated. They are based on materials that were in use many years ago and no longer have any relevance. The materials used for constructing and furnishing buildings today are radically different from those upon which fire ratings are based. Consider fire ratings overvalued, and plan for less time than they allow.

The requirements summarized in this section relate to the fundamental specifications of the *NFPA 101: Life Safety Code* relating to means of egress. For more detailed information concerning general requirements, means of egress, and other factors such as fire protection and fire protection equipment, refer to the actual code.

EXPLOSIVE HAZARDS

Many chemical and toxic substances used in modern organizations are flammable or combustible. Consequently, under certain conditions, they can explode. Working in these conditions involves hazards that require special precautions for handling, storing, transporting, and using such substances.

Health Hazards of Explosive Materials

The health hazards associated with explosions and fires are well known. The potential for serious injury or death from the force of a blast or from burns is very high. However, there are other hazards associated with explosive and combustible materials. These include skin irritation, intoxication, and suffocation.

Irritation can occur when the skin comes in contact with hazardous substances. The degree of irritation can range from minor to severe, depending on the type of substance, its concentration, and the duration of contact. Intoxication can occur when an employee breathes the vapours of combustible substances. This can cause impaired judgment, performance, and reaction time, which can, in turn, result in an accident. Finally, the vapours from combustible materials can accumulate in confined spaces. When this happens, the air becomes contaminated and is both toxic and explosive. In such cases, the hazard of suffocation must be added to those associated with explosives.[9]

SELF-ASSESSMENT IN FIRE PROTECTION

Health and safety personnel cannot be everywhere at the same time. Consequently, it is wise to enlist the assistance of supervisors and employees in fire protection. An excellent way to do this is to provide them with a self-assessment checklist that will guide them in scanning their areas of responsibility for fire hazards. Such checklists should contain at least the following questions:

1. Are portable fire extinguishers properly mounted, readily accessible, and available in adequate number and type?
2. Are fire extinguishers inspected monthly for both operability and general condition with appropriate notation made on their respective tags?
3. Are fire extinguishers recharged regularly and are the dates noted on their tags?
4. Are interior standpipes and valves inspected regularly?
5. Is the fire alarm system tested regularly?

6. Are employees trained in the proper use of fire extinguishers?

7. Are employees trained to know under what conditions they should help fight fires and under what conditions they should evacuate?

8. Are the nearest fire hydrants flushed annually?

9. Are the nearest fire hydrants maintained regularly?

10. Are avenues and ingress and egress clearly marked?

11. Are all avenues of ingress and egress kept free of clutter and other types of obstructions?

12. Are fire doors and shutters in good working condition?

13. Are fusible links in place and readily accessible?

14. Is the local fire department familiar with the facility and any specific hazards?

15. Is the automatic sprinkler system in good working order, maintained on a regular basis, given the proper overhead clearance, and protected from inadvertent contact damage?[10]

SUMMARY

1. Fire hazards are conditions that favour the ignition and spread of fire.

2. The elements required to start and sustain a fire are heat, fuel, oxygen, and a chemical chain reaction.

3. The product of combustion is energy in the form of heat.

4. By-products of combustion include light and smoke.

5. For a fire to start, there must be either a source of ignition or a sufficiently high temperature for the fuel.

6. Fire is an exothermic chemical reaction. Exothermic reactions generate heat. Endothermic reactions consume more heat than they generate.

7. Chemical reactions in a fire break down materials into basic elements.

8. Loose atoms bond with each other to create substances that were not originally present.

9. Cooling is one of the principal ways to control a fire or extinguish it.

10. Carbon is found in almost every flammable substance.

11. In a fire, released carbon atoms combine with oxygen to form either carbon dioxide or carbon monoxide.

12. Carbon dioxide can deplete oxygen concentrations in the air near the fire.

13. Carbon monoxide is a colourless, odourless, deadly gas.

14. Synthetic polymers in plastics and vinyls often form deadly toxic fumes when they are consumed, melted, or disintegrated in the presence of fire or high heat.

15. Liquid and solid fuels are first converted to a vapour before they burn.

16. The trend with regard to safety standards is away from the traditional specification-based approach to a performance-based approach.

17. Removing the fuel, starving the fire of oxygen, or cooling it below the combustion point may extinguish a fire.

18. An explosion is a very rapid, contained fire.

19. Heat always travels from a higher temperature to a lower one.

20. Excess heat is transferred to other objects by conduction, radiation, or convection.

21. Conduction is the transfer of direct thermal energy between two bodies that are touching or from one location to another within a body.

22. Radiation is the electromagnetic wave transfer of heat to a solid and includes alpha rays, beta rays, gamma rays, X-rays, neutrons, high-speed electrons, and high-speed protons.

23. Convection is the transfer of heat from one location to another by movement of hot gases.

24. Spontaneous combustion is rare, but not impossible.

25. Almost everything in the industrial environment can burn.

26. Fires are classified according to their properties, which relate to the fuels.

27. Class A fires involve solid fuels.

28. Class B fires involve flammable liquids and gases.

29. Class C fires involve live electricity.

30. Class D fires involve combustible metals.

31. Special categories include extremely active oxidizers and flammables containing oxygen.

32. All common packing materials burn easily.

33. Fire walls are defined by their ability to slow the spread of fire.

34. Wood and textiles can be treated to reduce their flammability.

35. The flash point is the lowest temperature at which vapours are produced in sufficient concentration to flash in the presence of a source of ignition.

36. The fire point is the lowest temperature at which vapours will continue to burn, given a source of ignition.

37. The auto-ignition temperature is the lowest point at which the vapours of a liquid or solid self-ignites without a source of ignition.

38. Flammable liquids have a flash point below 37.8°C (100°F).

39. Combustible liquids have a flash point at or above 37.8°C (100°F).

40. Flammable and combustible liquids are each divided into three classifications.

41. Most flammable liquids are lighter than water; therefore, water cannot be used to put out these fires.

42. Most gases are lighter than air.

43. Many of the gases present in smoke and at a fire site are toxic to humans.

44. Most fatalities from fire result from breathing toxic gases and smoke, or from suffocating because of a lack of oxygen.

45. A red, blue, yellow, and white diamond label is used to identify hazards present when a substance burns.

46. Natural and generated electricity play a major role in causing fires.

47. Heat, in the form of hot surfaces, can be a source of ignition.

48. Automatic fire detection systems employ different means of detecting a fire.

49. The best way to reduce fires is to prevent their occurrence.

Key Terms and Concepts

Auto-ignition temperature
Combustible
Combustion
Combustion point
Conduction
Convection
Endothermic
Exothermic

Explosion
Explosive range
Fire
Fire hazards
Fire point
Flammable
Flash point
Hypergolic

Ignition temperature
Kinetic energy
Means of egress
Radiation
Spontaneous combustion
Standpipe and hose systems

Review Questions

1. What are the four elements of the fire tetrahedron?

2. Fire is a chemical reaction. Explain the reaction.

3. Where is carbon found?

4. Compare and contrast carbon monoxide and carbon dioxide.

5. How is combustion of liquids and solids different from gases?

6. What are the three methods of heat transfer? Describe each.

7. What can happen to a pile of oil-soaked rags in a closed container? Describe the process.

8. In which direction does heat normally travel?

9. Name something in this room that will not burn.

10. What are the classes of fires?

11. What property do almost all packing materials share?

12. What are the differences between flash point, fire point, and auto-ignition temperature?

13. Which are more stable: combustible liquids or flammable liquids?

14. Which way do gases usually travel?

15. Describe the NFPA 704 hazards identification system.

16. In what ways can electricity cause a fire?

17. What are the leading causes of fire-related deaths?

18. What are some of the toxic chemicals often produced by fires?

19. What are some of the systems utilized by fire detectors?

20. What is the most successful lifesaving preparation for a fire disaster?

21. Explain the best ways to prevent an office fire.

22. What is the trend with regard to future fire safety standards?

23. Define the term *life safety*.

Weblinks

Canadian Association of Fire Chiefs

www.cafc.ca

The latest trends in fire safety can be found on this site, with links to provincial associations and other useful resources.

Canadian Fire Safety Association

www.canadianfiresafety.com

The Canadian Fire Safety Association's website shows how they promote fire safety through the use of seminars, safety training courses, informative newsletters, scholarships, and regular meetings.

National Fire Protection Association

www.nfpa.org

NFPA's website has interesting and informative articles for home and the workplace, along with links to international standards for fire and building safety, on which Canadian jurisdiction standards and codes are based.

National Research Council Canada

http://www.nrc-cnrc.gc.ca/eng/rd/construction/index.html

Links to and information on the National Fire and Building codes can be found here.

Endnotes

[1] National Fire Protection Association. *Fire Protection Handbook*, 18th ed. (Quincy, MA: NFPA, 1997), 112.

[2] Ibid., 132.

[3] C. Vogel. "Fires Can Raze Office Buildings." *Safety & Health* 144, no. 3: 26–27.

[4] A. E. Cote. "Will Fire Safety Standards Survive in the 21st Century?" *NFPA Journal* 85, no. 5: 42.

[5] Ibid.

[6] National Research Council of Canada. (June 15, 2001). *Construction Innovation* 6, no. 2 (Spring 2001). [Online]. Available: http://www.nrc-cnrc.gc.ca/eng/solutions/advisory/codes_centre/code_adoption.html. (Retrieved May 6, 2017).

[7] National Fire Protection Association. *NFPA 101: Life Safety Code* (NFPA 101) (Quincy, MA: NFPA, 2000), 101–119.

[8] Ibid., 101-26–101-50.

[9] Ibid.

[10] [Online]. Available: http://online.misu.nodak.edu/19577/BADM309checklist.htm.

Chapter 21
Radiation Hazards

Radiation hazards in the workplace fall into one of two categories: ionizing or nonionizing. This chapter provides prospective and practising health and safety professionals with the information they need concerning radiation hazards in both categories.

IONIZING RADIATION: TERMS AND CONCEPTS

An *ion* is an electrically charged atom (or group of atoms) that becomes charged when a neutral atom (or group of atoms) loses or gains one or more electrons as a result of a chemical reaction. If an electron is lost during this process, a positively charged ion is produced; if an electron is gained, a negatively charged ion is produced. To *ionize* is to become electrically charged or to change into ions. **Ionizing radiation** is radiation with enough energy to remove electrons from the orbit of an atom, causing the atom to become charged or ionized. Types of ionizing radiation, as shown in Figure 21–1, include alpha particles, beta particles, neutrons, X-radiation, gamma radiation, high-speed electrons, and high-speed protons.

ionizing radiation Radiation that becomes electrically charged or changed into ions. Radiation with enough energy to remove electrons from the orbit of an atom, causing the atom to become charged or ionized.

Figure 21–1 Types of ionizing radiation.

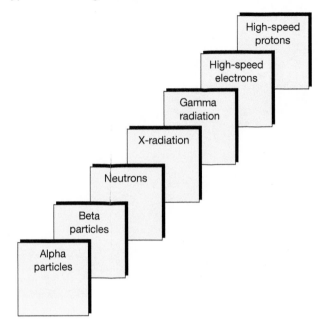

To understand the hazards associated with radiation, health and safety professionals need to understand the basic terms and concepts summarized in the following paragraphs:

- Radiation consists of energetic nuclear particles and includes alpha rays, beta rays, gamma rays, X-rays, neutrons, high-speed electrons, and high-speed protons.

- **Radioactive material** is material that emits corpuscular or electromagnetic emanations as the result of spontaneous nuclear disintegration.

- A **restricted area** is any area to which access is restricted in an attempt to protect employees from exposure to radiation or radioactive materials.

- An **unrestricted area** is any area to which access is not controlled because there is no radioactivity hazard present.

- A dose is the amount of ionizing radiation absorbed per unit of mass by part of the body or the whole body.

- **Rad** is a measure of the dose of ionizing radiation absorbed by body tissues stated in terms of the amount of energy absorbed per unit of mass of tissue. One rad equals the absorption of 100 ergs per gram of tissue.

- **Rem** is a measure of the dose of ionizing radiation to body tissue stated in terms of its estimated biological effect relative to a dose of 1 roentgen (r) of X-rays.

- **Sievert** is a single unit used to indicate the effective dose absorbed by various organs or tissues. One sievert (Sv) equals 100 rem (rem).

- **Air dose** is the dose measured by an instrument in the air at or near the area of the body that has received the highest dosage of radiation.

- **Personal monitoring devices** are required to be worn or carried by individuals who may be occupationally exposed to measure radiation doses received. Widely used devices include film badges, pocket chambers, pocket dosimeters, and film rings.

- A **radiation area** is any accessible area in which radiation hazards exist that could deliver doses such that (1) within 1 hour, a major portion of the body could receive more than 5 millirem; or (2) within 5 consecutive days, a major portion of the body could receive more than 100 millirem.

- A **high-radiation area** is any accessible area in which radiation hazards exist that could deliver a dose in excess of 100 millirem within 1 hour.

high-radiation area Any accessible area in which radiation hazards exist that could deliver a dose in excess of 100 millirem within 1 hour.

EXPOSURE OF EMPLOYEES TO RADIATION

The exposure of employees to ionizing radiation must be carefully controlled and accurately monitored. The Canadian Nuclear Safety Commission (CNSC), formerly the Atomic Energy Control Board of Canada, regulates the use of all radioactive material in Canada. In its legislation, the Nuclear Safety and Control Act, exposure limits to ionizing radiation are given for prescribed **dosimetry** periods. Figure 21–2 shows the maximum doses for individuals. Employers are responsible for ensuring that these dosages are not exceeded.

dosimetry The process of measuring or calculating the amount of ionizing radiation absorbed.

The energy absorbed by living tissue can cause biological changes that may lead to genetic or reproductive health effects. These effects of exposure are cumulative, so the prescribed exposure levels in Figure 21–2 are for periods of 1 and 5 years. The units used in the Canadian Nuclear Safety Commission Radiation Protection Regulations, sieverts (Sv), represent a large dosage that would have serious health effects if the worker suffered acute exposure of a similar magnitude. For example, 100 millisieverts (100 mSv) would increase the risk of developing cancer later in life to 5 in 1,000. One sievert (1 Sv) would increase that risk to 5 in 100 and 10 Sv would likely cause death within days or weeks.[1]

Figure 21–2 Ionizing radiation exposure limits.

Person	Period	Effective Dose (mSv)
Nuclear energy worker, including a pregnant nuclear energy worker [before she knows she's pregnant]	(a) One-year dosimetry period	50
	(b) Five-year dosimetry period	100
Pregnant nuclear energy worker [after she knows she's pregnant]	Balance of pregnancy	4
A person who is not a nuclear energy worker	One calendar year	1

Source: Based on *Radiation Protection Regulations.* (May 31, 2000). *Canada Gazette Part II* 134, no. 13: 1177–1178, 1183. Reproduced with the permission of the Minister of Public Works and Government Services, 2005.

CNSC is not the only agency that regulates radiation exposure. Health Canada has published Safety Code 6—Limits of Human Exposure to Radiofrequency Electromagnetic Fields in the Frequency Range from 3 kHz to 300 GHz. Safety Code 6 has been adopted by many organizations across Canada and referred to in a number of regulations, including the Canada Occupational Health and Safety Regulations. Industry Canada, which licenses radiocommunication equipment, approves where cell phone base stations are located, and conducts compliance assessments on cell phones and base stations, has also adopted Safety Code 6.[2]

PERSONAL MONITORING

Personal monitoring precautions are important for employees of companies that produce, use, release, dispose of, or store radioactive materials or any other source of ionizing radiation. Personal monitoring is routinely carried out by radiation workers in licensed nuclear facilities and by hospital employees who work with radioactive diagnostic equipment. During nuclear emergencies, monitoring equipment would be distributed by National Dosimetry Services to track and measure worker radiation exposure. National Dosimetry Services is licensed by CNSC and provincial regulatory authorities to provide dosimetry services throughout Canada. Various types of personal monitoring equipment are explained in Figure 21–3.

Figure 21–3 Personal monitoring equipment.

Personal monitoring is done with special radiation detection equipment that is designed to detect radiation from the different pathways:

- **Dosimeters** measure the external dose from nearby sources of radiation. They are not effective for monitoring skin contamination or radioactive dust that may have been inhaled into the body. There are three types of dosimeters:
  - *Badge dosimeters* record, but do not display, the dose; they are processed at a laboratory.
  - *Pencil dosimeters* display the dose and can be read by the user.
  - *Electronic dosimeters* display the dose on a digital readout.
- *Survey meters* measure external doses, and give an immediate reading of the strength and extent of the radiation around radioactive sources.
- *Hand-held contamination monitors* are portable units that are used to monitor surface contamination: radioactive particles on skin, hair, clothing, vehicles, or other objects that could be covered with radioactive dust.
- *Portal monitors* scan a person for surface contamination of the skin, hair, and clothing. The portal monitor looks like a doorframe. The person being monitored stands inside the frame for a few seconds until a reading has been registered.

dosimeter Measures the external dose from nearby sources of radiation.

Source: © All rights reserved. Monitoring Radiation Exposure. Health Canada, 2003. Adapted and reproduced with permission from the Minister of Health, 2016.

CAUTION SIGNS AND LABELS

Caution signs and labels have always been an important part of health and safety programs. This is particularly true in companies where radiation hazards exist. The universal colour scheme for caution signs and labels warning of radiation hazards is black or magenta superimposed on a yellow background.

Figure 21–4 shows the universal symbol for radiation. Along with the appropriate warning words, this symbol should be used on signs and labels. Figure 21–5 shows a warning

Figure 21–4 Universal radiation symbol.

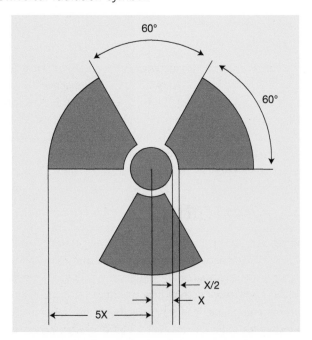

Source: Radiation Protection Regulations. (May 31, 2000). *Canada Gazette Part II* 134, no. 13: 1177–1178, 1183.

Figure 21–5 Sample warning sign.

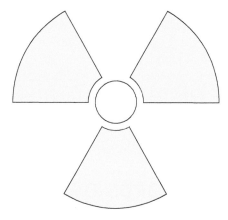

RAYONNEMENT - DANGER - RADIATION

sign and label that may be used in various radioactive settings. On containers, labels should also include the following information: (1) quantity of radioactive material, (2) kinds of radioactive materials, and (3) date on which the contents were measured.[3]

INSTRUCTING AND INFORMING PERSONNEL

It is critical that companies involved in producing, using, storing, handling, or transporting radioactive materials keep employees informed concerning radiation hazards and the appropriate precautions for minimizing them. Consequently, CNSC in its Radiation Protection Regulations has established specific requirements along these lines. Section 7 of these regulations is shown below:

> **7.** (1) Every licensee shall inform each nuclear energy worker, in writing, (*a*) that he or she is a nuclear energy worker; (*b*) of the risks associated with radiation to which the worker may be exposed in the course of his or her work, including the risks associated with the exposure of embryos and foetuses to radiation; (*c*) of the applicable effective dose limits and equivalent dose limits prescribed by sections 13, 14 and 15; and (*d*) of the worker's radiation dose levels.
>
> (2) Every licensee shall inform each female nuclear energy worker, in writing, of the rights and obligations of a pregnant nuclear energy worker under section 11 and of the applicable effective dose limits prescribed by section 13.
>
> (3) Every licensee shall obtain from each nuclear energy worker who is informed of the matters referred to in paragraphs (1)(*a*) and (*b*) and subsection (2) a written acknowledgement that the worker has received the information.[4]

STORAGE AND DISPOSAL OF RADIOACTIVE MATERIAL

Radioactive materials that are stored in restricted areas must be appropriately labelled, as described earlier in this chapter. Radioactive materials that are stored in unrestricted areas must be secured against unauthorized removal from the place of storage. This requirement precludes the handling and transport, intentional or inadvertent, of radioactive materials by persons who are not qualified to move them safely.

A danger inherent in storing radioactive materials in unrestricted areas is that an employee, such as a maintenance worker, may unwittingly attempt to move the container and damage it in the process. This could release doses that exceed prescribed acceptable limits. Low-level nuclear waste is often sent to the Chalk River Laboratories run by Atomic Energy of Canada Limited. Medium-level waste from nuclear power plants is usually stored on site in water-filled pools for years and then transferred to more permanent concrete bunkers or silos.

The storage and disposal of high-level radioactive waste is the topic of great controversy in Canada. Because of the massive volume of waste in existence and expected to be generated in the next four to five decades, permanent storage solutions are needed. Some of these materials will remain radioactive for thousands of years, so storage has to be very long term. At the heart of this debate is the proposal to store nuclear waste deep underground in stable geological structures of the Canadian Shield.

REPORTS AND RECORDS OF OVEREXPOSURE

During the control of an emergency or the consequent immediate remedial work, the dose may exceed the limits prescribed in sections 13 and 14 of the regulations.

> When a licensee becomes aware that a dose of radiation received by and committed to a person or an organ or tissue may have exceeded an applicable dose limit prescribed by section 13, 14 or 15, the licensee shall (*a*) immediately notify the person and the Commission of the dose; (*b*) require the person to leave any work that is likely to add to the dose; (*c*) conduct an investigation to determine the magnitude of the dose and to establish the causes of the exposure; (*d*) identify and take any action required to prevent the occurrence of a similar incident; and (*e*) within 21 days after becoming aware that the dose limit has been exceeded, report to the Commission the results of the investigation or on the progress that has been made in conducting the investigation.[5]

NONIONIZING RADIATION

nonionizing radiation Radiation on the electromagnetic spectrum that has a frequency of 10^{15} cycles per second (Hz) or less and a wavelength in metres of Hz 10^{-7} or more.

Nonionizing radiation is that radiation on the electromagnetic spectrum that has a frequency of 10^{15} cycles per second (Hz) or less and a wavelength in metres of Hz 10^{-7} or more. This low-frequency, long-wavelength end of the electromagnetic spectrum encompasses visible, ultraviolet, infrared, microwave, radio, and AC power frequencies. Radiation at these frequency levels does not have sufficient energy to shatter atoms and ionize them.[6] However, such radiation can cause blisters and blindness. In addition, there is mounting evidence of a link between nonionizing radiation and cancer.

The greatest concerns about nonionizing radiation relate to the following sources: visible radiation, ultraviolet radiation, infrared radiation, radio frequency and microwave radiation, extremely low frequency radiation, lasers, and **video display terminals**. The main concerns in each of these areas are explained in the following paragraphs. The section after that deals specifically with electromagnetic radiation (EMR) from power lines and other sources.

video display terminals (VDTs) A device on which computer data or graphics can be displayed.

visible radiation Radiation from light sources that create distortion and make the radiation visible.

1. **Visible radiation** comes from light sources that create distortion and make the radiation visible. This can be a hazard to employees whose jobs require colour perception. For example, 8 percent of the male population is red colour-blind and cannot properly perceive red warning signs.[7]

ultraviolet radiation Electromagnetic radiation with a frequency between visible violet light and X rays.

2. **Ultraviolet radiation** is electromagnetic radiation with a frequency between visible violet light and X rays. The most common source of ultraviolet radiation is the sun. Potential problems from ultraviolet radiation include sunburn, skin cancer, and cataracts. Precautionary measures include special sunglasses treated to block out ultraviolet rays and wearing protective clothing. Other sources of ultraviolet radiation include lasers, welding arcs, and ultraviolet lamps.[8]

3. **Infrared radiation** is electromagnetic radiation with a frequency less than that of visible light and greater than that of most radio waves. Infrared radiation creates heat. Consequently, the problems associated with this kind of nonionizing radiation involve heat stress and dry skin and eyes. Primary sources of infrared radiation are high-temperature processes such as the production of glass and steel.[9]

infrared radiation Electromagnetic radiation with a frequency less than that of visible light and greater than that of most radio waves.

4. *Radio frequency (RF)* and *microwave (MW) radiation* are electromagnetic radiation in the frequency range of 3 kilohertz (kHz) to 300 gigahertz (GHz). Usually MW radiation is considered a subset of RF radiation, although an alternative convention treats RF and MW radiation as two spectral regions. Microwaves occupy the spectral region between 300 GHz and 300 MHz, whereas RF or radio waves include 300 MHz to 3 kHz. RF and MW radiation are nonionizing in that there is insufficient energy—less than 10 electron volts (eV)—to ionize biologically important atoms. The primary health effects of RF and MW energy are considered to be thermal. The absorption of RF and MW energy varies with frequency. Microwave frequencies produce a skin effect—you can literally sense your skin starting to feel warm. RF radiation may penetrate the body and be absorbed in deep body organs without the skin effect that can warn an individual of danger.

   Research has revealed other nonthermal effects. All of the standards of Western countries have, so far, based their exposure limits solely on preventing thermal problems. In the meantime, research continues. Use of RF and MW radiation includes aeronautical radios, citizen's (CB) radios, cellular phones, processing and cooking of foods, heat sealers, vinyl welders, high-frequency welders, induction heaters, flow solder machines, communications transmitters, radar transmitters, ion implant equipment, microwave drying equipment, sputtering equipment, glue curing, and power amplifiers used in EMC and metrology (calibration).[10]

5. *Extremely low frequency (ELF) radiation* includes alternating current (AC) fields and nonionizing radiation from 1 Hz to 300 Hz. Because ELF frequencies are low (wavelengths are on the order of 1,000 km), static electromagnetic fields are created. ELF fields are considered separate, independent, nonradiating electric and magnetic fields. Electric and magnetic fields (EMFs) at 60 Hz are produced by power lines, electrical wiring, and electrical equipment. Electric fields are produced by voltage and increase in strength as the voltage increases. Electric field strength is measured in units of volts per metre (V/m). Magnetic fields are from the flow of current through wires or electrical devices and increase in strength as the current increases. Magnetic fields are measured in units of gauss (G) or tesla (T).

   Electrical equipment usually must be turned on for a magnetic field to be produced. However, electric fields are present even when equipment is turned off, as long as it is plugged in. Current research has focused on potential health effects of magnetic fields. Some inconclusive epidemiological studies have suggested increased cancer risk associated with estimates of magnetic field exposure. No similar associations have been reported for electric fields. Exposure to EMFs depends on the strength of the magnetic field sources, the distance from those sources, and the time spent in the magnetic field. The American Conference of Governmental Industrial Hygienists (ACGIH) has established occupational threshold limit values (TLVs) for static magnetic fields, sub-radio-frequency (30 kHz and below) magnetic fields, and sub-radio-frequency (30 kHz and below) static electric fields.[11]

6. **Lasers**, which amplify light by stimulated emission of radiation, are being used increasingly in modern industry. The hazards of lasers consist of a thermal threat to the eyes and the threat of electrocution from power sources. In addition, the smoke created by lasers in some processes can be toxic.[12]

lasers Light amplification by stimulated emission of radiation.

ELECTROMAGNETIC FIELDS IN THE WORKPLACE

electromagnetic fields (EMFs) Form of nonionizing radiation produced as electrical current flows.

The first studies of the potential effects on worker health of occupational exposure to electric and magnetic fields were published in the literature of the former Soviet Union in the mid-1960s. In these studies, electric switchyard workers reported a variety of subjective complaints, including problems with their cardiovascular, digestive, and central nervous systems.[13] Since then, numerous studies of the effects of **electromagnetic fields (EMFs)**, which is a form of nonionizing radiation produced as electrical current flows, on humans have been conducted. Although much of the research has been inconclusive in establishing a clear cause-and-effect relationship between EMFs and health problems, the case for a link between EMFs and a variety of health problems is strong. Consequently, health and safety professionals must be prepared to take appropriate precautions in the workplace.

According to Savitz, "associations reported between electric occupations and leukemia and brain cancer seem too consistent to be attributable to chance."[14] Occupations with a higher-than-normal incidence of leukemia and brain cancer are as follows:

- Telephone operators
- Electrical manufacturing workers
- Power plant workers
- Telecommunication workers
- Electrical engineers
- Electrical line workers
- Power station operators
- Electricians
- Cable splicers

The health problems most frequently associated with EMF exposure are brain cancer, acute myeloid leukemia, leukemia, and lymphatic leukemia.

The debate continues over the health effects of cell phone use and radiofrequency (RF) energy from Wi-Fi equipment. Some research supports a correlation between electromagnetic fields and brain cancer or leukemia, while some scientists strongly dispute these claims. Based on scientific evidence, Health Canada has determined that low-level exposure to (RF) energy from Wi-Fi equipment is not dangerous to the public. However one hazard that is disputed by few and supported by most Canadian jurisdictions is cell phone use while driving. In December 2002, Newfoundland and Labrador was the first province to pass legislation to ban cell phone use while driving, and all other jurisdictions except Nunavut have adopted similar legislation.

EMFs and Health Problems

Studies have shown that some employees exposed to high magnetic fields have increased cancer rates. However, such associations do not necessarily show that EMF exposures cause cancer (any more than the springtime association of robins and daffodils shows that one causes the other). Scientists have looked carefully at all of the EMF evidence, but they still disagree on the health effects of EMFs, except to say that better information is needed.[15]

Many studies report small increases in the rate of leukemia or brain cancer in groups of people living or working in high magnetic fields. Other studies have found no such increases. The most important data come from six recent studies of workers wearing EMF monitors to measure magnetic fields. All but one study found significantly higher cancer rates for men with average workday exposures above 4 milligauss. However, the results of these studies disagree in important ways, such as the type of cancer associated with EMF exposures. Consequently, scientists cannot be sure whether the increased risks are caused by EMFs or by other factors. A few preliminary studies have also associated workplace EMFs with breast cancer, and one study has reported a possible link between occupational EMF exposure and Alzheimer's disease. The data from all of these studies are too limited for scientists to draw conclusions.

An Appropriate Response for Safety Professionals

The research into the possible cause-and-effect relationship between EMF and health problems is inconclusive. On the other hand, the anecdotal and circumstantial evidence strongly suggests a link. How, then, is the health and safety professional to respond? According to William E. Feero,

> The emergence of new electrical technologies has produced an extremely complex electric and magnetic field environment in which we must live and work. Although there presently exist no universally accepted human exposure guidelines, current biological research may someday produce such limits. It is in anticipation of these exposure limits that electric and magnetic field management techniques are being investigated. At low frequencies, two categories of field management exist: cancellation and shielding. The particular class of control used will depend on several functions of the field and its source, and will be determined finally on a case-by-case basis.[16]

Cancellation Approach

Cancellation is an attenuation technique in which the magnetic fields produced by sources of electricity are, in effect, cancelled out. It works as follows: The magnetic field caused by alternating currents flowing through a given conductor are cancelled out or drastically reduced by currents flowing in the opposite conductors. The cancellation approach can be used for both single-phase and balanced multiphase systems.

According to Feero,

> Cancellation fields can be set up in some cases with very little cost penalty. In many cases, a principal source of magnetic fields is found to be the conductor systems leading to tools or power apparatus. In such relatively simple cases, these fields could be canceled via compaction of the conductor systems. For example, a low voltage device, either a 120 or 240V service, is typically supplied by a power cord and the fields any distance from the cord are rapidly attenuated. In the situation where the cords or leads have to be very close to the worker, the added precaution of twisting or interleaving of these leads with each other will further reduce the field. The net effect of twisting a pair of conductors is that each individual conductor appears to occupy the same space. Therefore, the fields are much more effectively canceled because the spacing between the conductors is reduced to nearly zero.

Electrical apparatus that consumes considerable energy would generally be supplied by three-phase cables rather than single-phase cables. If single-phase cables are used, care in bundling of the cables within cable trays and the routing of the cable trays can be a very effective control technology. In many instances where strong fields have been found near transformer vaults in buildings, the source of the magnetic field is the cable system leading to and from the transformer vault.

The magnetic field produced directly from most apparatus exhibits the characteristics of loop current source fields. Therefore, a simple control technique may be to move the device (i.e., a compressor motor in a refrigeration unit) to the back of the unit's housing. If the device's function does not permit it to be moved (handheld tools, for instance) then more sophisticated and possibly expensive techniques must be employed.[17]

SAFETY FACT TLVs and Personal Medical Devices

Routine exposures to static magnetic fields should not exceed 60 millitesla (mT) or the equivalent 600 gauss (G) for the whole body, or 600 mT (6,000 G) to the limbs on a daily time-weighted-average basis. Wearers of cardiac pacemakers and other personal electronic medical devices should be exposed to no more than 0.5 mT (5 G) on a daily time-weighted-average basis.

Shielding Approach

Shielding is another approach available for decreasing exposure to EMF. According to Feero,

> Shielding of magnetic fields requires either that the magnetic fields be diverted around the volume considered to be sensitive to the magnetic fields, or the magnetic fields be contained within the device that produces the fields. Effectively accomplishing shielding at either the source or the subject requires extreme care in choosing the shielding material. The electrical properties of ferromagnetic materials are very complex functions of magnetic field frequencies and magnitudes. For strong magnetic fields, the highly non-linear saturation characteristics of ferromagnetic materials have been widely recognized and reasonably adjusted to achieve source shielding. However, only a few engineers and physicists are aware of the effects of coerciveness at very low magnetizing forces. Subject shielding invariably involves weak magnetic fields. Ferromagnetic materials that are normally considered to have very high permeability may exhibit quite low permeability if being used to attempt to shield milligauss field levels. Thus, the problem of dynamic range encountered when trying to apply cancellation techniques reappears in a different form when attempting to utilize shielding techniques.[18]

Both cancellation and shielding are highly technical approaches requiring specialized knowledge. Health and safety professionals who are not specialists in electromagnetic fields may find it necessary to consult with EMF experts before attempting to implement either approach.

SAFETY FACT Reducing EMF Exposure in the Workplace

Employees are often exposed to electromagnetic fields in the workplace without even knowing it. It is important to inform employees about EMF and the associated hazards and to take steps to reduce exposure levels. Strategies for reducing exposure include the following:

- Because magnetic fields drop off significantly approximately 3 feet from the source, increase the distance between employees and sources of EMF.

- Substitute low-EMF-producing equipment (power supplies) wherever possible.
- Reduce the amount of time that employees are exposed to EMF sources.

SUMMARY

1. Widely used terms relating to ionizing radiation are *radiation, radioactive material, restricted area, unrestricted area, dose, rad, rem, sievert, air dose, personal monitoring devices, radiation area,* and *high-radiation area.*

2. Exposure of individuals to radiation must be carefully controlled and accurately monitored. Doses are typically measured in rems or sieverts.

3. Employers must require the use of personal monitoring devices such as film badges, pocket chambers, pocket dosimeters, and film rings.

4. Employees must be informed and instructed regarding potential radiation hazards, precautions that they should take, and records of exposure.

5. Radioactive materials that are stored in restricted areas must be appropriately labelled. Materials stored in unrestricted areas must be secured against unauthorized removal.

6. Radiation incidents that involve exposure beyond prescribed limits must be reported immediately to the Canadian Nuclear Safety Commission and investigated and the results or the status of the investigation reported within 21 days.

7. Nonionizing radiation is radiation on the electromagnetic spectrum that lacks sufficient energy to ionize atoms. This encompasses visible, ultraviolet, infrared, microwave, radio, and AC power frequencies.

8. Electromagnetic fields, or EMFs, encompass radiation from power lines and a long list of electrical appliances. Concerns about, and evidence of, a link between EMFs and cancer exist.

Key Terms and Concepts

Air dose
Dosimeter
Dosimetry
Electromagnetic fields
   (EMFs)
High-radiation area
Infrared radiation
Ionizing radiation

Lasers
Nonionizing radiation
Personal monitoring
   devices
Rad
Radiation area
Radioactive material
Rem

Restricted area
Sievert
Ultraviolet radiation
Unrestricted area
Video display terminals
   (VDTs)
Visible radiation

Review Questions

1. Define the following terms relating to ionizing radiation: *radiation, restricted area, dose, rem, sievert,* and *radiation area.*

2. Describe the types of personal monitoring devices used.

3. How should radioactive material be treated when stored in a unrestricted area?

4. Where is nuclear waste stored?

5. Describe the requirements in the case of radiation overexposure.

6. Define the term *nonionizing radiation.*

7. What are the primary sources of concern regarding nonionizing radiation?

8. What is the maximum dose of radiation allowed to the whole body during a 1- and 5-year period for a nuclear energy worker? For someone who is not a nuclear energy worker?

9. Describe the anecdotal and scientific evidence linking EMF to cancer.

Weblinks

Canadian Nuclear Safety Commission

www.nuclearsafety.gc.ca/eng

CNSC, the former Atomic Energy Control Board, has available on its website information on issues facing nuclear energy in Canada and links to nuclear energy legislation.

Health Canada

https://www.canada.ca/en/health-canada/services/environmental-workplace-health/radiation.html

Health Canada provides information on numerous health issues facing Canadians, including exposure to radiation from natural and artificial sources.

Endnotes

[1] Canadian Centre for Occupational Health and Safety. (May 23, 1999). "OHS Answers." [Online]. Available: http://www.ccohs.ca/oshanswers/phys_agents/ionizing.html. (Retrieved December 29, 2004).

[2] Health Canada. (December 3, 2002). "It's Your Health, Safety and the Safe Use of Cell Phones." [Online]. Available: http://www.hc-sc.gc.ca/english/iyh/products/cellphones.htm. (Retrieved December 29, 2004).

[3] Canadian Nuclear Safety Commission. (June 21, 2000). Radiation Protection Regulations. The Queen's Printer of Canada. [Online]. Available: http://www.nuclearsafety.gc.ca/eng/regulatory_information/pdf/sor203.pdf. (Retrieved December 29, 2004).

[4] Ibid.

[5] Ibid.

[6] American Conference of Governmental Industrial Hygienists. TLVs and BEIs (Cincinnati: ACGIH, 2001), 147.

[7] Ibid., 42.

[8] Ibid., 43.

[9] Ibid.

[10] OSHA. "Technical Links," 1. [Online]. Available: http://www.osha-slc.gov. (Retrieved June 2003).

[11] Ibid.

[12] Ibid.

[13] William E. Murray Jr. and Robert M. Patterson. "Electric and Magnetic Fields: What Do We Know?" American Industrial Hygiene Association Journal 54, no. 4 (April 1997): 164.

[14] David A. Savitz. "Overview of Epidemiologic Research on Electric and Magnetic Fields and Cancer." American Industrial Hygiene Journal 54, no. 4 (April 1993): 202.

[15] NIOSH. "Fact Sheet." [Online]. Available: http://www.cdc.gov/niosh/emf2.html. (Retrieved May 2001), 3.

[16] William E. Feero. "Electric and Magnetic Field Management." American Industrial Hygiene Journal 54, no. 4: 205. Copyright © The American Industrial Hygiene Association, www.aiha.org and The American Conference of Governmental Industrial Hygienists, www.acgih.org, reprinted by permission of Taylor & Francis Ltd, http://www.tandfonline.com on behalf of The American Industrial Hygiene Association and The American Conference of Governmental Industrial Hygienists.

[17] Ibid., 207–208.

[18] Ibid., 208–209.

Chapter 22
Noise and Vibration Hazards

The modern industrial work site can be a noisy place. This poses two health-and-safety-related problems. First, there is the problem of distraction. Noise can distract workers, disrupt their concentration, and mask audible warnings, which can lead to accidents. Second, there is the problem of hearing loss. Exposure to noise that exceeds prescribed levels can result in permanent hearing loss.

Health and safety professionals need to understand the hazards associated with noise and vibration, how to identify and assess these hazards, and how to prevent injuries related to them. This chapter provides the necessary information for prospective and practising health and safety professionals to do so.

HEARING LOSS PREVENTION TERMS

There are certain terms common to hearing loss prevention that must be understood by health and safety professionals. The reader may find the definitions in this section helpful when trying to understand the content of this chapter.

- **Baseline audiogram.** A valid audiogram against which subsequent audiograms are compared to determine if hearing thresholds have changed. The baseline audiogram is preceded by a quiet period to obtain the best estimate of the person's hearing at that time.

- **Continuous noise.** Noise of a constant level measured over at least one second using the "slow" setting on a sound level meter. Note that an intermittent noise (e.g., on for over a second and then off for a period) is both variable *and* continuous.

- **dB (decibel).** The unit used to express the intensity of sound. The decibel was named after Alexander Graham Bell. The decibel scale is a logarithmic scale in which 0 dB approximates the threshold of hearing in the midfrequencies for young adults, and in which the threshold of discomfort is between 85 and 95 dB and the threshold for pain is between 120 and 140 dB.

- **Dosimeter.** When applied to noise, this instrument measures sound levels over a specified interval, stores the measures, and calculates the sound as a function of sound level and sound duration. It describes the results in terms of dose, time-weighted average, and other parameters such as peak level, equivalent sound level, sound exposure level, and so on.

- **Exchange rate.** The relationship between intensity and dose. The federal government uses a 3-dB exchange rate. Thus, if the intensity of an exposure increases by 3 dB, the dose doubles. This may also be referred to as the *doubling rate*. While some provinces use a 5-dB exchange rate, others use a 3-dB exchange rate that provides a greater degree of protection.

- **Fit testing.** With all PPE, fit is an important consideration. A poor fit can undermine the effectiveness of any kind of PPE, including *hearing protection devices (HPDs)*. Fit testing is a process for ensuring the best possible fit of HPDs. The goal is to ensure that the HPD properly fits the individual as well as the situation.

- **Hazardous noise.** Any sound for which any combination of frequency, intensity, or duration is capable of causing permanent hearing loss in a specified population.

- **Conductive and sensorineural loss.** Hearing loss is often characterized by the area of the auditory system responsible for the loss. For example, when injury or a medical condition affects the *outer ear* or *middle ear* (i.e., from the pinna, ear canal, and eardrum to the cavity behind the eardrum that includes the ossicles), the resulting hearing loss is referred to as a *conductive* loss. When an injury or medical condition affects the *inner ear* or the auditory nerve that connects the inner ear to the brain (i.e., the cochlea and the VIIIth cranial nerve), the resulting hearing loss is referred to as a *sensorineural* loss. Thus, a welder's spark that damages the eardrum causes a conductive hearing loss. And because noise can damage the tiny hair cells located in the cochlea, noise causes a sensorineural hearing loss.

- **HTL (hearing threshold level).** The hearing level, above a reference value, at which a specified sound or tone is heard by an ear in a specified fraction of the trials. Hearing threshold levels have been established so that dB HTL reflects the best hearing of a group of persons.

- **Hz (hertz).** The unit measurement for audio frequencies. The frequency range for human hearing lies between 20 Hz and approximately 20,000 Hz. The sensitivity of the human ear drops off sharply below about 500 Hz and above 4,000 Hz.

- **Impulsive noise.** Generally used to characterize impact or impulse noise typified by a sound that rapidly rises to a sharp peak and then quickly fades. The sound may or may not have a "ringing" quality (such as striking a hammer on a metal plate or a gunshot in a reverberant room). Impulsive noise may be repetitive, or may be a single event (as with a sonic boom). If impulses occur in very rapid succession (e.g., some jackhammers), the noise is *not* described as impulsive.

- **Noise.** Any unwanted sound.

- **Noise dose.** The noise exposure expressed as a percentage of the allowable daily exposure. For example, if 85 dB(A) is the maximum permissible level, an 8-hour exposure to a continuous 85-dB(A) noise equals a 100 percent dose. If a 3-dB exchange rate is used in conjunction with an 85-dB(A) maximum permissible level, a 50 percent dose equals a 2-hour exposure to 88 dB(A) or an 8-hour exposure to 82 dB(A).

- **Noise-induced hearing loss.** A sensorineural hearing loss that is attributed to noise and for which no other etiology can be determined.

- **STS (standard threshold shift).** NIOSH uses this term to describe a change from baseline levels of 15 dB or more at any frequency from 400 through 6,000 Hz that is present on a retest in the same ear and at the same frequency. NIOSH recommends a confirmation audiogram within 30 days with the confirmation audiogram preceded by a quiet period of at least 14 hours.

- **TWA (time-weighted average).** A value, expressed in dB(A), computed so that the resulting average is equivalent to an exposure resulting from a constant noise level over an 8-hour period.

- **Lex.** This is an abbreviation for average exposure level adjusted for an 8-hour day. For example, when describing the Ontario regulations, the allowable noise limit is 90 dB(A) Lex.

CHARACTERISTICS OF SOUND

Sound is any change in pressure that can be detected by the ear. Typically, sound is a change in *air pressure*. However, it can also be a change in water pressure or any other pressure-sensitive medium. **Noise** is unwanted sound. Consequently, the difference between noise and sound is in the perception of the person hearing it (e.g., loud rock music may be considered "sound" by a rock fan but "noise" by a shift worker trying to sleep).

Sound and vibration are very similar. Sound typically relates to a sensation that is perceived by the inner ear as hearing. **Vibration**, on the other hand, involves oscillations of solid or semi-solid objects, is inaudible, and is perceived through the sense of touch. Sound can occur in any medium that has both mass and elasticity (air, water, and so on). It occurs as elastic waves that cross over (above and below) a line representing normal atmospheric pressure (Figure 22–1).

sound Any change in pressure that can be detected by the ear.

noise Unwanted sound.

vibration Oscillations of solid or semi-solid objects that can be perceived by the sense of touch.

Figure 22–1 Sound waves.

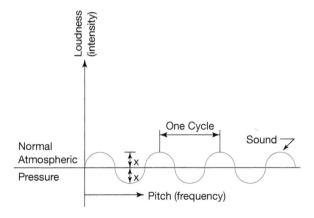

Normal atmospheric pressure is represented in Figure 22–1 by a straight horizontal line. Sound is represented by the wavy line that crosses above and below the line. The more frequently the sound waves cross the normal atmospheric pressure line (the shorter the cycle), the higher the pitch of the sound. The greater the vertical distance above and below the atmospheric pressure line (distance X), the louder or more intense the sound.

The unit of measurement used for discussing the level of sound and, correspondingly, what noise levels are hazardous is the **decibel (dB)**, or one-tenth of a *bel*. One decibel represents the smallest difference in the level of sound that can be perceived by the human ear. Figure 22–2 shows the decibel levels for various common sounds. The weakest sound that can be heard by a healthy human ear in a quiet setting is known as the **threshold of hearing** (1 dB(A)). The maximum level of sound that can be perceived without experiencing pain is known as the **threshold of pain** (140 dB(A)).

decibel (dB) The unit applied when measuring sound. One decibel equals one-tenth of a bel and is the smallest difference in the level of sound that can be perceived by the human ear.

threshold of hearing The weakest sound that can be heard by a healthy human ear in a quiet setting.

threshold of pain The maximum level of sound that can be perceived without experiencing pain.

Figure 22–2 Selected sound levels.

Source	Decibels (dB(A))
Whisper	20
Quiet library	30
Quiet office	50
Normal conversation	60
Vacuum cleaner	70
Noisy office	80
Power saw, lawn mower	90
Chain saw	90
Grinding operations	100
Passing truck	100
Gunshot blast	140
Jet aircraft	150
Rocket launching	180

The human ear is more sensitive at higher frequencies, so two sounds of equal magnitude but different frequencies will not seem equally loud. The A-weighted *sound pressure level*, abbreviated as *dB(A)*, represents a single number indicator of the relative loudness as perceived by the human ear. Sound level meters attenuate frequencies by different amounts so that the sound pressure level shown represents relative loudness as perceived by the human ear. While people typically judge a 10 dB increase in sound level to be the doubling of its intensity, a 6 dB increase is actually twice as loud. Most people can detect a change in sound levels as small as 2 to 3 dB.

The three broad types of industrial noise are described by McDonald as follows:

> **Wide band noise** is noise that is distributed over a wide range of frequencies. Most noise from manufacturing machines is wide band noise. **Narrow band noise** is noise that is confined to a narrow range of frequencies. The noise produced by power tools is narrow band noise. Finally, **impulse noise** consists of transient pulses that can occur repetitively or nonrepetitively. The noise produced by a jackhammer is repetitive impulse noise.[1]

wide band noise Noise that is distributed over a wide range of frequencies.

narrow band noise Noise that is confined to a narrow range of frequencies.

impulse noise Consists of transient pulses that can occur repetitively or nonrepetitively.

HAZARD LEVELS AND RISKS

The fundamental hazard associated with excessive noise is hearing loss. Exposure to excessive noise levels for an extended period can damage the inner ear so that the ability to hear high-frequency sound is diminished or lost altogether. Additional exposure can increase the damage until even lower frequency sounds cannot be heard.[2]

A number of different factors affect the risk of hearing loss associated with exposure to excessive noise. The most important of these are:

- Intensity of the noise (sound pressure level).
- Frequency of the noise.
- Type of noise (wide band, narrow band, or impulse).
- Distribution of the noise.
- Duration of daily exposure.
- Total duration of exposure (number of years).
- Age of the individual.
- Coexisting hearing disease.
- Nature of environment in which exposure occurs.
- Distance of the individual from the source of the noise.
- Position of the ears relative to the sound waves.[3]

Of these various factors, the most critical are the sound pressure level, frequency, duration, and distribution of noise (Figure 22–3). The unprotected human ear is at risk when exposed to sound levels exceeding 115 dB(A). Exposure to sound levels below 80 dB(A) is generally considered safe. Prolonged exposure to noise levels higher than 80 dB(A) should be minimized through the use of appropriate personal protective devices.

Figure 22–3 Critical noise risk factors.

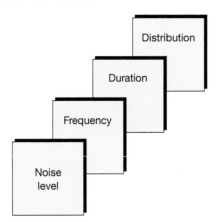

To decrease the risk of hearing loss, exposure to noise should be limited to a maximum 8-hour time-weighted average of 85 dB(A). The following general rules should be applied for dealing with noise in the workplace:

- Exposures of less than 80 dB(A) may be considered safe for the purpose of risk assessment.
- A time-weighted average (threshold) of 85 dB(A) should be considered the maximum limit of continuous exposure over 8-hour days without protection.[4]

In noisy work environments, the primary concern for the health and safety practitioner is the auditory effects on the worker, such as loss of hearing acuity or sensitivity. However, noise, like other environmental stressors, may have adverse effects on health, such as cardiovascular function (hypertension, changes in blood pressure and/or heart rate) and changes in breathing, annoyance, sleep, and physical and mental health.[5]

STANDARDS AND REGULATIONS

Since hearing loss is a factor of both the level and duration of exposure to loud noise, standards and regulations relating to noise hazards include limiting worker exposure level and duration. The noise exposure limits for each Canadian jurisdiction, which are often based on National Institute for Occupational Safety and Health (NIOSH) or American Conference of Governmental Industrial Hygienists (ACGIH) standards, are summarized in Figure 22–4. The maximum permitted exposure levels are based on an 8-hour day. When the magnitude of the noise exceeds these levels, some form of control is required to lower the sound level or duration of exposure to a point below the prescribed standard or regulation.

Figure 22–4 Noise exposure limits for Canadian jurisdictions.

Jurisdiction (federal, provincial, territorial)	Continuous Noise Maximum Permitted Exposure Level for 8 Hours: dB(A)	Exchange Rate dB(A)+	Impulse/Impact Noise Maximum Peak Pressure Level dB(peak)	Maximum Number of Impacts
Canada (Federal)	87	3	-	-
British Columbia	85	3	140	-
Alberta	85	3	-	-
Saskatchewan	85	3	-	-
Manitoba	85	3	-	-
Ontario	85	3	-	-
Quebec	90	5	140	100
New Brunswick	85	3	140	-
Nova Scotia	85	3	-	100
Prince Edward Island	85	3	-	-
Newfoundland and Labrador	85	3	-	-
Northwest Territories	85	*	140	100
Nunavut	85	*	140	-
Yukon Territory	85	3	140	90
*In both territories, the Mining Health and Safety Regulations reference 3 dBA.				

Source: Used with permission from Canadian Centre for Occupational Health and Safety.

exchange rate The increase in sound level that is permitted as the time of exposure is halved.

As the duration of the exposure is decreased, the permissible level is increased. The **exchange rate** indicates the increase in sound level that is permitted as the time of exposure is halved. In Quebec, for example, the maximum permitted exposure level for an 8-hour workday is 90 dB(A). With an exchange rate of 5 dB, the limit would be 95 dB(A) for 4 hours, 100 dB(A) for 2 hours and so on until 115 dB(A) is reached for 15 minutes, after which point no exposure without protection is permitted. Saskatchewan has a 3 dB(A) exchange rate that begins at 85 dB(A) for an 8-hour day, but also limits the maximum level to 115 dB(A). The federal Occupational Health and Safety Regulations also have a 3 dB(A) exchange rate, but start at 87 dB(A) for 8 hours. Of the three examples described, the Saskatchewan regulations provide the greatest degree of hearing protection for the worker.

It's been found that a variety of everyday activities can cause exposure to sound levels above 85 dBA, the occupational noise exposure limit for most Canadian jurisdictions. A few examples are:

- listening to music through headphones or earbuds
- attending a rock music concert
- mowing the lawn
- using a table saw
- driving a car on the highway with the windows open
- playing a musical instrument
- participating as a member of a band or orchestra
- using firearms regularly for hunting or target practice, without the appropriate hearing protection

Early signs of hearing loss include:

- trouble following a conversation when there is background noise (like at a social gathering or in a cafeteria)
- a sense that people mumble when they speak
- tinnitus – often referred to as ringing in the ears

Prevention is the only way to protect yourself from noise-induced hearing loss. There is no way to know how sensitive your ears are to damage from sounds until the damage is done.

Source: Government of Canada. (October 4, 2016). "Noise-Induced Hearing Loss." [Online]. Available: https://www.canada.ca/en/health-canada/services/healthy-living/your-health/environment/noise-induced-hearing-loss.html. (Retrieved August 12, 2017).

Hearing Hazards Monitoring

As with any health hazard, it is important to determine accurately the nature of the hearing hazard and to identify the affected employees. Those responsible for this aspect of the program must ensure that the exposures of all employees have been properly evaluated and that re-evaluations are conducted when changes in equipment or operations significantly alter working conditions. Recent evidence has indicated that aromatic solvents, metals, and petrochemicals may be associated with occupational hearing loss. Although studies are exploring the relationship between hearing loss and chemical exposures, there is insufficient information about this relationship to speculate on potential risk factors. Therefore, this section focuses on monitoring noise exposure, the major factor associated with occupational hearing losses. Hearing hazard exposure monitoring is conducted for various purposes, including:

- Determining whether hazards to hearing exist.
- Determining whether noise presents a safety hazard by interfering with speech communication or the recognition of audible warning signals.
- Identifying employees for inclusion in the hearing loss prevention program.
- Classifying employees' noise exposures for prioritizing noise control efforts and defining and establishing hearing protection practises.
- Evaluating specific noise sources for noise control purposes.
- Evaluating the success of noise control efforts.

Various measurement methods may be used, depending on the type of hearing hazard exposure monitoring that is being conducted. The most common types of monitoring are area surveys, dosimetry, and engineering surveys.

In an area survey, environmental noise levels are measured using a sound level meter to identify work areas where exposures are above or below hazardous levels and where more thorough exposure monitoring may be needed. The result is often plotted in the form of a "noise map" that shows noise level measurements for the different areas of the workplace.

Dosimetry involves the use of body-worn instruments (dosimeters) to monitor an employee's noise exposure over the work shift. Monitoring results for one employee can also represent the exposures of other workers in the area with similar noise exposures. It may also be possible to use task-based exposure methods to represent the exposures of other workers in different areas where exposures result from having performed the same tasks.

Engineering surveys typically employ more sophisticated acoustical equipment in addition to sound level meters. These may include octave-band analyzers and sound level recorders that furnish information on the frequency–intensity composition of the noise being emitted by machinery or other sound sources in various modes of operation. These measurements are used to assess options for applying engineering controls.

Engineering and Administrative Controls

Engineering and administrative controls are essential to achieve an effective hearing loss prevention program. Engineering and administrative controls represent the first two echelons in the hierarchy of controls: (1) remove the hazard, and (2) remove the worker. The use of these controls should reduce hazardous exposure to the point where the risk to hearing is eliminated or at least more manageable. Engineering controls are technologically feasible for most noise sources, but their economic feasibility must be determined on a case-by-case basis. In some instances, the application of a relatively simple noise control solution reduces the hazard to the extent that the other elements of the program, such as audiometric testing and the use of hearing protection devices, are no longer necessary. In other cases, the noise reduction process may be more complex and must be accomplished in stages over a period of time. Even so, with each reduction of a few decibels, the hazard to hearing is reduced, communication is improved, and noise-related annoyance is reduced as well.

It is especially important that organizations specify low noise levels when purchasing new equipment. Many types of previously noisy equipment are now available in noise-controlled versions. Consequently, a "buy quiet" purchasing policy should not require new engineering solutions in many cases.

For hearing loss prevention purposes, *engineering controls* are defined as any modification or replacement of equipment or related physical change at the noise source or along the transmission path (with the exception of hearing protectors) that reduces the noise level at the employee's ear. Typical engineering controls involve:

- Reducing noise at the source (e.g., installing a muffler).
- Interrupting the noise path (e.g., erecting acoustical enclosures and barriers).
- Reducing reverberation (e.g., installing sound-absorbing material).
- Reducing structure-borne vibration (e.g., installing vibration mounts and providing proper lubrication).

Administrative controls, defined as changes in the work schedule or operations that reduce noise exposure, may also be used effectively. Examples include operating a noisy machine on the second or third shift when fewer people are exposed, or shifting an employee to a less noisy job once a hazardous daily noise dose has been reached. Generally, administrative controls have limited use in industry because employee contracts seldom permit shifting from one job to another. Moreover, the practice of rotating employees between quiet and noisy jobs, although it may reduce the risk of substantial hearing loss in a few workers, may actually increase the risk of small hearing losses in many workers. A more practical administrative control is to provide for quiet areas where employees can gain relief from workplace noise. Areas used for work breaks and lunchrooms should be located away from noise.

Audiometric Evaluation

Audiometric evaluation is crucial to the success of the hearing loss prevention program in that it is the only way to determine whether occupational hearing loss is being prevented.

When the comparison of audiograms shows temporary threshold shift (a temporary hearing loss after noise exposure), early permanent threshold shift, or progressive occupational hearing loss, it is time to take swift action to halt the loss before additional deterioration occurs. Because occupational hearing loss occurs gradually and is not accompanied by pain, the affected employee may not notice the change until a large threshold shift has accumulated. However, the results of audiometric tests can trigger changes in the hearing loss prevention program more promptly, initiating protective measures and motivating employees to prevent further hearing loss.

As shown in Figure 22–5, audiometric testing requirements vary throughout Canadian jurisdictions. However, for maximum protection of employees who work in noisy environments, audiograms should be performed on these workers on the following occasions:

- Pre-employment.

- Prior to initial assignment in a hearing-hazardous work area.

- Annually as long as the employee is assigned to a noisy job (a time-weighted average exposure level equal to or greater than 85 dB(A)).

- At the time of reassignment out of a hearing-hazardous job.

- At the termination of employment.

Figure 22–5 Audiometric test requirements for Canadian jurisdictions.

Jurisdiction	Audiometric Testing Requirements
Canada (Federal)	No testing required.
British Columbia	Every 12 months.
Alberta	Every 24 months. Initial test within 6 months. Second within 12 months of employment.
Saskatchewan	Every 24 months.
Manitoba	Every 12 months.
Ontario	No testing required.
Quebec	Testing required, but time interval is not specified.
New Brunswick	No testing required.
Nova Scotia	Every 12 months.
Prince Edward Island	Every 12 months.
Newfoundland and Labrador	Every 12 months.
Northwest Territories and Nunavut	Every 12 months.
Yukon Territory	Every 12 months.

In addition, it is suggested that employees who are not exposed be given periodic audiograms as part of the organization's health care program. The audiograms of these employees can be compared to those of the exposed employees whenever the overall effectiveness of the hearing loss prevention program is evaluated. In an optimally effective program, the two employee groups show essentially the same amount of audiometric change.

Personal Hearing Protection Devices

A personal hearing protection device (or *hearing protector*) is anything that can be worn to reduce the level of sound entering the ear. Earmuffs, ear canal caps, and earplugs are the three principal types of devices. Each employee reacts individually to the use of these devices, and a successful hearing loss prevention program should be able to respond to the needs of each employee. Ensuring that these devices protect hearing effectively requires the coordinated effort of management, the hearing loss prevention program operators, and the affected employees.

Education and Motivation

Training is a critical element of a good hearing loss prevention program. In order to obtain sincere and energetic support by management and active participation by employees, it is necessary to educate and motivate both groups. A hearing loss prevention program that overlooks the importance of education and motivation is likely to fail because employees will not understand why it is in their best interest to cooperate, and management will fail to make the necessary commitment. Employees and managers who appreciate the precious sense of hearing and understand the reasons for, and the mechanics of, the hearing loss prevention program will be more likely to participate for their mutual benefit, rather than viewing the program as an imposition.

Record Keeping

Records quite often get the least attention of any of the program's components. However, audiometric comparisons, reports of hearing protector use, and the analysis of hazardous exposure measurements all involve the keeping of records. Unfortunately, records are often kept poorly because there is no organized system in place and, in many cases, those responsible for maintaining the records do not understand the records' value. People tend to assume that if they merely place records in a file or enter them into a computer, adequate record-keeping procedures are being followed.

Many companies have found that their record-keeping system is inadequate only when they discover that they need accurate information. This sometimes occurs during the processing of compensation claims. Problems can be avoided by implementing an effective record-keeping system, in which (1) management encourages that the system be kept active and accessible, (2) hearing loss prevention program implementers make sure that all of the information entered is accurate and complete, and (3) employees validate the information.

Hearing loss prevention program records should include all the following items for each phase of the program: (1) hearing loss prevention audit, (2) monitoring hearing hazards, (3) engineering and administrative controls, (4) audiometric evaluation, (5) personal hearing protective devices, (6) education and motivation, (7) record keeping, and (8) program evaluation. Each phase must be considered in order to evaluate the effectiveness of the hearing loss prevention program.

Program Evaluation

The primary goal of any hearing loss prevention program must be to reduce, and eventually eliminate, hearing loss due to workplace exposures. Although management may have the best intentions of implementing this goal and a company's hearing loss prevention program may have the appearance of being complete and in compliance with the legislative requirements, the program still may not achieve this goal. A thorough evaluation of the effectiveness of all the program's components is necessary to determine the extent to which the hearing loss prevention program is really working.

Management and program implementers should conduct periodic program evaluations to assess compliance with federal and provincial/territorial regulations and to ensure that hearing is being conserved. There are two basic approaches to following program evaluation: (1) assess the completeness and quality of the program's components, and (2) evaluate the audiometric data.

IDENTIFYING AND ASSESSING HAZARDOUS NOISE CONDITIONS

Identifying and assessing **hazardous noise** conditions in the workplace involves (1) conducting periodic noise surveys, (2) conducting periodic audiometric tests, (3) record keeping, and (4) follow-up action. Each of these components is covered in the following sections.

hazardous noise Any sound for which any combination of frequency, intensity, or duration is capable of causing permanent hearing loss in a specified population.

Noise Surveys

Conducting *noise surveys* involves measuring noise levels at different locations in the workplace. The devices that are most widely used to measure noise levels are sound level meters and dosimeters. A **sound level meter** produces an immediate reading that represents the noise level at a specific instant in time. A dosimeter provides a time-weighted average over a period of time, such as one complete work shift. A dosimeter also calculates the sound as a function of sound level and duration and describes the results in terms of dose, peak level, equivalent sound level, sound exposure level, and time-weighted average.[6] The dosimeter is the most widely used device because it measures total exposure. Using a dosimeter in various work areas and attaching a personal dosimeter to one or more employees is the recommended approach to ensure dependable, accurate readings.

sound level meter Meter that produces an immediate reading that represents the noise level at a specific instant in time.

Audiometric Testing

Audiometric testing measures the hearing threshold of employees. Tests conducted can detect changes in the hearing threshold of the employee. A negative change represents hearing loss within a given frequency range. The initial **audiogram** establishes a baseline hearing threshold. After that, audiometric testing should occur at least annually. Testing should not be done on an employee who has a cold or an ear infection or who has been exposed to noise levels exceeding 80 dB(A) within 14 to 16 hours prior to a test. Such conditions can produce invalid results.[7] When even small changes in an employee's hearing threshold are identified, more frequent tests should be scheduled.

audiometric testing Tests that measure the hearing threshold of employees.

audiogram The results of an audiometric test to determine the noise threshold at which a subject responds to different test frequencies.

Record Keeping

Figure 22–6 is an example of an audiometric form that can be used to record test results for individual employees. Such forms should be completed and kept on file to allow for sequential comparisons. It is also important to retain records containing a worker's employment history, including all past positions and the working conditions in those positions.

Follow-Up

Follow-up is critical. Failure to take prompt corrective action at the first sign of hearing loss can lead to permanent debilitating damage.

Hearing loss can occur without producing any evidence of physiological damage. Therefore, it is important to follow up on even the slightest evidence of a change in an employee's hearing threshold.

Figure 22–6 Sample audiometric test form.

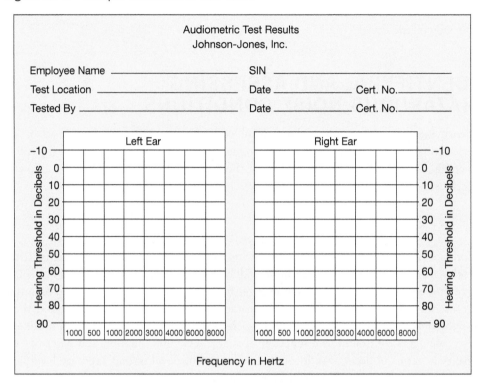

Follow-up can take a number of different forms, including these appropriate responses:

- Administering a retest to verify the hearing loss.

- Changing or improving the type of personal protection used.

- Conducting a new noise survey in the employee's work area to determine if engineering controls are sufficient.

- Testing other employees to determine if the hearing loss is isolated to the one employee in question or if other employees have been affected.

NOISE CONTROL STRATEGIES

Figure 22–7 illustrates the three components of a noise hazard. Noise can be reduced by engineering and administrative controls applied to one or more of these components. The most desirable noise controls are those that reduce noise at the source. The second priority

Figure 22–7 Three parts of a noise hazard.

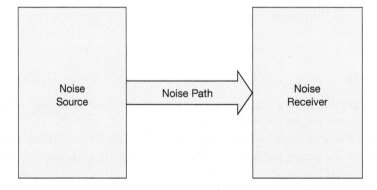

is to reduce noise along its path. The last resort is noise reduction at the receiver, using personal protective devices. The latter approach should never be substituted for the two former approaches.

The following paragraphs explain widely used strategies for reducing workplace noise at the source, along its path, and at the receiver:

- Noise can be reduced at its *source* by enclosing the source, altering the acoustical design at the source, substituting equipment that produces less noise, making alterations to existing equipment, or changing the process so that less noisy equipment can be used.

- Noise can be reduced along its *path* by moving the source farther away from receivers and improving the acoustical design of the path so that more sound is absorbed as it travels toward receivers.

- Noise can be reduced at the *receiver* by enclosing the worker, using personal protective devices, and changing job schedules so that exposure time is reduced.

Some of the noise reduction strategies explained in the preceding paragraphs are engineering controls; others are administrative controls. For example, enclosing a noise source and substituting less noisy equipment are both examples of engineering controls. Changing job schedules is an example of an administrative control. Health and safety professionals should be familiar with both types of controls.

Engineering Controls

Engineering controls consist of facility and equipment adjustments other than administrative and personal protection strategies made to reduce the noise level either at the source or within the worker's hearing zone. Following are some commonly used engineering controls. All these controls are designed to reduce noise at the source, along its path, or at the receiver. They focus primarily on the noise rather than on the employees who are exposed to it.

Maintenance

- Replacement or adjustment of worn, loose, or unbalanced parts of machines.
- Lubrication of machine parts and use of cutting oils.
- Use of properly shaped and sharpened cutting tools.

Substitution of machines

- Larger, slower machines for smaller, faster ones.
- Step dies for single-operation dies.
- Presses for hammers.
- Rotating shears for square shears.
- Hydraulic presses for mechanical presses.
- Belt drives for gears.

Substitution of processes

- Compression riveting for impact riveting.
- Welding for riveting.
- Hot working for cold working.
- Pressing for rolling or forging.

Reduce the driving force of vibrating surfaces by

- Reducing the forces used.
- Minimizing rotational speed.
- Isolating.

Reduce the response of vibrating surfaces by

- Damping.
- Additional support.
- Increasing the stiffness of the material.
- Increasing the mass of vibrating members.
- Changing the size to change resonance frequency.

Reduce the sound radiation from the vibrating surfaces by

- Reducing the radiating area.
- Reducing overall size.
- Perforating surfaces.

Reduce the sound transmission through solids by using

- Flexible mounting.
- Flexible sections in pipe runs.
- Flexible-shaft couplings.
- Fabric sections in ducts.
- Resilient flooring.

Reduce the sound produced by gas flow by

- Using intake and exhaust mufflers.
- Using fan blades designed to reduce turbulence.
- Using large, low-speed fans instead of smaller, high-speed fans.
- Reducing the velocity of fluid flow (air).
- Increasing the cross-section of streams.
- Reducing the pressure.
- Reducing the air turbulence.

Reduce noise transmission through air by

- Using sound-absorbent material on walls and ceilings in work areas.
- Using sound barriers and sound absorption along the transmission path.
- Completely enclosing individual machines.
- Using baffles.
- Confining high-noise machines to insulated rooms.[8]

Administrative Controls

Administrative controls are controls that reduce the exposure of employees to noise rather than reducing the noise. Administrative controls should be considered a second-level approach, with engineering controls given top priority. Smaller companies that cannot afford to reduce noise through engineering measures may use administrative controls instead. However, this approach should be avoided if at all possible.

Hearing Protection Devices

In addition to engineering and administrative controls, employees should be required to use appropriate *hearing protection devices (HPDs)*. It should be noted, however, that such devices are effective only if worn properly. Good hygiene practices are essential with the use, maintenance, and storage of any personal protective equipment, especially HPDs that enter the ear. Enforcement of the proper use of HPDs is difficult in some settings. The following four classifications of HPDs are widely used: enclosures, earplugs, superaural caps, and earmuffs.

Enclosures are devices that completely encompass the employee's head, much like the helmets worn by motorcycle riders.

Earplugs (also known as *aurals*) are devices that fit into the ear canal. *Custom-moulded earplugs* are designed and molded for the individual employee. *Premoulded earplugs* are generic in nature, are usually made of a soft rubber or plastic substance, and can be reused. *Formable earplugs* can be used by anyone. They are designed to be formed individually to a person's ears, used once, and then discarded.

Superaural caps fit over the external edge of the ear canal and are held in place by a headband.

Earmuffs, also known as *circumaurals*, cover the entire ear with a cushioned cup that is attached to a headband. Earplugs and earmuffs are able to reduce noise by 20 to 30 dB. By combining earplugs and earmuffs, an additional 3 to 5 dB of blockage can be gained.

Figures 22–8 through 22–10 are examples of various types of HPDs. Figure 22–8 illustrates ear, face, and head protection combined into one comprehensive device. Figure 22–9 contains two semi-insert earplugs which consist of two earplugs held over the ends of the ear canal by a rigid headband. Figure 22–10 displays soft, mouldable earplugs.

Figure 22–8 Earmuff-style HPD.

Chrisbrignell/Shutterstock

Figure 22–9 Canal-cap-style HPD.

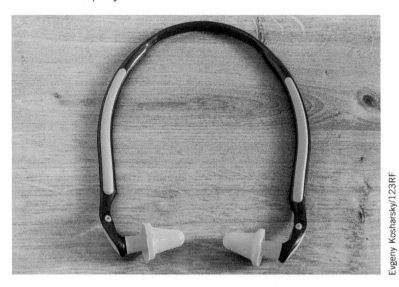

Evgeny Kosharsky/123RF

Figure 22–10 Earplug-style HPDs.

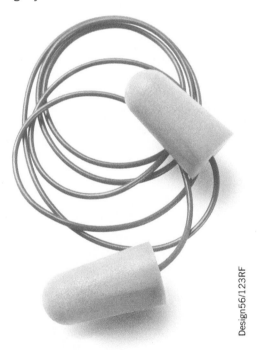

Design56/123RF

The effectiveness of HPDs can be enhanced through the use of technologies that reduce noise levels. These *active noise reduction (ANR)* technologies reduce noise by manipulating sound and signal waves. Such waves are manipulated by creating an electronic mirror image of sound waves that tends to cancel out the unwanted noise in the same way that negative numbers cancel out positive numbers in a mathematical equation. Using ANR in conjunction with enclosure devices or earmuffs can be an especially effective strategy.

Traditional, or passive, HPDs can distort or muffle sounds only at certain frequencies, particularly high-pitched sounds. *Flat-attenuation HPDs* solve this problem by using electronic devices to block all sound frequencies equally. This eliminates, or at least reduces, the distortion and muffling problems. Flat-attenuation HPDs are especially helpful for employees in settings where there is high-pitched sound that they should be able to hear, as well as for employees who have already begun to lose their ability to hear such sounds. The ability to hear high-pitched sounds is significant because warning signals and human voices can be high-pitched.

A benefit of ANR technologies is *optimization*. The amount of noise protection can be adjusted so that employees can hear as much as they should, but not too much. Too much noise can cause employees to suffer hearing loss. Too little noise can mean that they may not hear warning signals.

EVALUATING HEARING LOSS PREVENTION PROGRAMS

Hearing loss prevention programs should be evaluated periodically to ensure their effectiveness.[9] Such evaluations should have at least the following components: (1) training and education, (2) supervisor involvement, (3) noise measurement, (4) engineering and administrative controls, (5) monitoring and record keeping, (6) referrals, (7) hearing protection devices, and (8) administration. Following are checklists for each of these components.

Training and Education

Failures or deficiencies in hearing conservation programs (hearing loss prevention programs) can often be traced to inadequacies in the training and education of noise-exposed employees and those who conduct elements of the program.

- Has training been conducted at least once a year?
- Was the training provided by a qualified instructor?
- Was the success of each training program evaluated?
- Is the content revised periodically?
- Are managers and supervisors directly involved?

- Are posters, regulations, handouts, and employee newsletters used as supplements?
- Are personal counselling sessions conducted for employees having problems with hearing protection devices or showing hearing threshold shifts?

Supervisor Involvement

Data indicate that employees who refuse to wear hearing protectors or who fail to show up for hearing tests frequently work for supervisors who are not totally committed to the hearing conservation programs.

- Have supervisors been provided with the knowledge required to oversee the use and care of hearing protectors by subordinates?
- Do supervisors wear hearing protectors in appropriate areas?
- Have supervisors been counselled when employees resist wearing protectors or fail to show up for hearing tests?
- Are disciplinary actions enforced when employees repeatedly refuse to wear hearing protectors?

Noise Measurement

In order to be useful, noise measurements should be related to noise exposure risks and the prioritization of noise control efforts. In addition, the results should be communicated to the appropriate personnel, especially when follow-up actions are required.

- Were the essential or critical noise studies performed?
- Was the purpose of each noise study clearly stated? Have noise-exposed employees been notified of their exposures and apprised of auditory risks?
- Are the results routinely transmitted to supervisors and other key individuals?
- Are results entered into the health or medical records of noise-exposed employees?
- Are results entered into shop folders?
- If noise maps exist, are they used by the proper staff?
- Are noise measurement results considered when contemplating procurement of new equipment, modifying the facility, or relocating employees?
- Have there been changes in areas, equipment, or processes that have altered noise exposure? Have follow-up noise measurements been conducted?
- Are appropriate steps taken to include (or exclude) employees in the hearing loss prevention programs whose exposures have changed significantly?

Engineering and Administrative Controls

Controlling noise by engineering and administrative methods is often the most effective means of reducing or eliminating the hazard. In some cases, engineering controls will remove requirements for other components of the program, such as audiometric testing and the use of hearing protectors.

- Have noise control needs been prioritized?
- Has the cost effectiveness of various options been addressed?
- Are employees and supervisors apprised of plans for noise control measures?
- Are they consulted on various approaches?
- Will in-house resources or outside consultants perform the noise control measures?

- Have employees and supervisors been counselled on the operation and maintenance of noise control devices?
- Are noise control projects monitored to ensure timely completion?
- Has the full potential for administrative controls been evaluated? Are noisy processes conducted during shifts with fewer employees? Do employees have sound-treated lunch or break areas?

Monitoring Audiometry and Record Keeping

The skills of audiometric technicians, the status of the audiometer, and the quality of audiometric test records are crucial to hearing loss prevention program success. Useful information may be ascertained from the audiometric records as well as from the people who actually administer the tests.

- Has the audiometric technician been adequately trained, certified, and recertified as necessary?
- Do on-the-job observations of the technicians indicate that they perform a thorough and valid audiometric test, instruct and consult the employee effectively, and keep appropriate records?
- Are records complete?
- Are follow-up actions documented?
- Are hearing threshold levels reasonably consistent from test to test? If not, are the reasons for inconsistencies investigated promptly?
- Is the annual incidence of standard threshold shift greater than a few percent? If so, are problem areas pinpointed and remedial steps taken?
- Are audiometric trends (deteriorations) being identified, both in individuals and in groups of employees? (NIOSH recommends no more than 5 percent of workers showing 15 dB significant threshold shift, same ear, same frequency.)
- Do records show that appropriate audiometer calibration procedures have been followed?
- Is there documentation showing that the background sound levels in the audiometer room were low enough to permit valid testing?
- Are the results of audiometric tests being communicated to supervisors and managers as well as to employees?
- Has corrective action been taken if the rate of no-shows for audiometric test appointments is more than about 5 percent?
- Are employees incurring STS (significant threshold shift) notified in writing within at least 21 days? (NIOSH recommends immediate notification if retest shows 15 dB significant threshold shift, same ear, same frequency.)

Referrals

Referrals to outside sources for consultation or treatment are sometimes in order, but they can be an expensive element of the hearing loss prevention program and should not be undertaken unnecessarily.

- Are referral procedures clearly specified?
- Have letters of agreement between the company and consulting physicians or audiologists been executed?
- Have mechanisms been established to ensure that employees needing evaluation or treatment actually receive the service (e.g., transportation, scheduling, reminders)?

- Are records properly transmitted to the physician or audiologist, then back to the company?
- If medical treatment is recommended, does the employee understand the condition requiring treatment, the recommendation, and methods of obtaining such treatment?
- Are employees being referred unnecessarily?

Hearing Protection Devices

When noise control measures are not feasible, or until such time as they are installed, hearing protection devices are the only way to prevent hazardous levels of noise from damaging the inner ear. Making sure that these devices are worn effectively requires continuous attention on the part of supervisors and program implementers as well as noise-exposed employees.

- Have hearing protectors been made available to all employees whose daily average noise exposures are 85 dB(A) or above? (NIOSH recommends requiring HPD use if noises are equal to or exceed 85 dB(A) regardless of exposure time. To reduce the nonauditory effects of noise exposure, HPDs should be used any time the sound level is uncomfortable.)
- Are employees given the opportunity to select from a variety of appropriate protectors?
- Are employees fitted carefully with special attention to comfort?
- Are employees thoroughly trained, not only initially but at least once a year?
- Are the protectors checked regularly for wear or defects and replaced immediately if necessary?
- If employees use disposable hearing protectors, are replacements readily available?
- Do employees understand the appropriate hygiene requirements?
- Have any employees developed ear infections or irritations associated with the use of hearing protectors? Are there any employees who are unable to wear these devices because of medical conditions? Have these conditions been treated promptly and successfully?
- Have alternative types of hearing protectors been considered when problems with current devices are experienced?
- Do employees who incur noise-induced hearing loss receive intensive counselling?
- Are those who fit and supervise the wearing of hearing protectors competent to deal with the many problems that can occur?
- Do workers complain that protectors interfere with their ability to do their jobs? Are these complaints followed promptly with counselling, noise control, or other measures? Do protectors interfere with spoken instructions or warning signals?
- Are employees encouraged to take home their hearing protectors if they engage in noisy nonoccupational activities?
- Are potentially more effective protectors considered as they become available?
- Is the effectiveness of the hearing protector program evaluated regularly?
- Have at-the-ear protection levels been evaluated to ensure that either over- or underprotection has been adequately balanced according to the anticipated ambient noise levels?
- Is each hearing protector user required to demonstrate that he or she understands how to use and care for the protector? Are the results documented?

Administration

Keeping organized and staying current on administrative matters will help the program run smoothly.

- Have there been any changes in federal or provincial/territorial regulations? Have hearing loss prevention program policies been modified to reflect these changes?

- Are copies of company policies and guidelines regarding the hearing loss prevention program available in the offices that support the various program elements? Are those who implement the program elements aware of these policies? Do they comply?

- Are necessary materials and supplies being ordered with a minimum of delay?

- Are procurement officers refusing the hearing loss prevention program implementer's requests for specific hearing protectors or other hearing loss prevention equipment? If so, have corrective steps been taken?

- Is the performance of key personnel evaluated periodically? If such performance is found to be less than acceptable, are steps taken to correct the situation?

- Has the failure to hear warning shouts or alarms been tied to any accidents or injuries? If so, have remedial steps been taken?

OTHER EFFECTS OF NOISE HAZARDS

Hearing loss is the principal concern of health and safety professionals relating to noise hazards. However, hearing loss is not the only detrimental effect of excess noise. Noise can also cause communication problems, isolation, and productivity problems. According to S. L. Smith,

> Workers in noisy environments, even those where the noise is not loud enough to require hearing protection, often have trouble communicating with co-workers and supervisors. It is difficult for them to hear warning bells and signals, and they generally can't hold conversations with co-workers.[10]

Noise can also be detrimental to productivity by interfering with an employee's ability to think, reason, and solve problems. Not all employees respond to noise in this way, but many do. Can you concentrate on your studies in a noisy room? Some students can, whereas others cannot. If excessive noise makes it difficult for you to study, you will probably have the same problem on the job.

Isolation is another problem for some employees in a noisy environment. According to Smith, "While some workers benefit from the isolation provided by noise, it can have a significantly negative impact on employees who must act as a group or who must communicate frequently with supervisors or co-workers."[11] They can begin to feel left out and uninformed, the antithesis of the goal of a modern teamwork-oriented organization.

VIBRATION HAZARDS

Vibration hazards are closely associated with noise hazards because tools that produce vibration typically also produce excessive levels of noise. The strategies for protecting employees against the noise associated with vibrating tools are the same as those presented so far in this chapter. This section focuses on the other health and safety hazards associated with vibration.

Eastman explains the problems associated with vibration:

> Vibration-related problems are not only serious, they are widespread. Donald Wasserman, author of *Human Aspects of Occupational Vibration*, says that up to 8 million workers are exposed to some type of vibration hazard. Of these, it has been estimated that more than half will show some signs of injury.[12]

The types of injuries associated with vibration depend on its source. For example, workers who operate heavy equipment often experience vibration over the whole body. This can lead to problems ranging from motion sickness to spinal injury. However, the most common vibration-related problem is known as **hand-arm vibration syndrome (HAV)**. Eastman describes HAV as follows:

> The condition, a form of Raynaud's Syndrome, strikes an alarming number of workers who use vibrating power tools day in and day out as part of their jobs. For HAV sufferers, . . . the sensations in their hands are more than just minor, temporary discomforts. They are symptoms of the potentially irreversible damage their nerves and blood vessels have suffered. As the condition progresses, it takes less and less exposure to vibration or cold to trigger the symptoms, and the symptoms themselves become more severe and crippling.[13]

Environmental conditions and worker habits can exacerbate the problems associated with vibration. For example, working with vibrating tools in a cold environment is more dangerous than working with the same tools in a warm environment. Gripping a vibrating tool tightly will lead to problems sooner than using a loose grip. Smoking and excessive noise also increase the potential for HAV and other vibration-related injuries. What all of these conditions and habits have in common is that they constrict blood vessels, which in turn restricts blood flow to the affected part of the body.[14]

Injury Prevention Strategies

Modern health and safety professionals should know how to prevent vibration-related injuries. Prevention is especially important with HAV because the disease is thought to be irreversible. This does not mean that HAV cannot be treated. It can, but the treatments developed to date only reduce the symptoms. They do not cure the disease.

Following are prevention strategies that can be used by health and safety professionals in any company regardless of its size:

Purchase low-vibration tools Low-vibration tools are becoming more commonplace. Pneumatic tools are very popular in most industrial settings because of their high power, low cost, and low maintenance, but they have historically produced excessive noise and vibration. By implementing low-vibration technology into the design of high-quality power tools, vibration hazards have been dramatically reduced. Vibration abatement may be achieved through the design incorporated into the tool or through energy-absorbing handles, counterweights, or gloves. While energy-absorbing tools are generally more expensive, most trades workers choose this superior equipment for overall comfort and job satisfaction.

Limit employee exposure Although a correlation between cumulative exposure to vibration and the onset of HAV has not been scientifically quantified, there is strong suspicion in the health and safety community that such a link exists. For example, NIOSH recommends that companies limit the exposure of their employees to no more than 4 hours per day, 2 days per week.[15] Until the correlation between cumulative exposure and HAV has been quantified, health and safety professionals are well advised to apply the NIOSH recommendation.

Change employee work habits Employees can play a key role in protecting themselves if they know how. Health and safety professionals should teach employees who use vibration-producing tools the work habits that will protect them from HAV and other injuries. These work habits include the following: (1) wearing properly fitting thick gloves that can partially absorb vibration, (2) taking periodic breaks (at least 10 minutes every hour), (3) using a loose grip on the tool and holding it away from the body, (4) keeping tools properly maintained (i.e., replacing vibration-absorbing pads regularly), (5) keeping warm, and (6) using vibration-absorbing floor mats and seat covers as appropriate.[16]

Modern health and safety professionals should also encourage upper management to require careful screening of applicants for jobs involving the use of vibration-producing tools and equipment. Applicants who smoke or have other conditions that constrict blood vessels should be guided away from jobs that involve excessive vibration.

SUMMARY

1. *Sound* is any change in pressure that can be detected by the ear. Typically, sound is a change in air pressure. However, it can also be a change in water pressure or any other pressure-sensitive medium. The unit of measurement for sound is the decibel, or one-tenth of a bel.

2. The *threshold of hearing* is the weakest sound that can be detected by the human ear. The maximum sound that can be perceived without experiencing pain is known as the *threshold of pain.*

3. *Noise* is unwanted sound. Industrial noise is classified as *wide band noise, narrow band noise,* and *impulse noise.*

4. Several different factors affect the risk of hearing loss from excessive noise: (a) intensity of the noise, (b) frequency of the noise, (c) type of noise, (d) duration of daily exposure, (e) total duration of exposure, (f) age of the individual, (g) coexisting hearing disease, (h) nature of the environment, (i) distance of the receiver from the noise source, and (j) position of the ears relative to the sound waves.

5. Noise levels of less than 80 dB(A) are considered safe. A level of 85 dB(A) should be considered the maximum limit of continuous exposure over 8 hours without protection.

6. The exchange rate indicates the increase in sound level that is permitted as the time of exposure is halved. A lower exchange rate provides a greater degree of hearing protection.

7. Methods for identifying and assessing hazardous noise conditions include the following: (a) noise surveys, (b) audiometric tests, (c) record keeping, and (d) follow-up.

8. Noise reduction strategies are of three types: those that reduce noise at the source, those that reduce noise along its path, and those that reduce noise at the receiver.

9. Noise can be reduced by applying either engineering or administrative controls. Engineering controls attempt to reduce noise. Administrative controls limit human exposure to noise.

10. Vibration can cause physical problems ranging from motion sickness to spinal injury to hand-arm vibration syndrome (HAV). HAV is the most widespread of these problems. Because the physical damage associated with HAV may be irreversible, prevention is especially important.

11. HAV prevention strategies include purchasing low-vibration tools, limiting employee exposure, and changing employee work habits.

12. Hearing loss prevention programs should be evaluated periodically in the following areas: (a) training and education, (b) supervisor involvement, (c) noise measurement, (d) engineering and administrative controls, (e) monitoring and record keeping, (f) referrals, (g) hearing protection devices, and (h) administration.

Key Terms and Concepts

Audiogram
Audiometric testing
Decibel (dB)
Exchange rate
Hand-arm vibration
   syndrome (HAV)

Hazardous noise
Impulse noise
Narrow band noise
Noise
Sound
Sound-level meter

Threshold of hearing
Threshold of pain
Vibration
Wide band noise

Review Questions

1. Define the term *sound*.

2. What is the difference between sound and noise?

3. Differentiate between sound and vibration.

4. Describe the relationship between the pitch of sound and the cycle of sound waves.

5. List and briefly explain the three broad types of industrial noise.

6. Describe the various physiological problems associated with excessive noise.

7. List four factors that affect the risk of hearing loss from exposure to excessive noise.

8. At what sound level is it necessary to begin using some type of personal protection?

9. What are two precautions that should be considered when using HPDs?

10. Differentiate between engineering and administrative controls.

11. Define the following terms: *noise survey*, *audiometric testing*, and *follow-up*.

12. List three appropriate follow-up activities when an audiometric test reveals hearing loss in an employee.

13. Explain the four classifications of HPDs that are widely used.

14. Explain the main components of an evaluation of a hearing loss prevention program.

15. What is HAV? How can it be prevented?

Weblinks

Canadian Centre for Occupational Health and Safety

www.ccohs.ca/oshanswers/phys_agents

This CCOHS site has information to assist employers and workers in the recognition, assessment, and control of noise in the workplace.

Canadian Hearing Society

www.chs.ca

The Canadian Hearing Society provides services for those who are deaf, deafened, or hard of hearing. This website contains information on hearing and hearing loss prevention.

Noise Pollution Clearinghouse

www.nonoise.org

On this website you can find news and articles on different noise sources and links to those who control, monitor, and study noise pollution.

Endnotes

[1] National Institute for Occupational Safety and Hearing (NIOSH). *A Practical Guide to Preventing Hearing Loss*. Publication 96–110 (Washington, DC: NIOSH, 1999), 2. [Online]. Available: http://www.cdc.gov/niosh/96–110a.html.

[2] Ibid.

[3] J. B. Olishifski (revised by J. J. Standard). *Fundamentals of Industrial Hygiene* (Chicago: National Safety Council, 1996), 171.

[4] NIOSH. *A Practical Guide*, 4.

[5] Canadian Centre for Occupational Health and Safety. (June 3, 1999). "OHS Answers." [Online]. Available: http://www.ccohs.ca/oshanswers/phys_agents/non_auditory.html. (Retrieved December 28, 2004).

[6] NIOSH. *A Practical Guide*, 8.

[7] Ibid., 12.

[8] Olishifski. *Fundamentals of Industrial Hygiene*, 179.

[9] NIOSH. *A Practical Guide*, Appendix B, 1–6.

[10] S. L. Smith. "The 'Other' Effects of Noise." *Occupational Hazards* (January 1997): 79.

[11] Ibid.

[12] M. Eastman. "Vibration Shakes Workers." *Safety & Health* 143, no. 5: 32.

[13] Ibid.

[14] Ibid., 32–33.

[15] Ibid., 33.

[16] Ibid., 35.

Part 4
Contemporary Issues in Health and Safety

Chapter 23
Psychological Health and Safety

MAJOR TOPICS

- Psychological Health and Safety Defined
- The State of Psychological Health and Safety in Canada
- The Case for Psychological Health and Safety in Canada
- National Standard for Psychological Health and Safety in the Workplace
- Workplace Stress Defined
- Sources of Workplace Stress
- Human Reactions to Workplace Stress
- Measurement of Workplace Stress
- Shift Work, Stress, and Safety
- Improving Safety by Reducing Workplace Stress
- Safety Managers and Stress
- Post-Traumatic Stress Disorder (PTSD)
- Psychological Hazard Assessment

psychological health A state of well-being in which an individual realizes his or her own abilities, can cope with the normal stresses of life, can work productively, and is able to make a contribution to his or her community.

psychological safety A state of being protected from hazards that could affect psychological health.

The workplace plays an important role in the state of our **psychological health**. Since most adults spend the majority of their waking hours at work, the workplace can have a strong positive effect on our health, psychological health, and overall well-being. On the other hand, workplaces can be excessively stressful or toxic environments that contribute to the increasing prevalence of mental health problems and illnesses. The role of addressing these workplace challenges is increasingly placed upon health and safety professionals. As the focus on protecting workers' health and safety expands to include psychological health and safety, it is imperative that health and safety professionals are familiar with the issues surrounding mental health and the strategies to promote psychological health to ensure **psychological safety** in the workplace.

PSYCHOLOGICAL HEALTH AND SAFETY DEFINED

The terms *psychological* and *mental* are used synonymously in most literature and throughout this text. Good psychological health is a healthy state of mental well-being in which one can function normally in society and during everyday events. Psychological health is promoted and maintained by organizations through policies and programs that engage and empower the worker in respectful ways. Individuals take care of their psychological health through numerous choices, such as maintaining good relationships, exercise, work-life balance, and lifestyle choices that do not include recreational drugs or excessive alcohol consumption.

Psychological safety involves taking precautions to prevent harm to a person's psychological health. Organizations can enhance psychological safety through programs and policies that match assigned work to the workers' abilities; provide a comfortable work environment; acknowledge accomplishments; engage workers in decision-making; and deem any bullying, harassment, or violence unacceptable.

Shain defines a **psychologically safe workplace** as one that "does not permit harm to employee mental health in careless, negligent, reckless, or intentional ways." More simply, it is "one in which every practical effort is made to avoid reasonably foreseeable injury to the mental health of employees."[1] Mental health is an integral and essential component of **health**. The World Health Organization (WHO) constitution states, "Health is a state of complete physical, mental and social well-being, and not merely the absence of disease or infirmity." An important implication of this definition is that mental health is more than just the absence of mental disorders or disabilities.[2]

Exposure to acute psychological trauma or chronic exposure to less severe stressors in the workplace can have a profound effect on psychological health. When an event, action, neglect, or situation degrades psychological health, the worker may suffer a **psychological injury**. This is not to be confused with normal mood fluctuations and responses to daily stressors. For example, feeling upset, stressed, or even overwhelmed by an assignment would not necessarily constitute a psychological injury. However, if the ongoing exposure to these factors results in the development of post-traumatic stress disorder (PTSD), anxiety disorders, depression, or other mood disorders, we would then have a psychological injury.

psychologically safe workplace A workplace that does not permit harm to employee mental health in careless, negligent, reckless, or intentional ways.

health A state of complete physical, mental, and social well-being, and not merely the absence of disease or infirmity.

psychological injury When the exposure to a traumatic event, situation, or ongoing bullying or harassment causes a worker's psychological health to decline.

THE STATE OF PSYCHOLOGICAL HEALTH AND SAFETY IN CANADA

Each year, almost 7 million (or 1 in 5) Canadians experience a psychological health issue or illness. To further put this number in perspective, 2.2 million (or 1 in 15) have type 2 diabetes and 1.4 million (or 1 in 24) are living with heart disease. A March 2017 news release by the World Health Organization (WHO) stated that depression is the leading cause of ill health and disability worldwide. According to the same report, more than 300 million people are now living with depression, an increase of more than 18 percent between 2005 and 2015.[3]

Seventy percent of Canadian employees are concerned about the psychological health and safety of their workplaces, and 14 percent don't think theirs is healthy or safe at all. Such workplaces can take a detrimental personal toll as well as contribute to staggering economic costs. About 30 percent of short- and long-term disability claims in Canada are attributed to mental health problems and illnesses. The total cost from mental health problems to the Canadian economy exceeds $50 billion annually.[4]

In a 2012 news release, the Centre for Addictions and Mental Health (CAMH) reported the following statistics, cited from numerous sources, that show the scope of the mental health challenges we face in Canada. Listed below are just a sample of the points made:

- Young people aged 15 to 24 are more likely to experience mental illness and/or substance use disorders than any other age group.

- People with substance use problems are up to 3 times more likely to have a mental illness. More than 15 percent of people with a substance use problem have a co-occurring mental illness.
- People with mental illness and addictions are more likely to die prematurely than the general population.

According to a 2008 survey, 42 percent of Canadians were unsure whether they would socialize with a friend who has a mental illness.

- 70 percent believe attitudes about mental health issues have changed for the better compared to 5 years ago.
- 40 percent of respondents to a 2016 survey agreed they have experienced feelings of anxiety or depression but never sought medical help for it because of the stigma associated with these issues.
- Of Canadians aged 15 or older who report having a mental health need in the past year, one-third state that their needs were not fully met.
- The Mental Health Strategy for Canada recommends raising the proportion of health spending that is devoted to mental health to 9 percent by 2022.
- Individuals with a mental illness are much less likely to be employed. Unemployment rates are as high as 70 to 90 percent for people with the most severe mental illnesses.
- In any given week, at least 500,000 employed Canadians are unable to work due to mental health problems.
- The cost of a disability leave for a mental illness is about double the cost of a leave due to a physical illness.
- A small proportion of all health care patients account for a disproportionately large share of health care costs. Patients with high mental health costs incur over 30 percent more costs than other high-cost patients.

THE CASE FOR PSYCHOLOGICAL HEALTH AND SAFETY IN CANADA

The preceding points make a strong case for addressing the psychological health and safety challenges we face in Canadian workplaces. Guarding Minds @ Work (GM@W) examines the reasons why employers should assess and address the psychological health and safety of their organizations. In their approach, GM@W presents a case to address the health, business, and legal obligations related to psychological health and safety in the workplace.[5]

Mental health and well-being are fundamental to our collective and individual ability as humans to think, emote, interact, earn a living, and enjoy life. On this basis, the promotion, protection, and restoration of mental health can be regarded as a vital concern of individuals, communities, and societies throughout the world.[6]

Health Case

Linkages between psychological and physical health have been known and studied for decades. People with a long-term medical condition such as chronic pain are much more likely to also experience mood disorders. Conversely, people with a mood disorder are at much higher risk of developing a long-term medical condition. Mental illness can cut 10 to 20 years from a person's life expectancy.

In the section on stress, later in the chapter, we will discuss the physiological impact that psychological stress has on the worker. Like our physical health, our psychological health is determined by individual and environmental factors, including:

- Family history of illness and disease
- Health behaviours (e.g., smoking, exercise, substance use)

- Exposure to toxins
- Genetics
- Personal life circumstances and history
- Access to supports (e.g., timely healthcare, social connections)[7]

Business Case

Employee psychological health can have a profound positive or negative effect on the organization. A growing body of international evidence demonstrates that promotion, prevention, and early intervention show positive returns on investment.[8]

If employees' psychological health is degraded, the business may be impacted in the following ways:

- **Financial.** As noted above, depression and anxiety are rapidly becoming the main cause of disability in developed countries. Employers are facing increased disability premiums, rising health and benefits costs, and expenses associated with replacing absent employees.

- **Productivity.** In addition to absenteeism, psychological ill health is a significant contributor to **presenteeism**. That is, decreases in performance due to illness or injury while an employee is still at work. A recent study found that, compared to a variety of common disorders (e.g., asthma, migraine, arthritis), depression caused the greatest decline in work productivity and focus.

  presenteeism The act of being present at work but with reduced productivity, often due to ill health.

- **Safety.** The state of one's psychological health can contribute to accidents, incidents, and injuries. Most jobs require employees to have good concentration, social skills, and the ability to solve problems effectively. When these skills are undermined by mental health conditions, coworkers, customers, and employees are at risk of serious, and sometimes dire, outcomes.

- **Workplace morale.** Changes in a worker's behaviour or performance due to psychological health problems can be viewed as intentional or malicious. The resulting misunderstanding, resentment, and degraded relationships can erode workplace morale and, in turn, contribute to absenteeism and employee turnover.[9]

On the other hand, a psychologically healthy and safe workplace has meaningful benefits for organizations, including:

- **Improved recruitment and retention.** In today's job market, employees have higher expectations for their jobs. By providing a psychologically safe workplace, employers create and sustain a "great place to work" and will attract and keep the best workers.

- **Improved employee engagement.** An engaged employee is someone fully involved in, and enthusiastic about, his or her work. When employees are engaged, they view their interests as aligned with those of the company. They are more willing to extend an extra effort to assist clients, customers, and their colleagues. The net result is improved performance, productivity, and quality of goods and services.

- **Improved sustainability.** Organizations with psychologically healthy employees are more resilient and better equipped to survive and thrive when facing challenges.

- **Improved health and safety.** One of the fundamental needs we have is for physical safety. When workers know their health and safety is being protected, they can build better relationships, focus on their assigned work, and provide greater support for colleagues who might face psychological challenges.[10]

By taking purposeful action to control psychological hazards in the workplace, employers, human resource managers, and safety professionals will see tangible improvements in their business operations. Some data to measure and demonstrate positive improvements can be made by tracking the following metrics:

- Absenteeism rates
- Benefits costs
- Turnover rates
- Accident and injury rates
- Workers' compensation claims
- Disability rates[11]

Legal Case

While some jurisdictions have explicit provisions in their OHS legislation for the protection of workers' psychological health and safety, others may seek protection through general duty clauses or rely on other legal sources, such as employment standards or human rights. This lack of a clear standard creates a challenge for stakeholders. Decades ago, we were at the infancy of developing standards, best practises, and guidelines to protect workers' physical health. Today we are at a similar point in the evolution of psychological health and safety in the workplace. However, increasing pressure is mounting from numerous sources to create a new acceptable standard of conduct at work for the protection of workers' psychological health and safety.

This standard requires that people treat one another with fairness, civility, and respect regardless of their power or status within the organization. The overall effect of the new legal standards is that types of conduct that would most likely have been tolerated in the workplace even 5 years ago are no longer acceptable to the majority of judges and arbitrators. Given this, it is in employers' best interest to act in a proactive manner to prevent the risk of legal consequences.[12]

Discussion papers, reports, and commentaries by Dr. Martin Shain, written for the Mental Health Commission of Canada and Great-West Life, are widely believed to be the most influential work on the contemporary approach to psychological health and safety in the workplace. In his *Tracking the Perfect Legal Storm*, he describes the convergence of the seven legal sources of duty to provide a psychologically safe workplace.[13] See Figure 23–1.

Figure 23–1   Legal sources of duty to provide a psychologically safe workplace.

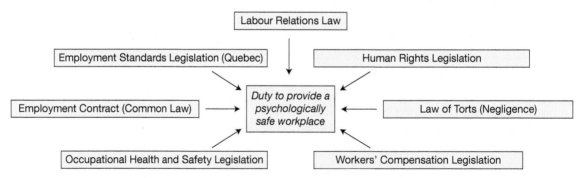

Source: Martin Shain, S.J.D. (May 2010) *Tracking the Perfect Legal Storm: Converging Systems Create Mounting Pressure to Create the Psychologically Safe Workplace.* An Update to "Stress, Mental Injury and the Law in Canada: A Discussion Paper for the Mental Health Canada 2009." Used with permission from Mental Health Commission of Canada.

Being passive or turning a blind eye to harassment, bullying, or violence in the workplace will no longer suffice as an adequate defense. Employers must proactively assess and control psychological hazards as they would any physical hazards in the workplace. The seven areas of law, as identified by Shain, that strengthen the duty to provide and maintain a psychologically safe workplace are summarized below:

1. **Human Rights Legislation.** Employers who discover that an employee is suffering from clinical depression have a duty to accommodate that employee to a reasonable degree, even in the absence of medical evidence. A provincial appeals court held that the general duty to accommodate applies even when the complainant does not declare his or her existing mental disability before being hired.

2. **Workers' Compensation Law.** The traditional refusal to accept claims for compensation of mental injury resulting in whole or in part from "gradual onset stress" (chronic stress) appears to be changing. The higher standard of proof in legislative provisions has been characterized as discrimination based on mental disability, and has been the target of a successful Canadian Charter of Rights and Freedoms challenge.

3. **The Law of Torts (Common Law).** Courts are on the brink of extending the reach of the torts of negligent and intentional suffering to govern the employment relationship as a whole, not just at the point where it is being dissolved. This makes the quality of the employment relationship in its entire course a target for legal intervention.

4. **Employment Contract.** The employment contract is evolving as judges allow so that it contains an implied duty to protect employee mental health, which is deemed to be included in the requirement that employers act in good faith at all stages of the employment relationship. Many employers will be interested to learn that a judge has found that certain overtime policies create systemic problems that contribute to a culture of overwork that affects every employee. Creating, by policy, a work environment in which overwork is encouraged represents a breach of the duty of good faith.

5. **Labour Law.** Arbitrators now routinely import implied terms for the protection of mental health into collective agreements. This labour law shield offers an impressive array of remedies to employees with claims of harassment and other forms of abuse. Labour law is also evolving as it struggles with balancing the rights of employees with mental disorders and the needs of employers to manage and direct work. "Hybrid" solutions that give direction to both the employee and employer are one method used to address these complex situations.

6. **Occupational Health and Safety Law.** Occupational health and safety law across the country is becoming more consistent in its application to psychological safety through various amendments to governing legislation. In most jurisdictions, harassment and violence have been added to the legislation as areas to which the general duty of due diligence applies.

7. **Employment Standards.** Quebec has led the country in placing protection from harassment at work and regulation of harm to mental health in general in the context of employment standards. Quebec case law also leads in detailing the boundary between frivolous and serious claims of mental injury. A relatively recent development in the realm of employment standards is legislation dealing with accessibility and treatment of those with mental disorders.[14]

NATIONAL STANDARD FOR PSYCHOLOGICAL HEALTH AND SAFETY IN THE WORKPLACE

Converging liabilities outlined by Dr. Martin Shain in the previous section created a raised awareness of employers' obligation to address the issue. The Canadian Mental Health Association (CMHA) commissioned the CSA Group to create the National Standard for Psychological Health and Safety in the Workplace. The content of the Standard was developed by a technical committee consisting of volunteers with significant experience and expertise in this subject matter. The membership included employers, organized labour, service providers, general interest (e.g., workplace mental health specialists), regulatory authorities, insurance providers, health and safety professionals, executives, government representatives, and experts in law and policy.

Launched in January 2013, the *National Standard of Canada for Psychological Health and Safety in the Workplace* is a set of voluntary guidelines, tools, and resources intended to guide organizations in promoting mental health and preventing psychological harm at work. The standard identifies thirteen workplace factors that impact psychological health. When assessing workplace hazards, organizations are asked to consider how each of the following items are addressed:

1. Psychological support
2. Organizational culture
3. Clear leadership and expectations
4. Civility and respect
5. Psychological job demands
6. Growth and development
7. Recognition and reward
8. Involvement and influence
9. Workload management
10. Engagement
11. Work/life balance
12. Psychological protection
13. Protection of physical safety

WORKPLACE STRESS DEFINED

Stress is a pathological, and therefore generally undesirable human reaction to psychological, social, occupational, or environmental stimuli.[15] Stress has been defined as the reaction of the human organism to a threatening situation.[16] The stressor is an external stimulus, and **stress** is the response of the human body to this stimulus.

stress A pathological, and therefore generally undesirable, human reaction to psychological, social, occupational, or environmental stimuli.

workplace stress The harmful physical and emotional responses that occur when the requirements of the job do not match the capabilities, resources, or needs of the worker.

This is a clinical definition of stress. Other definitions relate more directly to **workplace stress**. The National Institute for Occupational Safety and Health (NIOSH) defines job stress as "the harmful physical and emotional responses that occur when the requirements of the job do not match the capabilities, resources, or needs of the worker."[17]

Corporations tend to see stress as an individual-based problem that is rooted in an employee's lifestyle, psychological makeup, and personality. Unions view stress as the result of excessive demands, poor supervision, or conflicting demands.[18] According to Singer, "The best definition probably includes both sets of factors."[19]

However it is defined, stress is a serious problem in the modern workplace. In fact, The Canadian Health Association estimates that workplace stress and related illnesses cost the economy approximately $51 billion a year.[20]

Workplace stress involves the emotional state resulting from a perceived difference between the level of occupational demand and a person's ability to cope with this demand. Because preparations and emotions are involved, workplace stress is considered a subjective state. An environment that a worker finds to be stressful may generate feelings of tension, anger, fatigue, confusion, and anxiety.

Workplace stress is primarily a matter of person–workload fit. The status of the person–workload fit can influence the acceptance of the work and the level of acceptable performance of that work. The perception of workload may be affected by the worker's needs and his or her level of job satisfaction. The relationship between job demands and the worker's ability to meet those demands further influences workplace stress. Because workplace stress may be felt differently by different people in similar situations, it must be concluded that there are many causes of workplace stress.

SOURCES OF WORKPLACE STRESS

The sources of on-the-job stress may involve physical working conditions, work overload, **role ambiguity**, lack of **feedback**, personality, personal and family problems, or role conflict. These and other sources of workplace stress are discussed in the following paragraphs.

- *Task complexity* relates to the number of different demands made on the worker. A job perceived as being too complex may cause feelings of inadequacy that result in emotional stress. Conversely, repetitive and monotonous work may lack complexity, so that the worker becomes bored and dissatisfied with the job and experiences stress associated with the boredom.

- *Control* over the job assignment can also be a source of workplace stress. Most workers experience less stress when they participate in determining the work routine, including schedule and selection of tasks. Several studies have indicated that workers prefer to take control of their job assignments and that they experience less workload stress if given this opportunity.[21] A related source of stress that has been introduced in the age of high technology is from electronic monitoring. According to a study conducted at the University of Wisconsin at Madison, "Video display terminal workers who are electronically monitored suffered greater health problems than those who are not."[22]

- A *feeling of responsibility* for the safety of the general public has also been shown to be a stressor. Air traffic controllers are known to experience intense stress when their responsibility for public safety is tested by a near-accident event. A feeling of great responsibility associated with a job can transform a routine activity into a stress-inducing task.

- *Job security* involves the risk of unemployment. A worker who believes that his or her job is in jeopardy will experience anxiety and stress. The ready availability of other rewarding employment and a feeling that one's professional skills are needed reduce the stress associated with job security issues.

- An *organizational culture* that leaves an employee feeling left out, out of the loop, or ill-informed can cause stress. Organizations in which managers fail to communicate frequently and effectively with employees are creating high-stress environments for workers.

- *Work schedules* that are unpredictable, never-changing, or ever-changing can induce stress in employees. Employees have lives outside their jobs. Consequently, the ability to predict their work schedules is important. When work schedules are unpredictable, stress increases. Stress also increases when work schedules are inflexible—they cannot be changed no matter what other obligation the employee might have. On the other hand, ever-changing work schedules such as those associated with shift work can also increase the level of employee stress. The big-picture issue with regard to work schedules is the level of control employees have over their lives. The less control, the more stress.

- *Home and family problems* can create added stress for workers. There was a time when employees were expected to "leave their problems at the front door" when they came to work. This, of course, is a practical impossibility. The demands of raising children, working out of the home, job schedules, dealing with the conflicting agendas inherent in dual-career households, and otherwise handling the everyday work and home conflicts that inevitably arise can markedly increase an employee's stress level.

role ambiguity The condition that occurs when an employee is not clear concerning the parameters, reporting requirements, authority, or responsibilities of his or her job.

feedback An employee's opinion of a project or an employer's opinion about an employee's job performance.

task complexity The number of different demands made on the worker.

control When an employee participates in determining the work routine, including schedule and selection of tasks.

feeling of responsibility Being responsible for the welfare of his or her family may cause a worker to feel that options to take employment risks are limited.

job security The risk of unemployment and the accompanying sense—real or imagined—of having the potential for longevity in a job and having a measure of control concerning that longevity.

- *Work relationships* can lead to on-the-job stress. People are social beings by nature. They like to get along with those they spend a lot of time with. However, office politics, turf battles, and internal competition for recognition and rewards can be hard on work relationships. When employees do not get along with their fellow workers, stress levels increase.

- *Human resource management (HRM) issues* can be a source of workplace stress. People who work have a vested interest in their wages, salaries, working conditions, and benefits. If even one of these factors is a negative, employee stress levels can increase significantly. In addition to these factors, other stress-inducing HRM issues include underemployment, failure to get promoted, and working in a position that is clearly not valued by management.

- *Workload demands* can stimulate stress when they are perceived as being overwhelming. These demands may involve time constraints and cognitive constraints such as speed of decision-making and mandates for attention. Workload demands may also be physically overwhelming if the worker is poorly matched to the physical requirements of the job or is fatigued. Whenever the worker believes the workload to be too demanding, stress can result.

- *Psychological support* from managers and coworkers gives a feeling of acceptance and belonging and helps defuse stress. A lack of such support may increase the perception of a burdensome workload and result in greater levels of stress.

- The lack of *environmental safety* can also be a cause of stress. Feeling that one is in danger can be a stressor. Workers need to feel safe from environmental hazards such as extreme temperatures, pressure, electricity, fire, explosives, toxic materials, ionizing radiation, noises, and dangerous machinery. To reduce the potential for stress due to environmental hazards, workers should feel that their managers are committed to safety and that their company has an effective safety program.

Common Causes of Stress in the Workplace

A life insurance company poll of workers found that workplace stress may be caused by:

- The company was recently purchased by another company.
- Downsizing or layoffs have occurred in the past year.
- Employee benefits were significantly cut recently.
- Mandatory overtime is frequently required.
- Employees have little control over how they do their work.
- The consequences of making a mistake on the job are severe.
- Workloads vary greatly.
- Most work is machine-paced or fast-paced.
- Workers must react quickly and accurately to changing conditions.
- Personal conflicts on the job are common.
- Few opportunities for advancement are available.
- Workers cope with a great deal of bureaucracy in getting work done.
- Staffing, money, or technology is inadequate.
- Pay is below the going rate.
- Employees are rotated among shifts.[23]

It has long been known among health and safety professionals and practitioners of occupational medicine that stress can have a detrimental effect on attendance, productivity, employee retention, and morale. The sources of stress contained in this list are just some of the more common ones. There are many others. For example, technological developments have increased stress levels on the job.

The fact that cell phones can be obnoxiously intrusive and distracting has tended to increase stress levels at work. Continual change in the field of computer technology—change that forces workers to upgrade their skills almost as soon as they become comfortable with a given software package—has become a source of stress in the workplace. Stress has become such an all-pervasive source of health-and-safety-related problems that professionals in the field must acknowledge it and work to reduce its harmful effects like any other workplace hazard.

HUMAN REACTIONS TO WORKPLACE STRESS

Human reactions to workplace stress may be grouped into the following categories: subjective or emotional (anxiety, aggression, or guilt), behavioural (being prone to accidents or trembling), cognitive (inability to concentrate or make decisions), physiological (increased heart rate or blood pressure), and organizational (absenteeism or poor productivity). Continual or persistent stress has been linked to many physiological problems.[24] Initially, the effects may be psychosomatic, but with continued stress, the symptoms show up as actual organic dysfunction. The most common forms of stress-related diseases are gastrointestinal, particularly gastric or duodenal ulcers. Research has also linked some autoimmune diseases with increased long-term workplace stress.[25]

The human response to workplace stress can be compared to a rubber band being stretched. As the stress continues to be applied, the rubber band stretches until a limit is reached when the rubber band breaks. For humans, various physical and psychological changes are observed with the repetitive stimuli of stress. Until the limit is reached, the harmful effects can be reversed. With an increase in intensity or duration of the stress beyond the individual's limit, the effects on the human become pathological.

Hans Selye identified three stages of the human stress response: (1) alarm, (2) resistance, and (3) exhaustion.[26] The alarm reaction occurs when the stress of a threat is sensed. The **stage of alarm** is characterized by pallor, sweating, and an increased heart rate. This stage is usually short. It prepares the body for whatever action is necessary.

stage of alarm Characterized by pallor, sweating, and an increased heart rate.

When the stress is maintained, the **stage of resistance** initiates a greater physical response. The alarm symptoms dissipate and the body develops an adaptation to the stress. The capacity for adaptation during this stage is, however, limited.

stage of resistance The alarm symptoms dissipate and the body develops an adaptation to the stress.

Eventually, with sustained stress, the **stage of exhaustion** is reached. This stage is demonstrated by the body's failure to adapt to the continued stress. Psychosomatic diseases such as gastric ulcers, colitis, rashes, and autoimmune disorders may begin during this stage. The tendency to develop a specific stress-related disease may be partially predetermined by heredity, personal habits such as smoking, and personality.

stage of exhaustion This stage is demonstrated by the body's failure to adapt to the continued stress.

From an evolutionary viewpoint, the adverse effects of stress on health may be considered to be a maladaptation of humans to stress. What does this tell us? Either we (1) learn to do away with all stress (unlikely), (2) avoid all stressful situations (equally unlikely), (3) learn to adapt to being sick because of stress (undesirable), or (4) learn to adapt to workplace stress (the optimal choice). The first step in learning to adapt to stress is understanding the amount of stress to which we are subjected.

MEASUREMENT OF WORKPLACE STRESS

Workplace stress can be seen as an individual's psychological reaction to the work environment. Although psychological response cannot be directly measured in physical terms, one method commonly employed uses a measurement of mental workload. Mental workload can be measured in one of three ways:

1. With **subjective ratings**, the workers are asked to rate their perceived level of workload. The perceived workload is then viewed as a direct reflection of workplace stress. The workers may be asked to rate their mood in relation to the work situation.

subjective ratings Ratings that are less than objective and can be affected by emotions, human biases, presumptions, and perceptions.

The data gathered by this method are obviously subjective and state-dependent. State-dependent data are directly related to the circumstances or state under which they are collected and, therefore, have a built-in state bias.

2. **Behavioural time sharing** techniques require the simultaneous performance of two tasks. One of the tasks is considered the primary or most important; the other is of secondary importance. The decrease in performance efficiency of the secondary task is considered an index of workload for behavioural time sharing or human multitasking. Workplace stress is thought to increase as behavioural time sharing increases.

3. **Psychophysiological techniques** require simultaneous measurement of heart rate and brain waves, which are then interpreted as indexes of mental workload and workplace stress.

Behavioural time sharing and psychophysiological techniques are related to theoretical models, making data easier to interpret. These two techniques, however, also require sophisticated equipment and data collection methods.

Subjective ratings may be collected using questionnaires or survey instruments. These instruments may ask about the physical working conditions, the individual's health and mental well-being, and their perceived overall satisfaction with the job. The data may then be compared to standardized scales developed by various researchers.[27]

Psychosocial questionnaires evaluate workers' emotions about their jobs. Workers may be asked about job satisfaction, workload, pace, opportunities for advancement, management style, and organizational climate. Psychosocial questionnaires are another form of subjective ratings and are also subject to state-dependent bias in the data. Regardless of the measurement method, because workplace stress is dependent on personal awareness, no direct, objective means of measuring workplace stress are currently available.

SHIFT WORK, STRESS, AND SAFETY

Shift work can require some employees to work when the majority of people are resting. In some cases, shift work requires rotating between two or three different starting times, which may vary by 8 hours or more. Shift work has traditionally been required in industries such as health care, transportation, utilities, security, and, increasingly, retail sales.

Basic physiological functions are scheduled by the biological clock called the **circadian rhythm**. Many physical and psychological functions are affected by circadian rhythm. Blood pressure, heart rate, body temperature, and urine production are measurably slower at night. These same functions are normally faster during the day (active time). If a person takes a job starting at midnight, his or her body will still expect to be sleeping at night and active during the day.

Behavioural patterns also follow the circadian slower-at-night and more-active-during-the-day pattern. Sleep demand and sleep capacity for people aged fourteen or older is greatest at night and weakest during daylight hours. Alertness has been determined to be decreased at night.[28]

>>> **SAFETY FACT** Workplace Environment and Health

The physical and psychological health of working people is affected by their workplace environment. Autocratic, insensitive managers and supervisors are psychosocial factors that can degrade employees' physical and psychological health. When managers and supervisors show an interest in employees, empower them to participate, and provide positive reinforcement, fewer illnesses or cases of work-related depression are reported.

Workers surveyed have consistently reported lower job satisfaction with rotating shifts.[29] Day-shift workers with the same task definitions report higher job satisfaction and less stress than their second- or third-shift counterparts.[30] Rotating shifts over several weeks can result in desensitization to the circadian rhythms. With this desensitization comes a measurable loss in productivity, increased numbers of accidents, and reported subjective discomfort.[31] After returning to a predictable shift, workers regained their biological clocks and circadian rhythms.

Not working the normal day-shift hours results in an increase in workplace stress, with rotating shifts being the most stressful. From a safety viewpoint, shift workers are subjected to more workplace stress in terms of weariness, irritability, depression, and a lack of interest in work. Shift work increases workplace stress and may lead to a less safe worker.

Reducing the Stress Associated with Shift Work

Shift work is and will probably always be a fact of life for employees in certain occupations. About three out of ten workers in Canada work some type of shift work. To reduce the stress associated with shift work, health and safety professionals can apply the following strategies:

1. Encourage shift workers to exercise regularly. Regular exercise can have the double benefit of improving the quality of an individual's sleep and relieving pent-up stress.

2. Encourage shift workers to avoid caffeine, alcohol, or other drugs that can inhibit their ability to sleep.

3. If shift workers cannot sleep without some type of sleep aid, the dietary supplement melatonin or other natural sleep inducers should be recommended rather than sleeping pills that contain synthetic chemicals and can have side effects that might contribute to other stress-inducing effects.[32]

IMPROVING SAFETY BY REDUCING WORKPLACE STRESS

Not all sources of stress on the job can be eliminated, and employment screening is unlikely to identify all those who are sensitive to stress. People can learn to adapt to stress, however. Training can help people recognize and deal with stress effectively. Employees need to know what is expected of them at any given time and receive recognition when it is deserved. Managers can reduce role ambiguity and stress caused by lack of feedback by maintaining frequent communication.

Stress can result from low participation or lack of **job autonomy**. A manager can help employees realize their full potential by helping them match their career goals with the company's goals and giving them more control over their jobs.

job autonomy Control over one's job.

Managers can help design jobs in ways that lead to worker satisfaction, thereby lessening work stress. Physical stress can be reduced by improving the work environment and establishing a sound health and safety program. Managers can also assist in the effort to provide varied and independent work with good possibilities for contact and collaboration with fellow workers and for personal development.

Organizational approaches to coping with work stress include avoiding a monotonous, mechanically-controlled pace, standardized motion patterns, and constant repetition of short-cycle operations. Other stress-inducing work design features to avoid include jobs that do not make use of a worker's knowledge and initiative, that lack human contact, and that have authoritarian-type supervision.

There are also several individual approaches to coping with stress. One of the most important factors in dealing with stress is learning to recognize its symptoms and taking them seriously. Handling stress effectively should be a lifelong activity that gets easier with practice. Keeping a positive mental attitude can help defuse some otherwise stressful situations.

People can analyze stress-producing situations and decide what is worth worrying about. Individuals can effectively respond to a stressful workload by delegating responsibility instead of carrying the entire load. Relaxation techniques can also help reduce the effects of stress. Some common relaxation methods include meditation, biofeedback, music, and exercise.

>>> DISCUSSION CASE | What Is Your Opinion?

"We are beginning to see more and more stress-related problems. I'm afraid that if we don't deal with the issue, stress is going to cause even more serious injuries."

"Nonsense. We all have stress. There has always been stress on the job. It goes with the territory. A few employees go to a seminar on workplace stress and, all of a sudden, everyone is complaining about stress."

This discussion took place between the safety director and the CEO of Gulf Coast Electric Company. Is stress really a legitimate workplace hazard? What is your opinion?

The life insurance company study mentioned earlier found that the following strategies are can reduce workplace stress.

- Management recognizes workplace stress and regularly takes steps to reduce it.
- Mental health benefits are provided in the employee's health insurance coverage.
- The employer has a formal employee communications program to keep employees apprised of the company as a whole.
- Employees are given information on how to cope with stress.
- Workers have current, accurate, and clear **job descriptions**.
- Management and employees talk openly with one another.
- Employees are free to talk with each other during work.
- Employers offer exercise and other stress-reduction classes.
- Employees are recognized and rewarded for their contributions.
- Work rules are published and are the same for everyone.
- Child care programs are available.
- Employees can work flexible hours.
- Perks are granted fairly, based on a person's level in the organization.
- Workers have the training and **technology access** they need.
- Employers encourage work and personal support groups.
- Workers have a place and time to relax during the work day.
- Eldercare programs are available.
- Employees' work spaces are not crowded.
- Workers can put up personal items in their work areas.
- Management appreciates humour in the workplace.[33]

job descriptions Written specifications that describe the tasks, duties, reporting requirements, and qualifications for a given job.

technology access Access to time- and work-saving devices, processes, or equipment that are up to date.

Writing for *Occupational Hazards*, S. L. Smith recommends the following additional ways to reduce stress in the workplace:

- Match workload and pace to the training and abilities of employees.
- Make an effort to match work schedules with the personal lives of employees.
- Clearly define work roles.
- Before giving employees additional duties beyond their normal work roles, make sure they receive the necessary training.

- Promote teamwork among employees and encourage it throughout the organization.

- Involve employees in making decisions that affect them.

- Inform employees in a timely manner of organizational changes that might affect them.[34]

There is no one clear answer to workplace stress. The suggestions given here are a good starting place for management and employees to begin the process of being aware of and dealing effectively with workplace stress.

SAFETY MANAGERS AND STRESS

Health and safety management can be a stressful profession. Robert Scherer of Wright State University identified the following four conditions that frequently trigger stress among modern health and safety professionals:

- Role overload

- Coping with regulatory breakdown

- Communication breakdown

- Competing loyalties[35]

According to Scherer, health and safety professionals are sometimes overloaded when corporate downsizing occurs and they are delegated more and more responsibilities. Trying to keep up with the ever-changing multitude of regulations is a stress-inducing challenge. Communication relating to health and safety is always a challenge. However, when economic forces focus an organization's attention on other matters, it can be even more difficult than usual to get the health and safety message across. This increased difficulty can lead to increased stress. Line managers who are more concerned with meeting production quotas than with the safety of their employees sometimes try to influence health and safety managers, colleagues, and sometimes their friends to look the other way. This subjects health and safety managers to the pressures of competing loyalties.[36]

>>> **SAFETY MYTH** | Managers Cannot Reduce Employee Stress

Of course the workplace is stressful! This fact cannot be helped. Some people can handle stress and some cannot. There is nothing managers can do. Right? Wrong. There is a lot that managers can do. They can:

- provide training to help employees learn to recognize stress and deal with it,

- empower employees by giving them as much control as possible over their jobs,

- improve communication with employees,

- provide clear, understandable job descriptions that eliminate ambiguity,

- provide child care or child care assistance, and

- provide exercise and stress reduction programs.

There are many strategies that managers can employ to reduce stress on the job.

Scherer recommends that health and safety managers cope with these four common triggers of stress by applying the following strategies: (1) prioritize activities by focusing on those that present the most risk to the organization; (2) work closely with the organization's legal staff and subscribe to an online CD-ROM updating service; (3) formalize communication and hold regularly scheduled health and safety meetings for all operating employees; and (4) focus on the risks to the organization and refuse to take sides.[37]

POST-TRAUMATIC STRESS DISORDER (PTSD)

When people experience a frightening situation, they can experience nervousness, sleeplessness, or replaying the event over in their minds. These are normal feelings and reactions to traumatic events, and in most cases the negative reactions decrease over time. Post-traumatic stress disorder (PTSD) is a mental illness. It often involves exposure to trauma from single events that involve death or the threat of death or serious injury. PTSD may also be linked to ongoing emotional trauma, such as abuse in a relationship. Some jobs or occupations put people in dangerous situations. Military personnel, first responders (police, firefighters, and paramedics), doctors, and nurses experience higher rates of PTSD than other professionals.

PTSD can seriously disrupt a person's life through ongoing changes in thoughts or mood. There are a number of effective treatments and supports available for those suffering with PTSD. Counselling, particularly **cognitive-behavioural therapy (CBT)**, has been shown to be effective. Support groups, medication, and service dogs or companion animals are also very effective. Too often those afflicted withdraw from social interaction and, without professional help, turn to alcohol and drugs as a way to cope with PTSD.

cognitive-behavioural therapy (CBT) Therapy used to identify and change the unhelpful patterns of thinking that feed anxious thoughts.

Emergencies or even emergency response drills can trigger unwanted thoughts or emotions in some employees. When preparing a psychological health and safety program or conducting hazard assessments, consider the supports needed for those involved after the event. This could include a peer support network or a dedicated trauma response team. The potential psychological impact of workplace emergencies and the role of the trauma response team are discussed in the next chapter.

PSYCHOLOGICAL HAZARD ASSESSMENT

In Chapter 7 we discussed the importance of hazard assessments and their role in creating a structured *recognition, assessment, and control* process for hazards in the workplace. As part of the work site hazard assessment process, employers are required to identify work-related hazards and put measures in place to prevent harm to workers. Psychological hazards should be included in the hazard assessment process. The stressors or hazards we have identified in this chapter must be assessed for their potential impact on the worker and be appropriately controlled. Employers can show their commitment to a psychologically safe and healthy workplace by developing policies and procedures to prevent, control, and address psychological hazards.

SUMMARY

1. The workplace can have both positive and negative impacts on psychological health.

2. A psychologically safe workplace is one that does not permit harm to employee mental health in careless, negligent, reckless, or intentional ways.

3. Post-traumatic stress disorder (PTSD) is a psychological illness, usually brought on by exposure to a traumatic event, but it can also result from long-term stress, such as an abusive relationship or toxic workplace.

4. Seven areas of law that strengthen the duty to provide and maintain a psychologically safe workplace are: Human Rights Legislation, Workers' Compensation Law, The Law of Torts (Common Law), Employment Contract, Labour Law, Occupational Health and Safety Law, and Employment Standards.

5. The *National Standard of Canada for Psychological Health and Safety in the Workplace* is a set of voluntary guidelines, tools, and resources intended to guide organizations in promoting mental health and preventing psychological harm at work.

6. The standard, launched in 2013, identifies thirteen workplace factors that impact psychological health.

7. Stress is a pathological, and therefore generally undesirable, human reaction to psychological, social, occupational, or environmental stimuli.

8. Workplace stress is the harmful physical and emotional response that occurs when the requirements of the job do not match the capabilities, resources, or needs of the worker.

9. Sources of workplace stress include physical working conditions, work overload, role ambiguity, lack of feedback, personality, personal problems, and role conflict. Other sources of workplace stress are task complexity, lack of control over the job, public safety responsibility, lack of job security, organizational culture issues, work schedules, home and family problems, work relationships, human resource management (HRM) issues, lack of psychological support, and environmental safety concerns.

10. A life insurance company poll of workers found that workplace stress may be caused by company reorganizations or buyout; layoffs; cuts in benefits; mandatory overtime; little control over work; consequences of mistakes; varying workloads; work pace; changing conditions; personal conflicts on the job; lack of opportunity for advancement; bureaucracy; shortages of staff, money, or technology; low pay; or rotating shifts.

11. Human reaction to workplace stress may be grouped into five categories: (a) subjective, (b) behavioural, (c) cognitive, (d) physiological, and (e) organizational.

12. Long-term stress may eventually lead to autoimmune disease.

13. Until an individual's limit is reached, the effects of stress may be reversed. After that limit, with continuing stress, the effects can become pathological.

14. Research has shown three stages of human reaction to stress: (a) alarm, (b) resistance, and (c) exhaustion.

15. The best policy regarding stress is to learn to adapt to it. Efforts to rid the workplace of all sources of stress are unlikely to succeed.

16. Mental workload can be measured in three ways: (a) subjective ratings that are state-dependent, (b) behavioural time sharing, and (c) psychophysiological techniques.

17. Psychosocial questionnaires study how workers feel about their jobs.

18. Shift work occurs when the majority of people outside the workplace are at leisure. The circadian rhythm, or biological clock within the body, determines when a person will be comfortable either working or sleeping. Workers surveyed have reported lower job satisfaction with rotating shifts. Shift work may result in loss of productivity and an increased number of accidents.

19. All sources of stress on the job cannot be eliminated.

20. Managers can reduce workplace stress by reducing role ambiguity and increasing feedback and job autonomy. Managers can also lessen workers' stress by reducing exposure to physical hazards, varying the work pace, and eliminating monotonous or short-cycle operations.

21. Workplace stress reduction, according to a life insurance study, can be accomplished by providing employee mental health insurance benefits, improving employee–management communications, providing workers with information about how to deal with stress, providing job descriptions, talking with employees regularly, recognizing and rewarding contributions, having consistent work rules for all, and offering child care and eldercare programs. Other stress reducers include permitting flexible work hours, granting perks fairly, providing opportunities to talk with others during work, offering exercise and stress-reduction classes,

having work and personal support groups, giving adequate training and technology access, providing a place and time to relax, having uncrowded work spaces with places to put up personal items, and having a management that keeps a sense of humour.

22. Individuals can effectively respond to a stressful workload by delegating responsibility and learning how to relax. Relaxation methods include meditation, biofeedback, music, and exercise.

23. One of the most important factors in dealing with stress is learning to recognize its symptoms and taking the symptoms seriously.

24. Psychological hazards should be included in the hazard assessment process.

Key Terms and Concepts

Behavioural time sharing
Circadian rhythm
Cognitive-behavioural
    therapy (CBT)
Control
Feedback
Feeling of responsibility
Health
Job autonomy
Job descriptions

Job security
Presenteeism
Psychological health
Psychological injury
Psychologically safe
    workplace
Psychological safety
Psychophysiological
    techniques
Psychosocial questionnaires

Role ambiguity
Shift work
Stage of alarm
Stage of exhaustion
Stage of resistance
Stress
Subjective ratings
Task complexity
Technology access
Workplace stress

Review Questions

1. Describe the difference between psychological health and psychological safety.

2. Describe the characteristics of a psychologically safe workplace.

3. What are the three main considerations when making a case for promoting psychological health and safety.

4. What are the seven systems, referred to by Shain that contribute to the mounting pressure to create a psychologically safe workplace?

5. What are the key features of the *National Standard of Canada for Psychological Health and Safety in the Workplace*?

6. Define *stress*.

7. How is workplace stress different from general stress?

8. List five sources of workplace stress and give an on-the-job example for each source.

9. Explain why lack of job control/autonomy may cause workplace stress.

10. Give five categories of human reaction to workplace stress.

11. How are psychosomatic reactions to stress and actual physiological illness related?

12. How are some autoimmune diseases and workplace stress related?

13. Explain three stages of human reaction to stress.

14. Discuss efforts to rid the workplace of all causes of workplace stress.

15. Explain three ways in which mental workload can be measured.

16. What type of data do psychosocial questionnaires provide? Discuss the bias in this type of data.

17. Discuss how shift work causes workplace stress. Give suggestions for minimizing workplace stress from shift work.

18. Discuss at least five methods to reduce workplace stress, according to the life insurance company research.

19. Explain how individuals can reduce workplace stress.

20. Give specific steps that can be taken by managers to help reduce workplace stress.

21. What are the common causes of PTSD?

Weblinks

Canadian Mental Health Association (CMHA)

www.cmha.ca

CMHA is a national charity that helps maintain and improve mental health for all Canadians.

Canadian Centre for Occupational Health and Safety

http://www.ccohs.ca/topics/wellness/mentalhealth/

CCOHS provides information on identifying and dealing with workplace stress and offers advice on how to improve mental health.

Guarding Minds @ Work

www.guardingmindsatwork.ca

Guarding Minds @ Work (GM@W) is a unique and free comprehensive set of resources designed to protect and promote psychological health and safety in the workplace. Here you can find numerous psychological health and safety resources including information and links to the National Standard for Psychological Health and Safety in the Workplace. CAN/CSA-Z1003-13/BNQ 9700-803/2013.

Endnotes

[1] Martin Shain, S.J.D. "Stress, Mental Injury and the Law in Canada: A Discussion Paper for the Mental Health Commission of Canada." February 21, 2009. [Online]. Available: https://www.guardingmindsatwork.ca/info/safety_why/legal_case. (Retrieved June 3, 2017).

[2] Mental Health: Strengthening Our Response. Fact Sheet, April 2016. [Online]. Available: http://www.who.int/mediacentre/factsheets/fs220/en/. (Retrieved June 3, 2017).

[3] World Health Organization. "'Depression: Let's Talk' Says WHO, as Depression Tops List of Causes of Ill Health." [Online]. Available: http://www.who.int/mediacentre/news/releases/2017/world-health-day/en/. (Retrieved June 3, 2017).

[4] Mental Health Commission of Canada. "Focus Area, Workplace." [Online]. Available: http://www.mentalhealthcommission.ca/English/focus-areas/workplace. (Retrieved June 3, 2017). Used with permission.

[5] Guarding Minds @ Work. "Why Is Psychological Health and Safety Important?" [Online]. Available: https://www.guardingmindsatwork.ca/info/safety_why. (Retrieved June 3, 2017).

[6] Mental Health: Strengthening Our Response. Fact Sheet, April 2016. [Online]. Available: http://www.who.int/mediacentre/factsheets/fs220/en/. (Retrieved June 3, 2017).

[7] Guarding Minds @ Work. "The Health Case for Psychological Health and Safety." [Online]. Available: https://www.guardingmindsatwork.ca/info/safety_why/health_case. (Retrieved June 3, 2017). Used with the permission of Canadian Centre for Occupational Health and Safety.

8 Guarding Minds @ Work. "The Business Case for Psychological Health and Safety." [Online]. Available: https://www.guardingmindsatwork.ca/info/safety_why/business_case. (Retrieved June 3, 2017). Used with the permission of Canadian Centre for Occupational Health and Safety.

9 Ibid. Used with the permission of Canadian Centre for Occupational Health and Safety.

10 Ibid. Used with the permission of Canadian Centre for Occupational Health and Safety.

11 Ibid. Used with the permission of Canadian Centre for Occupational Health and Safety.

12 Guarding Minds @ Work. "The Legal Case for Psychological Health and Safety." [Online]. Available:https://www.guardingmindsatwork.ca/info/safety_why/legal_case.(RetrievedJune3, 2017). Used with the permission of Canadian Centre for Occupational Health and Safety.

13 Martin Shain, S.J.D. *Tracking the Perfect Legal Storm: Converging Systems Create Mounting Pressure to Create the Psychologically Safe Workplace*. An Update to "Stress, Mental Injury and the Law in Canada: A Discussion Paper for the Mental Health Commission of Canada 2009." (May 2010). [Online]. Available: http://www.mentalhealthcommission.ca/English/media/3051. Used with permission from Mental Health Commission of Canada.

14 Ibid. Used with permission from Mental Health Commission of Canada.

15 S. Minter. "Too Much Stress?" *Occupational Hazards* 61, no. 5 (May 1999): 49.

16 Ibid.

17 Ibid.

18 Ibid.

19 Ibid.

20 Sandra Hokansson. (2002). "Canada's Knowledge Economy Shift: The Social and Financial Implications." [Online]. Available: http://www.adecco.com/Channels/adecco/human+resources/adecco+viewpoint/workplace+stress+from+adecco+canada.asp. (Retrieved May 11, 2005).

21 E. Grandjean. *Fitting the Task to the Man* (New York: American Management Association, 1998), 176–77.

22 "Electronic Monitoring Causes Worker Stress." *Occupational Health & Safety Letter* 20, no. 21 (October 17, 1990): 168.

23 Minter. "Too Much Stress?" 51.

24 T. M. Fraser. *The Worker at Work* (New York: Wiley, 1997), 104, 110–11.

25 Ibid., 111.

26 Ibid., 111–15.

27 Grandjean. *Fitting the Task to the Man*, 177–78.

28 Fraser. *The Worker at Work*, 116–17.

29 Ibid.

30 Ibid.

31 Ibid.

32 Diann Morshead. "Stress and Shiftwork." *Occupational Health & Safety* 71, no. 4 (April 2002): 36–37.

33 Minter. "Too Much Stress?" 51.

34 S. L. Smith. "Combating Stress." *Occupational Hazards* (March 1994): 57.

35 R. Scherer. "Stress Homes in on Our Safety's Ranks." *Occupational Hazards* (January 1994): 156–57.

36 Ibid., 157.

37 Ibid.

Chapter 24
Preparing for Emergencies and Terrorism

Despite the best efforts of all involved, emergencies do sometimes occur. In recent years, Canadians have witnessed emergencies such as the Fort McMurray wildfire in 2016, the Ottawa Parliament Hill shooting in 2014, the Lac-Mégantic rail disaster in 2013, and the Cougar Helicopters Flight 91 crash off Newfoundland in 2009. Whether human-caused emergencies, natural disasters, or acts of terrorism, it is very important to respond in a way that minimizes harm to people and damage to property. This chapter provides prospective and practising health and safety professionals with the information they need to prepare for emergencies in the workplace and includes a section relating specifically to terrorism.

RATIONALE FOR EMERGENCY PREPARATION

An **emergency** is a potentially life-threatening situation, usually occurring suddenly and unexpectedly. Emergencies may be the result of natural or human causes. Public Safety Canada defines an emergency as "a present or imminent event that requires prompt

emergency A present or imminent event that requires prompt coordination of actions concerning persons or property to protect the health, safety, or welfare of people, or to limit damage to property or the environment.

coordination of actions concerning persons or property to protect the health, safety, or welfare of people, or to limit damage to property or the environment."[1]

Have you ever witnessed the timely, organized, and precise response of a professional emergency medical crew at an automobile accident? While passers-by and spectators may wring their hands and wonder what to do, the emergency response professionals quickly organize, stabilize the situation, and administer assistance. Their ability to respond in this manner is the result of preparation. As shown in Figure 24–1, preparation involves a combination of *planning, practising, evaluating,* and *adjusting* to specific circumstances.

Figure 24–1   Elements of emergency preparation.

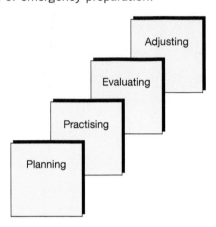

When an emergency occurs, immediate reaction is essential. Speed in responding can mean the difference between life and death or between minimal damage and major damage. Ideally, all those involved should be able to respond properly with a minimum of hesitation. This can happen only if all exigencies have been planned for and planned procedures have been practised, evaluated, and improved.

A quick and proper response—which results because of proper preparation—can prevent panic, decrease the likelihood of injury and damage, and bring the situation under control in a timely manner. Because no workplace is immune to emergencies, preparing for them is critical. An important component of preparation is planning.

EMERGENCY PREPAREDNESS LEGISLATION IN CANADA

Which jurisdiction's legislation applies to a specific situation will often be decided by the magnitude of the emergency. In the event of an emergency, it is also likely that various agencies from different jurisdictions will be involved in the initial response, the mediation, and the recovery processes. In Canada, legislation enacted by federal, provincial/territorial, or municipal governments may apply. The main piece of federal legislation is the Emergency Management Act.

The federal government, through Public Safety Canada, supports Canadians at all levels in preparing for and responding to emergencies. The **Emergency Management Act** limits the authority of the government of Canada and holds it accountable to Parliament when an emergency is declared. National emergencies usually differ from provincial emergencies

Emergency Management Act
Legislation that establishes rules that enable the Government of Canada to be ready to deal with emergencies in cooperation with the provinces and territories.

only in that the capacity to deal with the emergency exceeds that of the province or territory. The Emergency Management Act makes provisions to compensate disaster victims and protect Canadians' fundamental rights and freedoms.

The Emergency Management Act establishes rules that enable the Government of Canada to be ready to deal with emergencies in cooperation with the provinces and territories. The Emergency Management Act sets out the responsibilities and functions of the minister responsible for emergency preparedness with respect to the coordination and support of civil emergency plans, the enhancement of public awareness, and the conduct of training and education related to civil preparedness for emergencies;

- establishes the emergency preparedness responsibilities of all federal ministers in their respective areas of accountability;

- explicitly recognizes the interests of the provinces in relation to federal assistance provided during a provincial emergency;

- provides the legal basis for the Governor in Council to declare a provincial emergency to be of concern to the federal government, and to provide financial and other assistance requested by the affected province(s).[2]

Provincial or territorial legislation ensures that the province supports the response to national emergencies as well as assisting the municipal and individual response teams. The legislation varies, but the basic principles on which emergency management is based apply to each jurisdiction. They provide that (1) when the capabilities of the local

---

>>> **SAFETY FACT** | ## Provincial and Territorial Emergency Management Organizations

- **Alberta** Emergency Management Agency. Phone: (780) 422-9000. Toll-free (in Alberta): (780) 310-0000. www.aema.alberta.ca

- **British Columbia** Emergency Management BC. Phone: (250) 952-4913 / Emergency: (800) 663-3456. http://www2.gov.bc.ca/gov/content/safety/emergency-preparedness-response-recovery/preparedbc

- **Manitoba** Emergency Measures Organization. Phone: (204) 945-4772. Toll-free: (888)-267-8298. www.manitobaemo.ca

- **New Brunswick** Emergency Measures Organization. Phone: (506) 453-2133. Toll-free 24-hour line: (800) 561-4034. www2.gnb.ca/content/gnb/en/departments/jps/public_safety/content/emo.html

- **Newfoundland and Labrador** Fire and Emergency Services. Phone: (709) 729-3703. https://www.gov.nl.ca/fes/emo/programs.html#nldfap

- **Northwest Territories** Emergency Management Organization. Phone: (867) 873-7538 / 24-hour line: (867) 920-2303. http://www.maca.gov.nt.ca/en/services

- **Nova Scotia** Emergency Management Office. Toll-free 24-hour line: (866) 424-5620. www.gov.ns.ca/emo/

- **Nunavut** Emergency Management. Phone: (867) 975-5403 / Toll-free 24-hour line: (800) 693-1666. http://www.gov.nu.ca/community-and-government-services

- **Ontario** Office of the Fire Marshal and Emergency Management. Phone: (647) 329-1100 / Toll-free 24-hour line: (800) 565-1842. www.ontario.ca/beprepared

- **Prince Edward Island** Emergency Measures Organization. Phone: (902) 894-0385 / After hours: (902) 892-9365. www.peipublicsafety.ca

- **Quebec** Ministère de la sécurité publique. Phone (toll-free): (866) 644-6826. General information (Services Québec): (877) 644-4545. http://www.securitepublique.gouv.qc.ca/en.html

- **Saskatchewan** Emergency Management Organization. Phone: (306) 787-9563. http://www.saskatchewan.ca/

- **Yukon** Emergency Measures Organization. Phone: (867) 667-5220. Toll-free (within the Yukon): (800) 661-0408. http://www.community.gov.yk.ca/protectiveservices/about-yukon-emergency-measures-organization.html

Source: Government of Canada (January 15, 2015). "Emergency Management Organizations." [Online.] Available at: https://www.getprepared.gc.ca/cnt/rsrcs/mrgnc-mgmt-rgnztns-eng.aspx (Retrieved June 4, 2017).

community or municipality have been exhausted, progressively higher levels of government will provide resources, and (2) the provinces/territories will support national emergency response efforts.

Most municipalities are required by the province or territory to have an emergency response plan, although in some provinces this may apply only to specific larger cities. An example of a municipality exercising its legal authority is when a *state of local emergency* is declared. During a state of local emergency, the municipality may assume additional powers while implementing its emergency plan in order to protect the citizens from harm. During provincial or territorial emergencies, the province/territory may also exercise additional powers during a *state of emergency*, at which time it may or may not also seek federal assistance.

FIRST AID IN EMERGENCIES

Workplace emergencies often require a medical response. The immediate response is usually first aid. First aid consists of lifesaving measures taken to assist an injured person until medical help arrives. Because there is no way to predict when first aid may be needed, providing first-aid training to employees should be part of preparing for emergencies. In fact, most jurisdictions require that companies have at least one employee on site who has been trained in first aid.

First-aid requirements vary among all Canadian jurisdictions. The level of training (and type of equipment) required depends on factors such as:

- the number of employees
- the types of hazards present at the workplace
- the proximity to hospitals and other medical assistance

The legislation for each respective province and territory, or federally, will prescribe the specific requirements for training, equipment, contents of first-aid kits, reporting injuries, and record keeping. While some provinces and territories are collaborating to develop common standards or accept certification from neighbouring provinces, many variations exist. Common training requirements for most workplaces are the basic and advanced first-aid courses, also called *emergency* and *standard first aid*. As the potential for more serious injuries or the isolation of the workplace increases, so do the training requirements.

Basic-level first-aid training (emergency first aid) typically requires the student to learn emergency scene management and provide first aid for the following conditions:

- Shock, unconsciousness, fainting
- Breathing emergencies
- Wound care and bleeding
- Cardiopulmonary resuscitation (CPR)
- Use of automated external defibrillators (AEDs)

The second level (standard first aid) often includes:

- A secondary survey
- Fractures and their immobilization, muscle strains
- Head, spinal, abdominal, chest, eye, and pelvic injuries
- Medical conditions
- Heat and cold emergencies
- Evacuation and transportation

First-Aid Training Program

First-aid programs are available in most communities. The continuing education departments of community colleges and universities typically offer first-aid training. Classes can often be provided on site and customized to meet the specific needs of individual companies. The Canadian Red Cross and St. John Ambulance Canada are the two primary first-aid training providers in Canada. They provide first-aid training at various levels and for specific areas from babysitter safety to emergency response.

Beyond Training

Training employees in first-aid techniques is an important part of preparing for emergencies. However, training is only part of the preparation. In addition, it is important to do the following:

1. **Have well-stocked first-aid kits available.** First-aid kits should be placed throughout the workplace in clearly visible, easily accessible locations. They should be properly and fully stocked and periodically checked to ensure that they stay fully stocked.

2. **Have appropriate personal protective devices available.** With concerns about AIDS and hepatitis, administering first aid has become more complicated than in the past. The main concerns are with blood and other body fluids. Consequently, a properly stocked first-aid kit should contain rubber surgical gloves and face masks or mouthpieces for CPR.

3. **Post emergency telephone numbers.** The advent of 911 service has simplified the process of calling for medical care, police, or firefighting assistance. If 911 services are not available, emergency numbers for ambulance, hospital, police, fire department, LEPC (local emergency planning committee), and appropriate internal personnel should be posted at clearly visible locations near all telephones in the workplace.

4. **Keep all employees informed.** Some companies require all employees to undergo first-aid training; others choose to train one or more employees in each department. Regardless of the approach used, it is important that all employees be informed and kept up to date concerning basic first-aid information.

⟫⟫⟫ SAFETY FACT | First-Aid Kits

The Ontario Workplace Safety and Insurance Act prescribes the following minimum items be contained in first-aid kits where 15 to 200 people are employed.

- A current edition of the St. John Ambulance First Aid Manual
- 24 safety pins
- 1 basin, preferably stainless steel
- 48 adhesive dressings, individually wrapped
- 2 rolls of adhesive tape, 1 inch wide
- 12 rolls of 1-inch gauze bandage
- 48 sterile gauze pads, 3 inches square
- 8 rolls of 2-inch gauze bandage
- 8 rolls of 4-inch gauze bandage
- 6 sterile surgical pads suitable for pressure dressings, individually wrapped
- 12 triangular bandages
- splints of assorted sizes
- 2 rolls of splint padding

Along with the items listed, the employer shall ensure that the first-aid station has one stretcher and two blankets and is at all times in the charge of a worker who is a holder of a valid St. John Ambulance Standard First Aid Certificate (or its equivalent) and works in the immediate vicinity of the station.

HOW TO PLAN FOR EMERGENCIES

Responses to emergencies typically come from several people or groups of people, including medical, firefighting, security, and safety personnel as well as specialists from a variety of different fields. People in each of these areas have different but interrelated and often interdependent roles to play in responding to the emergency. Because of their disparate backgrounds and roles, organization and coordination are critical.

A company's **emergency response plan (ERP)** should clearly identify the different personnel and groups that respond to various types of emergencies and, in each case, who is in charge. One person should be clearly identified and accepted by all emergency responders as the **emergency coordinator**. This person should be knowledgeable, at least in a general sense, about the responsibilities of each individual emergency responder and how each relates to those of all other responders. This knowledge must include the order of response for each type of emergency set forth in the plan.

A company's health and safety professional is the obvious person to organize and coordinate emergency responses. However, regardless of who is designated, it is important that (1) one person is in charge, (2) everyone involved knows who is in charge, and (3) everyone who has a role in responding to an emergency is given ample opportunities to practise in simulated conditions that come as close as possible to real conditions.

Developing an ERP is a major step in preparing for emergencies. A preliminary step is to conduct a thorough analysis to determine the various types of emergencies that may occur. For example, depending on geography and the types of products and processes involved, a company may anticipate such emergencies as fires, chemical spills, explosions, toxic emissions, train derailments, hurricanes, tornadoes, lightning, floods, earthquakes, or volcanic eruptions.

A company's ERP should be a collection of small plans for each anticipated or potential emergency. The person developing the ERP has to consider the resources available locally and adjust the plan accordingly. For example, close proximity to a medical clinic or fire station would relieve the pressure from the areas of first aid and firefighting. However, a propane storage facility or densely populated residential area nearby would add to the potential seriousness of the emergency. These plans should have the following components:

1. **Procedures.** Specific, step-by-step emergency response procedures should be developed for each potential emergency.

2. **Coordination.** All cooperating agencies and organizations and emergency responders should be listed along with their telephone number and primary contact person.

3. **Assignments and responsibilities.** Every person who will be involved in responding to a given emergency should know his or her assignment. Each person's responsibilities should be clearly spelled out and understood. One person may be responsible for conducting an evacuation of the affected area, another for the immediate shutdown of all equipment, and another for telephoning for medical, fire, or other types of emergency assistance. When developing this part of the ERP, it is important to assign a backup person for each area of responsibility. Doing so ensures that the plan will not break down if a person assigned to a certain responsibility is one of the victims.

4. **Accident prevention strategies.** The day-to-day strategies to be used for preventing a particular type of emergency should be summarized in the ERP. In this way, the strategies can be reviewed, thereby promoting prevention.

5. **Schedules.** The plan should contain the dates and times of regularly scheduled practise drills. It is best to vary the times and dates so that practise drills don't become predictable and boring. Figure 24–2 is a checklist that can be used for developing an ERP.

emergency response plan (ERP) A written document that details the course of action to be taken in response to an emergency, with the goal of protecting the health, safety, and welfare of people while limiting damage to property and the environment.

emergency coordinator A person who is clearly identified in a company emergency response plan as the responsible party of the emergency situation.

Figure 24–2 Emergency planning checklist.

Type of Emergency

____Fire   ____Explosion
____Chemical spill   ____Toxic emission
____Train derailment   ____Hurricane
____Tornado   ____Lightning
____Flood   ____Earthquake
____Volcanic eruption

Procedures for Emergency Response

1. Controlling and isolating?
2. Communication?
3. Emergency assistance?
4. First aid?
5. Shutdown/evacuation/protection of workers?
6. Protection of equipment/property?
7. Egress, ingress, exits?
8. Emergency equipment (e.g., fire extinguishers)?
9. Alarms?
10. Restoration of normal operations?

Coordination

1. Medical care providers?
2. Fire service providers?
3. LEPC (local emergency planning committee) personnel?
4. Environmental protection personnel?
5. Civil defence personnel (in the case of public evacuations)?
6. Police protection providers?
7. Communication personnel?

Assignments and Responsibilities

1. Who cares for the injured?
2. Who calls for emergency assistance?
3. Who shuts down power and operations?
4. Who coordinates communication?
5. Who conducts the evacuation?
6. Who meets emergency responders and guides them to the emergency site?
7. Who contacts coordinating agencies and organizations?
8. Who is responsible for ensuring the availability and upkeep of fire extinguishers?
9. Who is responsible for ensuring that alarms are in proper working order?
10. Who is responsible for organizing cleanup activities?

Accident Prevention Strategies

1. Periodic safety inspections?
2. Industrial hygiene strategies?
3. Personal protective equipment?
4. Ergonomic strategies?
5. Machine safeguards?
6. Hand and portable power tool safeguards?
7. Material handling and storage strategies?
8. Electrical safety strategies?
9. Fire safety strategies?
10. Chemical safety strategies?

Schedules

1. Dates of practice drills:_____
2. Times of practice drills:_____
3. Duration of practice drills:_____

Peter, the safety manager for Dew-Line Manufacturing, made a request to the company president, Giovanni, that evacuation drills be conducted each quarter as opposed to semi-annually. Giovanni replied that the drills are a waste of time and are not required at all because the chance of an evacuation being necessary is very remote; and even if an alarm sounded, the workers know their way out of the building. Who is right in this case? What is your opinion?

EVACUATION PLANNING

In many situations, rapid egress from a facility can save lives or reduce injury. A written plan for the evacuation of the facility should be in place. Critical elements of the plan are the marking of exit routes, communications and alarms, outside assembly, and training and drills.

Marking of Exit Routes

Clearly identified and marked routes of egress are critical during a time of crisis (fire, natural disaster, terrorist attack, etc.). To ensure that routes of egress and all related evacuation response items are clearly marked, safety professionals should answer the following questions about the facilities for which they are responsible:

1. Are all exit, emergency exit, and non-exit doors clearly identified and marked?
2. Are there up-to-date evacuation route maps mounted at strategic locations throughout the facility?
3. Are all egress route aisles, hallways, and stairs marked clearly? Can the markings be seen in the event of darkness?
4. Are there low-level markings posted strategically throughout the facility that can be viewed in the event that smoke fills the facility?
5. Is all firefighting equipment clearly marked with directional signs so that it can be easily located in the event of an emergency?
6. Is all emergency first-aid equipment clearly marked with directional signs so that it can be easily located in the event of an emergency?
7. Are all electrical, chemical, and physical hazards identified and clearly marked?
8. Are all physical obstructions clearly outlined?
9. Are all critical shutdown procedures and equipment clearly identified and marked?
10. Are the handrails, treads, and risers on all stairs clearly marked?
11. In the case of multicultural workforce settings, are all signs and markings provided in a multilingual or pictogram format?[3]

Ensuring that all signs, pictograms, and other markings relating to facility evacuation are visible during power outages is critical. Battery backup systems are one approach that is widely used. However, there are environments in which even the smallest spark from a battery might set off an explosion. For this reason, some facilities find the use of photoluminescent signs a better alternative.

Photoluminescent signs and markings absorb normal light energy from their surroundings and then release this energy in the form of light during periods of darkness. Some of the better photoluminescent materials will give off light for as long as 24 hours and have a maintenance-free life expectancy of up to 25 years.

Communication and Alarm Procedures

People are so accustomed to false alarms in their lives that when the real thing occurs, it can be difficult to convince them that it's not just another drill. In addition, people tend to trust what they can see, smell, and hear. Consequently, if they cannot physically sense an emergency, they tend to ignore the warning. The communication component of a facility's evacuation plan should include procedures for early detection of a problem, procedures for reporting an emergency, procedures for initiating an evacuation, and procedures for providing the necessary information to employees who are being evacuated.[4]

Notifying employees of the emergency is the function of the facility's alarm system. However, just pulling the alarm switch is not sufficient communication. Once the alarm has been given, verbal instruction should be broadcast so that people know that the alarm is real (not just another drill) as well as specific actions they should take immediately. There must also be procedures for informing evacuated employees that the emergency is over and they can return to their work.

External communication procedures are also important. All employees should know how to notify outside authorities of the emergency. With the advent of 911 service, this problem has been simplified. However, do not assume that all employees will remember the number when under the stress of an emergency, or that they will remember to dial "9" or some other code to gain access to an outside line. This problem can be solved by placing clearly marked signs above or near telephones containing such messages as "In an emergency dial 911" or "In an emergency dial 9-911" (if it is necessary to first access an outside line).

Outside Assembly

The company's evacuation plan should include an assembly area to which employees go once evacuated.[5] This muster point should be well known by all employees, and employees should understand that it is critical to assemble there so that a headcount can be taken. In addition, there should be a backup assembly area known to all employees so they know where to go if the primary assembly area has been rendered inaccessible or hazardous.

Part of the evacuation plan relating to assembly areas must be devoted to transient personnel—non-employees such as vendors, visitors, contractors, and so on. How will they know where to assemble? Who will check to see that they have been notified of the emergency? These issues should be addressed in the evacuation plan.

Training and Drills

Training for evacuations is a critical element of the evacuation plan.[6] Developing a plan and then letting it just sit on the shelf gathering dust is a formula for disaster. Everything contained in the plan that requires action or knowledge on the part of employees should be part of the required evacuation training. Training should be provided when employees are first hired, and retraining should be provided periodically as various elements of the plan are updated.

Drills should be a major part of the training provided for employees. The old sports adage that says, "What you do in practise you will do in the game" applies here. When an emergency actually occurs should not be the first time employees have gone through the action required of them in an emergency.

DEALING WITH THE PSYCHOLOGICAL TRAUMA OF EMERGENCIES

In addition to the physical injuries and property damage that can occur in emergencies, modern health and safety professionals must also be prepared to deal with potential psychological damage. Psychological trauma among employees involved in workplace disasters is as common as it is among combat veterans. According to Johnson, "Traumatic incidents do not affect only immediate survivors and witnesses. Most incidents result in layers of victims that stretch far beyond those who were injured or killed."[7]

Trauma is psychological stress. It occurs as the result of an event, typically a disaster or some kind of emergency, so shocking that it impairs a person's sense of security or well-being. Johnson calls *trauma response* "the normal reactions of normal people to an abnormal event."[8] Traumatic events are typically unexpected and shocking, and they involve the reality or threat of death.

trauma Psychological stress.

Dealing with Emergency-Related Trauma

The typical approach to an emergency can be described as follows: Control it, take care of the injured, clean up the mess, and get back to work. Often, the psychological aspect is ignored. This leaves witnesses and other coworkers to deal with the trauma they've experienced on their own. "Left to their own inadequate resources, workers can become ill or unable to function. They may develop resentment toward the organization, which can lead to conflicts with bosses and co-workers, high employee turnover—even subconscious sabotage."[9]

It is important to respond to trauma quickly, within 24 hours if possible and within 72 hours in all cases. The purpose of the response is to help employees get back to normal by enabling them to handle what they have experienced. This is best accomplished by a team of people who have had special training. Such a team is typically called the **trauma response team (TRT)**. See Chapter 23, Psychological Health and Safety, for more information on psychological hazards.

trauma response team (TRT) Designated employees who are specially trained to provide initial response to traumatic events.

Trauma Response Team

A company's trauma response team may consist of health and safety personnel who have undergone special training or fully credentialed counselling personnel, depending on the size of the company. To complement the TRT, many large employers have established peer support networks of employees from all areas of the organization, who have basic training in trauma recognition and triage. In any case, the TRT should be included in the assignments and responsibilities section of the ERP.

The job of the TRT is to intervene as early as possible, help employees acknowledge what they have experienced, and give them opportunities to express how they feel about it to people who are qualified to help. The *qualified to help* aspect is very important. TRT members who are not counsellors or mental health professionals should never attempt to provide care that they are not qualified to offer. Part of the trauma training that health and safety professionals receive involves recognizing the symptoms of employees who need professional care and referring them to qualified care providers.

In working with employees who need to deal with what they have experienced but are not so traumatized as to require referrals for outside professional care, a group approach is best. According to Johnson, the group approach offers several advantages:

- It facilitates public acknowledgment of what the employees have experienced.

- It keeps employees informed, thereby cutting down on the number of rumours and horror stories that inevitably make the rounds.

- It encourages employees to express their feelings about the incident. This alone is often enough to get people back to normal and functioning properly.

- It allows employees to see that they are not alone in experiencing traumatic reactions (e.g., nightmares, flashbacks, shocking memories, and so on) and that these reactions are normal.[10]

Convincing Companies to Respond

Modern health and safety professionals may find themselves having to convince higher management of the need to have a TRT. Some corporate officials may not believe that trauma even exists. Others may acknowledge its presence but view trauma as a personal problem that employees should handle on their own.

In reality, psychological trauma that is left untreated can manifest itself as post-traumatic stress disorder, the same syndrome experienced by some war veterans. This disorder is characterized by "intrusive thoughts and flashbacks of the stressful event, the tendency to avoid stimulation, paranoia, concentration difficulties, and physiological symptoms such as rapid heartbeat and irritability."[11]

In today's competitive marketplace, companies need all of their employees operating at peak performance levels. Employees experiencing trauma-related disorders will not be at their best. Health and safety professionals should use this rationale when it is necessary to convince higher management of the need to provide a company-sponsored trauma response team.

RECOVERING FROM DISASTERS

Many organizations put a great deal of effort into planning for disaster response, including emergency evacuation. The primary function of **emergency planning** is to prevent injuries and protect life, but what about after the disaster? The secondary function of emergency planning should include provisions to expedite the return to normal operation.

Accordingly, a comprehensive disaster recovery plan should have at least the following components: recovery coordinator, recovery team, recovery analysis and planning, damage assessment and salvage operations, recovery communications, and employee support and assistance. The overall goal of a disaster recovery plan is to get an organization fully operational again as quickly as possible.

emergency planning Developing procedures to reduce the negative effects of an emergency. An emergency plan will have provisions for reducing fatalities and injuries; limiting the damage to equipment, facilities, and products; and expediting the return to normal operation.

Recovery Coordinator

There must be one person who has ultimate responsibility and authority for disaster recovery. This person must have both the ability and the authority to take command of the situation, assess the recovery needs, delegate specific responsibilities, approve the necessary resources, interact with outside agencies, and activate the organization's overall response.

Recovery Team

The recovery team consists of key personnel to whom the disaster coordinator can delegate specific responsibilities. These responsibilities include facility management, security, human resources, environmental protection (if applicable), communications, and the various personnel needed to restart operations.

Recovery Analysis and Planning

This phase involves assessing the impact of the disaster on the organization and establishing both short- and long-term recovery goals. The more recovery analysis and planning that can be done, the better. One of the ways to do this is to consider various predictable scenarios and plan for them. This is the business equivalent of the war-gaming activities that take place in the military.

Damage Assessment and Salvage

This component of the plan has two elements: *preparedness* and *recovery*. The preparedness element should include the following information: (1) a comprehensive inventory of all property at the facility in question; (2) a checklist of the items on the inventory that are essential for maintaining the facility; (3) a list of all personnel who will aid in the recovery (make sure to have fully trained and qualified backup personnel in case a primary player is not available or is injured during the emergency); (4) a list of all vendors, contractors, and so on whose assistance will be needed during the damage assessment and salvage phases of recovery; (5) a worksheet that can be used to document all actions taken during recovery operations; and (6) procedures for quickly establishing a remote operational site.

The recovery element should include procedures for (1) securing workspace for the recovery team and coordinator; (2) identifying areas of the facility that must be accessible; (3) maintaining security at the facility against looting and vandalism; (4) analyzing and inspecting damage to the facility and reporting it to the recovery coordinator; (5) assessing the extent of damage to goods, supplies, and equipment; (6) photographing and videotaping damage to the facility; (7) taking appropriate action to prevent additional damage to the facility; (8) repairing, restoring, and resetting fire detection and suppression equipment; and (9) investigating accidents.

Recovery Communications

Communication is one of the most important considerations in disaster recovery. This component of the plan should deal with both who is to be notified and how that is to take place. The "how" aspects concern backup procedures for telephone service, email, and so forth. Will cell phones be used? Will radio stations be part of the mix? Will two-way "walkie-talkie"-type radios be used for communicating on site? The following list contains the people and organizations who might have to be contacted as part of the disaster recovery operation:

- Customers
- Vendors and suppliers
- Insurance representatives
- Employees' families
- Appropriate authorities
- Media outlets (radio and television stations and newspapers)

Employee Support and Assistance

After a disaster, employees are likely to need various types of assistance, including financial, medical, and psychological. The following steps for developing this component of the disaster recovery plan are recommended:

1. Determine postdisaster work schedules and provide them to employees. Include overtime work if it will be necessary, and make sure employees know that flexibility in scheduling work hours will be important until the recovery is complete.
2. Plan for the whole range of employee-assistance services that might be needed, including medical, transportation, financial, shelter, food, water, clothing, and psychological services (trauma, shock, and stress counselling).
3. Plan for the provision of grief counselling. The best way to handle this is to assign grief counselling to the company's employee assistance program provider.
4. Plan for the possible need to relocate the facility as part of disaster recovery.
5. Plan to give employees opportunities to participate in personal actions taken on behalf of fatally injured employees and their families. Work for employee consensus before deciding what to do for these families.

6. Plan to fully inform all employees about what happened, why, how the company is responding in the short term, and how it will respond in the long term. Be sure to build in ways to let employees know the company cares about them and will do everything possible to protect their safety.[12]

TERRORISM IN THE WORKPLACE

Terrorism is the use of violence or threats of violence by individuals or groups against civilians or property. Although Canada has a peaceful history, there have been hundreds of terrorist attacks.[13] Among the more notable were the 1970 FLQ crisis in Quebec, which resulted in the murder of cabinet minister Pierre Laporte and the 1985 Air India Bombing. (Although Canada was not directly attacked, the bombing of an Air India flight from Toronto in 1985 resulted in the death of 329 people, most of whom were Canadian.)

More recently, in October 2014, Michael Zehaf-Bibeau was shot and killed after he killed Canadian soldier Corporal Nathan Cirillo at the National War Memorial and then stormed the Parliament Buildings. In January 2017, six people were dead and nineteen injured after a shooting incident at a Quebec City mosque. But the events of September 11 brought the threat of terrorism one step closer and have made the fear of terrorism more a part of our daily consciousness. The Canadian Security Intelligence Service (CSIS) warns, "Not only were there a number of Canadians among the approximately 3,000 victims of the World Trade Center attack but, because of Canada's solidarity with the United States in pursuing those responsible, our country—along with other western democracies—has now become a potential target for terrorist activity."[14]

terrorism The unlawful use or threat of violence or sabotage, usually against the public, as a politically-motivated means of attack or coercion.

Role of the Employer

There is no question that the threat of terrorist attacks has become an ever-present reality in today's workplace. Because this is the case, employers clearly have a role to play in preparing for terrorist attacks, taking all prudent precautions to prevent them, and in responding properly should an attack occur. Because terrorism threatens the health and safety of employees, it is more than just a security issue; it is also an occupational health and safety issue.

The roles of employers and health and safety professionals relating to terrorism in the workplace are summarized below:

- **Run a safe and caring operation.** Employees watch the nightly news and read their morning newspapers. They know what is going on in their world. As a result, many are discomfited by the possibility that they or their workplace might become the target of a terrorist attack. Consequently, the first responsibility of the employer is to run a safe operation in which employees know their safety is a high priority. Many of the engineering, administrative, training, and enforcement actions taken to make the workplace safe from occupational hazards will also help mitigate the threat of terrorism.

- **Listen to employees.** Employees are concerned about the threat of terrorism, and they have a right to be. Employers should take the concerns of employees seriously, and deal with them by answering questions, communicating openly and frequently, and referring employees who need professional help to the employee assistance program.

- **Train employees.** Security and safety procedures do little good unless employees know what they are and how to use them. In addition, personnel in certain positions need to have specialized knowledge relating to terrorism. For example, mailroom personnel need to be trained in how to screen incoming mail for biohazards and explosives.

- **Communicate.** Talk with employees openly and frequently. Let them know what the company knows. It is better for employees to hear news from the company than to receive it in the form of third-party gossip and rumors. Before giving out information, however, it is a good idea to verify it. Check with local authorities or go online to http://www.snopes.com to debunk rumors and gossip.

- **Know your personnel.** Institute background checks as part of the hiring process. Make sure that supervisors get to know their direct reports well enough to sense when something is wrong with one of them. If inconsistencies in normal behavioural patterns occur, address them right away.

- **Empower personnel.** Empower employees to back away from a situation that does not feel right or that makes them uncomfortable. Be flexible in allowing them to have time off for family activities. This can be especially important for employees who have worked longer than normal hours during particularly busy times.

- **Harden the site against external threats and restrict access.** Insulate the workplace from negative outside influences, control who has access to the workplace, and take all necessary steps to reduce the exposure of employees to potential threats. Call in security experts if necessary to help develop and implement the necessary controls.

- **Remove any barriers to clear visibility around the facility.** The better employees can see around them, the less likely it will be that a terrorist will be able to pull off a surprise attack. The trees, shrubs, and bushes that make the perimeter of the facility and parking lot so attractive can be used by unauthorized personnel to hide while attempting to gain access.

- **Have and enforce parking and delivery regulations.** Arrange parking spaces so that no car is closer than 100 feet to a building. This will lessen the likelihood of damage from a car bomb. In addition, have strict delivery procedures so that terrorists posing as delivery personnel do not gain access through this means.

- **Make sure that visitors can be screened from a distance.** Arrange the facility so that visitors are channeled into a specific area, an area in which they can be viewed by company personnel from a distance. This will lessen the likelihood of a terrorist gaining access by overpowering or killing access-control personnel.

- **Keep all unstaffed entrance doors locked and alarmed.** Employees need to be able to get out of the building through any exit door, but access into the building should be channelled through doors staffed by access-control personnel.

- **Make air intakes and other utilities inaccessible to everyone except designated maintenance personnel.** Releasing toxic material into the air intake is one way terrorists could harm the highest possible number of people. The likelihood of this happening can be decreased by locating air intakes in inaccessible locations.

- **Prevent access to roofs and upper stories.** Terrorists who cannot gain access on the ground floor might simply gain entry through doors and other openings on the roof. Consequently, it is important to keep roof doors locked from the outside and alarmed. They should open from the inside, but doing so should trigger an alarm. It is also important to establish control procedures for emergency escape routes from the roof and upper stories so that these avenues are not used by terrorists trying to gain access into the building.

- **Secure trash containers.** The grounds should be kept free of debris and clutter. Further, trash containers should be secured either by keeping them inside the building's wall or, if kept outside, at a distance from the building.

- **Ensure that employees, contractors, and visitors wear badges.** Establish a system in which all employees, contractors, and visitors must wear badges in order to gain access to the facility. Require identification of all visitors and an internal sponsor before providing them with badges. Have visitors sign in and out on every visit.

- **Have an emergency response plan and practise it periodically.** Plan for all predictable exigencies and practise the various components of the plan on a regular basis.
- **Be cautious of information placed on your company's website.** Make sure that your company's website does not contain information that can be used by terrorists, such as detailed maps, floor plans, or descriptions of hazardous materials stored on site.
- **Keep up to date with the latest safety and security strategies.** Crime Prevention Through Environmental Design (CPTED) should become part of the knowledge base of health and safety professionals. For the latest information concerning CPTED, visit the following website periodically: http://www.cpted.net/.
- **Protect the integrity of your facility's key system.** Terrorists can use any key from your facility to make their own master key if they know how, and many do. To make matters worse, they share information about how to make master keys via the Internet. The following procedures will help protect the integrity of your facility's key system: (a) restrict access to keys (including restroom keys), (b) consider not using master keys, and (c) switch from a key system to an electronic keycard or fingerprint recognition system.[15]

Securing Hazardous Materials

Clearly, one of the tactics of terrorists is to convert hazardous materials used in the workplace into weapons of mass destruction. Consequently, it is important for facilities that produce, use, or store any type of hazardous materials to develop, implement, and enforce a security program that denies terrorists access to these materials.[16] "The goal of the security plan should be to implement measures that deter, detect, delay, or defeat the threat. Deterrence can be improved by using highly visible measures and randomness. This is cost-efficient and complicates the threatening person or group's planning."[17]

A hazmat security plan should have two broad components: *personnel security* and *physical security*. The fundamental elements of the personnel component of the plan are to (1) determine who should be granted access to the materials, (2) conduct comprehensive background checks on all individuals who require access, (3) submit employees who require access to psychological screening to ensure stability, and (4) require identification badges with photographs or fingerprints of those with authorized access.

The physical security component consists of measures taken to prevent or control access to the hazardous materials in question. Security practices in this component should be integrated and layered by using a combination of measures including fences, lights, electronic alarm systems, guards, reaction forces, and the *two-person rule* which requires two employees to be present in order to gain access to the hazardous materials.

RESUMING BUSINESS AFTER A DISASTER

After a disaster in the workplace—regardless of whether the source of the disaster was natural, accidental, or terrorist-related—a comprehensive hazard assessment should be completed with the help of competent professionals before business is resumed. Before resuming business, an organization should consider the following factors:[18]

- **Structural integrity.** Has the structural integrity of the building been checked by competent engineering professionals to ensure that it is safe to enter?
- **Utility checks.** Have all utilities—gas, electricity, water, sewer—been checked to ensure that there are no leaks, cracks, loose wires, and so on? Have the appropriate utility companies given their approval for reopening? Remember that if reopening involves the use of electric generators, these devices should not be used inside the building because they can create a carbon monoxide hazard.

- **Cleanup protection.** Make sure that cleanup crews are properly protected from any hazardous materials or conditions that might have been created by the disaster. Make sure they properly use the appropriate personal protective gear and comply with all applicable health and safety regulations and procedures as they clean the facility.

- **Health and sanitation.** Kitchens, bathrooms, and any area in which food or potentially hazardous or toxic substances are stored should be checked and thoroughly cleaned to prevent the exposure of employees and customers to hazardous conditions.

- **Air quality.** Make sure the air quality in the facility is tested before allowing personnel to enter the building. Certain types of disasters, such as hurricanes, might cause the proliferation of mold and mildew. The air should be checked for any potentially hazardous biological or chemical agents that could be harmful to humans.

- **Ventilation.** Make sure that all types of ductwork and ventilation have been checked for the presence of potentially harmful biological and chemical agents, as well as for dust and debris that might impede airflow. Once it appears that ventilations systems are clean, have the air-conditioning and heating systems started up and all ventilation systems checked again before allowing personnel back into the building. When the air-conditioning and heating systems are restarted, blow cold air through them, even in winter. This will help prevent the growth of mold in the ventilation ducts.

- **Walls, ceilings, and floors.** Check walls and ceilings to ensure that no materials are in danger of falling off—inside for occupants and outside for pedestrians. Check floors for any hazards that might contribute to slipping and falling.

- **Safety equipment.** Check all fire extinguishers, all types of alarms, and any other safety equipment to determine whether it has been damaged. Make sure that all safety equipment is in proper working order before allowing personnel to reenter the facility.

- **Lighting.** Ensure that all illumination devices are in proper working order and that all personnel have the required amount of illumination to do their jobs. Employees should not return to work unless the necessary illumination is available and working.

- **Hazardous waste removal.** Any type of potentially hazardous material that is left lying around after the disaster should be collected and properly disposed of. Broken glass, debris, litter, and sharp-edged material should be removed before employees are allowed to return to work.

- **Machines and equipment.** All machines and equipment should be checked carefully before they are reenergized. All electrical, gas, hydraulic, fill, drain, and plumbing lines should be checked for leaks and proper connections before the machines are energized for use.

- **Furniture.** Check all furniture to ensure its structural integrity. Make sure that fasteners, braces, and supports have not been damaged during the emergency, or that furniture has not become unstable due to water damage.

SUMMARY

1. An *emergency* is a present or imminent event that requires prompt coordination of actions concerning persons or property to protect the health, safety or welfare of people, or to limit damage to property or the environment. Emergencies may be the result of natural or human causes.

2. Preparing for emergencies involves planning, practising, evaluating, and adjusting. An immediate response is critical in emergencies.

3. The federal government, through Public Safety Canada, supports Canadians at all levels in preparing for and responding to emergencies.

4. Because there is no way to predict when first aid may be needed, part of preparing for emergencies should include training employees to administer first aid.

5. In addition to providing first-aid training, it is important to have well-stocked first-aid kits readily available, have personal protective devices available, post emergency telephone numbers, and keep all employees informed.

6. For proper coordination of the internal emergency response, it is important that one person be in charge and that everyone involved knows who that person is.

7. A company's emergency action plan should be a collection of small plans for each anticipated emergency. These plans should have the following components: procedures, coordination, assignments and responsibilities, accident prevention strategies, and schedules.

8. Critical elements of an evacuation plan are as follows: marking of exit routes, communications and alarms, outside assembly, and training and drills.

9. ERPs should be customized to include procedures, coordination, assignments and responsibilities, accident prevention strategies, and schedules.

10. Some organizations have staff trained as peer support counsellors to assist the emergency response team in identifying and providing early intervention.

11. Trauma is psychological stress. It typically results from exposure to a disaster or emergency so shocking that it impairs a person's sense of security or well-being. Trauma left untreated can manifest itself as post-traumatic stress disorder. This disorder is characterized by intrusive thoughts, flashbacks, paranoia, concentration difficulties, rapid heartbeat, and irritability.

12. A disaster recovery plan should have at least the following components: recovery coordinator, recovery team, recovery analysis and planning, damage assessment and salvage operations, recovery communications, and employee support and assistance.

13. Employers can help decrease the likelihood of a terrorist attack on their facilities by taking the following actions: Run a safe and caring operation; listen to employees; train employees; communicate; know your personnel; empower personnel; harden the site against external threats and restrict access; remove any barriers to clear visibility around the facility; have and enforce parking and delivery regulations; make sure that visitors can be screened from a distance; keep all unstaffed entrance doors locked from the outside and alarmed; make air intakes and other utilities inaccessible to everyone except designated personnel; prevent access to roofs and upper stories; secure trash containers; ensure that employees, contractors, and visitors wear badges; have an emergency response plan and practise it periodically; be cautious about what information is placed on your company's website; keep up to date with the latest safety and security strategies; and protect the integrity of your facility's key system.

14. Secure hazardous materials so that terrorists cannot gain access to them for use in making bombs and other weapons of mass destruction. A hazmat security plan should have two components: personnel security and physical security.

15. All systems, conditions, and potential hazards should be checked and corrected as appropriate before resuming business after a disaster.

Key Terms and Concepts

Emergency

Emergency coordinator

Emergency planning

Emergency Management Act

Emergency response plan (ERP)

Terrorism

Trauma

Trauma response team (TRT)

Review Questions

1. Define the term *emergency*.

2. Explain the rationale for emergency preparation.

3. What types of natural or human-induced emergencies are most likely to happen in your region of the country?

4. Describe the agreements in place to address first-aid requirements for employers and workers who work in more than one province or territory.

5. Explain how you would provide first-aid training if you were responsible for setting up a program at a company.

6. Besides training, what other first-aid requirements should a company have?

7. What is trauma?

8. Why should a company include trauma response in its ERP?

9. Describe how a company may respond to the trauma resulting from a workplace emergency.

10. What elements should a disaster recovery plan contain?

11. How can employers prepare for the threat of terrorism?

12. What considerations should be made before resuming business after a disaster?

Weblinks

Public Safety Canada

www.publicsafety.gc.ca

The federal government's public safety website is a useful resource for individuals or businesses for dealing with major emergencies and terrorism. A list of addresses and websites for provincial and territorial emergency measures organizations is available in the Safety Fact box earlier in the chapter.

New West Partnership Trade Agreement (NWPTA)

www.newwestpartnershiptrade.ca

The New West Partnership Trade Agreement (NWPTA) is an accord that creates a barrier-free, interprovincial market for goods, services, and labour mobility.

Endnotes

[1] Public Safety Canada. "National Emergency Response System." (December 15, 2015). Available: https://www.publicsafety.gc.ca/cnt/rsrcs/pblctns/ntnl-rspns-sstm/index-en .aspx. (Retrieved August 12, 2017).

2 Government of Canada. Justice Laws Website. Emergency Management Act S.C. 2007, c. 15. [Online]. Available: http://laws-lois.justice.gc.ca/eng/acts/E-4.56/FullText.html. (Retrieved June 11, 2017).

3 S. Larson. "Heading for the Exits." *Occupational Health & Safety* 72, no. 2 (February 2003): 60.

4 C. Schroll. "Evacuation Planning: A Matter of Life and Death." *Occupational Hazards* (June 2002): 50–54.

5 Ibid., 54.

6 Ibid., 54.

7 E. Johnson. "Where Disaster Strikes." *Safety & Health* 145, no. 2: 29.

8 Ibid., 28.

9 Ibid., 29.

10 Ibid., 30.

11 National Safety Council. "Trained for Trauma." *Safety & Health* 145, no. 2: 32.

12 U.S. Office of Personnel Management. "Handling Traumatic Events." [Online]. Available: opm.gov/policy-data-oversight/worklife/reference-materials/traumaticevents.pdf. (Retrieved August 13, 2017).

13 *The Canadian Encyclopedia*. "Terrorism and Canada." [Online]. Available: http://www.thecanadianencyclopedia.ca/en/article/terrorism/. (Retrieved June 10, 2017).

14 Canadian Security Intelligence Service. (August 9, 2002). "Counter-Terrorism." [Online]. Available: http://www.csis-scrs.gc.ca/eng/operat/ct_e.html. (Retrieved January 23, 2005).

15 C. Dawson. "The Role of the Employer in Domestic Security." *Occupational Hazards* (January 2002): 31–32.

16 D. M. Petroff. "Security of Hazardous Materials." *Occupational Health & Safety* 72, no. 4 (April 2003): 44–48.

17 Ibid., 48.

18 American Society of Safety Engineers. "ASSE Offers Business Resumption Safety Checklist." *Occupational Health & Safety*. [Online]. Available: ohsonline.com/stevens/ohspub.nsf/d3d5b4f938b22b6e8625670c006bc58/6600. (Retrieved July 10, 2013).

Chapter 25
Computers, Automation, and Robots

robot A machine capable of conducting complex tasks, often created to increase productivity or accuracy, or to reduce worker stress and injury.

robotics Interdisciplinary field of science and engineering that deals with the design, construction, and control of robots.

automation The state of being operated automatically.

Automation of the workplace has changed, and continues to change, how work is done. The introduction of automated processes that involve computers and **robots** has changed the environment of the modern workplace and what is needed to succeed in it. The proliferation of automated systems and **robotics** can be seen in workplaces ranging from warehouses to fast food restaurants to manufacturing. These advanced technological systems can dramatically increase productivity and, at the same time, reduce worker stress and injury from tasks associated with numerous occupations.

IMPACT OF AUTOMATION ON THE WORKPLACE

The advent of **automation** in the workplace was the next logical step on a continuum of developments intended to enhance productivity, quality, and competitiveness. This continuum began when humans first developed simple tools to assist them in doing work. This was the age of hand tools and manual work. It was eventually superseded by the age of mechanization during the Industrial Revolution. During the age of mechanization, machines were developed to do work previously done by humans using hand tools. The 1960s saw the beginnings of broad-based efforts at automating mechanical processes and systems.

These early attempts at automation resulted in islands of automation—or individual automated systems lacking electronic communication with other related systems. Examples of islands of automation are a stand-alone computer numerical control milling machine or a personal computer-based word-processing system, neither of which is connected to other related systems. Local area networks (LANs) for integrating personal computers are an example of integration in the office. Computer-integrated manufacturing is an example in the factory.

These developments impact the workplace. According to Ebukuro, automation and integration have the following effects on workers:

- Reducing the amount of physical labour workers must perform.

- Increasing the amount of mental work required.

- Polarizing work into mental jobs and labour-intensive jobs.

- Increasing the stress levels of managers.

- Decreasing the need for traditional blue-collar workers.

- Decreasing the feelings of loyalty that workers feel toward employers.

- Increasing workers' feelings of powerlessness and helplessness.[1]

These various effects of automation are resulting in a marked increase in the amount of stress experienced by workers. Two factors in particular lead to increased levels of stress: rapid, continual change and an accompanying feeling of helplessness. With automation, the rate of change has increased. As a result, workers must continually learn and relearn their jobs with little or no relief. In addition, automated machines do more of the work that used to be done by humans.

Workplace stress is a complex concept involving physiological, psychological, and social factors. People become stressed when there is an imbalance between the demands placed on them and their ability to respond.[2] Automation appears to be increasing the instances in which such an imbalance occurs. This chapter focuses on the health and safety concerns associated with computers, robots, and automation, and the appropriate measures for dealing with these concerns. Refer to Chapter 23 for detailed information on the causes and effects of workplace stress.

HUMAN–ROBOT INTERACTION

Every new tool developed to enhance the ability of humans to work efficiently and effectively has brought with it a new health and safety hazard. This is particularly the case with industrial robots. What makes robots more potentially dangerous than other machines can be summarized as follows: (1) their ability to be hacked or sabotaged through programming, (2) their flexibility and range of motion, (3) their speed of movement, and (4) their power.

Robots are so widely used now that they are no longer the oddity they once were. Consequently, there is plenty of human–robot interaction in modern industry. The innovative hub for automation and use of robots in Canada is in the manufacturing field, especially in the automotive manufacturing industry where sophisticated robots perform tasks that require greater strength, endurance, and precision than can be provided by humans. Robots can also spare workers from exposure to hazardous environments created by welding, painting, or cleaning processes. According to Yamashita, "At ordinary factories human workers and robots coexist, creating such problems as cooperation and competition between man and machines and safety."[3]

How does human–robot interaction differ from human interaction with other machines? This is an important question for health and safety professionals. According to

Lena Martensson of the Royal Institute of Technology in Stockholm, Sweden, the modern factory has, or is moving toward having, the following characteristics:

- Workers will supervise machine systems rather than interact with individual pieces of production equipment.
- Workers will communicate with machines via video display terminals on which complex information processed by a computer will be displayed.
- Workers will be supported by expert systems for fault identification, diagnosis, and repair.[4]

Robots and other intelligent computer-controlled machines play an increasingly important role in modern industry. As this evolves, health and safety professionals must be concerned about the new workplace hazards that will be created.

HEALTH AND SAFETY PROBLEMS ASSOCIATED WITH ROBOTS

Robots are being used in industry for such applications as arc welding, spot welding, spray painting, materials handling and assembly, and loading and unloading of machines. Figure 25–1 is an example of a modern industrial robot being used in typical applications. According to the US National Safety Council, the principal hazards associated with robots are as follows:

- Being struck by a moving robot while inside the work envelope. The work envelope of a robot is the total area within which the moving parts of the robot actually move. Figure 25–2 is an example of a robot's work envelope.
- Being trapped between a moving part of a robot and another machine, object, or surface.
- Being struck by a workpiece, tool, or other object dropped or ejected by a robot.[5]

Figure 25–1 Industrial robot.

Rainer Plendl/Shutterstock

Until a worker enters the work envelope of a robot, there is little probability of an accident. However, whenever a worker enters a functioning robot's work envelope, the probability becomes very high. The only logical reason for a worker to enter the work envelope of an engaged robot is to teach it a new motion.

Figure 25–2 A robot's work envelope.

Model 762

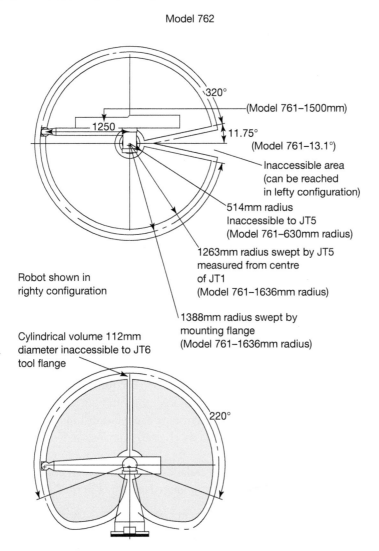

320°

(Model 761–1500mm)

1250

11.75°

(Model 761–13.1°)

Inaccessible area
(can be reached
in lefty configuration)

514mm radius
Inaccessible to JT5
(Model 761–630mm radius)

1263mm radius swept by JT5
measured from centre
of JT1
(Model 761–1636mm radius)

Robot shown in
righty configuration

1388mm radius swept by
mounting flange
(Model 761–1636mm radius)

Cylindrical volume 112mm
diameter inaccessible to JT6
tool flange

220°

Source: Courtesy of Unimation, Inc.

Minimizing the Health and Safety Problems of Robots

If human workers never had to enter a work envelope, the health and safety problems associated with robots would be minimal. However, workers must occasionally do so. Therefore health and safety professionals must be concerned with ensuring safe human–robot interaction.

The US National Safety Council recommends several strategies for minimizing the hazards associated with robots. The general strategies are summarized as follows:

- Ensure a glare-free, well-lit robot site. The recommended light intensity is 538.2–1076.4 Lux (lumen per m) (or 50–100 foot-candles [lumen per ft]).

- Keep the floors in and around the robot site carefully maintained, clean, and free of obstructions so that workers do not trip or slip into the work envelope.

- Keep the robot site free of associated hazards such as blinding light from welding machines or vapours from a paint booth.

- Equip electrical and pneumatic components of the robot with fixed covers and guards.

- Clear the work envelope of all nonessential objects and make sure all safeguards are in place before starting the robot.

- Apply lockout and proper test procedures before entering the work envelope.

- Remove and account for all tools and equipment used to maintain the robot before starting it.[6]

Because of the gradual evolution of robots and many other complex automated processes, they are not specifically mentioned in the safety legislation for most Canadian jurisdictions, but are usually considered to be the same as any other industrial machine. CSA, however, provides a comprehensive set of guidelines for the selection, installation, use, and maintenance of such equipment in its Z432, *Safeguarding of Machinery* standards. Safety personnel should be familiar with these standards along with the regulations covering their jurisdiction when robots are used in the workplace.

INDUSTRIAL MEDICINE AND ROBOTS

industrial medicine A specialized field that is concerned with work-related health and safety issues.

Industrial medicine is a specialized field that is concerned with work-related health and safety issues. Practitioners of **industrial medicine** are becoming increasingly concerned with the interaction of humans and automated machines, particularly robots and computers. They are concerned about maladaptation to an automated environment.

According to Masamitsu Oshima of Japan's Medical Information System Development Center, maladaptation can manifest itself as an urge to quit work, fatigue, problems with human relations, a drop in work performance, social pathological phenomena such as drug use or crime, mood swings, a loss of motivation, and accidents.[7] Practitioners of industrial medicine are concerned with improving the relationship between humans and automated machines by establishing methods whereby humans can work more adequately with the machines.[8]

Oshima makes the following recommendations for improving the interaction between humans and robots, computers, and other automated machines in the high-tech workplace:

- Match the human system and the computer system.

- Position machine systems as human-supportive systems.

- Adapt human–computer interaction to human use.

- Initiate job-changing opportunities.

- Allow suitable rest periods for users of automated equipment.

- Vitalize the workplace.

- Encourage recreation.

- Promote the effective use of nonworking hours.

- Increase the contact with nature.

- Free people from hazardous, dirty, and harmful jobs.

- Shorten working hours and promote work sharing.

- Expand human contact.

- Harmonize people, things, and the environment ergonomically.[9]

It should be obvious from reviewing this list that it was developed with the Japanese culture in mind. However, these recommendations can also be applied to the Canadian workplace. As human workers continually increase the amount of their interaction with automated machines, the potential for maladaptation also increases. One key to preventing maladaptation is to design automated systems around the needs of humans rather than designing them in a vacuum and then expecting humans to adapt. Another is to pay special attention to establishing and maintaining human contact for workers who interact primarily with automated machines and systems. These are areas in which attentive health and safety professionals can have a positive impact.

TECHNOLOGICAL ALIENATION IN THE AUTOMATED WORKPLACE

As technology has become more widely used in the workplace, particularly automated technology, some workers have come to resent its impact on their lives. This concept is known as **technological alienation**. According to Gary Benson of the University of Wyoming, this concept has several meanings, all of which encompass one or more of the following:

- **Powerlessness** is the feeling that workers have when they are not able to control the work environment. Powerless workers may feel that they are less important than the technology with which they work and that they are expendable.

- **Meaninglessness** is the feeling that workers get when their jobs become so specialized and technology-dependent that they cannot see the meaning in their work as it relates to the finished product or service.

- **Normlessness** is the phenomenon in which people working in a highly automated environment can become estranged from society. Normless people lose sight of society's norms, rules, and mores.[10]

technological alienation The frame of mind that results when employees come to resent technology and the impact that it has on their lives.

powerlessness The feeling that workers have when they are not able to control the work environment.

meaninglessness The feeling that workers get when their jobs become so specialized and technology-dependent that they cannot see the meaning in their work as it relates to the finished product or service.

normlessness The phenomenon in which people working in a highly automated environment can become estranged from society.

>>> SAFETY FACT   CTDs Are More Than Carpal Tunnel Syndrome

The personal computer has become an all-pervasive and universal tool. Jobs from the shop floor to the executive office now involve frequent, repetitive computer use. This means that people in the workplace are typing and clicking at an unprecedented pace. Frequent and, for some, constant computer use has led to an explosion of injuries heretofore seen mostly in the meatpacking industry. Collectively, these injuries are known as *cumulative trauma disorders (CTDs)*.

Cumulative trauma disorders are caused by forceful or awkward hand movements repeated frequently over time. Other aggravating factors include poor posture, an improperly designed workstation, and job stress. CTDs occur to the muscles, nerves, and tendons of the hands, arms, shoulders, and neck. Carpal tunnel syndrome is a common diagnosis for a broad range of occupations, but is only one of many CTDs.

Benson investigated what he considers to be the most devastating form of technological alienation—**mindlessness**.[11] Mindlessness is the result of the process of "dumbing down" the workplace. This is a concept that accompanied automation. In the past, machines have been used to do physical work previously done by human workers. With the advent of computers, robots, and automation, machines began doing mental work. According to Benson,

mindlessness The result of the process of "dumbing down" the workplace and setting people up to not have to use their minds or think in order to do their work.

> The net result is jobs and work environments where people do not have to use their minds or think to do their work—an environment where computers, robots, and other forms of high technology do the thinking.[12]

Mindlessness on the job should be of interest to health and safety professionals because of the other problems it can create. According to Benson, these problems include an increase in alcoholism, drug abuse, employee theft, work-related accidents, absenteeism, sick-leave abuse, turnover rates, and employee personal problems. Mindlessness can also lead to a decrease in job performance, productivity, and work quality.[13]

Each of these problems can, in turn, increase the potential for health and safety problems on the job. Employees who abuse alcohol and drugs represent a serious threat in the workplace. Absent employees force their coworkers to double up. High turnover results in a steady influx of inexperienced workers. Employees with personal problems may not be properly focused on accident prevention measures. Finally, when productivity and quality fall, supervisors can feel so much pressure to improve performance that they overlook or put aside safety precautions. These are the potentially negative health and safety effects of mindlessness in the automated workplace.

According to Benson,

> What is needed now are more employees who are aware of and willing to do something about the problem and more research into the phenomenon and causes of the solutions for mindlessness in technological alienation. This is surely a phenomenon of modern-day worklife that must be dealt with effectively—and immediately.[14]

MINIMIZING THE PROBLEMS OF AUTOMATION

The infusion of technology into the workplace has presented health and safety professionals with an entirely new set of challenges. Among the most pressing of these is the need to identify and minimize the new health and safety problems specifically associated with automation. Behavioural scientist A. B. Cherns developed a "sociotechnical system theory" for doing so that consists of the following components: variance control, boundary location, work group organization, management support, **design process**, quality of work life, and an ergonomics management program.[15]

design process A plan of action for reaching a goal.

Although the sociotechnical system theory was developed in 1977, it has even more relevance now than it did then. According to Yoshio Hayashi of Japan's Keio University,

> The safety and health of workers in this high technology age cannot be discussed within the conventional framework of one worker assigned to one machine. . . . The socio-technical system may be roughly understood if the *man* and *machine* in the man–machine system are replaced by *socio* and *technical* respectively. It refers to a system composed of a work group and high technology.[16]

The various components in the sociotechnical system theory explain what must happen if humans and technological systems are going to work together harmoniously and safely. Health and safety professionals can apply the theory as they work to minimize the potential problems associated with automation in the modern workplace. These components can be summarized as follows:

- *Variance control* involves controlling the unexpected events that can be introduced by new technologies. For example, a runaway, out-of-control industrial robot introduces unexpected safety hazards at variance with the expectations of workers and management. Variance control involves bringing the situation under control and establishing appropriate preventive measures for the future.

- The concept of *boundary location* involves the classification of work. What specific tasks are included in an employee's job description? Does a robot technician just operate the robot, or is he or she also required to teach and maintain the robot? The accident prevention measures learned by an employee should cover all tasks in his or her job description.

- The concept of *work group organization* involves identifying the tasks that a work group is to perform and how these tasks are to be performed. The key is to make sure that all work group members have the training needed to effectively and safely accomplish all tasks assigned to them.

- *Management support* is perhaps the most important of the components of the sociotechnical system theory. It states that, in the age of high technology, managers must be willing to accept occasional temporary declines in productivity without resorting to shortcuts or improvement efforts that may be unsafe or unhealthy. Management must be willing to emphasize safety in spite of temporary declines in productivity.

- The *design process* component refers to the ability of an organization to design itself in ways that promote productivity, quality, competitiveness, safety, and health. It also involves the ability to continually redesign as technological advances and other circumstances dictate.

- *Quality of work life* involves determining ways to promote the morale and best interests of workers. The key is to ensure that technology extends the abilities of humans and that technological systems are *human centred*. In other words, it is important to ensure that people control systems rather than vice versa.

- An *ergonomics management program* consists of activities undertaken to prevent ergonomics-related injuries and disorders. Such a program should have at least the following components: work-site analysis, hazard control, health surveillance, and training. Refer to Chapter 14 for a detailed explanation of this concept.[17]

If the sociotechnical system theory is fully applied, the health and safety hazards of the automated workplace can be minimized. Health and safety professionals can play a key role in making sure the theory is applied. To play such a role, these professionals must be technicians, diplomats, trainers, and lobbyists. They must work with the technical aspects of variance control, boundary location, work group organization, and the design process. They must be diplomats in working with supervisors and employees in promoting adherence to safe work practices. They must be trainers in order to ensure that all employees know how to apply safe work practices and appropriate accident prevention techniques. Finally, they must be lobbyists as they continually interact with management to establish and maintain management support for safety, health, and quality of life issues.

Safety Measures for Automated Systems

The sociotechnical system theory discussed in the previous section is broad and conceptual in nature. Modern health and safety professionals also need to know specific measures that can be taken to minimize the hazards associated with robots and other automated systems. Minoru Goto of the Nissan Motor Company's safety department developed specific safety measures in the categories of technological systems, auxiliary equipment, and training.[18]

Examples of safety measures that can be used at the technological systems level include:

- Construction of a safety fence around the system that defines the work envelope of the system.

- Control of the speed of movement of system components when working inside the work fence.

- Installation of an emergency stop device that is coloured red and placed in an easily accessible location.

- Location of the control panel for the system outside of the safety fence.

- Establishment of automatic shutdown switches that activate any time a system component goes beyond its predetermined operational range.[19]

Safety measures relating to training include training system operators to work safely within the work envelope and to work together as a team when interacting with the system. Maintenance workers should be trained on the technical aspects of maintaining all machines and equipment that make up the system. This is important because the safety level of the system is the sum of the safety levels of its individual components. A system with four properly operating components and just one faulty component is an unsafe system.[20]

CHALLENGE FOR THE FUTURE

Much more effort has gone into developing automated systems to improve productivity than has gone into the appropriate matching of people and technology. Now, with the speed of technical development being what it is, the health and safety problems associated with automation, particularly stress-related problems, are likely to increase. According to Kensaburo Tsuchiya of Japan's University of Occupational Health and Safety, the challenge for the future is "to create jobs which are free from stress and musculoskeletal overloads while at the same time being challenging and interesting for the individual."[21]

The future holds a number of problems that will have to be addressed to meet Tsuchiya's challenge. The most prominent of these are as follows:

- Increasingly intense international competition may magnify the tendency for companies to neglect health and safety precautions in favour of short-term productivity gains.
- The level of mental stress is likely to increase as the automated manipulation of information forces workers to try continually to handle too much information that is poorly understood.
- Automation and competition are likely to increase the level of anxiety as workers are required to make split-second decisions while knowing that their actions or inactions may have dire consequences.

occupational diseases
Pathological conditions brought about by workplace conditions or factors.

- New **occupational diseases** relating to mental, visual, and musculoskeletal problems may arise whose remedies must be sought through a combination of ergonomics, psychology, occupational medicine, and design.
- There is likely to be increased introduction of robots into the workplace with even less foresight that will, in turn, introduce more unexpected health and safety risks.
- Ignorance may lead to the introduction of automation in an office or factory in forms that do not require workers to think, reason, or make judgments, giving rise to alienation and frustration.
- An aging workforce will continue to raise new issues concerning the special needs of older workers and their interaction with automated technologies.[22]

Because they are likely to face these inhibitors, the health and safety professionals of the future must be prepared to deal with them. They need to know what has to happen if the inhibitors are to be overcome. Tsuchiya suggests the following strategies for enhancing the health and safety of tomorrow's automated workplace:

- Technological systems and processes must be designed to take into account the physical, mental, and emotional needs of human workers.
- Workers will need training and continual retraining so that they can effectively and efficiently operate technological systems and interact with them from the perspective of mastery rather than inadequacy.

ergonomists Scientists who study the interaction of workers and their surroundings.

- Health and safety professionals, management, workers, psychologists, **ergonomists**, and practitioners of occupational medicine will have to work together as a team in all aspects of the health and safety program.
- The quality of work life and health and safety considerations will have to receive as much attention in the design and implementation of automated systems and processes as do economic and technological concerns.

- Additional research will have to be conducted to determine more clearly the psychological and physiological effects of human interaction with automated technologies.

- Much more comprehensive accident reporting will be needed. Implementation of the "critical incident" reporting system used in commercial aviation may be considered by companies for collecting health and safety data.

- Ergonomists should become involved in accident prevention. They should focus their accident prevention activities on accident and error analysis and simulation of accidents for training purposes. They should also be involved in systems design; human performance; cognitive performance; workload and methods design; the study of factors contributing to accidents and injuries related to equipment, tool, and workstation design; and issues relating to an aging and more diverse workforce.[23]

Tsuchiya sums up his thoughts regarding the future of the automated workplace as it relates to health and safety:

> A motivating, satisfying and good quality job should be consistent with a safe, healthy and efficient automated workplace. Intermediate stages of new technologies sometimes lead to repetitive and monotonous tasks and these must be replanned to minimize adverse reactions to them. Where technology reduces the number of operators, isolation should be avoided for safety and to increase social contacts to reduce stress. When people can work or act together in small groups, even for a short period of the working day, human and productivity advantages can arise (e.g., group discussion of production activities). Where technologies or products are changing rapidly a workforce with good intercommunications can be even more important in keeping productivity high.[24]

AUTONOMOUS VEHICLES

For decades **autonomous vehicles** have been used in manufacturing and warehousing environments. For the most part these materials-handling machines are confined to a fixed area and a set path, which enables many of the safety hazards to be mitigated with barriers or relatively simple safety devices or programming. However, with rapid technological advances and competition among the automotive and technology companies, autonomous vehicles are destined to become commonplace on our streets.

autonomous vehicles Vehicles capable of navigating without human assistance.

Autonomous vehicles are capable of navigating without human assistance and often use a range of technological applications to detect their surroundings including terrain, obstacles, location, and environment. Many of the features on which the *self-driving* or *driverless* vehicles operate have evolved from safety systems incorporated into our cars. Anti-lock brakes, adaptive cruise control, traction control, navigation systems, backup cameras, steering assist, park assist, sophisticated computer systems for entertainment and comfort, and advanced drivetrain systems have all contributed to the development of autonomous vehicles.

The impact of autonomous vehicles will be felt far beyond the materials-handling and transportation industries. Consider the prevalence of vehicles and driving in our work and everyday lives, or even our daily commute. If only a small percentage of traffic accidents were avoided, hundreds of lives could be saved and immeasurable pain, suffering, and costs could also be avoided. The personal and public safety implications will be far reaching. The number and severity of these crashes could be dramatically reduced with autonomous vehicles, especially since 95 percent of all traffic fatalities are the result of human error.[25]

We are in the early days of this emerging technology and have already seen high-profile incidents being reported. As new technologies and systems are developed, new hazards will be recognized. For example, driverless vehicles, which are connected wirelessly for software updates and monitoring, are prone to cyber-hacking. This technology also lends itself to concerns around privacy and unauthorized monitoring of driving behaviour.

While autonomous vehicles are already statistically significantly safer than those driver controlled, accidents are inevitable. If a component fails on a vehicle, most drivers are able to make split-second complex decisions to compensate for the malfunction and navigate their car to safety—will autonomous vehicles be able to handle these unanticipated events? How will rural settings, with poorly marked roads, be navigated? Currently the ability to summon a vehicle from a garage or parkade exists, which is entering Level 4 automation level. When this technology progresses, so that you can summon your vehicle to your work or airport, who looks after the scene if an accident occurs on the way? Insurance companies, vehicle manufacturers, government regulators, and safety professionals will continue to seek out ways to mitigate these hazards and ongoing challenges.

>>> **SAFETY FACT** | **Automated Driving Systems**

The Society of Automotive Engineers (SAE) defines six levels of vehicle automation in their standard J3016: Taxonomy and Definitions for Terms Related to On-Road Motor Vehicle Automated Driving Systems.

Level 0—No automation: The driver controls all driving.

Level 1—Driver assistance: Computer may assist with features such as cruise control.

Level 2—Partial automation: The car can steer, accelerate, and decelerate without the driver touching the steering wheel or pedals, but the driver must be ready to take over instantly.

Level 3—Conditional automation: The car is responsible for driving, monitoring the environment, and making decisions. The driver has to be ready to take over at this level as well.

Level 4—High automation: The car can drive in all situations, in well-mapped locations.

Level 5—Full automation: No option for driver control.

While technological changes will enhance productivity and, in most cases, improve worker safety, many new challenges will be created for human resources and safety professionals. Who will operate and program these robots? Will jobs be lost? What fundamental level of literacy will be required by the new workforce? Numerous ethical dilemmas will arise when these machines fail to operate as planned or when they make a "choice" that causes harm to a person. The unintended consequences to both physical and psychological health that arise with any advances in technology will continue to be addressed as safety professionals strive for continuous improvement and zero harm to workers.

SUMMARY

1. The introduction of automation in the workplace has had several different effects on workers, including reducing the amount of physical labour required, increasing the amount of mental work required (in some cases), polarizing work into mental jobs and labour-intensive jobs, increasing stress levels, decreasing the need for blue-collar workers, decreasing loyalty of workers, and increasing feelings of powerlessness and helplessness.

2. What makes robots potentially dangerous to humans is their ability to be hacked or sabotaged through programming, their flexibility and range of motion, their speed of movement, and their power.

3. Specific health and safety risks associated with robots include the following: being struck by a moving robot while inside the work envelope, entrapment between a moving robot and another machine, and being struck by a workpiece, tool, or other object dropped or ejected by a robot.

4. There are numerous strategies for minimizing the health and safety hazards of robots and other automated machines. They include ensuring a well-lit, glare-free robot site; maintaining good housekeeping around the robot site; keeping the robot site free of associated hazards (bright light from welding, paint vapours); having fixed covers over the electrical and pneumatic components of the robot; keeping the work envelope clear of all nonessential objects; using appropriate lockout and test procedures; and removing maintenance tools and supplies from the work envelope before starting the robot.

5. Maladaptation to automated technologies could manifest itself as an urge to quit work, fatigue, problems with human relations, a drop in work performance, social pathological phenomena such as drug use or crime, mood swings, a loss of motivation, and accidents.

6. Technological alienation is the frame of mind that results when employees come to resent technology and the impact that it has on their lives. It is characterized by feelings of powerlessness, meaninglessness, and normlessness.

7. Mindlessness is the result of the dumbing down of the workplace so that workers are not required to use their minds in their work.

8. Problems associated with mindlessness include an increase in alcoholism, drug abuse, employee theft, work-related accidents, absenteeism, sick-leave abuse, turnover rates, and employee personal problems.

9. The sociotechnical system theory consists of the following components: variance control, boundary location, work group organization, management support, design process, quality of work life, and an ergonomic management program.

10. Problems that are likely to be associated with automation in the future include the following: the tendency to overlook health and safety precautions for short-term productivity gains may be exacerbated by increasingly intense international competition; the level of mental stress to which workers are subjected is likely to increase; the level of anxiety will increase as workers are required to make split-second decisions; new occupational diseases are likely to be introduced; increased introduction of robots will introduce more unexpected health and safety risks; the tendency to dumb down the workplace is likely to continue; and new issues concerning special needs of older workers will arise.

11. Strategies for overcoming anticipated future problems include better design of technological systems; training and continual retraining; teaming health and safety professionals with management, workers, psychologists, ergonomists, and practitioners of occupational medicine; giving quality of work life and health and safety considerations as much attention as economic and technological concerns; more research; better accident reporting; and the involvement of ergonomists in accident prevention.

12. Of all motor vehicle accidents that occur, 95 percent are caused by human error. Autonomous vehicles can impact the workplace and workers by reducing exposure to hazards associated with driving.

Key Terms and Concepts

Automation	Meaninglessness	Powerlessness
Autonomous vehicles	Mindlessness	Robot
Design process	Normlessness	Robotics
Ergonomists	Occupational diseases	Technological alienation
Industrial medicine		

Review Questions

1. Briefly summarize how automation has changed the workplace.

2. List five effects that automation of the workplace has had on workers.

3. Explain the four factors that make robots more potentially dangerous than other machines.

4. List and explain the specific hazards associated with human–robot interaction.

5. Explain four specific strategies for minimizing the hazards associated with interacting with a robot.

6. List five strategies for minimizing the potential for occurrences of maladaptation.

7. Define the following automation-related terms: *technological alienation, powerlessness, meaninglessness, normlessness,* and *mindlessness.*

8. Mindlessness in the workplace can lead to a number of other problems. Name five of them.

9. What effect may increasingly intense international competition and the need to improve productivity have on workplace health and safety in the future?

10. What hazards and benefits will be created with driverless vehicles?

Weblinks

Futurism

www.futurism.com

This website is an excellent source for the latest research and news on technology and its impact on science, work, government, and society.

Transport Canada

www.tc.gc.ca/eng/motorvehiclesafety/safevehicles-vehicle-safety-related-technologies-1068.htm

The Advanced Vehicle Technologies page has information on emerging vehicle technology and regulations for vehicles used on Canadian roads.

Canadian Centre for Occupational Health and Safety (CCOHS)

www.ccohs.ca/oshanswers/ergonomics/sitting/sitting_overview.html

One significant effect that automation and computers has on workers is the excessive sitting we do at work. This CCOHS link has information on the effect of and solutions to this new health problem facing many workers.

Endnotes

[1] R. Ebukuro. "Alleviation of the Impact of Microelectronics on Labour." *Occupational Health and Safety in Automation and Robotics.* K. Noro, ed. (Chicago: National Safety Council, 1987), 5.

[2] O. Ostberg. "Emerging Technology and Trends in Blue-Collar Stress." *Occupational Health and Safety,* 17.

[3] T. Yamashita. "The Interaction Between Man and Robot in High Technology Industries." *Occupational Health and Safety,* 140.

[4] L. Martensson. "Interaction Between Man and Robots with Some Emphasis on 'Intelligent' Robots." *Occupational Health and Safety*, 144.

[5] National Safety Council. *Robots*, Data Sheet 1–717–85 (Chicago: National Safety Council, 1991), 1.

[6] Ibid., 9.

[7] M. Oshima. "The Role of Industrial Medicine at the Man–Robot Interface." *Occupational Health and Safety*, 284–285.

[8] Ibid., 284.

[9] Ibid., 285.

[10] G. Benson. "Mindlessness: A New Dimension of Technological Alienation—Implications for the Man–Machine Interface in High Technology Work Environments." *Occupational Health and Safety*, 326–327.

[11] Ibid., 328.

[12] Ibid.

[13] Ibid., 232.

[14] Ibid., 336.

[15] A. B. Cherns. "Can Behavioral Science Help Design Organizations?" *Organizational Dynamics*, 44–64.

[16] Y. Hayashi. "Measures for Improving the Occupational Health and Safety of People Working with VDTs or Robots—Small-Group Activities and Safety and Health Education." *Occupational Health and Safety*, 383.

[17] Ibid., 384.

[18] M. Goto. "Occupational Safety and Health Measures Taken for the Introduction of Robots in the Automobile Industry." *Occupational Health and Safety*, 399–417.

[19] Ibid., 404–408.

[20] Ibid., 411–413.

[21] K. Tsuchiya. "Summary Report on the Fifth University of Occupational and Environmental Health International Symposium." *Occupational Health and Safety*, 422.

[22] Ibid., 422–426.

[23] Ibid.

[24] Ibid., 425–426.

[25] Andrew Choi. *Future*. (October 28, 2016). "Governments Are Investing in Self-Driving Cars Because They Will Save Lives." [Online]. Available: https://futurism.com/governments-are-investing-in-self-driving-cars-because-they-will-save-lives/. (Retrieved June 24, 2017).

Chapter 26
Ethics and Safety

Practically everyone agrees that the business practices of industrial firms should be above reproach with regard to ethical standards. Few people are willing to defend unethical behaviour. And for the most part, industry in Canada operates within the scope of accepted legal and ethical standards.

This is important because "companies and business people who wish to thrive long-term must adopt sound ethical decision-making practices. Companies and people who behave in a socially responsible manner are much more likely to enjoy ultimate success than those whose actions are motivated solely by profits. Knowing the difference between right and wrong and choosing what is right is the foundation for ethical decision-making. In many cases, doing the right thing often leads to the greatest financial, social, and personal rewards in the long run."[1]

However, unethical behaviour does occur frequently enough that modern health and safety professionals should be aware of the types of ethical dilemmas that they may occasionally face, and they should know how to deal with such issues.

AN ETHICAL DILEMMA

According to Stead, Worrell, and Stead,

> Managing ethical behavior is one of the most pervasive and complex problems facing business organizations today. Employees' decisions to behave ethically or unethically are influenced by a myriad of individual and situational factors. Background, personality, decision history, managerial philosophy, and reinforcement are but a few of the factors which have been identified by researchers as determinants of employees' behavior when faced with ethical dilemmas.[2]

Consider the following example of an ethical dilemma:

Mil-Tech Manufacturing Company is a Department of National Defence contractor that produces air- and watertight aluminum containers for shipping non-nuclear munitions such as missiles, bombs, and torpedoes. Business has been good and Mil-Tech is prospering. However, the company's management team has a problem.

Mil-Tech has been awarded a contract to produce 10,000 boxes in 6 months. The company's maximum capacity is currently 1,000 boxes per month. Unless Mil-Tech can find a way to increase its capacity, the company will be forced to add new facilities, equipment, and personnel—an expensive undertaking that will quickly eat up the projected profits of the new contract.

The most time-consuming bottleneck in the production of the boxes is the painting process, the last step. The problem is with the paint that Mil-Tech uses. It poses no health, safety, or environmental hazards, but it is difficult to apply and requires at least 2 hours to dry. Clearly, the most expeditious way to increase productivity is to find a paint that is easier to apply and takes less time to dry.

The production manager has been searching frantically for a substitute paint for 2 weeks and has finally found one. The new paint is easy to apply, and it dries almost on contact. However, it is extremely toxic and can be dangerous to anyone exposed to it at any time before it dries. Personal protective equipment and other hazard-prevention techniques can minimize the health problems, but they must be used properly with absolutely no shortcuts. In addition, it is recommended that every employee who will work with the paint complete 3 full days of training.

Mil-Tech's management team is convinced that the union will not consent to the use of this paint even if the personal protective equipment is purchased and the training is provided. To complicate matters, the supplier of the paint cannot provide the training within a timeframe that meets Mil-Tech's needs. In a secret meeting, top management officials decide to purchase personal protective equipment, use the new paint, and forego the training. More important, the management team decides to withhold all information about the hazards associated with the new paint.

Camillo Garcia, Mil-Tech's health and safety manager, was not invited to the secret meeting. However, the decisions made during the meeting were slipped to him anonymously. Garcia now faces an ethical dilemma. What should he do?

If he chooses to do nothing, Mil-Tech employees may be inappropriately exposed to an extremely hazardous substance. If he confronts the management team with what he knows, he could fall into disfavour or even lose his job. If he shares what he knows with union leaders, he may be called on to testify about what he knows. This is an example of the type of ethical dilemma that health and safety professionals might face on the job.

ETHICS DEFINED

There are many definitions of the term *ethics*. However, no one definition has emerged as universally accepted. According to Paul Taylor, the concept can be defined as "inquiry into the nature and grounds of morality where morality is taken to mean moral judgments, standards, and rules of conduct."[3] According to Arlow and Ulrich, ethical dilemmas in the workplace are more complex than ethical situations in general.[4] They involve societal expectations, competition, and social responsibility—as well as the potential consequences of an employee's behaviour on customers, coworkers, competitors, and the public at large. The result of the often conflicting and contradictory interests of workers, customers, competitors, and the general public is a natural tendency for ethical dilemmas to occur frequently in the workplace.

Whenever ethics is the topic of discussion, such terms as *conscience*, *morality*, and *legality* are frequently heard. Although these terms are closely associated with ethics, they do not, by themselves, define it. For the purpose of this book, **ethics** is defined as the study of morality within a context established by cultural and professional values, social norms, and accepted standards of behaviour.

Morality refers to the values that are subscribed to and fostered by society in general and individuals within society. Ethics attempts to apply reason in determining rules of human conduct that translate morality into everyday behaviour. **Ethical behaviour** is that which falls within the limits prescribed by morality.

How, then, does a health and safety professional know if someone's behaviour is ethical? Ethical questions are rarely black and white. They typically fall into a grey area between the two extremes of right and wrong. Personal experience, self-interest, point of view, and external pressure often cloud this grey area further.

Guidelines for Determining Ethical Behaviour

Guidelines are needed for health and safety professionals to use when trying to sort out matters that are not clearly right or wrong. First, however, it is necessary to distinguish between the concepts of *legal* and *ethical*. They are not the same thing. Just because an option is legal does not necessarily mean it is ethical.

In fact, it is not uncommon for people caught in the practice of questionable behaviour to use the "I didn't do anything illegal" defence. A person's behaviour can be well within the scope of the law and still be unethical. The following guidelines for determining ethical behaviour assume that the behaviour in question is legal (Figure 26–1):

- Apply the **morning-after test**. This test asks, "If you make this choice, how will you feel about it tomorrow morning?"

- Apply the **front-page test**. This test encourages you to make a decision that would not embarrass you if printed as a story on the front page of your hometown newspaper.

- Apply the **mirror test**. This test asks, "If you make this decision, how will you feel about yourself when you look in the mirror?"

- Apply the **role-reversal test**. This test requires you to trade places with the people affected by your decision and view the decision through their eyes.

- Apply the **common-sense test**. This test requires you to listen to what your instincts and common sense are telling you. If it feels wrong, it probably is.

Figure 26–1 Guidelines for determining what is ethical.

Guidelines for Ethical Choices

1. Apply the morning-after test.
2. Apply the front-page test.
3. Apply the mirror test.
4. Apply the role-reversal test.
5. Apply the common-sense test.

ethics The study of morality within a context established by cultural and professional values, social norms, and accepted standards of behaviour.

ethical behaviour Behaviour that falls within the limits prescribed by morality.

morning-after test Encourages people to make choices based on how they will feel about their decision the next day.

front-page test Encourages people to make a decision that would not embarrass them if it were printed as a story on the front page of their hometown newspaper.

mirror test Encourages people to make choices based on how they will feel about their decision when they look in the mirror.

role-reversal test Requires a person to trade places with the people affected by the decision that he or she made and to view the decision through their eyes.

common-sense test Requires a person to listen to what instincts and common sense are telling him or her.

Blanchard and Peale suggest their own test for deciding what the ethical choice is in a given situation.[5] Their test consists of the following three questions:

- Is it legal?
- Is it balanced?
- How will it make me feel about myself?

If a potential course of action is not legal, no further consideration is in order. If an action is not legal, it is also not ethical. If an action is balanced, it is fair to all involved. This means that health and safety professionals and their team members have responsibilities that extend well beyond the walls of their unit, organization, and company. If a course of action is in keeping with your own moral structure, it will make you feel good about yourself. Blanchard and Peale also list the following "Five P's of Ethical Power":

- **Purpose.** Individuals see themselves as ethical people who let their conscience be their guide and in all cases want to feel good about themselves.
- **Pride.** Individuals apply internal guidelines and have sufficient self-esteem to make decisions that may not be popular with others.
- **Patience.** Individuals believe right will prevail in the long run, and they are willing to wait when necessary.
- **Persistence.** Individuals are willing to stay with an ethical course of action once it has been chosen and see it through to a positive conclusion.
- **Perspective.** Individuals take the time to reflect and are guided by their own internal barometer when making ethical decisions.[6]

These tests and guidelines will help health and safety professionals make ethical choices in the workplace. In addition to internalizing the guidelines themselves, health and safety professionals may want to share these values with all employees with whom they interact.

ETHICAL BEHAVIOUR IN ORGANIZATIONS

Research by Trevino suggests that ethical behaviour in organizations is influenced by both individual and social factors.[7] Trevino identified three personality measures that can influence an employee's ethical behaviour: (1) ego strength, (2) Machiavellianism, and (3) locus of control.

An employee's **ego strength** is his or her ability to undertake self-directed tasks and to cope with tense situations. A measure of a worker's **Machiavellianism** is the extent to which he or she will attempt to deceive and confuse others. **Locus of control** is the perspective of workers concerning who or what controls their behaviour. Employees with an internal locus of control feel that they control their own behaviour. Employees with an external locus of control feel that their behaviour is controlled by external factors (e.g., rules, regulations, their health and safety professional, and so on).

Preble and Miesing suggest that social factors also influence ethical behaviour in organizations.[8] These factors include gender, role differences, religion, age, work experience, nationality, and the influence of other people who are significant in an individual's life. Luthans and Kreitner state that people learn appropriate behaviour by observing the behaviour of significant role models (parents, teachers, public officials, and so on).[9] Because health and safety professionals represent a significant role model for their team members, it is critical that they exhibit ethical behaviour that is beyond reproach in all situations.

ego strength   An employee's ability to undertake self-directed tasks and to cope with tense situations.

Machiavellianism   The extent to which an employee will attempt to deceive and confuse others.

locus of control   The perspective of workers concerning who or what controls their behaviour.

In addition to the various tests that can be used for determining ethical behaviour, there are also numerous models:

- Categorical imperative (black and white)
- Conventionalistic ethic (anything legal is ethical)
- Disclosure rule (explain actions to a wide audience)
- Doctrine of the mean (virtue through moderation)
- Golden Rule (do unto others . . .)
- Intuition rule (you will know what is right)
- Market ethic (whatever makes a profit is right)
- Means-end ethic (end justifies the means)

- Might-equals-right ethic (self-explanatory)
- Organizational ethic (loyalty to the organization)
- Practical imperative (treat people as ends, not means)
- Equal freedom (full freedom unless it deprives another)
- Proportionality ethic (good outweighs the bad)
- Professional ethic (do only what can be explained to your peers)
- Revelation ethic (answers revealed by prayer)
- Rights ethic (protect rights of others)
- Theory of justice (impartial, even-handed)

HEALTH AND SAFETY PROFESSIONALS' ROLE IN ETHICS

Using the guidelines set forth in the previous section, health and safety professionals should be able to make responsible decisions concerning ethical choices. Unfortunately, deciding what is ethical is much easier than actually doing what is ethical. In this regard, trying to practise ethics is like trying to diet. It is not so much a matter of knowing you should cut down eating; it is a matter of following through and actually doing it.

It is this fact that defines the role of health and safety professionals with regard to ethics. Their role has three parts. First, they are responsible for setting an example of ethical behaviour. Second, they are responsible for helping fellow employees identify the ethical choices when facing ethical questions. Finally, health and safety professionals are responsible for helping employees follow through and actually undertake the ethical option once the appropriate choice has been identified. In carrying out their roles, health and safety professionals can adopt one of the following approaches (Figure 26–2): the best-ratio approach, the black-and-white approach, or the full-potential approach.

Figure 26–2 Three basic approaches to handling ethical problems.

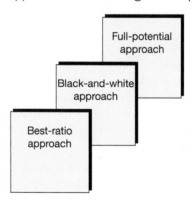

Best-Ratio Approach

best-ratio approach People are basically good and, under the right circumstances, behave ethically.

The **best-ratio approach** is the pragmatic approach. Its philosophy is that people are basically good and, under the right circumstances, behave ethically. However, under certain conditions, they can be driven to unethical behaviour. Therefore, the health and safety professional should do everything possible to create conditions that promote ethical behaviour and try to maintain the best possible ratio of good choices to bad. When hard decisions must be made, the appropriate choice is the one that does the most good for the most people. This is sometimes referred to as *situational ethics*.

Black-and-White Approach

Using the **black-and-white approach**, right is right, wrong is wrong, and circumstances are irrelevant. The health and safety professional's job is to make ethical decisions and carry them out. It is also to help employees choose the ethical route. When difficult decisions must be made, health and safety professionals should make fair and impartial choices regardless of the outcome.

black-and-white approach Right is right, wrong is wrong, and circumstances are irrelevant.

Full-Potential Approach

Health and safety professionals who use the **full-potential approach** make decisions based on how the outcomes affect the ability of those involved to achieve their full potential. The underlying philosophy is that people are responsible for realizing their full potential within the confines of morality. Choices that can achieve this goal without infringing on the rights of others are considered ethical.

full-potential approach People are responsible for realizing their full potential within the confines of morality.

Decisions made may differ, depending on the approach selected. For example, consider the ethical dilemma presented at the beginning of this chapter. If the health and safety manager, Camillo Garcia, applies the best-ratio approach, he may decide to keep quiet, encourage the proper use of personal protective equipment, and hope for the best. On the other hand, if he takes the black-and-white approach, he will be compelled to confront the Mil-Tech management team with what he knows.

THE COMPANY'S ROLE IN ETHICS

Industrial firms have a critical role to play in promoting ethical behaviour among their employees. Health and safety professionals cannot set ethical examples alone or expect employees to behave ethically in a vacuum. A company's role in ethics can be summarized as (1) creating an internal environment that promotes, expects, and rewards ethical behaviour; and (2) setting an example of ethical behaviour in all external dealings (Figure 26–3).

Figure 26–3 Ethics cannot be practised in a vacuum. The company has a critical role to play.

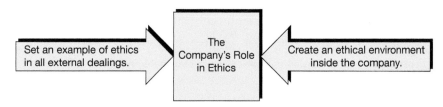

Creating an Ethical Environment

A company creates an ethical environment by establishing policies and practices that ensure that all employees are treated ethically and then enforcing these policies. Do employees have the right of due process? Do employees have access to an objective grievance

The city council members are in a real quandary about the request from International Plastics Corporation (IPC) to open a new plant on a hundred-acre plot owned by the city. On the one hand, the city needs the new jobs that the IPC plant would bring—badly. High unemployment is the city's most serious problem, and every member of the city council ran on a job-creation platform in the last election. On the other hand, the council members have learned that IPC is not always a good corporate citizen in spite of its claims to the contrary.

Several cities with IPC plants have had problems enforcing their health and safety regulations. The consensus among other cities is that IPC officials say all of the right things until contracts are signed. Then, all of a sudden, they begin to procrastinate, stonewall, and break promises. Should the city council allow IPC to build the new plant? What is your opinion?

procedure? Are there appropriate health and safety measures to protect employees? Are hiring practices fair and impartial? Are promotion practices fair and objective? Are employees protected from harassment based on race, gender, or other reasons? A company that establishes an environment that promotes, expects, and rewards ethical behaviour can answer yes to all of these questions.

One effective way to create an ethical environment is to develop an ethics philosophy and specific written guidelines for implementing that philosophy, which are shared with all employees. Stelco Inc., Canada's largest steel producer, has a Code of Ethics and Business Conduct that it shares with all employees. The code begins with the following statement of philosophy:

> Stelco is committed to conducting its business affairs in compliance with all applicable laws, statutes and regulations and expects its employees acting on its behalf to do likewise. In addition business dealings among employees and by employees, with customers, shareholders and suppliers, community organizations and governmental and regulatory authorities must be based on principles of honesty, integrity and the ethical standards outlined below. [10]

This statement sets the tone for all employees at Stelco. It lets them know that higher management not only supports ethical behaviour but also expects it. This approach makes it less difficult for health and safety professionals when they find themselves caught in the middle between the pressures of productivity and the maintenance of safe work practices.

An ethics credo shows employees that they have obligations extending well beyond their work units and that how they perform their work can have an impact, negative or positive, on fellow employees, the company, customers, and the country. Although the emphasis on ethics in the workplace is relatively new, the concept is not. According to Shanks, Robert Wood Johnson, the leader who built Johnson & Johnson into a major international corporation, developed an ethics credo for his company as early as the mid-1940s.[11]

Johnson's credo read as follows:

- To customers and users: quality and service at reasonable prices.
- To suppliers: a fair opportunity.
- To employees: respect, equal opportunity, and a sense of job security.
- To communities: a civic responsibility.
- To the environment: protection.
- To shareholders: a fair return.[12]

Written philosophies and guidelines such as those developed by Stelco and Johnson & Johnson are the first step in creating an ethical environment in the workplace. Health and safety professionals can play a key role in promoting ethical behaviour on the job by encouraging higher management to develop written ethics philosophies, credos, and guidelines and then by modelling the behaviour that they encourage.

Setting an Ethical Example

Companies that take the "Do as I say, not as I do" approach to ethics will not succeed. Employees must be able to trust their company to conduct all external and internal dealings in an ethical manner. Companies that do not pay their bills on time; companies that pollute; companies that place short-term profits ahead of employee health and safety; companies that do not live up to advertised quality standards; companies that do not stand behind their guarantees; and companies that are not good neighbours in their communities are not setting a good ethical example. Such companies can expect employees to mimic their unethical behaviour.

In addition to creating an ethical internal environment and handling external dealings in an ethical manner, companies must support health and safety professionals who make ethically correct decisions. This support must be given not just when such decisions are profitable, but in all cases. For example, in the ethical dilemma presented earlier in this chapter, say Camillo Garcia decided that his ethical choice was to confront the management team with his knowledge of the hazards associated with the new paint. Management gave the order to withhold critical information. This is obviously the profitable choice in the short run. But is it the ethical choice? If Camillo Garcia does not think so, will Mil-Tech stand behind him? If not, everything else that the company does to promote ethics will fail.

HANDLING ETHICAL DILEMMAS

No person will serve long as a health and safety professional without confronting an ethical dilemma. How, then, should one proceed when faced with such a dilemma? There are three steps (Figure 26–4):

1. Apply the various guidelines presented earlier in this chapter for determining what is ethical.
2. Select one of the three basic approaches to handling ethical questions.
3. Proceed in accordance with the approach selected, and proceed with consistency.

Figure 26–4 Handling ethical dilemmas.

Steps for Handling Ethical Dilemmas

1. Apply the guidelines.
2. Select the approach.
3. Proceed accordingly and consistently.

Apply the Guidelines

In this step, as a health and safety professional, you should apply as many of the tests set forth in Figure 26–1 as necessary to determine the ethically correct decision. In applying these guidelines, attempt to block out all mitigating circumstances and other factors that tend to cloud the issue. At this point, the goal is only to identify the ethical choice. Deciding whether to implement the ethical choice comes in the next step.

Select the Approach

When deciding how to proceed after Step 1, you have three basic approaches. These approaches, as set forth in Figure 26–2, are the best-ratio, black-and-white, and full-potential approaches. These approaches and their ramifications can be debated ad infinitum; however, selecting an approach to ethical questions is a matter of personal choice. Factors that will affect the ultimate decision include your personal makeup, the expectations of the company, and the degree of company support.

Proceed with the Decision

The approach selected in Step 2 will dictate how you should proceed as a health and safety professional. Two things are important in this final step. The first is to proceed in strict accordance with the approach selected. The second is to proceed consistently. **Consistency** is critical when handling ethical dilemmas. Fairness is a large part of ethics, and consistency is a large part of fairness. The grapevine will ensure that all employees know how a health and safety professional handles an ethical dilemma. Some will agree, and some will disagree, regardless of the decision. Such is the nature of human interaction. However, regardless of the differing perceptions of the problem, employees respect consistency. Conversely, even if the decision is universally popular, you may lose respect if the decision is not consistent with past decisions.

consistency The rules are enforced in the same manner every time with no regard to any outside factors.

QUESTIONS TO ASK WHEN MAKING DECISIONS

Health and safety professionals often must make decisions that have ethical dimensions. A constant state of tension often exists between meeting production schedules and maintaining employee safety. Health and safety professionals usually are right in the middle of these issues. Following are some questions that can and should be asked by managers when making decisions about issues that have ethical dimensions. Health and safety professionals should ask these questions themselves, and they should encourage other decision makers within their organizations to do the same.

- Has the issue or problem been thoroughly and accurately defined?
- Have all dimensions of the problem (productivity, quality, cost, safety, health, and so on) been identified?
- Would other stakeholders (employees, customers) agree with your definition of the problem?
- What is your real motivation in making this decision? Meeting a deadline? Outperforming another organizational unit or a competitor? Self-promoting? Getting the job done right? Protecting the health and safety of employees? Some combination of these?
- What is the probable short-term result of your decision? What is the probable long-term result?
- Who will be affected by your decision and in what way? In the short term? In the long term?
- Did you discuss the decision with all stakeholders (or all possible stakeholders) before making it?
- Would your decision withstand the scrutiny of employees, customers, colleagues, and the general public?

Safety professionals should ask themselves these questions, but, equally important, they should insist that other managers do so. The manager responsible for meeting this month's production quota may be so focused on the numbers that he or she overlooks safety. The manager who is feeling the pressure to cut production costs may make decisions that work in the short term but have disastrous consequences in the long term. Questions such as those posed above can help managers broaden their focus and consider the long-range impact when making decisions.

ETHICS AND WHISTLE-BLOWING

What can health and safety professionals do when their employer is violating legal or ethical standards? The first option, of course, should be to bring violations to the attention of appropriate management executives through established channels. In most cases, this will be sufficient to stop the illegal or unethical behaviour. But what about those occasions when the health and safety professional is ignored or, worse yet, told to "mind your own business"? These are the types of situations that have led to the concept of **whistle-blowing**, which can be defined as the act of informing an outside authority or media outlet of alleged illegal or unethical acts on the part of an organization or individual.

whistle-blowing Act of informing an outside authority or media outlet of alleged illegal or unethical acts on the part of an organization or individual.

Problems with Whistle-Blowing

Even when the illegal or unethical practice in question threatens the health and safety of employees, some people still don't like whistle-blowers. There is often a "don't tell" mentality that causes whistle-blowers to be shunned and viewed as outcasts. As children we learned not to be tattletales. Many adults still seem to hold to this philosophy.

>> **DISCUSSION CASE** | What Is Your Opinion?

Following are two ethical dilemmas that a health and safety professional may face. What is the right thing to do in each case? What is your opinion?

- You are the safety director for West Coast Power Company. Your son is a line worker for a branch of the company that is located in another city. He is visiting you while recuperating from a back injury for which he is collecting workers' compensation. While visiting, he jogs, lifts weights, and plays softball with friends. You finally realize that he is not really injured. What should you do?

- The manufacturing director and the union representative have just had a chin-to-chin argument about

removing the new machine guards from the milling machines. They have asked you—the company's safety director—to mediate the dispute. According to the manufacturing director, "We ran these machines for 5 years without an accident. The only reason we put them on was because some government inspector suggested it. They're fine when we are not in a hurry, but they slow us down when the rush is on. Unless we remove the guards, this job will not be shipped on time." The union representative counters by saying, "These machines are dangerous." What is the right thing to do here? What is your opinion?

The "don't be a tattletale" attitude is only one of the problems that work against whistle-blowing. Others are as follows:

- **Retribution.** People who blow the whistle on their employer may be subjected to retribution. They may be fired, transferred to an undesirable location, or reassigned to an undesirable job. They may also be shunned. There are numerous ways—legal ways—for an employer to take retribution against a whistle-blower.

- **Damaged relationships and hostility.** Blowing the whistle about an illegal or unethical practice can often damage relationships. Somebody in the company—by acts of commission or omission—is responsible. That person or those persons may be disciplined as a result. When this happens, people tend to choose a side, which, in turn, leads to damaged relationships. Damaged relationships are often manifested as hostility directed toward the whistle-blower.

- **Loss of focus.** Whistle-blowers often find that their time, energy, and attention are overtaken by the events surrounding the claim of illegal or unethical behaviour. Rather than focusing on doing their jobs, they find themselves dealing with retribution, damaged relationships, and hostility.

- **Scapegoating.** Negative consequences certainly can occur as a result of whistle-blowing. Because of this, some health and safety professionals may decide to ignore the issue or to raise it to the next level of management and let it drop there. The problem with this approach is the issue of *accountability*. When an employee is injured or the environment is damaged, the actions of health and safety professionals are certain to be closely scrutinized. "Did you know about the hazardous condition?" "Did you do everything in your power to prevent the accident or incident?" These types of questions are always asked when litigation is brought, as is often the case. An irresponsible organization facing charges of negligence may begin looking for a convenient scapegoat. One obvious candidate in such situations is the organization's chief health and safety professional.

Most statutes that protect the whistle-blower were developed with environmental protection or employment standards in mind. However, some legislation, such as the Ontario Occupational Health and Safety Act, prohibits the employer from taking reprisals against a worker who is acting in compliance with the act.

>>> DISCUSSION CASE | What Is Your Opinion?

Jack Wilson, safety director for Leader, Inc., is facing a dilemma. His employer is seeking registration as an ISO 14000 company. Internal assessments and trial audits show that the company is ready and will probably pass the registration audit with flying colours. If so, Leader will be able to double its business in just 2 years. A European company is looking for a partner in Canada. Leader wants to be that partner, but ISO 14000 registration is a prerequisite.

Leader looks good on paper, but Jack Wilson knows of a least two serious environmental problems that the company is covering up rather than correcting. Leader's Environmental Management Plan, required by ISO 14000, shows that the environmental problems have been corrected. They haven't. Worse yet, Jack Wilson has been warned to say or do nothing that may jeopardize Leader's ISO 14000 registration. On the other hand, if the environmental problems in question are not corrected soon, the community's water supply could be contaminated in the future. What should Jack Wilson do?

SUMMARY

1. Ethics is the study of morality. Morality refers to the values that are subscribed to and fostered by society. Ethics attempts to apply reason in determining rules of human conduct that translate morality into everyday behaviour.

2. Ethical behaviour is that which falls within the limits prescribed by morality.

3. *Legal* and *ethical* are not the same. If something is illegal, it is also unethical. However, just because something is legal does not mean that it is ethical. An act can be legal but unethical.

4. To determine if a choice is ethical, you can apply the following tests: morning-after, front-page, mirror, role-reversal, and common-sense.

5. Health and safety professionals have a three-pronged role with regard to ethics. They are responsible for setting an ethical example, helping employees to identify the ethical choices when facing ethical questions, and helping employees to follow through and actually undertake the ethical option.

6. Health and safety professionals have three approaches available in handling ethical dilemmas: best-ratio, black-and-white, and full-potential.

7. The company's role in ethics is to create an ethical environment and to set an ethical example. An effective way to do this is to develop a written ethics philosophy and share it with all employees.

8. Three personality characteristics that can influence an employee's ethical behaviour are ego strength, Machiavellianism, and locus of control.

9. People facing ethical dilemmas should apply the tests for determining what is ethical, select one of the three basic approaches, and proceed consistently.

10. Whistle-blowing is the act of informing an outside authority or the media of alleged illegal or unethical acts on the part of an organization or individual.

Key Terms and Concepts

Best-ratio approach	Ethical behaviour	Machiavellianism
Black-and-white approach	Ethics	Mirror test
Common-sense test	Front-page test	Morning-after test
Consistency	Full-potential approach	Role-reversal test
Ego strength	Locus of control	Whistle-blowing

Review Questions

1. Define the term *ethics*.
2. Define the term *morality*.
3. Briefly explain each of the following ethics tests: morning-after, front-page, mirror, role-reversal, and common sense.
4. List and briefly describe the Five P's of Ethical Power as set forth by Blanchard and Peale.
5. List the individual and social factors that may influence an employee's ethical behaviour.
6. What is the health and safety professional's role with regard to ethics?
7. Briefly explain the following approaches to handling ethical behaviour: best-ratio, black-and-white, and full-potential.
8. Briefly explain a company's role with regard to ethics.
9. Explain how one should proceed when facing an ethical dilemma.
10. Write a brief ethics philosophy for a chemical company.
11. What questions should health and safety professionals ask when making decisions that have an ethical component?
12. Explain the most common problems associated with whistle-blowing.

Weblinks

EthicsWeb.ca

www.ethicsweb.ca

The EthicsWeb.ca website provides useful tools for developing your own code of ethics and also has links to several organizations and associations of an ethical nature.

Values and Ethics of the Public Service

www.canada.ca/en/government/publicservice/values.html

The federal government's web page, Values and Ethics of the Public Service, provides information about diversity and employment equity, official languages, and other values of the public service.

Endnotes

[1] "A Definition for Business Ethics." [Online]. Available: business.lovetoknow.cora/wiki/A_Definition_for_Business_Ethics. (Retrieved July 13, 2013).

[2] E. W. Stead, D. L. Worrell, and J. G. Stead. "An Integrative Model for Understanding and Managing Ethical Behavior in Business Organizations." *Journal of Business Ethics* 5, no. 9: 233.

[3] P. Taylor. *Principles of Ethics: An Introduction* (Encino, CA: Dickson, 1975), 96.

[4] P. Arlow and T. A. Ulrich. "Business Ethics, Social Responsibility, and Business Students: An Empirical Comparison of Clark's Study." *Akron Business and Economic Review* 4, no. 3: 17–23.

[5] K. Blanchard and N. V. Peale. *The Power of Ethical Management* (New York: Ballantine Books), 10–17.

[6] Ibid., 79.

[7] L. K. Trevino. "Ethical Decision Making in Organizations: A Person-Situation Interactionist Model." *Academy of Management Review* 11, no. 3: 601–617.

[8] J. F. Preble and P. Miesing. "Do Adult MBA and Undergraduate Business Students Have Different Business Philosophies?" Proceedings of the National Meeting of the American Institute for the Decision Sciences (November 1984), 346–348.

[9] F. Luthans and R. Kreitner. *Organizational Behavior Modification and Beyond: An Operant and Social Learning Approach* (Glenview, IL: Scott Foresman).

[10] Stelco, Inc. (March 2003). "Code of Ethics and Business Conduct." [Online]. Available: http://www.stelco.com/code/CodeofEthics-ENG-Mar03.pdf. (Retrieved March 12, 2005).

[11] D. C. Shanks. "The Role of Leadership in Strategy Development." *Journal of Business Strategy* (January/February 1989): 32.

[12] Ibid., 33.

Chapter 27
Violence, Harassment, and Bullying in the Workplace

On June 15, 2012, five armoured car security guards were dispatched to the University of Edmonton to replenish cash in two ATMs. Four of the team entered the HUB Mall while one guard stayed with the armoured vehicle. After entering the small secure vestibule, two guards began to load the machine while being watched by a supervisor. Standing inside the secure steel door, Travis Baumgartner removed his .38 caliber pistol from its holster and shot his three colleagues—twice each, at point-blank range. He then left and went to the armoured vehicle and shot the guard there three times. Three of the guards were killed that night. The fourth guard was shot in the head and, after a year of surgery and rehabilitation, made an unexpected recovery.

WORKPLACE VIOLENCE

The immeasurable trauma and suffering caused by the events on that June evening is an example of extreme **workplace violence**. However, these types of events are becoming more frequent in our workplaces. Incidents of purely "criminal" violence by intruders into the workplace against retail and service employees in restaurants, stores, gas stations, banks, and taxis are shockingly frequent. CCOHS lists health care employees, correctional officers, social services employees, teachers, municipal housing inspectors, public works employees, and retail employees among the occupational groups most at risk from workplace violence. Violent incidents of every kind are increasing and can occur in any workplace.[1]

workplace violence Any action, conduct, threat, or gesture of a person toward an employee in their work place that can reasonably be expected to cause harm, injury, or illness to that employee.

The increased incidence and severity of violence against health care workers has been attributed to two main factors. On the one hand, austerity measures have resulted in inadequate staffing and poor levels of service that can lead to third-party violence by patients and their families, who often have to endure long waiting times and poor access to treatment. This inflicts significant stress on health workers, contributes to a culture of coworker violence and harassment, and leads to reduced staff morale and, ultimately, to workers leaving their jobs. On the other hand, health care is a largely feminized sector, and unions have highlighted gender-based violence against nurses in particular.[2]

We tend to think of violence as a physical assault. However, CCOHS describes workplace violence as "any act in which a person is abused, threatened, intimidated or assaulted in his or her employment." Rumours, swearing, verbal abuse, pranks, arguments, property damage, vandalism, sabotage, pushing, theft, physical assaults, psychological trauma, anger-related incidents, rape, arson, and murder are all examples of workplace violence.[3] In Chapter 23, we discussed the psychological impact these events can have on the worker, as well as the implications for the business.

In the federal jurisdiction, the Canada Labour Code, Occupational Health and Safety Regulations, Part XX contains a broad definition of workplace violence that is not restricted to "physical injury." Rather, violence is defined as "any action, conduct, threat or gesture of a person towards an employee in their work place that can reasonably be expected to cause harm, injury or illness to that employee." Nor is workplace violence limited to incidents that occur within a traditional workplace. Work-related violence can occur at off-site business-related functions (conferences, trade shows), at social events related to work, in clients' homes or away from work but resulting from work (a threatening telephone call to your home from a client).[4]

⟫⟫ SAFETY FACT — Workplace Violence in the News

The following list of news stories appearing on the OHS Canada website is a mere sample of workplace violence challenges faced across the country.

- Police lay murder charge in fatal stabbing at Calgary medical clinic.
- Social workers fear for their safety in "no-go zones": B.C. union.
- Two arrested after scuffle with security at Sask. legislature.
- Union calls for better anti-violence policies at psychiatric facility.
- B.C. Health Minister taking action on violence.

- TTC requests police help to investigate subway assault.
- City of St. John's meeting with taxi-industry reps to reduce violence.
- B.C. Nurses' Union vows to press charges for violent incidents.
- Bill to help protect transit operators comes into force.
- Police officer shot at Alberta casino dies.
- Violent assault on nurse spurs call for OH&S charges.
- Domestic violence study reveals troubling findings.

Source: OHS Canada. [Online]. Available: www.ohscanada.com.

Most Canadian jurisdictions have, or are in the process of developing, legislation to explicitly address violence in the workplace. Even for those without specific laws to protect workers from violence, the provisions of most Canadian health and safety statutes impose a general duty on employers to take reasonable precautions to protect each worker. For example, in Ontario the employer has a general duty to "take every precaution reasonable in the circumstances to ensure a worker's safety." That general duty has been interpreted as encompassing a general obligation to take reasonable steps to protect workers from violence.[5]

RISK-REDUCTION STRATEGIES

Figure 27–1 is a checklist that can be used by employers to reduce the risk of workplace violence in their facilities. Most of these risk-reduction strategies grow out of the philosophy of *crime reduction through environmental design (CRTED)*.[6] CRTED has the following four major elements, to which the author has added a fifth (administrative controls).

- Natural surveillance
- Control of access
- Establishment of territoriality
- Activity support
- Administrative controls

Figure 27–1 Checklist for workplace violence risk reduction.

> ✓ Identify high-risk areas and make them visible. Secluded areas invite violence.
>
> ✓ Install good lighting in parking lots and inside all buildings.
>
> ✓ Minimize the handling of cash by employees and the amount of cash available on the premises.
>
> ✓ Install silent alarms and surveillance cameras where appropriate.
>
> ✓ Control access to all buildings (employee badges, visitor check-in and check-out procedure, visitor passes, and so on).
>
> ✓ Discourage working alone, particularly late at night.
>
> ✓ Provide training in conflict resolution as part of a mandatory employee orientation.
>
> ✓ Conduct background checks before hiring new employees.
>
> ✓ Train employees how to handle themselves and respond when a violent act occurs on the job.
>
> ✓ Develop policies that establish ground rules for employee behaviour and responses in threatening or violent situations.
>
> ✓ Nurture a positive, harmonious work environment.
>
> ✓ Encourage employees to report suspicious individuals and activities or potentially threatening situations.
>
> ✓ Deal with allegations of harassment or threatened violence promptly before the situation escalates.
>
> ✓ Take threats seriously and act appropriately.
>
> ✓ Adopt a *zero-tolerance* policy toward threatening or violent behaviour.
>
> ✓ Establish a *violence hot line* so that employees can report potential problems anonymously.
>
> ✓ Establish a *threat-management team* with responsibility for preventing and responding to violence.
>
> ✓ Establish an *emergency response team* to deal with the immediate trauma of workplace violence.

The following explains how these elements can help avoid workplace violence:

1. **Natural surveillance.** This strategy involves designing, arranging, and operating the workplace in a way that minimizes secluded areas. Making all areas inside and outside the facility easily observable allows for natural surveillance.

natural surveillance Designing, arranging, and operating the workplace in a way that minimizes secluded areas.

control of access Channelling the flow of outsiders to an access-control station.

2. **Control of access.** One of the most common occurrences of workplace violence involves an outsider entering the workplace and harming employees. The most effective way of stopping this type of incident is to control access to the workplace. Channelling the flow of outsiders to an access-control station, requiring visitors' passes, issuing access badges to employees, and isolating pickup and delivery points can minimize the risk of violence perpetrated by outsiders.

establishment of territoriality Giving autonomy to employees to recognize strangers in their workplace territory.

3. **Establishment of territoriality.** This strategy involves giving employees control over the workplace. With this approach, employees move freely within their established territory but are restricted in other areas. Employees come to know everyone who works in their territory and can, as a result, immediately recognize anyone who shouldn't be there.

activity support Maximizing the number of employees conducting natural surveillance via work flow and traffic patterns.

4. **Activity support.** Activity support involves organizing work flow and natural traffic patterns in ways that maximize the number of employees conducting natural surveillance. The more employees observing the activity in the workplace, the better.

administrative controls Limiting employee exposure to hazardous conditions.

5. **Administrative controls.** Administrative controls consist of management practices that can reduce the risk of workplace violence. These practices include establishing policies, conducting background checks, and providing training for employees.

>>> **DISCUSSION CASE** | **What Is Your Opinion?**

A man walks into an office building and asks to see his wife. The man is well known to the other employees, one of whom escorts him to his wife's workstation. Suddenly, the man pulls out a gun and shoots his wife and another employee who tries to intervene. Is the employer at fault? What is your opinion about this incident involving an employee-related outsider?

Another way to reduce the risk of workplace violence is to ensure that managers understand the social and cultural factors that can lead to it. These factors fall into two broad categories: individual and environmental factors.

Individual Factors Associated with Violence

The factors explained in this section can be predictors of the potential for violence. Employees and individuals with one or more of the following factors may respond to anger, stress, or anxiety in a violent way.

1. **Record of violence.** Past violent behaviour is typically an accurate predictor of future violent behaviour. Consequently, thorough background checks should be a normal part of the employment process.

2. **Membership in a hate group.** Hate groups often promote violence against the subjects of their prejudice. Hate-group membership on the part of an employee should raise a red flag in the eyes of management.

3. **Psychotic behaviour.** Individuals who incessantly talk to themselves, express fears concerning conspiracies against them, say that they hear voices, or become increasingly dishevelled over time may be prone to violence.

4. **Romantic obsessions.** Workplace violence is often the result of romantic entanglements or love interests gone awry. Employees who persist in making unwelcome advances may eventually respond to rejection with violence.

5. **Depression.** People who suffer from depression are prone to hurt either themselves or someone else. An employee who becomes increasingly withdrawn or overly stressed may be suffering from depression.

6. **Finger-pointing.** Refusal to accept responsibility is a factor often exhibited by perpetrators of workplace violence. An employee's tendency to blame others for his or her own shortcomings should raise the caution flag.

7. **Unusual frustration levels.** The workplace has become a competitive, stressful, and sometimes frustrating place. When frustration reaches the boiling point, the emotional explosion that results can manifest itself in violence.

8. **Obsession with weapons.** Violence in the workplace often involves a weapon (gun, knife, or explosive device). A normal interest in guns used for hunting or target practice need not raise concerns. However, an employee whose interest in weapons is unusually intense and focused is cause for concern.

9. **Drug dependence.** It is common for perpetrators of workplace violence to be drug abusers. Consequently, drug dependence should cause concern not only for all of the usual reasons but also for its association with violence on the job.

Environmental Factors Associated with Violence

The environment in which employees work can contribute to workplace violence. An environment that produces stress, anger, frustration, feelings of powerlessness, resentment, and feelings of inadequacy can increase the potential for violent behaviour. The following factors can result in such an environment:

1. **Dictatorial management.** Dictatorial, overly authoritative management that shuts employees out of the decision-making process can cause them to feel powerless, as if they have little or no control over their jobs. Some people respond to powerlessness by striking out violently—a response that gives them power, if only momentarily.

2. **Role ambiguity.** One of the principal causes of stress and frustration on the job is role ambiguity. Employees need to know for what they are responsible, how they will be held accountable, and how much authority they have. When these questions are not clear, employees become stressed and frustrated, factors often associated with workplace violence.

3. **Partial and inconsistent supervision.** Supervisors who play favourites engender resentment in employees who aren't the favourite. Supervisors who treat one employee differently than another or one group of employees differently than another group also cause resentment. Employees who feel that they are being treated unfairly or unequally may show their resentment in violent ways.

4. **Unattended hostility.** Supervisors who ignore hostile situations or threatening behaviour are unwittingly giving tacit approval. An environment that accepts hostile behaviour will have hostile behaviour.

5. **No respect for privacy.** Supervisors and managers who go through the desks, files, toolboxes, and work areas of employees without first getting their permission can make employees feel invaded or even violated. Violent behaviour is a possible response to these feelings.

6. **Insufficient training.** Holding employees accountable for performance on the job without providing the training that they need to perform well can cause them to feel inadequate. People who feel inadequate can turn their frustration inward and become depressed or turn it outward and become violent.

The overriding message in this section is twofold: First, managers should endeavour to establish and maintain a positive work environment that builds employees up rather than tearing them down. Second, managers should be aware of the individual factors that can contribute to violent behaviour and respond promptly if employees show evidence of these factors.

Workplace Analysis

workplace analysis An in-depth study of the workplace that is used to identify hazards.

Workplace analysis is the same process used by health and safety professionals to identify other potentially hazardous conditions that are not related to workplace violence. Worksite analysis should be ongoing and have at least four components (Figure 27–2). An effective way to conduct an ongoing program of workplace analysis is to establish a threat-assessment team with representatives from all departments and led by the organization's chief health and safety professional.

Figure 27–2 Four components of workplace analysis.

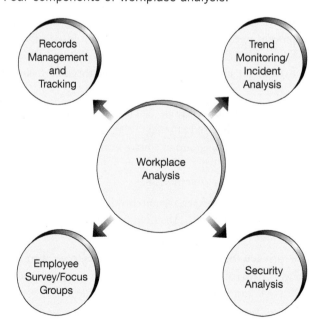

Records monitoring and tracking   The purpose of *records monitoring and tracking* is to identify and chart all incidents of violence and threatening behaviour that have occurred within a given time frame. Records to analyze include the following: incident reports, police reports, employee evaluations, and letters of reprimand. Of course, individual employees' records should be analyzed in confidence by the human resources member of the team. The type of information that is pertinent includes the following:

- Where, specifically, did the incident occur?
- What time of day or night did the incident occur?
- Was the victim an employee? Customer? Outsider?
- Was the incident the result of a work-related grievance? Personal?

Trend monitoring and incident analysis   *Trend monitoring* and *incident analysis* may prove helpful in determining patterns of violence. If there have been enough incidents to create one or more graphs, the team will want to determine if the graphs suggest one or more trends. If the organization has experienced only isolated incidents, the team may want to monitor national trends. By analyzing both local and national incidents, the team can generate information that will be helpful in predicting and, thereby, preventing workplace violence. The team should look for trends in severity, frequency, and types of incidents.

Employee surveys and focus groups   Employees are one of the best sources of information concerning workplace hazards. This is also true when it comes to identifying vulnerabilities to workplace violence. Employee input should be solicited periodically through either *written employee surveys* or *focus groups* or both. Where are we vulnerable? What practices put our employees at risk? These are the types of questions that should be asked of employees. An effective strategy for use with focus groups is to give participants case studies of incidents that occurred in other organizations. Then ask such questions as, Could this happen here? Why, or why not? How can we prevent such incidents from occurring here?

Security analysis   Is the workplace secure, or could a disgruntled individual simply walk in and harm employees? It is important to ask this question. The team should periodically perform a *security analysis* of the workplace to identify conditions, situations, procedures, and practices that make employees vulnerable. The types of questions to ask include the following:

- Are there physical factors about the facility that make employees vulnerable (e.g., areas that are isolated, poorly lit, infrequently travelled, or unobservable)?
- Is there a process for handling disgruntled customers? Does it put employees at risk?
- Are the prevention strategies that are already implemented working?
- Is the training provided to employees having a positive effect? Is more training needed? Who needs the training? What kind of training is needed?
- Are there situations in which employees have substantial amounts of money in their possession, on or off site?
- Are there situations in which employees are responsible for highly valuable equipment or materials late at night or at isolated locations?

Hazard Prevention and Control

Once hazardous conditions have been identified, the strategies and procedures necessary to eliminate them must be put in place. The two broad categories of prevention strategies are engineering controls and administrative controls, just as they are with other health and safety hazards. In addition to these, organizations should adopt post-incident response strategies as a way to prevent future incidents.

Engineering controls The prevention of workplace violence requires *engineering controls* that serve the same purpose as engineering controls relating to other hazards. They either remove the hazard or they create a barrier between it and employees. Engineering controls typically involve changes to the workplace. Examples include the following:

- Installing devices and mechanisms that give employees a complete view of their surroundings (e.g., mirrors, glass or clear plastic partitions, interior windows, and so on).

- Installing surveillance cameras and television screens that allow for monitoring of the workplace.

- Installing adequate lighting, particularly in parking lots.

- Pruning shrubbery and undergrowth outside and around the facility.

- Installing fencing so that routes of egress and ingress to company property can be channeled and, as a result, better controlled.

- Arranging outdoor sheds, storage facilities, recycling bins, and other outside facilities for maximum visibility.

Administrative controls Whereas engineering controls involve making changes to the workplace, *administrative controls* involve making changes to how work is done. This amounts to changing work procedures and practices. Administrative controls fall into four categories (Figure 27–3).

Figure 27–3 Categories of administrative controls.

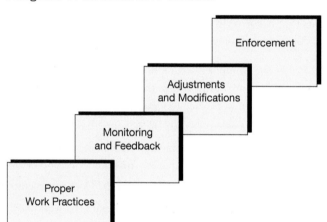

- Minimizing the vulnerability of employees. For example, if a driver has to make deliveries in a high-crime area, the company may employ a security guard to go along, change delivery schedules to daylight hours only, or both.

- Monitoring and providing feedback ensures that proper work practices are being used and that they are having the desired effect. For example, a company may establish a controlled-access system in which visitors must check in at a central location and receive a visitor's pass. Is the system being used? Are all employees sticking to specified procedures? Has unauthorized access to the workplace been eliminated?

- Making adjustments and modifications to violence prevention practices if it becomes clear from monitoring and feedback that they are not working or that improvements are needed.

- Enforcing practices by applying meaningful sanctions when employees fail to follow the established and proper work practices. An employee who has been fully informed concerning a given administrative control, has received the training needed to practise it properly, but consciously decides not to follow the procedure should be disciplined appropriately.

Post-incident response Post-incident response relating to workplace violence is the same as post-incident response relating to traumatic accidents. The first step is to provide immediate medical treatment for injured employees. The second step involves providing psychological treatment for traumatized employees. This step is even more important in cases of workplace violence than with accidents. Employees who are present when a violent incident occurs in the workplace, even if they don't witness it, can experience the symptoms of psychological trauma shown in Figure 27–4. Employees experiencing such symptoms or any others growing out of psychological trauma should be treated by professionals such as psychologists, psychiatrists, clinical nurse specialists, or certified social workers. In addition to one-on-one counselling, employees may also be enrolled in support groups. The final aspect of post-incident response is the investigation, analysis, and report. In this step, safety professionals determine how the violent incident occurred and how future incidents may be prevented, just as post-accident investigations are handled.

Figure 27–4 Symptoms of psychological trauma in cases of workplace violence.

- ✓ Fear of returning to work
- ✓ Problems in relationships with fellow employees and/or family members
- ✓ Feelings of incompetence
- ✓ Guilt feelings
- ✓ Feelings of powerlessness
- ✓ Fear of criticism by fellow employees, supervisors, and managers

Training and Education

Training and education are as fundamental to the prevention of workplace violence as they are to the prevention of workplace accidents and health-threatening incidents. A complete health and safety training program should include a comprehensive component covering all aspects of workplace violence (e.g., workplace analysis, hazard prevention, proper work practices, and emergency response). Such training should be provided on a mandatory basis for supervisors, managers, and employees.

>>> **SAFETY FACT** Aggressive Employees Threaten Productivity

No one wants to work with or around an aggressive person. As a result, aggressive employees cause tardiness, absenteeism, and turnover. All three of these factors are known to harm productivity. Consequently, it is important to deal with aggressive employees through counselling, aggression-management training, or even termination.

DOS AND DON'TS FOR SUPERVISORS

Supervisors can play a pivotal role in the prevention of workplace violence. Following are some rules that will enhance the effectiveness of supervisors in this regard:

- *Don't* try to diagnose the personal, emotional, or psychological problems of employees.

- *Don't* discuss an employee's drinking, drug use, or other addiction unless it occurs on the job. Restrict comments to performance.

- *Don't* preach to employees. Counsel employees about attendance, tardiness, and job performance, not about how they should live their lives.

- *Don't* cover up for employees or make excuses for inappropriate behaviour. Misguided kindness may allow problems to escalate and get out of hand.

- *Don't* create jobs to get problem employees out of the way. Stockpiling an employee simply gives him or her more time to brood and allow resentment to build.

- *Don't* ignore the warning signs explained earlier in this chapter. The problems that they represent will not simply go away. Sooner or later, they will have to be handled. Sooner is better.

- *Do* remember that chemical dependence and emotional problems tend to be progressive. Left untreated, they get worse, not better.

- *Do* refer problem employees to the employee assistance program or to other mental health service providers.

- *Do* make it clear to employees that job performance is the key issue. They are expected to do what is necessary to maintain and improve their performance.

- *Do* make it clear that inappropriate behaviour will not be tolerated.[7]

DOMESTIC VIOLENCE IN THE WORKPLACE

domestic violence Any form of abuse, mistreatment, or neglect that a child or adult experiences from a family member, or from someone with whom they have an intimate relationship; also used synonymously with *family violence*.

Domestic violence is a workplace issue because it can affect employee productivity, lead to absenteeism, affect workplace morale, incur litigation costs and penalties, and put workers at a greater risk of injury due to a lack of focus. Worksafe BC describes workplace violence as a range of behaviours or actions taken by a person to control and dominate another person. Domestic violence is characterized by abusive, coercive, forceful, or threatening acts or words used by one member of a family, household, or intimate relationship against another. Domestic violence may take the form of physical, emotional, sexual, financial, and/or spiritual abuse. The forms of abuse may differ, but the motivation is ultimately the same: the control of the victim by the abuser.[8]

Along with the impact already mentioned, domestic violence can also have a serious effect on workers' physical and mental health. Coworkers who witness violence in the workplace are also prone to the same negative effects as the victims. There is a growing recognition of the need for victims of domestic violence to be away from work to address their situation. Organizations such as the Yukon Teachers' Association have negotiated special leave that can be used when workers need time off due to domestic violence. Manitoba and Ontario have also legislated that employers provide paid leave to these employees so they can get the legal, medical, psychological, or other help needed.

Incorporating workplace domestic violence education into staff training or meetings is an effective means of bringing the issue to light and helping workers identify the signs as outlined in Figure 27–5. Experts from social agencies or anti-violence groups can often help with education and training. The goals of the workplace domestic violence education training are to:

- Increase awareness about the effects domestic violence has on workplace health and safety.

Figure 27–5 Signs of domestic violence.

Work productivity	Social behaviour	Escalating abuse
Your employee is ...		
• Having trouble concentrating • Often arriving late • Missing work more frequently than usual • Less productive • Making excuses for poor work performance • Receiving frequent phone calls and emails from a partner	• Behaving differently than usual • Appearing withdrawn and isolated • Engaging in fewer social activities than usual • Making last-minute cancellations • Using drugs and/or alcohol to cope • Apologizing for a partner's behaviour	• Appearing flustered by incoming phone calls or emails from a partner • Trying to cover up bruises and scratches (e.g., wearing long sleeves or turtleneck tops in summer) • Showing signs of strangulation—this is a major risk factor for future homicide of women • Receiving unannounced visits from a partner at work • Acting nervous when a partner shows up at the workplace • Being followed to/from work by a partner

Source: Addressing Domestic Violence in the Workplace: A Handbook for Employers Outside of B.C. [Online]. Available: https://www.worksafebc.com/en/resources/health-safety/books-guides/addressing-domestic-violence-in-the-workplace-a-handbook-for-employers-outside-of-bc?lang=en. Used with the permission of WorkSafeBC (Workers' Compensation Board).

- Decrease the stigma attached to victims of domestic violence.
- Encourage employees to talk about domestic violence in general and to report threats.
- Ensure and improve confidence that disclosure of domestic violence will lead to an appropriate response from the employer and coworkers.
- Reduce employee risk from domestic violence in the workplace.[9]

EMERGENCY PREPAREDNESS PLAN

To be prepared for properly handling a violent incident in the workplace, employers should form a crisis management team.[10] The team should have only one mission—immediate response to violent acts on the job—and be chaired by a health and safety professional. Team members should receive special training and be updated regularly. The team's responsibilities should be as follows:

- Undergo trauma response training.
- Handle media interaction.
- Operate telephone and communication teams.
- Develop and implement, as necessary, an emergency evacuation plan.
- Establish a backup communication system.
- Calm personnel after an incident.
- Debrief witnesses after an incident.
- Ensure that proper security procedures are established, kept up to date, and enforced.

- Help employees deal with post-traumatic stress.
- Keep employees informed about workplace violence as an issue, how to respond when it occurs, and how to help prevent it.

WORKPLACE HARASSMENT AND BULLYING

Employers need to be aware that psychological harm can be inflicted upon a worker through the actions of their peers and supervisors. In Chapter 23 we discussed these psychological hazards and the effect they can have on mental health. Often we hear news about **harassment** and **bullying** in prominent organizations and institutions such as the Royal Canadian Mounted Police (RCMP), banks, and even in the Canadian Senate. If this behaviour can occur in these institutions that we expect to uphold a high ethical standard, bullying and harassment can take place in your workplace as well. The call to identify and control bullying and harassment is being strengthened through evolving legislation, progressive workplaces, and organizations that lead the development and research around psychological health and safety in the workplace.

Harassment and bullying are among the leading causes of psychological injuries in our workplaces. Because these behaviours are often subtle and occur over an extended period, they are usually difficult to identify. The Canadian Human Rights Commission defines harassment as "a form of discrimination. It involves any unwanted physical or verbal behaviour that offends or humiliates. Generally, harassment is a behaviour that persists over time. Serious one-time incidents can also sometimes be considered harassment."[11]

In some jurisdictions, situations that relied on human rights for a remedy are now addressed through enhanced definitions of harassment in provincial legislation. For example, Manitoba's OHS regulations define harassment as

> any objectionable conduct, comment or display by a person that
>
> (a) Is directed at a worker in a workplace;
>
> (b) Is made on the basis of race, creed, religion, colour, sex, sexual orientation, gender, determined characteristics, political beliefs, political association or political activity, marital status, family status, source of income, disability, physical size or weight, age, nationality, ancestry or place of origin; and
>
> (c) Creates a risk to the health of the worker.[12]

Bullying, like harassment or violence, can inflict physical or psychological harm, but usually involves repeated incidents or a pattern of behaviour that is intended to intimidate, offend, degrade, or humiliate a particular person or group of people and is described as "the assertion of power through aggression."[13] The following list provides examples of bullying:

- Spreading malicious rumours, gossip, or innuendo.
- Excluding or isolating someone socially.
- Undermining or deliberately impeding a person's work.
- Physically abusing or threatening abuse.
- Removing areas of responsibilities without cause.
- Constantly changing work guidelines.
- Establishing impossible deadlines that will set up the individual to fail.
- Withholding necessary information or purposefully giving the wrong information.
- Making jokes that are "obviously offensive" by spoken word or e-mail.
- Intruding on a person's privacy by pestering, spying, or stalking.

harassment Engaging in malicious comments or conduct that is known, or ought reasonably to be known, to be unwelcome against a worker in a workplace.

bullying Workplace bullying is repeated, unreasonable or inappropriate behaviour directed toward a worker or group of workers that creates a risk to health and safety.

- Assigning unreasonable duties or workload that is unfavourable to one person (in a way that creates unnecessary pressure).

- Underwork—creating a feeling of uselessness.

- Yelling or using profanity.

- Criticising a person persistently or constantly.

- Belittling a person's opinions.

- Unwarranted (or undeserved) punishment.

- Blocking applications for training, leave, or promotion.

- Tampering with a person's personal belongings or work equipment.[14]

Workers may be distressed by some acts or comments of their supervisor, but should note that bullying and harassing behaviour does *not* include:

- Expressing differences of opinion.

- Offering constructive feedback, guidance, or advice about work-related behaviour.

- Reasonable action taken by an employer or supervisor relating to the management and direction of workers or the place of employment (e.g., managing a worker's performance, taking reasonable disciplinary actions, assigning work).[15]

SUMMARY

1. Canadian workplaces are not free from violence, especially for health care workers and women.

2. Employees 65 years and older are more likely to be victims than younger employees.

3. A violent act can be considered an on-the-job incident, even if it is committed away from the workplace.

4. The concept of crime reduction through environmental design (CRTED) has four major elements: natural surveillance, control of access, establishment of territoriality, and activity support. The author has added another: administrative controls.

5. Violence is not a completely unpredictable event, and certain factors can be predictors of the potential for violence. Employees and individuals with one or more of the following factors may be more likely than others to become violent: past record of violence, membership in a hate group, psychotic behaviour, romantic obsessions, depression, finger-pointing, unusual frustration levels, obsession with weapons, drug dependence.

6. An environment that produces stress, anger, frustration, feelings of powerlessness, resentment, and feelings of inadequacy can also increase the potential for violence. The following factors in the work environment can increase the likelihood of violent behaviour: dictatorial management; role ambiguity; partial and inconsistent supervision; unattended hostility; no respect for privacy; insufficient training. Managers should be aware of the individual factors that can contribute to violent behaviour and respond promptly if employees show evidence of these factors; they should endeavour to establish and maintain a positive work environment that builds employees up rather than tearing them down.

7. Domestic violence is a workplace issue because it can affect employee productivity, lead to absenteeism, affect workplace morale, incur litigation costs and penalties, and put workers at a greater risk of injury due to a lack of focus.

8. Some employers and jurisdictions provide paid leave to victims of domestic violence so they can get the legal, medical, psychological, or other help needed.

9. Managing violent incidents should be included in an organization's emergency preparedness plan.

10. Harassment and bullying can have the same physiological and psychological effects on the worker and workplace as violence.

11. Reasonable employee supervision, direction, and discipline should not be considered harassment or bullying.

Key Terms and Concepts

Activity support	Domestic violence	Natural surveillance
Administrative controls	Establishment of	Workplace analysis
Bullying	territoriality	Workplace violence
Control of access	Harassment	

Review Questions

1. What factors contribute to the increase of violence toward health care workers?
2. What legislation regarding violence is in place in your particular jurisdiction?
3. Defend or refute the following statement: A violent act that occurs away from the employer's premises cannot be considered work related.
4. Explain the concept of crime reduction through environmental design (CRTED).
5. What measures can be taken to reduce the risk of violence on the job?
6. Considering the controls and strategies outlined in the chapter, what factors can you identify that make the prevalence of violence high for the taxi and retail industries?
7. What are some of the telltale signs that a coworker may be a victim of domestic violence?
8. What makes harassment and bullying difficult to identify?

Weblinks

Canadian Human Rights Commission

www.chrc-ccdp.gc.ca/eng

Learn about discrimination, human rights, and your obligation under these laws.

Canadian Centre for Occupational Health and Safety

www.ccohs.ca/oshanswers/psychosocial/violence.html

This CCOHS web page provides workers and employers with information to identify signs of potential workplace violence and answers to other questions on the topic.

WorkSafeBC

www.worksafebc.com/en/health-safety/hazards-exposures/violence

Find some of Canada's most comprehensive and progressive information on workplace violence, domestic violence, bullying, and harassment.

Endnotes

1 Cheryl A. Edwards. *Workplace Violence & Harassment in Canada: Ontario's OHS Provisions in Perspective*. November 26, 2010. [Online]. Available: http://www.cba.org/cba/cle/PDF/ adm10_edwards_paper_2.pdf. (Retrieved June 26, 2017).

2 International Labour Office. Bureau for Workers' Activities (ACTRAV). *Violence and Harassment Against Women and Men in the World of Work: Trade Union Perspectives and Action*. (Geneva: ILO), 2017. [Online]. Available: http://www.ilo.org/actrav/info/pubs/ WCMS_546645/lang–en/index.htm. (Retrieved June 28, 2017).

3 Canadian Centre for Occupational Health and Safety. OSH Answers Fact Sheets. *Violence in the Workplace*. [Online]. Available: http://www.ccohs.ca/oshanswers/psychosocial/violence .html. (Retrieved June 28, 2017).

4 Ibid.

5 Cheryl A. Edwards. *Workplace Violence & Harassment in Canada: Ontario's OHS Provisions in Perspective*. November 26, 2010. [Online]. Available: http://www.cba.org/cba/cle/PDF/ adm10_edwards_paper_2.pdf. (Retrieved June 26, 2017).

6 Janice L. Thomas. "A Response to Occupational Violent Crime." *Professional Safety* 37(b) (June 1992): 27–31.

7 Illinois State Police. *Do's and Don'ts for the Supervisor*. [Online]. Available: http://www .state.il.us/isp/viowkplc/vwpp6c.htm.

8 WorkSafeBC. *Addressing Domestic Violence in the Workplace: A Handbook for Employers*. [Online]. Available: https://www.worksafebc.com/en/health-safety/hazards-exposures/ violence/domestic-violence. (Retrieved June 28, 2017).

9 *Addressing Domestic Violence in the Workplace: A Handbook for Employers Outside of B.C.* [Online]. Available: https://www.worksafebc.com/en/resources/health-safety/books-guides/ addressing-domestic-violence-in-the-workplace-a-handbook-for-employers-outside-of- bc?lang=en. (Retrieved June 28, 2017).

10 Illinois State Police. *Do's and Don'ts for the Supervisor*. [Online]. Available: http://www .state.il.us/isp/viowkplc/vwpp8.htm.

11 The Canadian Human Rights Commission. *What Is Harassment?* [Online]. Available: http://www.chrc-ccdp.gc.ca/eng/content/what-harassment. (Retrieved June 28, 2017).

12 Manitoba. *Workplace Safety and Health Regulation, M.R. 217/2006*. Available at http:// web2.gov.mb.ca/laws/regs/current/_reg.php?reg=217/2006. (Retrieved January 15, 2018).

13 CCOHS. *Bullying in the Workplace*. [Online]. Available: http://www.ccohs.ca/oshanswers/ psychosocial/bullying.html. (Retrieved June 28, 2017).

14 Ibid.

15 Ibid.

Chapter 28
Health, Wellness, and Lifestyle

Worker health is a fundamental necessity for workers and the workplace to succeed and thrive. Since most people spend a substantial part of their day at work, or engaged in work, it is essential that the workplace does not negatively impact their ability to be productive or enjoy life. Employers have a business, moral, social, and legal obligation to protect the health and well-being of their workers.

Workers' expectations of their employers are rising—not only are they demanding to be kept free from harm, but they want the workplace to enhance their health and well-being. This is reflected in how organizations of all sizes are addressing worker health and wellness. In Canada and around the world, the importance of good health is being noted. For example, two of the nine principles upon which the World Health Organization's (WHO) constitution is based are:

1. Health is a state of complete physical, mental, and social well-being, and not merely the absence of disease or infirmity.

2. The enjoyment of the highest attainable standard of health is one of the fundamental rights of every human being without distinction of race, religion, political belief, economics, or social condition.[1]

Policies and programs that promote health and wellness benefit the worker, the organization, and society. Healthy workers are more productive, improve workplace morale and engagement, and reduce medical costs for the employer and the health care system. It should be noted that although our publicly funded health care system means that organizations assume less cost of treating health problems, workplace health and wellness initiatives can produce considerable savings for employers. Direct savings can be seen through reduced cost of employer-funded medical benefits programs. And indirect costs associated with missed work, presenteeism, and lower productivity can be curtailed.

HEALTH AND WELLNESS

Some employers faced with mounting health care and workers' compensation costs are looking for innovative ways to keep their workers safe and healthy. One innovation that is gaining popularity as a way to promote health and safety is the **wellness program**. A wellness program is any program designed to help and encourage employees to adopt a healthier lifestyle. These programs, which are sponsored by various organizations and government agencies, benefit all parties by reducing the number of accidents, their severity, and the associated cost and suffering.

wellness program Any program designed to help and encourage employees to adopt a healthier lifestyle.

A typical wellness, or **health promotion**, program includes diet and exercise under the supervision of an appropriately qualified professional, stress management activities, and special activities designed to help high-risk employees overcome such lifestyle-related behaviours as smoking and overeating. Healthy workers are more resilient and are better able to cope with the physical and psychological demands placed on them in the workplace.

health promotion A range of interventions, policies, or programs aimed at proactively protecting and promoting workers' health.

Company-sponsored health and wellness programs often have some very beneficial outcomes, as pointed out by Dianne Dyck in a *Benefits Canada* magazine article:

- Canada Life, based in Toronto, developed a health promotion program in 1978 which was independently evaluated over a 10-year period. The program showed a return of $6.85 on each corporate dollar invested based on reduced employee turnover, greater productivity, and decreased medical claims by participating employees.

- A review of worldwide wellness studies by Dr. Ray Shephard for the Canadian government found that workplace wellness programs have a return on investment of between $1.95 to $3.75 per employee, per dollar spent.

- A 1997 Labour Canada study showed that employees who smoke cost companies between $2,308 to $2,613 more per year than non-smoking employees. This is due to increased absenteeism, lost productivity, and increased health and life insurance premiums.

- According to a Government of Ontario report called "The High Cost of a Sedentary Lifestyle," up to half of the burden of medical costs could be prevented by changes in personal lifestyle. Physical activity, in particular, has the potential to reduce both acute and chronic demands on the health care system, with a reduction in employee turnover and absence, an increase in productivity, a reduction in absenteeism, and a decreased risk of industrial injury.[2]

WORK-LIFE BALANCE / WORK-FAMILY BALANCE

The terms **work-life balance** and **work-family balance** are often used synonymously. Work-life balance is often described as having four elements: work, family, friends, and self. "Balance" is subjective and does not mean equal time engaged in work and non-work activities, but rather is influenced by the worker's personal situation, such as where they are in terms of raising a family and other commitments outside of work. The stress of balancing competing demands on workers can have harmful effects on a workers' psychological and physical health, as described in Chapter 23.

work-life balance An effective and equitable relationship between the demands of work commitments and those outside of work.

work-family balance An effective and equitable relationship between the demands of work commitments and those of the family.

In 2010, the Bureau de Normalisation du Québec (BNQ) introduced *Standard BNQ 9700-820, Work-Family Balance*. Its goal is to make work-family balance an integral part of human resources management in organizations. The standard sets out requirements necessary for work-family balance in keeping with the characteristics and realities of organizations and their workers.[3] The changes in the labour force over the past few decades and the need to promote work-family balance in order to attract workers is expressed in the standard's preamble:

> Along with this constant pressure to adapt, it has become more widely recognized that an organization's key strength resides in its labour force. The portrait of an active population has however changed considerably over time. The past model of the father as the sole bread winner is long gone. The labour force is now made up of almost as many women as men, often parents of young children or caregivers to dependent adults, related to them or not. The labour force is now more skilled. Add that to the new generation of employees whose expectations and attitudes toward work are different of those of past generations. Although they are clearly committed to work, they are also clearly striving for greater work-life balance.[4]

>>> **DISCUSSION CASE** | **What Is Your Opinion?**

"I need to create a shift schedule for the Christmas/New Year's break. Unfortunately, an acute care hospital can't close its doors because it's a public holiday," said Gayle, the nursing manager. "Just as we have done in the past, we will give priority to the nurses who have children at home."

Cailin, who had been scheduled to work the past three Christmases, spoke up. "I appreciate people wanting to spend time with family during the holidays, but my interests are just as important and I feel I am being punished for not having children."

Martin added, "I agree. We all have equal entitlement to pursue our interests away from work and our family status should not be factored into the scheduling."

What is your opinion?

FLEXIBLE WORK ARRANGEMENTS

work-life conflict Incompatible demands between work and non-work commitments.

Todays' safety practitioner often works in collaboration with their human resources department to develop and implement opportunities for workers to address work-family or **work-life conflicts**. Employers continuously search for ways to maximize worker participation and engagement. For some groups of workers this may include policies and programs that provide more time for family. For other workers the goal is to find time outside work for study, volunteering, taking care of their own health, or participating in sports and recreation.

Having options about how work is organized makes managing work and life demands possible by allowing employees to work on nontraditional work schedules and in locations that better fit their personal or family needs. Alternatively, employers may initiate various schedules to meet their customer needs. For employers, **flexible work arrangements** provide a means to reduce the loss of skills and experience and the high cost of recruitment and retention in a competitive labour market. Employers who provide flexible work options gain a competitive edge in the labour market by becoming "employers of choice."[5]

flexible work arrangements Alternative work schedules from the traditional working day or week.

According to CCOHS, common flexible work arrangements include:

1. **Flex time.** Flex time is an arrangement where employees work a full day but they can vary their working hours. These arrangements are usually established with specific guidelines so that a "core" working day exists. Flex time is usually arranged in advance with the employee and employer or supervisor; and a set range of start and finish times are established. The total hours of work are not usually affected by this arrangement.

For example, an employee may choose to start between 7:30 and 9:30 a.m., and finish between 3:30 and 5:30 p.m. This arrangement establishes that core hours are between 9:30 a.m. and 3:30 p.m., when all employees will be at work. Lunch periods are usually mandatory and for a set length (30 to 90 minutes). Employees should maintain their start/finish times so that a routine is established and coworkers can become accustomed to one another's schedules.

2. **Reduced hours/Part-time.** Employees may choose to work fewer than the standard 37.5 or 40 hours of work per week. These arrangements may be on a temporary or permanent basis depending on individual circumstances. It may also be considered in some cases for employees with health problems or disabilities. Work hours may be negotiated, or they may be chosen to coincide with peak workload hours, depending on the type of business. However, employee benefits and qualification for government programs (such as employment insurance or pension plans) may be affected, and should be examined thoroughly before commencing.

3. **Compressed workweek.** A compressed workweek occurs when an employee works for longer periods of time per day or shift in exchange for a day off. Employees may start earlier or finish later than the normal workday. Compressed workweeks are often initiated by the employee, but sometimes the employer may initiate the option to improve operational efficiency, to maximize production (reduced daily start-up costs), or to establish longer business hours that can enhance customer service.

   Common arrangements for a 40-hour workweek are: working 10 hours per day for 4 days a week; working 1 extra hour per day with 1 day off every 2 weeks; or working .5 extra hours per day with 1 day off every 3 to 4 weeks.

4. **Telework/Telecommuting.** Telework or telecommuting occurs when people do at least some of their regular work from home instead of going into the office. Details such as hours of work and how communications occur between the teleworker, coworkers, and customers need to be outlined. See the Canadian Centre for Occupational Health and Safety weblink at the end of this chapter for the OSH Answers document on telework/telecommuting.

5. **Job sharing.** Job sharing occurs when two or more people share one or more positions or sets of duties. It should be clear before starting how these arrangements affect pay, benefits, and holidays. It is very important that those in a job-sharing arrangement work effectively as a team and communicate well. Job sharing may be an option when few part-time positions are available within the company.

6. **Banking of hours/Annualized hours.** This arrangement allows employees to choose, within negotiated boundaries, their days and hours of work to the maximum for a set period of time. This period of time may be weekly, monthly, or yearly. Such arrangements are often a combination of flex time and compressed workweek and can help reduce the amount of overtime hours required. These arrangements may be suited to fields where there is variation in demands such as peak hours or seasons.

7. **Gradual retirement.** Gradual retirement allows employees to reduce their working hours or their workload over a period of time rather than switching from full-time employment to retirement abruptly. This phased period can be used to train the replacement employee, to help others adjust to restructuring within the company, or to adjust for the redistribution of tasks among the remaining employees.

8. **Leaves and sabbaticals.** Leaves and sabbaticals are authorized periods of time away from work without loss of employment rights. Paid or unpaid leaves are usually granted for family, health care, education, or leisure reasons. Sabbaticals are usually paid (or partially funded) and occur on a regular basis in addition to vacation time. In some cases, self-funded leaves are also possible where a portion of the employee's salary is withheld and returned to the employee as "pay" during the time away from work.[6]

The 2017 federal budget included, for the first time, a measure to help balancing work and family that allows federally-regulated workers to request flexible work arrangements from their employers. The budget document states that things like the ability to have "flexible start and finish times and the ability to work from home" will have to be considered. While these changes would apply to Canadians whose work is regulated by the Canada Labour Code, the lead of the federal government will likely be followed by provincial and territorial jurisdictions in coming years.

LIFESTYLE IMPACTS ON THE WORKPLACE

Many health and wellness programs are aimed at curbing negative lifestyle practices such as smoking, drug use, inactivity, and poor dietary habits. Employers who are aware of the connection between workers' lifestyle and their performance are more likely to invest in health promotion programs and policies that promote a healthy lifestyle. Progressive organizations employ a number of strategies to improve worker well-being, productivity, recruitment, and retention. In addition to those already covered, employers can also address lifestyle challenges through on-site programs or facilities, or collaborate with external providers to develop a healthier workforce.

Smoking Cessation

Smoking is a major cause for concern within a workplace because it can have a direct impact on both smokers and nonsmokers, and ultimately the organization. Smokers tend to use more sick leave than nonsmokers, and it is estimated that around 20 percent of workplace fires are started by cigarettes or discarded matches, which in turn can lead to higher insurance premiums. Smoking is an important contributing factor in the top three causes of death and ill health: coronary artery disease, cancers, and strokes.[7]

A Conference Board of Canada news release states that "on average, each smoker cost their employer an estimated $4,256 in 2012—more than $3,800 in lost productivity due to unsanctioned smoking breaks and more than $400 in lost productivity due to absenteeism. On average, each daily smoker and recent quitter took almost two and a half more sick days in 2010 compared to employees who have never smoked The overall economic costs of smoking borne by businesses and society were estimated at $11.4 billion in 2010. Three-quarters of current smokers are working—and most want to break the habit. Smoking is also responsible for large losses in economic activity, due to its association with increased risk of short- and long-term disability and premature mortality. The prevalence rate of daily smokers in a typical Canadian company is estimated to fall by 35 percent by 2025 if a workplace cessation program is introduced."[8]

▶▶▶ SAFETY FACT   Smoking in the Workplace

"The workplace is an ideal setting to combat smoking and Canadian businesses have a strong financial incentive to help smokers quit, especially in industries like construction, mining, and transportation that employ predominantly male blue-collar workers. The prevalence of smoking is much higher than average in these industries, and employers are less likely to offer effective cessation programs, benefits, policies, or practices."

—Fares Bounajm, Economist, Canadian Alliance for Sustainable Health Care and co-author of *Smoking Cessation and the Workplace: Benefits of Workplace Programs*.[9]

Source: Conference Board of Canada. *Up in Smoke: Smokers Cost Their Employers More Than $4,000 Each Per Year.* [Online.] Available: http://www.conferenceboard.ca/press/newsrelease/13-10-29/up_in_smoke_smokers_cost_their_employers_more_than_4_000_each_per_year.aspx. Used with the permission of Conference Board of Canada.

These statistics make a strong case for employers to invest in smoking cessation programs or to include smoking cessation products and treatments in their benefits plan. Options range from pharmaceutical to psychoeducational approaches to smoking cessation. The potential for the indirect effect of one worker quitting smoking can have a huge effect on the workplace. Eliminating the direct cost for lost productivity is obvious, but, in addition, other workers would be motivated by the worker's boosted confidence, focus, engagement, and self-esteem.

DRUGS AND ALCOHOL IN THE WORKPLACE

One of the most pernicious causes of accidents on the job is chemicals — but not the kind industrial hygienists generally concern themselves with.[10] The chemicals alluded to here are the illicit drugs and alcohol used by employees. Drugs and alcohol are the root cause or contributing cause of many accidents on the job every year. Consequently, safety professionals need to be on guard for employees who are drug and alcohol abusers.

When a worker's alertness, accuracy, or ability to quickly respond to their environment is limited, productivity and safety can be compromised. Impairment by drugs and alcohol can contribute to serious accidents and interfere with the accuracy and efficiency of work. Other ways that substance abuse may cause problems at work include:

- after-effects of substance use (hangover, withdrawal) affect job performance
- absenteeism, illness, and/or reduced productivity
- preoccupation with obtaining and using substances while at work, which interferes with attention and concentration
- illegal activities at work, including selling illicit drugs to other employees
- psychological or stress-related effects due to substance abuse by a family member, friend, or coworker that affects another person's job performance[11]

Workplace drug and alcohol testing is a controversial issue both in Canada and around the world. Legal experts, policy makers, and human resources professionals are challenged with balancing worker safety with an individual's human rights. The growing use of medical marijuana and the imminent legalization of cannabis in Canada will create even greater complexity for human resources and safety policy makers. Most jurisdictions currently appear to limit legislative involvement to safety-critical industries such as transportation. While some high-profile human rights challenges have taken place, many private industry businesses appear to be able to create testing programs and policies that suit their business purposes without significant opposition.

In Canada, workplace policies cannot be deemed discriminatory to those with a drug or alcohol addiction. Dependency on drugs or alcohol is deemed to be a **disability**, and provincial human rights commissions—or, in the case of industries that fall under federal jurisdiction, the Canadian Charter of Rights and Freedoms—would consider any imposed restrictions to be a form of **discrimination**. Employers have the **duty to accommodate** those with disabilities up to a point of **undue hardship.** And many employers are able to implement workplace drug and alcohol testing in occupations with a bona fide occupational safety requirement. Tests have been developed by the Supreme Court of Canada to determine whether employers have followed the appropriate process to designate occupations having **bona fide** safety requirements.

The United States has been a leader in implementing drug and alcohol prevention programs on a larger scale than other areas of the world, and as such has developed policies and procedures regarding testing in the workplace. Canadian companies that do cross-border business with the United States have to follow US legislation regarding testing, most notably in the transportation industry.

disability A condition or affliction that inhibits a person from carrying out normal or routine activities.

discrimination Bias or prejudice resulting in unfair treatment.

duty to accommodate An employer's obligation to make every reasonable effort, short of undue hardship, to accommodate workers who may be discriminated against under human rights legislation.

undue hardship An obligation that places a burden on the employer that is not in proportion to the reciprocal cost or benefit.

bona fide Made or carried out in good faith without malice or intention to deceive.

Even a serious medical condition may not be enough to change behaviour. A recent Statistics Canada study looked at changes in smoking, physical activity, alcohol consumption, and diet among 5,404 Canadians age fifty or older with heart disease, cancer, stroke, respiratory disease, or diabetes. Participants were questioned every 2 years between 1994/95 and 2006/07.

After being diagnosed, participants made surprisingly few behaviour changes. Three-quarters of smokers didn't quit, few people changed their diet, and the number who were physically active didn't change (except among those with diabetes). Alcohol consumption declined, but the reductions were rarely statistically significant.

Source: Benefits Canada. *Do Wellness Incentives Work?* [Online]. Available: http://www.benefitscanada.com/benefits/health-wellness/do-wellness-incentives-work-63193. (Retrieved July 1, 2017). Used with the permission of Benefits Canada.

According to the Ontario Human Rights Commission, a drug and alcohol testing policy that respects human rights and may be justifiable under the Code is one that:

- is based on a rational connection between the purpose of testing (minimizing the risk of impairment to ensure safety) and job performance,

- shows that testing is necessary to achieve workplace safety,

- is put in place after alternative, less intrusive methods for detecting impairment and increasing workplace safety have been explored,

- is used only in limited circumstances such as for-cause, post-incident, or post-reinstatement situations,

- does not apply automatic consequences following positive tests,

- does not conflate substance use with substance addiction,

- is used as part of a larger assessment of drug or alcohol addiction (for example, employee assistance programs, drug education and awareness programs, and a broader medical assessment by a professional with expertise in substance use disorders or a physician who provides a process for inquiring into possible disability),

- provides individualized accommodation for people with addictions who test positive, to the point of undue hardship,

- uses testing methods that are highly accurate, able to measure current impairment, are minimally intrusive, and provide rapid results,

- uses reputable procedures for analysis, and

- ensures confidentiality of medical information and the dignity of the person throughout the process.[12]

Establishing drug-free workplace programs is typically the responsibility of the human resources department. However, health and safety professionals should be aware of the workplace problems that can be caused by alcohol and drug abuse. Further, if a cross-functional team of representatives from various departments is convened by the human resources department for the purpose of developing a drug-free workplace program, the chief health and safety professional for the organization should be a member of that team.

Obesity

obesity Abnormal or excessive fat accumulation that may impair health. The World Health Organization (WHO) and Dieticians of Canada consider a body mass index (BMI) of thirty and over to be obese.

Obesity rates in Canada, as in other parts of the developed world, have increased dramatically over the last few decades. Since obesity is strongly linked to many chronic diseases, including diabetes, coronary heart disease, and hypertension, rates of these diseases are also on the rise. As a result, workplaces and the Canadian health care system are significantly affected.[13]

Canadians with a body mass index (BMI) greater than thirty are 4 times as likely to have diabetes, 3.3 times as likely to have high blood pressure, and 1.5 times as likely to have heart disease.

Overweight workers have higher rates of absenteeism and claims for workers' compensation, medical care, and short-term disability. Obese workers take more time off from work and have more diseases.[14] Being overweight can obviously impede performance and create further health risks for workers—such as firefighters and construction workers whose jobs require physical exertion—but can also cause problems for food servers and more sedentary workers, such as cashiers who stand for long periods.

There are labour force characteristics that are correlated with obesity and being overweight. A higher proportion of male blue-collar workers are obese than men with white-collar jobs—similarly, higher obesity rates are found among men whose usual daily activities or work habits include doing heavy work or carrying very heavy loads. Working longer hours or doing shift-work also increases the prevalence of obesity.[15] **Sedentary** work contributes to obesity and a myriad of related health problems.

sedentary A state of little or no physical activity—usually sitting.

We often hear that "sitting is the new smoking." Research clearly shows a link between sedentary behaviour and increased risk for chronic diseases. In fact, 4 out of 5 Canadians risk developing chronic conditions such as cancer, heart disease, or type 2 diabetes; 6 out of 10 adults are overweight.[16] Canadian adults spend about 70 percent of their waking hours being sedentary; Canadian office workers spend 77 to 80 percent of their working hours in prolonged sitting periods. The Public Health Agency of Canada's Sit Kicker program is a nationwide initiative focused on encouraging Canadians who work in office settings to reduce sedentary behaviour.[17] All employers need to develop strategies to limit sedentary work and the impact it has on workers.

>>> **SAFETY FACT** Body Mass Index (BMI)

Body mass index (BMI) is a simple index of weight-for-height that is commonly used to classify adults as underweight, healthy, overweight, or obese. It is defined as a person's weight in kilograms divided by the square of their height in meters (kg/m2). Depending on your BMI number, you will be classified as:

- **Underweight** (BMI less than 18.5). Health risks associated with being underweight include osteoporosis, infertility, and impaired immune functioning. Underweight may also indicate an eating disorder or other underlying illness.

- **Healthy weight** (BMI 18.5 to 24.9). This may lower your risk for developing weight-related health problems.

- **Overweight** (BMI 25 to 29.9) or **Obese** (BMI 30 and over). You are at greater risk of developing diabetes, heart disease, and some types of cancer, including endometrial, breast, ovarian, prostate, liver, gallbladder, kidney, and colon.

  See the Dieticians of Canada weblinks at the end of his chapter for assessments tools and calculators.

Source: Data from Dietitians of Canada.

EMPLOYEE ASSISTANCE PROGRAMS (EAPs)

Employee and Family Assistance Programs, also known as Employee and Family Assistance Programs (EFAPs), are usually employer-funded and provide various services and counselling to employees and their families. Most large employers have EAPs administered by their human resources departments and provided by an external organization. The earliest iterations of EAPs were those arising from efforts in the early 1900s to address social conditions leading to subsequent employee performance concerns. However, the prominence of alcohol abuse after World War II is where the strongest roots of EAPs are found.

After the war, thousands of soldiers who were traumatized from the horrors they had seen turned to alcohol as they struggled to reclaim their place in society. The problems associated with excessive alcohol consumption led to the first employee assistance programs in 1945. Until 1975, alcohol was the primary focus of the EAPs. During the following decade other worker problems such as marital concerns, family issues, and prescription/non-prescription drug abuse all began to fall under the expanding EAP umbrella.[18] Today, EAPs have evolved to cover a broad range of employee issues and offer a suite of services that include lifestyle, legal, financial, and numerous counselling and psychological health services.

EAPs usually offer free and confidential assessments, short-term counselling, referrals, and follow-up services for employees and their families. Employees can get assistance with a range of personal problems or work-related problems that may impact their job performance, health, and mental and emotional well-being. These service providers are often the first source of support sought by employers to support and counsel their employees after traumatic or violent incidents in the workplace. Employees can access the services directly or through their supervisor or manager, who should be familiar with the program and how employees can get the support they need. Most EAP providers also facilitate group training sessions that address prominent or arising workplace concerns, such as psychological health, violence, bullying and harassment, and others.

SUMMARY

1. Employers have a business, moral, social, and legal obligation to protect the health and well-being of their workers.

2. The WHO states that health is not merely the absence of disease or infirmity and that the enjoyment of the highest attainable standard of health is one of the fundamental rights of every human being.

3. Promoting worker health and wellness can produce considerable direct and indirect savings to the employer.

4. Health and wellness promotion and programs have shown to produce a favourable return on investment.

5. Work-life balance is often described as having four elements: work, family, friends, and self.

6. Flexible work arrangements can include: flex time, reduced hours/part-time, compressed workweek, telework/telecommuting, job sharing, banking of hours/ annualized hours, gradual retirement, and leaves and sabbaticals.

7. Although the new generation of workers are clearly committed to work, they are also clearly striving for greater work-life balance

8. Negative lifestyle practices such as smoking, drug use, inactivity, and poor dietary habits can affect worker performance.

9. Smoking is a major cause for concern within a workplace because of the lost productivity and the cost associated with short- and long-term disability.

10. Drug and alcohol testing is a challenge because of the balance required between safety and human rights.

11. Overweight workers have higher rates of absenteeism and claims for workers' compensation, medical care, and short-term disability.

12. Sedentary work contributes to obesity and a myriad of related health problems.

13. Employee Assistance Programs (EAPs) offer assistance with a range of personal problems or work-related problems that may impact job performance, health, and mental and emotional well-being.

Key Terms and Concepts

Bona fide	Health promotion	Wellness program
Disability	Obesity	Work-family balance
Discrimination	Sedentary	Work-life balance
Duty to accommodate	Undue hardship	Work-life conflict
Flexible work arrangements		

Review Questions

1. What are the WHO's views on health?

2. How can a worker's health impact the workplace?

3. What are the benefits of health and wellness promotion for employers?

4. How have work-life balance expectations changed during the past few decades?

5. List eight flexible work arrangements.

6. Explain why smoking is such a cause for concern to employers.

7. List the direct and indirect ways that drug and alcohol use can cause problems in the workplace.

8. Why are drug and alcohol testing programs challenging for Canadian employers?

9. How does the workplace contribute to obesity? What are the effects?

10. Describe the services usually provided by Employee Assistance Programs (EAPs)?

Weblinks

Dieticians of Canada

www.dietitians.ca/your-health/assess-yourself/assess-your-bmi/bmi-adult.aspx

Along with numerous resources on diet and nutrition, the Dieticians of Canada website has a BMI calculator and other assessments tools.

Canadian Centre for Occupational Health and Safety

https://ccohs.ca/oshanswers/hsprograms/telework.html

This CCOHS web page provides workers and employers with information on telework/telecommuting.

Albertaquits.ca

www.albertaquits.ca/

This website connects smokers to effective free resources to support them on their path to quit smoking.

The Canadian Human Rights Reporter

www.cdn-hr-reporter.ca/content/chrr-online

The Canadian Human Rights Reporter Inc. (CHRR) is a not-for-profit organization established to promote access to human rights laws in Canada. CHRR publishes human rights legislation and decisions of tribunals, boards of inquiry, and courts from all jurisdictions.

Government of Canada, Department of Justice

www.justice.gc.ca/eng/cj-jp/marijuana/law-loi.html

The status of cannabis legislation in Canada is updated on this site.

Endnotes

[1] World Health Organization. *Constitution of WHO: Principles.* [Online]. Available: http://www.who.int/about/mission/en/. (Retrieved July 1, 2017). Reprinted from Publication Constitution of WHO: principles, Copyright (1946).

[2] Dianne Dyck. (January 1999). "The Wellness Package." *Benefits Canada* magazine. [Online]. Available: http://www.benefitscanada.com/content/legacy/Content/1999/01-99/ben46.html. (Retrieved November 15, 2004). Used with the permission of Benefits Canada.

[3] Bureau de normalisation du Québec (BNQ). BNQ 9700-820/2010. *Work-Family Balance.* [Online]. Available: https://www.bnq.qc.ca/en/standardization/health-and-work/work-family-balance.html. (Retrieved July 1, 2017).

[4] Ibid.

[5] Government of South Australia. *What Is Work Life Balance?* [Online]. Available: https://www.safework.sa.gov.au/worklifebalance/wlb_show_page.jsp?id=111580. (Retrieved July 1, 2017).

[6] Canadian Centre for Occupational Health and Safety (CCOHS). *Flexible Work Arrangements.* [Online]. Available: https://www.ccohs.ca/oshanswers/psychosocial/flexible.html. (Retrieved July 1, 2017). Used with the permission of Canadian Centre for Occupational Health and Safety.

[7] Healthy Working Lives. *Smoking Policy.* [Online]. Available: http://www.healthyworkinglives.com/advice/Legislation-and-policy/employee-issues/smoking. (Retrieved July 1, 2017).

[8] Conference Board of Canada. *Up in Smoke: Smokers Cost Their Employers More Than $4,000 Each Per Year.* [Online]. Available: http://www.conferenceboard.ca/press/newsrelease/13-10-29/up_in_smoke_smokers_cost_their_employers_more_than_4_000_each_per_year.aspx. Used with the permission of Conference Board of Canada.

[9] Ibid.

[10] Stephen G. Minter. "The Safety Threat from Within." *Occupational Hazards* 64, no. 4 (April 2002): 8.

[11] Government of Canada (Canadian Centre on Occupational Health and Safety, 2008). *Substance Abuse in the Workplace.* [Online]. Available: http://www.ccohs.ca/oshanswers/psychosocial/substance.html. (Retrieved December 22, 2011).

[12] Ontario Human Rights Commission. *Policy on Drug and Alcohol Testing 2016.* [Online]. Available: http://www.ohrc.on.ca/en/policy-drug-and-alcohol-testing-2016. (Retrieved July 15, 2017). © Queen's Printer for Ontario, 2016. Reproduced with permission.

[13] Public Health Agency of Canada. *Chronic Diseases and Injuries in Canada.* Volume 32, no. 2, March 2012. [Online]. Available: http://www.phac-aspc.gc.ca/publicat/hpcdp-pspmc/ 32-2/ar-01-eng.php. (Retrieved July 14, 2017).

[14] *OHS Canada* Magazine. "Tightening the Belt." [Online]. Available: http://www.ohscanada .com/features/tightening-the-belt/. (Retrieved July 14, 2017).

[15] Ibid.

[16] Public Health Agency of Canada. News Release: *Government of Canada Invests in Program to Combat Sedentary Behaviour in the Workplace.* [Online]. Available: https:// www.canada.ca/en/public-health/news/2017/03/government_of_canadainvestsinpro- gramtocombatsedentarybehaviourin.html. (Retrieved July 17, 2017).

[17] Ibid.

[18] Manualife.com. *A Brief History of the Employee Assistance Program.* [Online]. Available: http://groupbenefits.manulife.com/Canada/GB_v2.nsf/LookupFiles/ EBNQ305EAPHistory/$File/EAPHistory.htm. (Retrieved July 1, 2017).

Glossary

absorption Entry through the skin and into the bloodstream.

acceleration Increase in the speed of a falling object before impact.

accident An unplanned or unexpected event that results in injuries to people or loss of product or process.

accident investigation The process of collecting facts to determine the cause of an accident.

accident prevention The act of preventing a happening that may cause loss or injury to a person.

accident report Records the findings of an accident investigation, the cause or causes of an accident, and recommendations for corrective action.

accident scene The area where an accident occurred.

accident/incident theory Theory of accident causation in which overload, ergonomic traps, or a decision to err lead to human error.

accident-analysis report Report identifying the root cause of an accident.

acclimatization Process by which the body becomes gradually accustomed to heat or cold in a work setting.

ACGIH American Conference of Governmental Industrial Hygienists. A professional association that develops and publishes recommended exposure limits for chemical and physical agents.

act Document containing laws made by provincial legislature or federal parliament.

activity support Maximizing the number of employees conducting natural surveillance via work flow and traffic patterns.

acute effects and exposures The effects of short-term exposure.

adjustable guards Devices that provide a barrier against a variety of different hazards associated with different production operations.

administrative controls Limiting employee exposure to hazardous conditions.

AIDS Acquired immunodeficiency syndrome, the condition caused by the human immunodeficiency virus (HIV).

air dose Dose measured by an instrument in the air at or near the area of the body that has received the highest dosage of radiation.

alternating current Electrical current in which the direction of flow alternates from one direction to the other.

altitude sickness A form of hypoxia associated with high altitudes.

amperes The unit of measurement for electrical current.

ancestry A person's line of descent.

anesthetics Substances that can inhibit the normal operation of the central nervous system without causing serious or irreversible effects, when carefully controlled.

anti-labour laws Nineteenth-century laws that strongly favoured employers.

aseptic necrosis A delayed effect of decompression sickness involving damage to marrow generation and healthy bone cells.

asphyxiants Substances that can disrupt breathing so severely as to cause suffocation.

assumption of risk Based on the theory that people who accept a job assume the risks that go with it. It says employees who work voluntarily should accept the consequences of their actions on the job rather than blaming the employer.

audiogram The results of an audiometric test to determine the noise threshold at which a subject responds to different test frequencies.

audiometric testing Tests that measure the hearing threshold of employees.

auto-ignition temperature The lowest temperature at which a vapour-producing substance or a flammable gas will ignite without the presence of a spark or a flame.

automatic ejection A system that ejects work pneumatically or mechanically.

automatic feed A system that feeds stock to the machine from rolls.

automation The state of being operated automatically.

autonomous vehicles Vehicles capable of navigating without human assistance.

avian influenza An infectious disease of birds caused by type A strains of the influenza virus.

bacteria Microscopic single-cell organisms found in food, water, and air.

barometer Scientific device for measuring atmospheric pressure.

behavioural time sharing A technique requiring the simultaneous performance of two tasks.

bends Common name for decompression sickness.

best-ratio approach People are basically good and, under the right circumstances, behave ethically.

bill Law in draft form.

biological agents Living things or substances produced by living things that may cause harm to humans.

biological exposure indices (BEIs) Procedures used to determine the amount of material absorbed into the human body.

biological hazards Living things, or products of living things, that can cause illness and disease in humans.

black-and-white approach Right is right, wrong is wrong, and circumstances are irrelevant.

blackball To ostracize an employee.

bloodborne pathogens Disease-producing agents found in the blood.

body surface area (BSA) When assessing the severity of burns, the amount of body surface area that is covered with burns is an important factor.

bona fide Made or carried out in good faith without malice or intention to deceive.

bonding Method used to connect two pieces of equipment by a conductor. It involves eliminating the difference in static charge potential between materials.

Boyle's law The product of a given pressure and volume is constant with a constant temperature.

British North America (BNA) Act, 1867 Established the constitutional layout of the new country, Canada, including the powers of the provincial and federal governments.

bulk shipment A shipment of a hazardous product that is contained without intermediate packaging.

bullying Workplace bullying is repeated, unreasonable or inappropriate behaviour directed toward a worker or group of workers that creates a risk to health and safety.

Canada Labour Code Legislation that sets out the rights and duties of federal employees who work under federal jurisdiction. About 10% of the Canadian workforce is covered by the Canada Labour Code.

Canadian Centre for Occupational Health and Safety (CCOHS) A federal government agency established to research and provide safety information resources to all Canadian workers.

Canadian Human Rights Act Legislation passed by the Parliament of Canada in 1977, to protect the basic human rights of all Canadians.

carcinogen Any substance that can cause a malignant tumour or a neoplastic growth.

carpal tunnel syndrome (CTS) An injury to the median nerve inside the wrist.

causal relationship A situation in which an action leads to a certain result.

ceiling The level of exposure that should not be exceeded at any time for any reason.

central factor The main issue or factor in a problem or act.

certification A designation or acknowledgment from an accrediting body that a person is qualified to conduct work in a particular field.

cervical radiculopathy Compression of the cervical vertebrae in the neck.

chain of infection A series of conditions that allow a disease to spread.

chemical agents Single elements or compounds that may be toxic to humans.

chemical burns Burn damage to the skin caused by chemicals such as acids and alkalies.

chemical hazards Hazards that are caused by exposure to harmful chemical substances.

chokes Coughing and choking, resulting from bubbles in the respiratory system.

chronic effects and exposures The effects of exposure over time.

circadian rhythm A person's biological clock.

circuit tester An inexpensive piece of test equipment with two wire leads capped by probes and connected to a small bulb.

code A set of standards, rules, or regulations relating to a specific area.

code of ethics A set of rules that govern behaviour or conduct, based on the organization's moral principles.

Code of Hammurabi Developed by the ruler Hammurabi around 1780 B.C. during the time of the Babylonians, this code encompassed all of the laws of the land at that time. The significant aspect for our purposes is that it contained clauses dealing with injuries, allowable fees for physicians, and monetary damages assessed against those who injured others.

coefficient of friction A numerical correlation of the resistance of one surface against another surface.

cognitive-behavioural therapy (CBT) Therapy used to identify and change the unhelpful patterns of thinking that feed anxious thoughts.

cold stress Physical or mental stress that results from working in cold conditions.

combination theory The actual cause of an accident is best explained by combining many models.

combustible Any substance with a flash point of 37.8°C (100°F) or higher.

common-sense test Requires a person to listen to what instincts and common sense are telling him or her.

competitiveness The ability to succeed and prosper consistently in the marketplace whether it is local, regional, national, or global.

conduction The transfer of direct thermal energy between two bodies that are touching or from one location to another within a body.

conductors Substances that have many free electrons at room temperature and can conduct electricity.

confined space An area with limited means of egress that is large enough for a person to fit into, but is not designed for occupancy.

consent of the governed The phrase is most commonly cited from the American Declaration of Independence. It refers to a government's just right to exercise power only when it is validated by the consent of those governed.

consistency The rules are enforced in the same manner every time with no regard to any outside factors.

Constitution Act, 1982 Provided Canada with a new constitution that included the charter of rights and freedoms.

continuity tester Tool used to determine whether a conductor is properly grounded or has a break in the circuit.

contributory negligence An injured worker's own negligence contributed to the accident. If the actions of employees contributed to their own injuries, the employer is absolved of any liability.

control of access Channelling the flow of outsiders to an access-control station.

control When an employee participates in determining the work routine, including schedule and selection of tasks.

contusions Bruises resulting from a blow.

convection The transfer of heat from one location to another by way of a moving medium.

corporate image How a company is perceived to interact with its workers, customers, and community.

cost allocation Spreading the cost of workers' compensation appropriately and proportionately among industries, ranging from the most to the least hazardous.

cost The amount of money needed to produce a product, not to be confused with "price," which is the amount of money needed to purchase a product after the cost has been marked up.

cost–benefit The relationship between the cost of a remedy and the benefit it produces.

creeps Itchy, crawling, rashy feeling in the skin caused by bubble formation in the skin.

critical burns Second-degree burns covering more than 30% of the body and third-degree burns covering over 10% of the body.

critical injury Injury in which a specified degree of seriousness has been reached. The specific requirements for classifying an injury as "critical" are provided in the statutes of some jurisdictions.

crushing Occurs when a part of the body is caught between two hard surfaces that progressively move together, thereby crushing anything between them.

CSA Group Formerly, the Canadian Standards Association. Independent agency that develops standards for the performance of many products inside and outside of the workplace.

cultural barriers Rules, expectations, or norms of a culture that often impede full participation in a new setting. Language and religion are common cultural barriers.

cumulative trauma disorders (CTDs) Injuries caused by forceful or awkward movements repeated frequently over time.

cutting Occurs when a body part comes in contact with a sharp edge.

Dalton's law of partial pressures In a mixture of theoretically ideal gases, the pressure exerted by the mixture is the sum of the pressures exerted by each component gas of the mixture.

decibel (dB) The unit applied when measuring sound. One decibel equals one-tenth of a bel and is the smallest difference in the level of sound that can be perceived by the human ear.

decompression sickness Sickness that can result from the decompression that accompanies a rapid rise from sea level to at least 5,500 metres (18,044 feet) or a rapid ascent from around 40 to 20 metres (131 to 66 feet) under water.

dermis (also called *cutis* or *corium*) The inner layer of human skin.

design flaw A defect in equipment or in the work space that can lead to an accident or injury.

design process A plan of action for reaching a goal.

destructive testing Testing by these methods destroys the material being checked.

direct costs Identifiable costs incurred as a result of an accident.

direct current An electrical current flowing in one direction only.

disability A condition or affliction that inhibits a person from carrying out normal or routine activities.

disability management A set of practices intended to reduce the human and financial cost that workplace injuries and illness have on the worker and workplace.

disabling injury rate The disabling injury rate represents the probability or risk of a disabling injury or disease to a worker. The disabling injury rate is similar to the lost time rate although it covers a broader range of injuries, including those that are less severe in nature (do not require time away from work). The rate represents the number of claims per 100 people per year.

discrimination Bias or prejudice resulting in unfair treatment.

domestic violence Any form of abuse, mistreatment, or neglect that a child or adult experiences from a family member, or from someone with whom they have an intimate relationship; also used synonymously with *family violence*.

domino theory Injuries are caused by the action of preceding factors. Removal of the central factor negates the action of the preceding factors and, in so doing, prevents accidents and injuries.

dose The amount of a substance, agent, or energy that enters the body; radiation dose is the amount of ionizing radiation absorbed per unit of mass any part of the body or the whole body.

dose threshold The minimum dose required to produce a measurable effect.

dosimeter Measures the external dose from nearby sources of radiation.

dosimetry The process of measuring or calculating the amount of ionizing radiation absorbed.

double insulation A means of increasing electrical equipment safety.

due diligence A measure of prudence and care that a reasonable person would exercise under the circumstances.

duty to accommodate A set of practices intended to reduce the human and financial cost that workplace injuries and illness have on the worker and workplace.

duty to accommodate An employer's obligation to make every reasonable effort, short of undue hardship, to accommodate workers who may be discriminated against under human rights legislation.

dysbarism The formation of gas bubbles due to rapid ambient pressure reduction.

ego strength An employee's ability to undertake self-directed tasks and to cope with tense situations.

electrical hazards Potentially dangerous situations related to electricity (e.g., a bare wire).

electrical system grounding When one conductor of the circuit is connected to the earth.

electricity The flow of negatively charged particles called *electrons* through an electrically conductive material.

electrolytes Minerals that are needed for the body to maintain the proper metabolism and for cells to produce energy.

electromagnetic fields (EMFs) Form of nonionizing radiation produced as electrical current flows.

electromechanical devices Contact bars that allow only a specified amount of movement between the worker and the hazard.

electrons Negatively charged particles.

electrostatic hazards Shocks from static electricity discharge.

emergency A present or imminent event that requires prompt coordination of actions concerning persons or property to protect the health, safety, or welfare of people, or to limit damage to property or the environment.

emergency coordinator A person who is clearly identified in a company emergency response plan as the responsible party of the emergency situation.

Emergency Management Act Legislation that establishes rules that enable the Government of Canada to be ready to deal with emergencies in cooperation with the provinces and territories.

emergency planning Developing procedures to reduce the negative effects of an emergency. An emergency plan will have provisions for reducing fatalities and injuries; limiting the damage to equipment, facilities, and products; and expediting the return to normal operation.

emergency response plan (ERP) A written document that details the course of action to be taken in response to an emergency, with the goal of protecting the health, safety, and welfare of people while limiting damage to property and the environment.

employee engagement The positive relationship the employee has with their organization. Highly engaged employees have an interest in the organization's success and will exert more discretionary effort into their assigned tasks.

employee negligence Condition that exists when an employee fails to take necessary and prudent precautions.

employer liability In 1877, the Employer's Liability Law was passed and established the potential for employers to be liable for accidents that occurred in the workplace.

employer-biased laws A collection of laws that favoured employers over employees in establishing a responsibility for workplace safety.

endothermic Chemical reactions that consume more heat than they generate.

engineering controls Strategies such as the design of tools, equipment, workplace, or processes that eliminates the hazard at the source.

environment The aggregate of social and cultural conditions that influence the life of an individual.

environmental factors Characteristics of the environment in which an employee works that can affect his or her state of mind or physical conditions, such as noise or distractions.

environmental heat Heat that is produced by sources outside the body.

epidemiological theory Theory that the models used for studying and determining epidemiological relationships can also be used to study causal relationships between environmental factors and accidents or diseases.

epidermis The outer layer of human skin.

ergonomic hazards Factors within the workplace environment that can harm the musculoskeletal system.

ergonomic traps Unsafe conditions unintentionally designed into a workstation.

ergonomics The science of conforming the workplace and all of its elements to the worker.

ergonomists Scientists who study the interaction of workers and their surroundings.

establishment of territoriality Giving autonomy to employees to recognize strangers in their workplace territory.

ethical behaviour Behaviour that falls within the limits prescribed by morality.

ethics The study of morality within a context established by cultural and professional values, social norms, and accepted standards of behaviour.

evolved gas effects Happens when gas is being absorbed faster than it is being exhaled. These bubbles of gas, which are often nitrogen, may form in the blood and other tissues.

exchange rate The increase in sound level that is permitted as the time of exposure is halved.

exothermic Chemical reactions that create heat.

experience rating The recent safety performance of the company is rated and reflected in the premiums charged.

experience rating The recent safety performance of the company is reflected in the premiums charged.

expiration When pressure within the lungs is greater than atmospheric pressure, air moves down a pressure gradient from the lungs to the outside.

explosion A very rapid, contained fire.

explosive range The concentrations of a vapour or gas in air that can ignite from a source.

feedback An employee's opinion of a project or an employer's opinion about an employee's job performance.

feeling of responsibility Being responsible for the welfare of his or her family may cause a worker to feel that options to take employment risks are limited.

fellow servant rule Employers are not liable for workplace injuries that result from negligence of other employees.

fire hazards Conditions that favour the ignition and spread of fire

fire or combustion A chemical reaction between oxygen and a combustible fuel.

fire point The minimum temperature at which the vapours or gas continue to burn, given a source of ignition.

first-degree burns Burns that result in a mild inflammation of the skin known as erythema.

fixed guards Guards that provide a permanent barrier between workers and the point of operation.

flammable Any substance with a flash point below 37.8°C (100°F).

flash point The lowest temperature for a given fuel at which vapours are produced in sufficient concentrations to flash in the presence of a source of ignition.

flexible work arrangements Alternative work schedules from the traditional working day or week.

fluid loss Depletion of necessary body fluids, primarily through perspiration.

foreign object Any object that is out of place or in a position to trip someone or cause a slip.

Foster Wheeler (FW) study Seventeen-year study conducted by Foster Wheeler, a large United Kingdom construction company, to determine if a link exists between workplace safety and productivity.

four-to-one ratio The distance from the wall to the base of the ladder should be 1/4 (up to 1/3) the distance from the ground to the top of the ladder.

freeze The inability to voluntarily release one's grip from a conductor of electricity.

frequency The number of events in a given time; the number of cycles per second in hertz (Hz).

friable asbestos Asbestos that is in a state of crumbling deterioration. When asbestos is in this state, it is most dangerous.

front-page test Encourages people to make a decision that would not embarrass them if it were printed as a story on the front page of their hometown newspaper.

full-potential approach People are responsible for realizing their full potential within the confines of morality.

fungi Simple plants that feed on dead or living tissue of other organisms.

fuses Consist of a metal strip or wire that will melt if a current above a specific value is conducted through the metal.

gates Guards that provide a barrier between the danger zone and workers.

general duty clause Legislation found in each Canadian jurisdiction to ensure that OHS obligations, which are not explicitly stated, are met.

global marketplace The worldwide economic market in which many companies must compete for business.

good housekeeping Proper cleaning and maintenance of a work area.

ground fault When the current flow in the hot wire is greater than the current in the neutral wire.

ground fault circuit interrupter (GFCI) Detects the flow of current to the ground and opens the circuit, thereby interrupting the flow of current.

Ham Commission Royal commission headed by Dr. James Ham in 1975, dealing with miners' illnesses, laid the foundation for Ontario's first Occupational Health and Safety Act.

hand-arm vibration syndrome (HAV) A form of Raynaud's syndrome that afflicts workers who use vibrating power tools frequently over time.

harassment Engaging in malicious comments or conduct that is known, or ought reasonably to be known, to be unwelcome against a worker in a workplace.

harmful environment A work environment in which physical or psychological factors exist that are potentially hazardous.

hazard A condition with the potential of causing injury to personnel, damage to equipment or structures, loss of material, or lessening of the ability to perform a prescribed function.

hazard analysis A systematic process for identifying hazards and recommending corrective action.

hazardous condition A condition that exposes a person to risks.

hazardous noise Any sound for which any combination of frequency, intensity, or duration is capable of causing permanent hearing loss in a specified population.

hazardous products A product covered by the Hazardous Products Act that meets the criteria to be included in one or more of the WHMIS 2015 hazard classes.

health A state of complete physical, mental, and social well-being, and not merely the absence of disease or infirmity.

health and safety professional An individual whose profession (job) is to be concerned with health and safety measures in the workforce.

health promotion A range of interventions, policies, or programs aimed at proactively protecting and promoting workers' health.

heat strain The overall physiological response resulting from heat stress.

heat stress The net heat load to which a worker is exposed from the combined contributions of metabolic cost of work, environmental factors, and clothing requirements.

hepatitis An infection or inflammation of the liver.

hierarchy of controls A system of hazard control methods ranging from most effective (elimination) to least effective (personal protective equipment).

high-radiation area Any accessible area in which radiation hazards exist that could deliver a dose in excess of 100 millirem within 1 hour.

horizontal work area The limits of the horizontal plane in which a worker is required to perform a task. A good horizontal work area is designed and positioned so that it does not require a worker to bend forward or to twist the body from side to side.

human error A mistake that is made by a human, not a machine.

human factors The science of human data applied to the environment, workplace, machine, tool, device, or system.

human factors theory Attributes accidents to a chain of events ultimately caused by human error.

human immunodeficiency virus (HIV) The virus that causes acquired immunodeficiency syndrome (AIDS).

humidification Adding moisture to the air to reduce electrical static.

hygiene According to the World Health Organization (WHO), "Hygiene refers to conditions and practices that help to maintain health and prevent the spread of diseases."

hypergolic Fuels that ignite spontaneously on contact with an oxidizer.

hyperoxia Too much oxygen or oxygen breathed under too high a pressure.

hypothermia The condition that results when the body's core temperature drops to dangerously low levels, below 35°C (95°F).

hypoxia Too little oxygen getting to body tissues.

ignition temperature (or combustion point) The temperature at which a given fuel can burst into flame.

immunization The process whereby a person is made immune or resistant to an infectious disease, typically by the administration of a vaccine. Vaccines stimulate the body's own immune system to protect the person against subsequent infection or disease.

impact accidents Involve a worker being struck by or against an object.

impact The consequences of an action or event.

impulse noise Consists of transient pulses that can occur repetitively or nonrepetitively.

inanimate power Power that is lacking life or spirit. During the Industrial Revolution, humans and animals were replaced with inanimate power (e.g., steam power).

inappropriate activities Activities undertaken with disregard for established safety procedures.

inappropriate response A response in which a person disregards an established safety procedure.

incentives Rewards for desirable performance.

income replacement Replacement of current and future income, based on 90% of net pay for most jurisdictions.

indirect costs Uninsured costs that are not directly identifiable with workplace accidents.

industrial hygiene A profession dedicated to the recognition, assessment, and control of workplace stressors that may cause injuries, illnesses, or discomfort for workers.

industrial hygiene An area of specialization in the field of industrial health and safety that is concerned with predicting, recognizing, assessing, controlling, and preventing environmental stressors in the workplace that can cause sickness or serious discomfort.

industrial medicine A specialized field that is concerned with work-related health and safety issues.

infection The body's response to contamination by a disease-producing microorganism.

Information Age The current period of our history brought on by computers and digital technology. The proliferation of microcomputers and these technologies fostered by the enhancement of the global economy.

infrared radiation Electromagnetic radiation with a frequency less than that of visible light and greater than that of most radio waves.

ingestion Entry through the mouth.

inhalation Entry of gases, vapours, dust, smoke, fumes, aerosols, or mists into the body by breathing in.

injection Entry into the body through punctured skin.

inspiration When atmospheric pressure is greater than pressure within the lungs, air flows down this pressure gradient from the outside into the lungs.

insulators Substances that have few free electrons and that resist the flow of electrical current.

interlocked guards Guards that shut down the machine when the guard is not securely in place or is disengaged.

interlocks Mechanisms that automatically break the circuit when an unsafe situation is detected.

internal factors Factors that can add a burden on a person and interfere with his or her work, such as personal problems.

internal responsibility system A mechanism to allow employers, supervisors, and workers to monitor one another's actions and ensure compliance with legislation.

International Organization for Standardization (ISO) An independent, non-governmental worldwide organization of 163 national standards bodies that develop voluntary, consensus-based, market relevant international standards.

intravenous drug user One who is administered drugs by means of injecting them directly into their veins.

ionizers Devices that ionize the air surrounding a charged surface to provide a conductive path for the flow of charges.

ionizing radiation Radiation that becomes electrically charged or changed into ions. Radiation with enough energy to remove electrons from the orbit of an atom, causing the atom to become charged or ionized.

irritants Substances that cause irritation to the skin, eyes, and the inner lining of the nose, mouth, throat, and upper respiratory tract.

job autonomy Control over one's job.

job descriptions Written specifications that describe the tasks, duties, reporting requirements, and qualifications for a given job.

job security The risk of unemployment and the accompanying sense—real or imagined—of having the potential for longevity in a job and having a measure of control concerning that longevity.

kinetic energy The energy resulting from a moving object.

laboratory label Label required on controlled products that are intended solely to be used or tested in a lab. There are two types of laboratory labels: supply house labels and sample labels.

lagging indicators A record of incidents that already happened. A reactive measure of OHS program success.

lanyard A flexible line for connecting the body belt or body harness to a deceleration device, lifeline, or anchorage.

lasers Light amplification by stimulated emission of radiation.

latency period Time after exposure to a hazardous product before symptoms appear.

laws Rules that limit behaviour.

leading indicators A record of systems or measures in place. A proactive measure of OHS program success.

legal obligation A duty to which one is bound by law.

legislation Laws brought into force by a legislative body.

let-go current The highest current level at which a person in contact with a conductor of electricity can release the grasp of the conductor.

lethal concentration The concentration in air that causes death to the test subject when inhaled.

lethal dose The dose that is highly likely to cause death in the test subject by exposure through any means other than inhalation.

lifting hazards Any factors that, if not properly dealt with, may lead to an injury from lifting.

lightning Static charges are from clouds, involving very high voltage and current, that follow the path of least resistance to the earth.

literacy Knowledge of a particular area, usually referring to one's ability to read and write.

load A device that uses currents.

lockout/tagout system A system for incapacitating a machine until it can be made safe to operate. *Lockout* means physically locking up the machine so that it cannot be used without removing the lock. *Tagout* means applying a tag that warns employees not to operate the machine in question.

locus of control The perspective of workers concerning who or what controls their behaviour.

lost time The amount of time that an employee is unable to work due to an injury.

lost time injuries Injuries or illnesses due to a work-related accident or exposure to a noxious substance that results in an employee missing work and for which the employee receives compensation for lost income.

lost time rate Indicates the probability of lost time for each 100 person-years worked. The lost-time rate is calculated by dividing the number of lost-time claims by the person-years worked estimate, and multiplying the result by 100.

Machiavellianism The extent to which an employee will attempt to deceive and confuse others.

Magna Carta Charter enacted in 1215 that limited the power of King John of England.

manual materials handling (MMH) Moving goods or equipment without the aid of machinery.

meaninglessness The feeling that workers get when their jobs become so specialized and technology-dependent that they cannot see the meaning in their work as it relates to the finished product or service.

means of egress A route for exiting a building or other structure.

mechanical hazards Hazards associated with power-driven machines, whether automated or manually operated.

mechanical injuries Injuries that have occurred due to misuse of a power-driven machine.

medical rehabilitation Designed to provide the needed medical care to the injured employee until he or she is pronounced fit to return to work.

metabolic heat Produced within a body as a result of activity that burns energy.

methicillin-resistant Staphylococcus aureus (MRSA) A type of bacteria that is resistant to many antibiotics.

mindlessness The result of the process of "dumbing down" the workplace and setting people up to not have to use their minds or think in order to do their work.

minor burns All first-degree burns are considered minor as well as second-degree burns covering less than 15 percent of the body.

mirror test Encourages people to make choices based on how they will feel about their decision when they look in the mirror.

moderate burns Second-degree burns covering less than 30% of the body and third-degree burns covering less than 10% of the body.

modified work Altered duties after an injury or disease to accommodate the workers' limitations or rehabilitation while permitting the worker to avoid losing time from work.

moral obligation A duty to which one is bound by one's values, but not legally.

morning-after test Encourages people to make choices based on how they will feel about their decision the next day.

mutate Undergo or cause to undergo genetic change. For pathogens, each mutation requires a new vaccine.

narcotics Substances that produce numbness or stupor.

narrow band noise Noise that is confined to a narrow range of frequencies.

natural surveillance Designing, arranging, and operating the workplace in a way that minimizes secluded areas.

needlestick injuries Injuries obtained through inadvertent puncture of the skin with hypodermic needles.

negative pressures Pressures below atmospheric level.

neoplasm Cancerous tissue or tissue that might become cancerous.

neutrons Particles that neutralize the negative charge of electrons. They act as temporary energy repositories between positively charged particles called *protons* and *electrons*.

nip point (pinch point) Point of convergence of two parts, with at least one moving.

noise Unwanted sound.

nondestructive testing Testing by these methods does not harm the material being tested.

nonionizing radiation Radiation on the electromagnetic spectrum that has a frequency of 10^{15} cycles per second (Hz) or less and a wavelength in metres of Hz 10-7 or more.

nonskid footwear Shoes that have special nonskid soles.

normlessness The phenomenon in which people working in a highly automated environment can become estranged from society.

obesity Abnormal or excessive fat accumulation that may impair health. The World Health Organization (WHO) and Dieticians of Canada consider a body mass index (BMI) of thirty and over to be obese.

objectivity Rules are enforced equally, regardless of employee or management status, within the company.

occupational accidents Unplanned events that cause injury to a worker.

occupational diseases Pathological conditions brought about by workplace conditions or factors.

Occupational Health and Safety Act Legislation that sets out the rights and duties of all parties in the workplace for the protection of workers against hazards on the job.

Ohm's law Description of the relationship among volts, ohms, and amps. One ohm is the resistance of a conductor that has a current of one amp under the potential of one volt.

ohms Measure of resistance.

open ground Condition in which electrical wiring is connected improperly and has no path to ground.

open-ended Questions that do not lead the witness to give certain answers or suggest any prejudgment of the answers.

organized labour A group of employees who join together to fight for the rights of all employees (i.e., unions).

orientation The process of introducing new employees to the organization, its rules, culture, and expectations.

overexertion The result of employees working beyond their physical limits.

overload An imbalance between a person's capacity at any given time and the load that person is carrying in a given state.

parasite An animal or plant that lives in or on a host.

pathogens Biological agents that can cause illness and disease in humans.

personal monitoring devices Devices worn or carried by an individual to measure radiation doses received.

personal protective equipment (PPE) Any type of clothing or device that puts a barrier between the worker and the hazard (e.g., safety goggles, gloves, hard hats, and so on).

photoelectric devices Optional devices that shut down the machine any time the light field is broken.

physical hazards Substances, tools, equipment, activities, and forms of energy that can cause injury or illness to exposed workers.

placards Alternative or temporary label used when workplace labels are not practical.

point-of-operation guards Machine guards that provide protection right at the point where the user operates the machine.

post-traumatic stress disorder (PTSD) Post-traumatic stress disorder (PTSD) is a serious condition that can develop after a person has experienced or witnessed a traumatic or terrifying event in which serious harm occurred or was threatened. While PTSD is most often linked with military personnel or first responders, it may also be linked to ongoing emotional trauma, such as exposure to chronic bullying, harassment, or an abusive relationship at work.

powerlessness The feeling that workers have when they are not able to control the work environment.

preceding factors Factors that led up to an accident.

predispositional characteristics Human personality characteristics that can have a catalytic effect in causing an accident.

preliminary hazard analysis (PHA) Conducted to identify potential hazards and prioritize them according to the likelihood of an accident or injury being caused by the hazard and the severity of injury, illness, or property damage that could result if the hazard caused an accident.

presenteeism The act of being present at work but with reduced productivity, often due to ill health.

pressure hazard A hazard caused by a dangerous condition involving pressure.

pressure The force exerted against an opposing fluid or solid distributed over a surface.

presumptive legislation Presumptive legislation links a particular occupation with a disease or condition that has been shown to be a hazard associated with that occupation. As a result of this linkage, if an individual employed in the occupation covered by the presumption contracts a disease or condition that is specified in the presumptive law, then that disease or condition is presumed to have come from that occupation. In this case, the burden of proof shifts from the employee to the employer to demonstrate that the condition was not in fact associated with the occupation but with another cause.

primary witness An eyewitness to an accident.

principal's office syndrome When an accident witness is unable to communicate freely about what they saw because he or she is intimidated or uncomfortable in the interview situation.

probability The statistical likelihood of an action or event taking place.

productivity The concept of comparing output of goods or services to the input of resources needed to produce or deliver them.

proof pressure tests Tests in which containers are "proofed" by subjecting them to specified pressures for specified periods.

protons Positively charged particles.

psychological health A state of well-being in which an individual realizes his or her own abilities, can cope with the normal stresses of life, can work productively, and is able to make a contribution to his or her community.

psychological injury When the exposure to a traumatic event, situation, or ongoing bullying or harassment causes a worker's psychological health to decline.

psychological safety A state of being protected from hazards that could affect psychological health.

psychologically safe workplace A workplace that does not permit harm to employee mental health in careless, negligent, reckless, or intentional ways.

psychophysiological techniques Require simultaneous measurement of heart rate and brain waves, which are then interpreted as indexes of mental workload and workplace stress.

psychosocial hazards Any hazards that affect the mental well-being or mental health of the worker.

psychosocial questionnaires Questionnaires that evaluate workers' emotions about their jobs.

pullback devices Devices that pull the operator's hands out of the danger zone when the machine starts to cycle.

puncturing Results when an object penetrates straight into the body and pulls straight out, creating a wound in the shape of the penetrating object.

quality A measure of the extent to which a product or service meets or exceeds customer expectations.

quality management (QM) A way of managing a company that revolves around a total and willing commitment of all personnel at all levels to quality.

rad A measure of the dose of ionizing radiation absorbed by body tissues stated in terms of the amount of energy absorbed per unit of mass of tissue.

radiant heat The result of electromagnetic nonionizing energy that is transmitted through space without the movement of matter within that space.

radiation The electromagnetic wave transfer of heat to a solid and includes alpha rays, beta rays, gamma rays, X-rays, neutrons, high-speed electrons, and high-speed protons.

radiation area Any accessible area in which radiation hazards exist that could deliver doses such that (1) within 1 hour, a major portion of the body could receive more than 5 millirem; or (2) within 5 consecutive days, a major portion of the body could receive more than 100 millirem.

radioactive material Material that emits corpuscular or electromagnetic emanations as the result of spontaneous nuclear disintegration.

radio-frequency devices Capacitance devices that brake the machine if the capacitance field is interrupted by a worker's body or another object.

radiography A form of imaging using small doses of ionizing radiation, as opposed to visual light. X-rays are used in medical radiology to view the internal body systems and in industrial radiography to see internal structures or defects in mechanical parts.

receptacle wiring tester A device with two standard plug probes for insertion into an ordinary 110-volt outlet and a probe for the ground. It is used to detect an improperly wired receptacle (outlet).

re-enactment A technique in which a witness to an accident goes through the same set of actions as the accident victim in order to demonstrate what happened. The witness should simulate the actions rather than actually performing them or there may be another accident.

regulations Specific rules that support other legislation.

repetitive motion Short-cycle motion that is repeated continually.

repetitive strain injuries (RSI) A broad and generic term that encompasses a variety of injuries resulting from cumulative trauma to the soft tissues of the body.

resistance A tendency to block flow of electric current.

response time The amount of time between when an order is placed and when the product is delivered.

restraint devices Devices that hold back the operator from the danger zone.

restricted area Any area to which access is restricted in an attempt to protect employees from exposure to radiation or radioactive materials.

retrofit Renovating rather than replacing.

right to know Workers' basic right to be informed of any hazards that exist in the workplace.

right to participate Workers' basic right to participate in their own safety (e.g., via committees).

right to refuse Workers' basic right to refuse work that they believe is unsafe.

risk The likelihood and severity of harm from exposure to a hazard.

risk analysis An analytical methodology normally associated with insurance and investments.

risk assessment The process of quantifying the level of risk.

robot A machine capable of conducting complex tasks, often created to increase productivity or accuracy, or to reduce worker stress and injury.

robotics Interdisciplinary field of science and engineering that deals with the design, construction, and control of robots.

role ambiguity The condition that occurs when an employee is not clear concerning the parameters, reporting requirements, authority, or responsibilities of his or her job.

role-reversal test Requires a person to trade places with the people affected by the decision that he or she made and to view the decision through their eyes.

safety culture The collective beliefs, values, attitudes, and perceptions toward safety in the workplace.

safety management system A business tool that provides a comprehensive and structured approach to identifying hazards and controlling risks in the workplace.

safety marks Transportation of Dangerous Goods labelling convention used for the quick identification of dangerous goods.

safety movement Began during World War II when all of the various practitioners of occupational health and safety began to see the need for cooperative efforts. This movement is very strong today.

safety policy A written description of an organization's commitment to maintaining a safe and healthy workplace.

safety trip devices Devices that include trip wires, trip rods, and body bars that stop the machine when tripped.

secondary witness Someone who was present at the scene of an accident but did not actually see the accident.

second-degree burns Burns that result in blisters forming on the skin.

sedentary A state of little or no physical activity—usually sitting.

semiautomatic ejection A system that ejects the work using mechanisms that are activated by the operator.

semiautomatic feed A system that uses a variety of approaches for feeding stock to the machine.

semiconductors Substances that are neither conductors nor insulators.

severe acute respiratory syndrome (SARS) A respiratory infection similar to pneumonia.

severity The magnitude of the results of an event or action.

shearing Results from forces being applied to a body by two contacting parts moving parallel to the plane of contact.

shift work Employees work at different times of the day instead of during the same hours.

shock A depression of the nervous system.

short circuit A circuit in which the load has been removed or bypassed.

short-term exposure limit The maximum concentration of a given substance to which employees may be safely exposed for up to 15 minutes without suffering irritation, chronic or irreversible tissue change, or narcosis to a degree sufficient to increase the potential for accidental injury, impair the likelihood of self-rescue, or reduce work efficiency.

sick building syndrome A set of ailments associated with a workplace. The symptoms can include watering eyes and runny nose, fatigue, dizziness, dry and/or itchy skin, headaches, sore throat, nose bleeds, and nausea.

sievert A single unit used to indicate the effective dose absorbed by various organs or tissues. The effective dose or Sv is used to assess the risk to humans, but not plants or other animals.

situational characteristics Factors that can change from setting to setting and have a catalytic effect in causing an accident.

situational factors Environmental factors that can affect an employee's safety and that can differ from situation to situation.

slip and fall Accidents that occur when the worker's centre of gravity is suddenly thrown out of balance.

social environment The general value system of the society in which an individual lives, works, grows up, and so on.

sound Any change in pressure that can be detected by the ear.

sound level meter Meter that produces an immediate reading that represents the noise level at a specific instant in time.

spontaneous combustion Result of sufficient fuel and heat from decomposing organic material for ignition.

sprains The result of torn ligaments.

stage of alarm Characterized by pallor, sweating, and an increased heart rate.

stage of exhaustion This stage is demonstrated by the body's failure to adapt to the continued stress.

stage of resistance The alarm symptoms dissipate and the body develops an adaptation to the stress.

standard An operational principle, criterion, or requirement pertaining to working conditions, methods, equipment, or materials in the workplace.

standpipe and hose systems Systems that provide the hose and pressurized water for firefighting.

static electricity A surplus or deficiency of electrons on the surface of a material.

statute Law made by provincial legislature or federal parliament.

step and fall An accident that occurs when a person's foot encounters an unexpected step down.

strains The result of overstretched or torn muscles.

stress A pathological, and therefore generally undesirable, human reaction to psychological, social, occupational, or environmental stimuli.

stressors Stimuli that cause stress.

stump and fall An accident that occurs when a worker's foot suddenly meets a sticky surface or a defect in the walking surface.

subjective ratings Ratings that are less than objective and can be affected by emotions, human biases, presumptions, and perceptions.

supplier label Identified by the WHMIS broken border, the supplier label is required as a condition of sale of hazardous products.

systems theory Views a situation in which an accident may occur as a system comprising the following elements: person (host), machine (agency), and environment.

task complexity The number of different demands made on the worker.

TDG Act, 1992 Federal legislation governing the transportation of dangerous goods.

tearing Occurs when shear, friction, and/or blunt force causes the separation of skin layers.

technological alienation The frame of mind that results when employees come to resent technology and the impact that it has on their lives.

technology access Access to time- and work-saving devices, processes, or equipment that are up to date.

tendinitis Painful result of small tears in the tendon from overwork.

tenosynovitis A condition resulting from an excess buildup of fluid that causes pressure on the surrounding nerve.

terms of reference A set of rules under which the health and safety committee is to operate.

terrorism The unlawful use or threat of violence or sabotage, usually against the public, as a politically-motivated means of attack or coercion.

tertiary witness Someone who may have information that is relevant to an accident investigation although they were not present when the accident happened.

third-degree burns Burns that penetrate through both the epidermis and the dermis. They may be fatal.

three E's of safety Engineering, education, and enforcement.

threshold limit values (TLVs) The levels of exposure at which all employees may be repeatedly exposed to specified concentrations of airborne substances without fear of adverse effects. Exposure beyond TLVs is considered hazardous.

threshold of hearing The weakest sound that can be heard by a healthy human ear in a quiet setting.

threshold of pain The maximum level of sound that can be perceived without experiencing pain.

time-weighted average The level of exposure to a toxic substance to which a worker can be repeatedly exposed on a daily basis without suffering harmful effects.

total safety management (TSM) The principles of quality management (QM) applied to safety management.

toxic substances Substances that have a negative effect on the health of a person or interfere with the normal biological function of a person.

transactional leadership A leadership style that focuses on the role of supervision, organization, compliance with rules, and group performance.

transformational leadership A leadership style that engages employees by inspiring, developing, and empowering them. Transformational leadership motivates followers by creating a vision of an ideal future state.

trapped gas effects With a decrease in pressure, gases in the body increase in volume. These occurrences often cause pain or discomfort and may result in injuries if the pressure change is rapid.

trauma Psychological stress.

trauma response team (TRT) Designated employees who are specially trained to provide initial response to traumatic events.

trip and fall An accident that occurs when a worker encounters an unseen foreign object in his or her path.

tunnel syndromes Injuries caused by compression of the nerves passing through a tunnel (a conduit formed by ligaments and other soft tissues).

two-hand controls Controls that require the operator to use both hands concurrently to activate the machine.

UL label Underwriters Laboratories is a world-leading organization in product safety testing and certification.

ultrasonic testing Use of acoustic waves for detecting foreign objects.

ultraviolet radiation Electromagnetic radiation with a frequency between visible violet light and X rays.

undue hardship An obligation that places a burden on the employer that is not in proportion to the reciprocal cost or benefit.

undue hardship Worker accommodation beyond the point of incurring reasonable difficulty in terms of health and safety or financial hardship on the organization.

unrestricted area Any area to which access is not controlled because no radioactivity hazard is present.

unsafe act An act that is not safe for an employee.

unsafe behaviour The manner in which people conduct themselves that is unsafe to them or to another.

useful consciousness A state of consciousness in which a person is clearheaded and alert enough to make responsible decisions.

vacuums Areas where there is little or no matter, creating an area of negative pressure (pressure below atmospheric level).

value added The difference between what it costs to produce a product and the value the marketplace puts on it (what it costs to purchase it).

vertical work area The limits of the vertical plane in which a worker is required to perform a task. A good vertical work area is designed and positioned so that workers are not required to lift their hands above their shoulders or bend down in order to perform any task.

vibration Oscillations of solid or semi-solid objects that can be perceived by the sense of touch.

video display terminals (VDTs) A device on which computer data or graphics can be displayed.

virus A microscopic organism that invades a host to reproduce.

visible radiation Radiation from light sources that create distortion and make the radiation visible.

vocational rehabilitation Involves providing the education and training needed to prepare the worker for a new occupation.

voltage Measures the potential difference between two points in a circuit.

water hammer A series of loud noises caused by pressurized liquid flow suddenly stopping.

watts Measure of electrical power.

wellness program Any program designed to help and encourage employees to adopt a healthier lifestyle.

wet bulb globe temperature (WBGT) A measure of the heat stress in direct sunlight, which takes into account temperature, humidity, wind speed, and solar heat load.

whistle-blowing Act of informing an outside authority or media outlet of alleged illegal or unethical acts on the part of an organization or individual.

WHMIS Workplace Hazardous Materials Information System. A national communication system implemented on October 31, 1988, that provides the worker with information on the production, use, storage, and safe handling of hazardous materials in the workplace. The program was updated to WHMIS 2015, to align with the Globally Harmonized System of Classification and Labelling of Chemicals (GHS).

wide band noise Noise that is distributed over a wide range of frequencies.

work envelope The total three-dimensional area established by a robot's full range of motion, within which the moving parts of a robot actually move.

workers' compensation A no-fault, employer-paid, insurance program developed to allow injured employees to be compensated appropriately without having to take their employers to court.

work-family balance An effective and equitable relationship between the demands of work commitments and those of the family.

work-life balance An effective and equitable relationship between the demands of work commitments and those outside of work.

work-life conflict Incompatible demands between work and nonwork commitments.

workplace accidents Unplanned events at an employee's place of work that result in injury or loss.

workplace analysis An in-depth study of the workplace that is used to identify hazards.

workplace injuries Injuries that occur while an employee is at work.

workplace label Required on hazardous products in the workplace, but may have less content than supplier labels.

workplace stress The harmful physical and emotional responses that occur when the requirements of the job do not match the capabilities, resources, or needs of the worker.

workplace violence Any action, conduct, threat, or gesture of a person toward an employee in their work place that can reasonably be expected to cause harm, injury, or illness to that employee.

work-related musculoskeletal disorders (WMSDs) A group of painful disorders of muscles, tendons, and nerves.

zero potential State of a neutral electrical charge.

Index

Mutate, 197
Myofacial muscle damage, 228

N

Narcotics, 162–163
Narrow band noise, 360
National Fire Code of Canada (NFC), 336–337
National Fire Protection Association (NFPA), 330, 331
Natural surveillance, 451
Needlestick injuries
    defined, 205
    responding to, 206
    safety needles and, 205–206
Negative pressures, 300–301
Neoplasm, 163
Neutrons, 309
Nip point hazards, 236, 237
Nitrogen narcosis, 293
Noise, 358, 359
    control strategies, 368–373
    exposure limits, 362
    hazard levels and risks, 360–361
    hazardous, 358
    impulse, 360
    impulsive, 358
    narrow band, 360
    standards and regulations, 362–367
    wide band, 360
Noise dose, 359
Noise hazards
    effects of, 377
    monitoring, 363–364
    parts of, 368
Noise-induced hearing loss, 359
Noise surveys, 367
Nondestructive testing, 300
Nonionizing radiation, 350–351
Nonschedule disabilities, 74
Nonskid footwear, 256
Normlessness, 427
North American Industry Classification System (NAICS), 81

O

Obesity, 470–471
Objectivity, 60
Occupational accidents, 11
Occupational diseases, 11
    automation and, 430
    worker's compensation and, 69
Occupational Health and Safety Act
    Ontario's, 6, 8, 59–60, 62
    Saskatchewan's, 5–6
Occupational health and safety committees, 62–64
    duties of, 63
    requirements for, 63
    terms of reference for, 63–64
Occupational health and safety law, 389
Occupational health nurses, 49–50
Occupational physicians, 50
Ocean Ranger disaster, 8
Ohms, 310

Ohm's law, 310–311
Ontario Factories Act, 4
Ontario Workmen's Compensation Act, 5
Open-ended format, of interview, 133
Open ground, 314
Organizational culture, 391
Organized labour, 9–10
Orientation, 42, 43
Overexertion, 86
Overload, 113

P

Parasites, 198
Partial pressures, 292
Particulate respirators, 205
Pathogens, 96
Performance appraisal instrument, 34
Permanent electrical safety device (PESD), 320
Permanent partial disability, 74
Permanent total disability, 75
Personal commitment, gaining, 20–21
Personal monitoring devices, 346
Personal protective equipment (PPE), 61, 85, 103, 270–271
    for asbestos removal, 165
    chemical agents and, 170
Personnel security, 417
Photoelectric devices, 242
Photoelectric fire sensors, 332
Physical hazards, 95, 112, 186–187
Physical security, 417
Physical stress, 213–214
Pinch-point hazards, 236
Placards, 191
Point-of-operation devices, 242–243
Point-of-operation guards, 239–242
Portable fire extinguishers, 334
Posner, Barry Z., 19
Post-incident response, workplace violence, 457
Post-traumatic stress disorder (PTSD), 6, 73, 96, 385, 398
Powered industrial truck, 271–272
Powerlessness, 427
Preceding factors, 112
Predispositional characteristics, 116
Pregnancy, physical work and, 114
Preliminary hazard analysis (PHA), 96–98
Presenteeism, 387
Pressure
    atmospheric, 292
    defined, 291
    partial, 292
    units of, 291
Pressure hazards
    boilers and, 293–294
    defined, 291
    measurement of, 299–300
    reduction of, 300–301
    sources of, 292–293
Pressure vessels
    cracking hazards in, 296–297
    nondestructive testing of, 297–298
Presumptive legislation, 6, 72–73
Primary witnesses, 132

Principal's office syndrome, 133
Probability, 98
Problem-solving strategies, ergonomics, 220–225
    seated control work, 221
    seated repetitive work with light parts, 220
    seated work with larger parts, 221
    standing for heavy lifting and carrying, 222–223
    standing work, 222
    video display terminals, 224–225
    work with hands above the chest, 223
    work with hand tools, 223
Productivity
    and competitiveness, 144–145
    and cost, 147
Professional associations, 52
Proof pressure tests, 300
Protons, 309
Psychological hazards, assessment of, 398
Psychological health/safety
    business case, 387–388
    defined, 384, 385
    health case, 386–387
    legal case, 387–389
    state of, 385–386
    in workplace, national standard for, 389–390
Psychological injury, 385
Psychologically safe workplace, 385
Psychological support, 392
Psychophysiological techniques, 393
Psychosocial questionnaires, 393
Puffer, Tim, 25
Pullback devices, 242
Pulp digester vessels, 297
Pyrophor hypergolic, 328

Q

Quality, 147
    and competitiveness, 145–146
    defined, 145
Quality management (QM), 149–150
Quality of work life, 429

R

Rad, 346
Radiant heat, 277
Radiation, 327
    defined, 346
    exposure of employees to, 347
    extremely low frequency, 351
    infrared, 351
    ionizing, 345–346, 347
    microwave, 351
    nonionizing, 350–351
    personal monitoring precautions, 347–348
    ultraviolet, 350
    visible, 350
Radiation area, 346
Radiation hazards, 345
    caution signs and labels, 348–349
    instructing and informing personnel, 349
    reports and records of overexposure, 350
    storage and disposal of radioactive material, 349–350